CHEMISTRY RESEARCH AND APPLICATIONS

RUTHENIUM

SYNTHESIS, PHYSICOCHEMICAL PROPERTIES AND APPLICATIONS

CHEMISTRY RESEARCH AND APPLICATIONS

Additional books in this series can be found on Nova's website under the Series tab.

Additional e-books in this series can be found on Nova's website under the e-book tab.

CHEMISTRY RESEARCH AND APPLICATIONS

RUTHENIUM

SYNTHESIS, PHYSICOCHEMICAL PROPERTIES AND APPLICATIONS

GARY P. KEELER
EDITOR

New York

For permission to use material from this book please contact us:
Telephone 631-231-7269; Fax 631-231-8175
Web Site: http://www.novapublishers.com

Additional color graphics may be available in the e-book version of this book.

Library of Congress Cataloging-in-Publication Data

Ruthenium : synthesis, physicochemical properties and applications / [edited by] Gary P. Keeler.
pages cm. -- (Chemistry research and applications)
Includes bibliographical references and index.
ISBN 978-1-63321-657-0 (hardcover)
1. Ruthenium. I. Keeler, Gary P., editor.
QD181.R9R88 2014
546'.632--dc23

2014028265

Published by Nova Science Publishers, Inc. † New York

CONTENTS

PREFACE

Ruthenium is exceedingly rare, as it is only the 74th most abundant metal on Earth. The element is generally found in ores with the other platinum group metals in the Ural Mountains and in North and South America. Ruthenium containing-complexes are well suited for biological application owning to the unique properties of ruthenium. For example, ruthenium complexes have been utilized as cellular imaging tools, radiopharmaceutical imaging tools, and as replacements to platinum-based drugs in fighting several diseases such as cancer, malaria, *Leishmania major*, and *Trypanosoma cruzi*, to name a few. This book discusses the synthesis of ruthenium as well as the physicochemical properties and applications.

Chapter 1 – Ruthenium containing-complexes are well suited for biological application owning to the unique properties of ruthenium. For example, ruthenium complexes have been utilized as cellular imaging tools, radiopharmaceutical imaging tools, and as replacements to platinum-based drugs in fighting several diseases such as cancer, malaria, *Leishmania major*, and *Trypanosoma cruzi* to name a few. This chapter will discuss a brief history and coordination chemistry of several ruthenium-containing complexes and their uses in solving some of the world's problems.

Chapter 2 – This chapter discusses the chemistry of several ruthenium-containing complexes and their roles in the conversion of solar energy into chemical and electrical energy. In this chapter, subsections will include polypyridyl ruthenium dyes which are currently being developed for their use in the manufacture of solar cells and mixed-metal and non-mixed-metal complexes for the production of hydrogen in various media.

Chapter 3 – Transition metals and transition metal complexes have been of great value to medicine for half a century. For example, cisplatin, cis-diaminedichloroplatinum(II), has been a key chemotherapy drug since its FDA approval in 1978. Vanadium, chromium, and magnesium have been proposed for many years in the treatment of diabetes. Ruthenium complexes have been extensively studied as potential photodynamic chemotherapy drugs over the past decade. In this chapter, the authors will review the roles played by ruthenium coordination complexes and ruthenium organometallic complexes in the treatment of a variety of illnesses, including uses as antimalarial, antimicrobial, and anticancer agents.

Chapter 4 – Organometallic chemistry and particularly organotransition metal complexes have been an intensive area of research which growth was mainly motivated by the impressive achievements in the field of homogeneous catalysis. In fact, the development of catalysis served as foundation for many important industrial processes. Moreover, the fascinating properties of organometallic compounds encouraged the development of its chemistry for several other applications, ranging from material chemistry, where several technological applications were found (integrated optics, molecular switches, dye-sensitized solar cells (DSSCs), organic light emitting diodes (OLED's), to bioinorganic chemistry where they appear as potential drugs for several diseases (cancer, diabetes, malaria, etc.). In this frame, ruthenium organometallic complexes have revealed a prominent role in all these areas due to their great scope in molecular engineering. The vast diversity of frameworks and structures, associated with their stability in several oxidation states, bonding modes and electronic features place ruthenium compounds among the most successful organotransition metal complexes studied to date. In particular, η^5-monocyclopentadienylruthenium derivatives ("RuCp") have been thoroughly studied due to the promising results in the field of nonlinear optics. More recently, the "RuCp" fragment emerged in the new fascinating bioorganometallic subject, displaying important results in the area of potential agents for cancer therapy. These apparent greatly incongruent endeavors might find some common explanation in the unique characteristics of this versatile metal fragment. This chapter presents an overview of the work published during the last two decades in the fields of nonlinear optics and bioorganometallic chemistry concerning the "RuCp" scaffold. An outlook of the synthetic methods involved and the relevant properties for each purpose is also discussed. It will be shown the versatility of the "RuCp" on the design of different organometallic environments, with structural features aiming a particular application.

Chapter 5 – In this contribution, the catalytic activity of a plethora of ruthenium complexes in the isomerization of allylic and propargylic alcohols in non-conventional solvents [water, ionic liquids (*ILs*), glycerol and Deep Eutectic Solvents (*DESs*)] is reviewed. On the one hand, the search for organic reactions proceeding with efficiency, selectivity and atom economy has emerged as a prime goal in synthetic chemistry. Among the organic reactions that proceed with atom economy, isomerization reactions are typical examples because no by-products are generated. To this regard, the ruthenium-catalyzed isomerizations of readily accessible allylic and propargylic alcohols, mainly giving carbonyl compounds, provide a simple synthetic route to these very valuable raw materials in organic chemistry. On the other hand, combination of ruthenium-catalyzed isomerization reactions and non-conventional solvents has led in recent years to the development of a huge number of new and *greener* synthetic methodologies. In this chapter, an overview of the progress achieved on the ruthenium-catalyzed isomerization of allylic and propargylic alcohols in environmentally-friendly solvents will be presented, with special emphasis on synthetic applications.

Chapter 6 – The problem related to the presence of Platinum Group Metals (PGMs) in the environment has raised much attention and great interest in the scientific community. This is due to the fact that the PGMs are widely used in various fields, such as anticancer drugs, jewels production, photographic operations, industrial catalysts, and especially autocatalytic converters. In the last case, their continuous use and deterioration implies a considerable release of these metals in the environment. It should be noted that the metals initially used in autocatalytic converters were platinum, palladium and rhodium, but in recent years such PGMs were gradually and partially replaced, or alloyed with osmium and especially ruthenium. Their addition in the manufacture of autocatalytic converters helps them withstand high temperatures and wear, thus increasing the product life. Thus, the increasing use of autocatalytic converters shows two decidedly conflictual effects on the environment: an evident and drastic reduction of the concentration levels of lead, and, at the same time, an equally evident and widespread increase of the PGMs concentration, and in particular of ruthenium, due to its increasing use in recent years. This work proposes a voltammetric method for the determination of ultra-trace ruthenium in environmental samples: airborne particulate matter, vegetables, superficial waters, mussels, clams and soils/sediments. To better validate the proposed analytical procedure, a critical comparison with spectroscopic measurements — electrothermal atomic absorption spectroscopy (ET–AAS) because of its well established and tested robustness — has been also carried out and discussed here. All the parameters of interest for the set-up of an analytical method, such as trueness and precision (accuracy), limit of detection and quantification, selectivity and, especially, sensitivity were taken into account.

Chapter 7 – Sunlight provides the necessary energy for all life through a process called photosynthesis. With today's increasing demand for energy and the diminishing fossil fuel resources, there exists a need to move the society towards a sustainable energy economy. The light-driven splitting of H_2O to H_2 and O_2 thus constitutes an attractive option for solving this energy crisis. However, because of the kinetic and thermodynamic complexity associated with the processes occurring in the natural photosynthetic machinery, reproducing this represents a great scientific challenge. Currently the development of efficient and robust catalysts for oxidizing H_2O to O_2 constitutes the primary bottleneck for advancing towards a carbon-neutral society. This has attracted significant attention to the construction of molecular complexes that are able to carry out the demanding four-electron oxidation of H_2O in the pursuit of viable catalysts that can be used for commercial applications. The design of mono- and dinuclear Ru complexes that can efficiently adapt to accommodate a wide variety of stable redox states is a powerful strategy to overcome the difficulties encountered in H_2O oxidation. This chapter thus aims at describing and discussing the key aspects and rapid progress of this field, which has certainly contributed to understanding and advancing the art of oxidizing H_2O in artificial photosynthesis.

Chapter 8 – The design and study of new drugs is one of the main challenges in different areas of science for at least two reasons: (i) the cancer has not been defeated and (ii) many bacteria rapidly develop resistance to existing drugs. Development of new drugs is strongly connected with the model of transport, activation of compounds in biological environment, and by the mode of interaction with molecule which is considered the primary target. That is why the recognition of target molecules and processes that determine the activity in biological environment is an imperative for the development of new drugs. A DNA molecule is particularly important for the functioning of biological systems and is considered to be the primary target for anticancer agents. DNA tends to interact by covalent binding with metal complex or non-covalently through two general modes: (i) major and minor groove-bound way stabilized by hydrophobic, electrostatic, and hydrogen-bonding interactions and (ii) through an intercalative interaction in which planar, hetero-aromatic moiety slides between the DNA base pairs. In the case of antimicrobial agents, the drug diffusion through the cell wall is usually major barrier and determining process for the drug activity into the cell. Progressive study of ruthenium complexes with Schiff bases derived from salicylaldehyde and various amines, as candidates for the development of new drugs, is based on several reasons: (i) Ru(III) is isoelectronic with Fe(III) and is found to be readily transported by plasma proteins, (ii) Salicyilideneimines derived from extended planar aromatic amines intercalate DNA, (iii) Many Schiff bases derived from salicyladehyde exhibit antimicrobial activity, especially significant activity against gram-positive bacteria *S. Aureus* and (iv) Since lipid membranes of bacteria favors diffusion of lipid-soluble materials, lipophilicity may be systematically varied on both, salicylaldehyde and amines aromatic rings. Syntheses of salicylideneimines and their complexes are not demanding. Imines, also known as azomethines or Schiff bases, are compounds represented by the general formula $R_1R_2C=NR_3$. A common method for the preparation of the imines is the condensation reaction of salicylaldehyde with the appropriate amine. The reaction can be accelerated by acid catalysis and is generally carried out by refluxing a mixture of a carbonyl compound and an amine. Syntheses of ruthenium complexes are usually carried out in reaction of $RuCl_3$ with appropriate imine(s) in absolute alcohol solution. From chemical point of view ruthenium complexes with salicylideneimine ligands are thermodynamically stable and resistant to hydrolysis. Kinetically, Ru(II) compounds are more labile than Ru(III). The Ru(III)/Ru(II) electrode potentials depend on the type and number of donor atoms. The electronic effect of nitrogen from azomethine group and phenolate oxygen on reduction potential is different. More electronegative and smaller oxygen atom, hard in character, stabilizes Ru(III), while nitrogen as softer, prefers lower oxidation state. Systematic alteration of the coordination mode of salicylideneimine ligands in octahedral ruthenium complexes and the consequent fine-tuning of the formal electrode potential are crucial for prospective use of these compounds as electron-transfer mediators and the development of new sensors and catalysts.

Chapter 9 – Polymeric organometallic ruthenium systems have been known for more than 50 years, and their chemistry and synthetic pathways have been extensively studied mainly for their reaction patterns to give an array of neutral and cationic ruthenium complexes which in turn shows to be highly reactive complexes. Worldwide research over the last few decades on the synthesis and reactivity of ruthenium complexes in solution gave rise to a range of different versatile and stable catalysts which are increasingly employed in organic synthesis. These complexes find widespread use in the synthesis of complex organic molecules which have application in the pharmaceutical, plastic and other commercial industries. The ongoing search for inexpensive and trivial synthetic routes to these chemo- and regio-selective ruthenium complexes have in many accounts made use of polymeric ruthenium precursors, and is still of interest to date. Some of these polymeric complexes also exhibit other interesting physical properties which renders them useful for other applications. This chapter covers the initial discovery of selected organometallic polymeric- and oligomeric Ru(0), Ru(I), and Ru(II) species for the specific application as highly reactive synthons to fine organo- and inorganic ruthenium complexes, their associated solid state structures that has been investigated, and their reactions involving both stoichiometric and catalytic amounts of these complexes with a wide range of ligands under various reaction conditions. Modern approaches to other polymeric ruthenium species that has been synthesized in the last 15 years are also discussed. Selected reactions, reactions with ligands, and selected characterization of the polymeric complexes have been tabulated and are included herein.

In: Ruthenium
Editor: Gary P. Keeler

ISBN: 978-1-63321-657-0

Chapter 1

SOLVING SOME OF THE WORLD'S PROBLEMS WITH RUTHENIUM COMPLEXES: THEIR ROLE IN IMAGING AND BIOMEDICAL APPLICATIONS

Jimmie L. Bullock, Michael J. Celestine and Alvin A. Holder*
Department of Chemistry and Biochemistry,
Old Dominion University, Norfolk, Virginia, US

ABSTRACT

Ruthenium containing-complexes are well suited for biological application owning to the unique properties of ruthenium. For example, ruthenium complexes have been utilized as cellular imaging tools, radiopharmaceutical imaging tools, and as replacements to platinum-based drugs in fighting several diseases such as cancer, malaria, *Leishmania major*, and *Trypanosoma cruzi* to name a few. This chapter will discuss a brief history and coordination chemistry of several ruthenium-containing complexes and their uses in solving some of the world's problems.

ABBREVIATIONS

5CNU	5-cyanouracil
A*β*	amyloid-*β*
acac	acetylacetonate
AD	Alzheimer's disease
Azpy	2-phenylazopyridine
bbn_n	bis[4(40-methyl-2,20-bipyridyl)]-1,n-alkane
BIDA	*N*-(4-(n-butyl)-acetanilide)iminodiacetic *acid*
bipb	bis(imidazo[4,5-*f*]-1,10-phenanthrolin-2-yl)benzene

* Corresponding author: Alvin A. Holder. Department of Chemistry and Biochemistry, Old Dominion University, 4541 Hampton Boulevard, Norfolk, VA 23529-0126, USA. Telephone: 757-683-7102 and e-mail: aholder@odu.edu.

bmbp	2,6-bis(6-methylbenzimidazol-2-yl)pyridine)
$bpibH_2$	1,4-bis([1,10]phenanthroline-[5,6-d]-imidazol-2-yl)benzene
bpm	2,2'- bipyrimidine
bpy	2,2'- bipyridine
CppH	2-(2-pyridyl)pyrimidine-4-carboxylic acid
CTDNA	calf thymus deoxyribonucleic acid
CTZ	clotrimazole
CQ	chloroquine
DIP	4,7-diphenyl-1,10-phenanthroline
DISIDA	*N*-(2,6-diisopropylacetanilide)iminodiacetic *acid*
DMNPB	3-(4,5-dimethoxy-2-nitrophenyl)-2-butyl
DMSO	dimethyl sulfoxide
DNA	Deoxyribonucleic acid
dpp	2,9-di(pyrid-2′-yl)-1,10-phenanthroline
dppz	dipyrido[3,2-a:2',3'-c]phenazine
dpq	2,3-bis(2-pyridyl)quinoxaline)
en	ethylenediamine = 1,2-diaminoethane
HAT	1,4,5,8,9,12-hexaazatriphenylene
Im	imidazole
KTZ	ketoconazole
$mbpibH_2$	1,3-bis(1,10-phenanthroline-[5,6-d]imidazol-2-yl)benzene
Me_2bpy	4,4'-dimethyl-2,2'-bipyridine
MeCN	acetonitrile
MLCT	metal-to-ligand charge-transfer
NTD	neglected tropical disease
PAIDH	2-pyridyl-1H-anthra[1,2-d]imidazole-6,11-dione
PAn_3	tris(*o*-anisyl)phosphane
pbt	2-(2-pyridinyl)benzothiazole
PDT	photodynamic therapy
PGM	platinum group metal
Ph_2phen	4,7-diphenyl-1,10-phenanthroline
$phen_2DTT$	1,4-bis(1,10-phenanthrolin-5-ylsulfanyl)butane-2,3-diol
phen	1, 10-phenanthroline
PIPIDA	(*N*,α-(*p*-isopropyl acetanilide) iminoacetic acid)
pta	1,3,5-triaza-7-phosphatricyclo-[3.3.1.1]decane
sal-*L*-tryp	*N*-salicylidene-*L*-tryptophanate
SBI	sterol biosynthesis inhibitors
SOS	2-mercaptoethyl ether
terpy	2,2';6',2"-*terpyridine*
tpeb	1,3,5-tris(4-pyridylethynyl)benzene
thz	1,3-thiazole
tpphz	tetrapyrido[3,2-a:2',3'-c:3",2"-h:2'",3'"-j]phenazine
tpy	2, 2':6', 2"-terpyridine

HISTORY

Ruthenium is a Group 8A metal that has the symbol **Ru**, an atomic number of 44 (electronic configuration = [Kr] $4d^7$ $5s^1$), and an atomic weight of 101.07 g mol^{-1}. [1] It is named after Ruthenia, the Latin word for Rus' which referred to the people, region, and medieval states (9th to 12th centuries) of the Kievan Rus' polities. Jedrzej Sniadecki claimed to have produced ruthenium in 1807 but he withdrew his claim of the discovery after other scientists failed to replicate his findings. [2] Jons Berzelius and Gottfried Osann nearly discovered ruthenium in 1827 when the duo examined residues left over after dissolving crude platinum obtained from the Ural Mountains (Western Russia to northwester Kazakhstan) in *aqua regia.* [3] Osann thought he had found three new metals, one of which he named "ruthenium," however, discrepancies led to controversy among Berzelius and Osann. [1] With these first two discoveries never verified, a third attempt by Karl Klaus in 1844, generally recognized as the discoverer, showed that Osann's ruthenium oxide sample was very impure but that it did in fact contain a new metal, ruthenium. [4] Klaus obtained six grams of ruthenium from a portion of crude platinum that is insoluble in *aqua regia.* [1, 4] Figure 1 below shows a photograph of the silvery white metallic forms of the pure ruthenium metal.

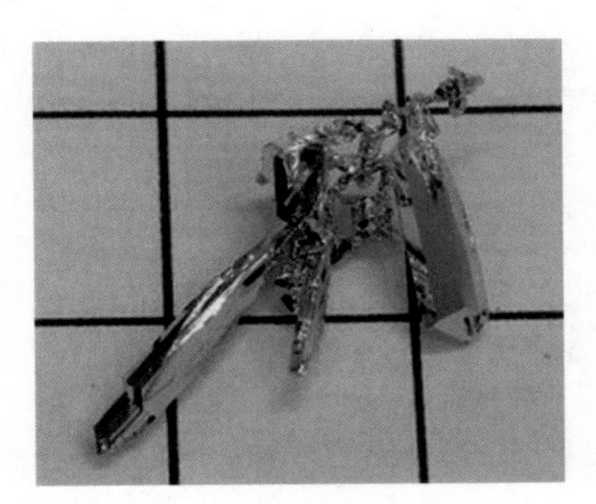

Figure 1. A photograph of ruthenium metal [5].

OCCURRENCE AND PRODUCTION OF RUTHENIUM

Ruthenium is exceedingly rare, as it is only the 74th most abundant metal on Earth. [2] The element is generally found in ores with the other platinum group metals in the Ural Mountains and in North and South America. Small but commercially important quantities are also found in pentlandite $(Fe, Ni)_9S_8$ extracted from Sudbury, Ontario, Canada and in pyroxenite deposits in South Africa. The native form of ruthenium is a very rare mineral (Ir replaces part of Ru in its structure).

Roughly 12 tons of ruthenium is mined each year with estimated global reserves of 5,000 tons. [2] The composition of the platinum group metal (PGM) mixtures varied widely based on geochemical formation. PGM mixtures isolated from South Africa generally contain on average 11% ruthenium while PGMs mined in the former USSR contains only 2% ruthenium. [6] Johnson Matthey lists the base price of ruthenium metal with minimal impurity (99.9% pure) as $72 per ounce.

Ruthenium metal has been found in the free-state; and there are a few naturally occurring minerals such as laurite (ruthenium sulfide), and ruthenarsenite (ruthenium nickel arsenide). All are rare and none act as a commercial source of ruthenium. Ruthenium is commercially obtained as a by-product from nickel and copper mining and processing as well as by the processing of other PGM ores. During electro-refining of copper and nickel, noble metals such as silver, gold and the platinum group metals settle to the bottom of the cell as *anode mud*, which forms the starting point for their extraction. [7] To separate the metals, they must first be brought into solution. Several methods are available depending on the separation process and the composition of the mixture; two representative methods are fusion with sodium peroxide followed by dissolution in *aqua regia*, [8, 9] and dissolution in a mixture of chlorine with hydrochloric acid. [8, 10, 11] Osmium, ruthenium, rhodium and iridium can be separated from platinum and gold and base metals based on their insolubility in *aqua regia*. Rhodium can then be separated from the residue by treatment of the solid residue with molten sodium bisulfate. The insoluble residue, which contains Ru, Os and Ir is then treated with sodium oxide, in which Ir is insoluble, producing water-soluble Ru and Os salts. After oxidation to the volatile oxides, RuO_4 is separated from OsO_4 by precipitation of $(NH_4)_3RuCl_6$ with ammonium chloride or by distillation or extraction with organic solvents of the volatile osmium tetroxide. [12] Hydrogen is then finally used to reduce ammonium ruthenium chloride yielding a powder. [9] The first method to precipitate the ruthenium with ammonium chloride is similar to the procedure that Smithson Tennant and William Hyde Wollaston used for their separations of osmium, iridium, palladium, and rhodium [13-15].

Several methods are now suitable for industrial scale production. In either case, the product is reduced using hydrogen, yielding the metal as a powder or sponge that can be treated using powder metallurgy techniques or by argon-arc welding [16].

Fission products of ^{235}uranium contain significant amounts of ruthenium, as well as the lighter platinum group metals and therefore used nuclear fuels serve as another potential source of ruthenium.

However, the complicated extraction process is expensive and the radioactive isotopes of ruthenium present would make storage for several half-lives of the decaying isotopes necessary; further increasing the cost associated with ruthenium production via this process. The financial costs assoiciated with this method of ruthenium isolation are unattractive and no large-scale extraction has been conducted [17, 18].

Physical Properties

In its pure form ruthenium is a hard, white metal and has four crystal modifications and does not tarnish at room temperatures, but will oxidize in air at 800 °C. It possesses the 10th highest melting point of 2334 °C, the 19th highest density of 12.27 g cm^{-3}, and a Mohs hardness of 6.5. It possesses one of the lowest thermal expansions of all elements (6.4 μM m^{-1} K^{-1}), and a thermal conductivity of 117 W m^{-1} K^{-1}. [19] The metal is not attacked by acids, but will dissolve in fused alkalis.

If potassium chlorate is added to this solution, it oxidizes explosively. It can be plated by electrodeposition or by thermal decomposition methods.

Other Properties

Ruthenium, situated in the middle of the second row of transition metals, lies right at the heart of the periodic table. Its position bestows upon it properties which are not present in early- or late-transition metals. It is unique from the rest of its brethren amongst the platinum group (group 8A), as it possesses an atypical electron configuration in its outermost shell as shown in table 1.

All group 8A elements have two electrons in the outermost shell except ruthenium, as one of its outermost electrons has transferred to a lower shell. A similar effect can be observed with neighboring metals niobium, rhodium, and palladium.

There are seven stable, naturally occurring ruthenium isotopes. In addition to these seven isotopes, 34 radioactive isotopes have been discovered. Of these radioisotopes, the most stable are ^{106}Ru with a half-life of 373.59 days, ^{103}Ru with a half-life of 39.26 days and ^{97}Ru with a half-life of 2.9 days [1, 2].

Fifteen other radioisotopes have been characterized with atomic weights ranging from 89.93 amu (^{90}Ru) to 114.928 amu (^{115}Ru). Most of these have half-lives that are less than five minutes except ^{95}Ru (half-life: 1.643 hours) and ^{105}Ru (half-life: 4.44 hours) [1].

The primary decay mode before the most abundant isotope, ^{102}Ru, is electron capture and the primary mode after is beta emission. The primary decay product before ^{102}Ru is technetium and the primary decay product after is rhodium [1].

Table 1. Electron configurations for group 8A elements

Z	Element	Electron Configuration
26	Iron	$[Ar]\ 3d^6\ 4s^2$
44	Ruthenium	$[Kr]\ 4d^7\ 5s^1$
76	Osmium	$[Xe]\ 4f^{14}\ 5d^6\ 6s^2$
108	Hassium	$[Rn]\ 5f^{14}\ 6d^6\ 7s^2$

Basic Chemistry

The chemistry of ruthenium bears minimal resemblance to that of iron except in some solids such as sulfides or phosphides. The oxidation state of ruthenium range from 0 to +8, and -2. The most common states are +2, +3, and +4. The oxidation states and stereochemistries are summarized in table 2. Although lower oxidation states are known, these mainly only exist with π-bonding ligands. For the most common oxidation sates, there is great complexity as many of the compounds can undergo reversible oxidation and reduction reactions to yield species with the same structure but different oxidation states.

Ruthenium metal can be oxidized to ruthenium(IV) oxide which can be oxidized a second time by sodium metaperiodate to ruthenium tetroxide, RuO_4, a strong oxidizing agent with a structure and properties analogous to osmium tetroxide. The properties of ruthenium and osmium compounds are often very similar. The uses of ruthenium in coordination chemistry are numerous. Derivatives of bipyridine and terpyridine are well known, the most well-known of course being the luminescent tris(bipyridine)ruthenium(II) chloride.

Table 2. Oxidation States and Stereochemistry of Ruthenium [20]

Oxidation state	Coordination number	Geometry	Examples
Ru^{-II}	4	Tetrahedral	$[Ru(CO)_4]^{2-}$, $[Ru(diphos)_2]^{2-}$
Ru^{0}, d^8	5	tbp[d]	$[Ru(CO)_5]$, $[Ru(CO)_3(PPh_3)_2]$
Ru^{I}, d^7	6[a]		$[\eta^5\text{-}C_5H_5Ru(CO)_2]_2$
Ru^{II}, d^6	5 5 6[b]	See text tbp[d] Octahedral	$RuCl_2(PPh_3)_3$ $RuHCl(PPh_3)_3$ $[RuNOCl_4]^{2-}$, $[Ru(bpy)_3]^{2+}$, $[Ru(NH_3)_6]^{2+}$, $RuCl_2CO(PEtPh_2)_3$
Ru^{III}, d^5	4 6[b]	Distorted tetrahedral Octahedral	$Ru_2(CH_2SiMe_3)_6$[c] $[Ru(NH_3)_5Cl]^{2+}$,$[RuCl_5H_2O]^{2-}$, K_3RuF_6
Ru^{IV}, d^4	4 4 5 6[b] 7	Square Tetrahedral tbp[d] Octahedral Distorted pentagonal bipyramidal	$Ru[N(2,6\text{-}Pr^iC_6H_3)]_2(PMe_3)_2$ $[Ru(c\text{-}C_6H_{11})_4]$ $[Ru(SR)_4(MeCN)]$ K_2RuCl_6, RuO_2[c] $[RuCl(S_2CNMe_2)_3]$
Ru^{V}, d^3	5 6	 Octahedral	$[Ru_2(O)_2(CH_2SiMe_3)_6]$[c] $KRuF_6$, $(RuF_5)_4$
Ru^{VI}, d^2	4 5 6	Tetrahedral sp[e] tbp[d] Octahedral	RuO_4^{2-} $[RuNCl]^-$ $[RuO_3(OH)_2]^{2-}$ RuF_6
Ru^{VII}, d^1	4	Tetrahedral	RuO_4^-
Ru^{VIII}, d^0	4	Tetrahedral	RuO_4

[a]If η^5-C_5H_5 is assumed to occupy three coordination sites
[b]Most common states for Ru
[c]Metal-metal bond present
[d]Trigonal bipyramidal
[e]Square pyramidal

Aqua Ions of Ruthenium

The aqua ions of ruthenium(II), ruthenium(III), and ruthenium(IV) are arguably the most important, of which the divalent, diamagnetic, pink $[Ru\ (H_2O)_6]^{2+}$ is the most important, as it serves as a useful starting material for the synthesis of numerous ruthenium complexes. It is most commonly produced by the reduction of an aqueous solution of RuO_4 with lead [21].

The Pb^{2+} is removed after treatment with H_2SO_4 and the $[Ru(H_2O)_6]^{2+}$ is isolated as a toluene sulfonate following ion exchange treatment. The tosylates is readily converted to the triflate by ion exchange [20].

The +2 ion is readily oxidized in air to a yellow species $[Ru(H_2O)_6]^{3+}$ which possesses a reduction potential of 0.23 V. [20] The water ligands in the +2 species can also be substituted by halides such as Cl^- and other anions or by neutral ligands such as MeCN and DMSO; rate constants for these monosubstitutions have been obtained and reported in literature. [22] The +2 aqua ions are also capable of catalyzing several other reactions in solutions, such as dimerization of ethylene via the intermediates $[Ru(C_2H_4)(H_2O)_5]^{2+}$ and $[Ru(C_2H_4)_2(H_2O)_4]^{2+}$ which have been isolated as tosylates. [23, 24] It is also capable of polymerizing norbornenes [25].

Ruthenium(IV) aqua ions, $H_n[Ru_4O_6(H_2O)_{12}]^{(4+n)+}$, are generally obtained upon electrochemical oxidation of $[Ru(H_2O)_6]^{2+}$ in HBF_4. Although the structures are not fully characterized, the $Ru_4O_6^{4+}$ core with two single and two double oxo-bridges appears to be present [26].

Use of Ruthenium Halide Salts in Syntheses

Ruthenium halide salts are very important in synthesis. The most prevalent precursor is ruthenium trichloride ($RuCl_3{\cdot}nH_2O$), a red solid, is poorly defined chemically but very versatile synthetically. [14] It is generally synthesized by evaporating a concentrated solution of HCl and RuO_4. Ru(II) chloro complexes, which are often deep blue in color, can be obtained from $RuCl_3{\cdot}nH_2O$ by reducing it via electrochemical or chemical methods.

The blue solutions made by this reduction are used as starting materials in multiple syntheses including: Cp_2Ru, phosphine complexes, bipyridyl complexes, [27] $[Ru(bpy)_3]^{2+}$, *cis*-$[Ru(bpy)Cl_2]^+$, *cis*-$[Ru(bpy)_2Cl_2]$, [28] $[RuCl_6]^{3-}$, a pyridylpeptide complex, [29] and $[Ru(acac)_3]$ [30].

Creutz-Taube Complex and Analogues

A series of complexes featuring two Ru atoms bridged by bidentate ligands which facilitate a degree of electron transfer have been synthesized. The prototype has been extensively studied and was named after the discoverers Carol Creutz and Henry Taube. [31] The Creutz-Taube ion shown in figure 2 ($[Ru(NH_3)_5]_2(C_4H_4N_2)^{5+}$) illustrates the advantages that ruthenium complexes possess for examining redox reactions. Many analogues of this ion have been prepared using different bridging ligands.

Other complexes have been extensively studied for the insight that they may provide about the processes of electron exchange in bimolecular redox reactions and about the general character of electron transmission through chemical systems, to include spectroscopic phenomena associated with such processes. These ions generally possess mixed valencies, II-III (5+), but II-II (4+) and III-III (6+) salts have also been isolated. Crystal structures are consistent with symmetrical ions even in the II-III case.

Aromatic Pyridine and Polypyridine-Containing Complexes

Complexes containing pyridines, bipyridines, terpyridines, and other polypyridines differ considerably from those which contain only NH_3 and aliphatic amines.

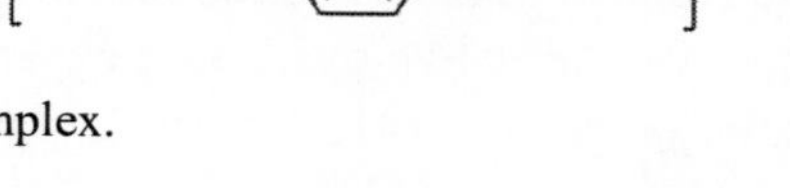

$$\left[(H_3N)_5RuN\langle\rangle NRu(NH_3)_5\right]^{5+}$$

Figure 2. The Creutz-Taube Complex.

They have been and continue to be intensively studied due to the unusual properties of photoinduced energy migration and charge separation, luminescence, photocatalytic reactions, and water activation.

They are involved in the construction of double-helical complexes, [32] as complexes that bind to DNA, [33-38] and used as molecular rods and wires for fast electron transfers [39].

$[Ru(bpy)_3]^{2+}$ is the most extensively studied ruthenium based sensitizer in photodriven chemical and physical processes such as photolysis of water. The excited structure of the excited ion is the result of a transfer of an electron from the t_2g orbital to one of the ligands π^* orbitals. This excited state then reverts to the ground state by photoemission without chemical reaction unless suitable reactants are present. This process is distinctly different than the process observed for simple amines, which respond to photoexcitation by prompt aquation or oxidization as shown by equations 1 and 2 below:

$$[Ru(NH_3)_5L]^{2+} + H_2O \xrightarrow{h\nu} [Ru(NH_3)_5H_2O]^{2+} \text{ or } [Ru(NH_3)_4L(H_2O)]^{2+} \quad (1)$$

$$[Ru(NH_3)_5L]^{2+} + H^+ \xrightarrow{h\nu} [Ru(NH_3)_5L]^{3+} + 1/_2\, H_2 \quad (2)$$

Examples of more complicated ligands that show luminescent behaviors are as shown below:

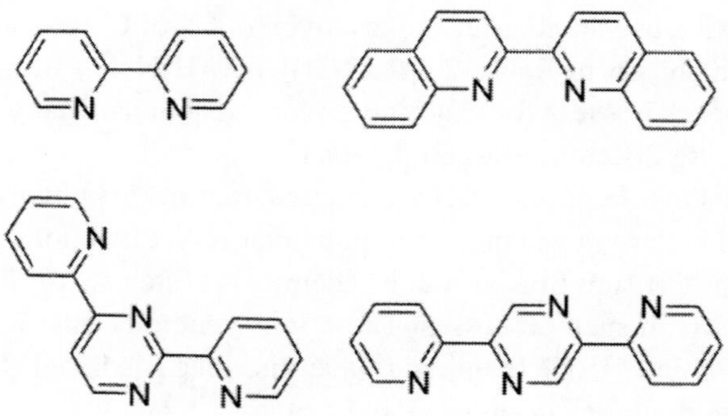

N N N N

N N N N N N N N

Uses of Ruthenium and Its Complexes

Due to ruthenium's unique properties, it has application over a wide spectra of areas. It is often used in alloys, as a catalyst in various chemical reactions, medicinal applications ranging from immunosuppresssants to sensors, solar cells, and electronics.

The metal is one of the most effective hardeners for platinum and palladium, and it is often alloyed with these metals to make electrical contacts for severe wear resistance. [40] In this application, only very thin plated films are required to achieve the necessary wear-resistance making it a cost effective alternative over more expensive metals such as rhodium which possess many of the same properties. [41, 42] These thin coats are generally applied via electroplating or sputtering techniques. [43] A ruthenium-molybdenum alloy has been shown to be superconductive at 10.6 K. [44, 45] Additionally, ruthenium is occasionally added to jewelry to make it harder. Corrosion resistant deep water pipes constructed of titanium are improved over a hundredfold by the addition of 0.1% ruthenium. [46, 47] Ruthenium is also used in some advanced high-temperature single-crystal super alloys, with applications including the turbine blades in jet engines. Several nickel based superalloy compositions are described in the literature [48, 49].

Ruthenium is a versatile catalyst. It can be the utilized to catalyze the splitting of hydrogen sulfide (H_2S) through light, using an aqueous suspension of cadmium sulfide (CdS) particles loaded with ruthenium dioxide.

This process is used to facilitate the removal of H_2S in oil refinement and other industrial processes [50].

Organometallic ruthenium carbene and alkylidene complexes have been found to be highly efficient catalysts for olefin metathesis, [51, 52] a process often utilized in organic and pharmaceutical chemistry.

Ruthenium compounds in general are well-suited for medicinal applications. [53-55] They have been investigated as immunosuppressants, [56] nitric oxide scavengers/deliverers, [57, 58] anti-microbial [59-62] and anti-malarial agents. [63] The fluorescence of some ruthenium complexes is quenched by oxygen, which has led to their use as optode sensors for oxygen. [64] Ruthenium red, $[(NH_3)_5Ru\text{-}O\text{-}Ru(NH_3)_4\text{-}O\text{-}Ru(NH_3)_5]^{6+}$, is a biological stain used to stain polyanionic molecules such as pectin and nucleic acids for light microscopy and electron microscopy. [65] The beta-decaying isotope ^{106}ruthenium is used in radiotherapy of eye tumors, mainly malignant melanomas of the uvea. [66] Ruthenium-complexes are at the forefront of anti-cancer research. [67] Compared with platinum complexes such as cisplatin, ruthenium complexes show greater resistance to hydrolysis and more selective action on tumors. NAMI-A and KP1019 whose structures are shown below in figure 3 are two ruthenium-based drugs undergoing clinical evaluation against metastatic tumors and colon cancers. Some ruthenium complexes absorb light throughout the visible spectrum and these complexes are being pursued for their potential application in various areas of solar energy technologies.

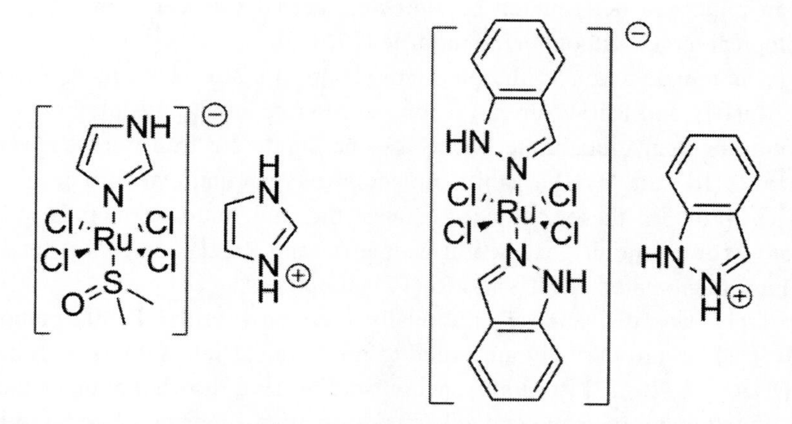

Figure 3. Structures of (left to right) NAMI-A and KP1019, the first ruthenium anticancer complexes to enter clinical trials.

For example, [Ru((4,4-dicarboxyl-2,2'-bipyridine)(4,4'-bis(p-hexyloxystyryl)-2,2-bipyridine)$(NCS)_2$] and [Ru((4,4-dicarboxyl-2,2'-bipyridine)(4,4'-bis(p-methoxystyryl)-2,2'-bipyridine)$(NCS)_2$] have been used for light absorption in dye-sensitized solar cells, a promising new low-cost solar cell system. [68] In addition, polymers containing pendant polypyridyl ruthenium complexes absorbed to metal-oxide surfaces are currently being investigated for their light-harvesting properties [69].

Chemical vapor deposition of ruthenium is used as a method to produce thin films of pure ruthenium on substrates. These films show promising properties for the use in microchips and for the giant magnetoresistive read element for hard disk drives. Ruthenium was also suggested as a possible material for microelectronics because its use is compatible with semiconductor processing techniques [70].

PROPERTIES SUITED TO BIOLOGICAL APPLICATIONS

Over the last few decades, coordination complexes containing d^6 metal centers and polypyridyl ligand architectures have been developed as structure- and site-specific DNA binding agents. [71, 72] Due to the attractive photophysical properties, much research has been focused on complexes containing ruthenium metal centers and, more recently, attention has shifted to the use of these complexes in biological systems.

As the rules that govern the cellular uptake and localization of these systems are determined numerous applications ranging from cellular imaging to therapeutics are rising [73, 74].

There are three main properties that make ruthenium compounds well suited to medicinal application: (i) rate of ligand exchange, (ii) the range of accessible oxidation states, and (iii) the ability of ruthenium to mimic iron in binding to certain biological molecules. [4] Many ruthenium complexes have been evaluated for clinical applications, particularly in the treatment of cancer, due in part, to Ru(II) and Ru(III) complexes having similar ligand exchange kinetics to those of Pt(II) complexes and cellular division rates. [74] Ligand exchange is an important determinant of biological activity, as very few metal-based drugs reach the biological target without being modified [75].

Ruthenium is unique amongst the platinum group in that each of its common oxidation states Ru(II), Ru(III), and Ru(IV) are all readily accessible under physiological conditions. In a biological environment glutathione, ascorbate and single electron transfer proteins can be used to reduce Ru(III) and Ru(IV), while molecular oxygen and cytochrome oxidase readily oxidize Ru(II). [75] In these oxidation states the ruthenium center is predominantly hexacoordinate with essentially octahedral geometry, and Ru(II) complexes tend to be more biologically inert than related Ru(III) and Ru(IV) complexes.

Coordinatively saturated and subsitutionally inert polypyridyl Ru(II) compounds have cytotoxic effect which are partially attributed to noncovalent interactions with nucleic acids, particularly DNA. [38, 76, 77] Recently, several studies have shown that other factors such as modification of cell membrane and cell adhesion properties, topoisomerase I and II inhibition, [78] or mitochondrial-mediated apoptosis, [76] could be responsible for cytotoxicity. The low toxicity of ruthenium drugs is derived from the fact that ruthenium can mimic iron in biological systems. This fact allows it to bind to many biomolecules, including serum transferrin and albumin. [79] These two proteins are used by mammals to solubilize and transport iron; as such ruthenium possesses natural advantages over Pt-based drugs. Since rapidly dividing cells, for example cancer cells, have a greater requirement for iron, they increase the number of transferrin receptors located on their cell surfaces, thereby sequestering more of the circulating metal-loaded transferrin [80].

RUTHENIUM COMPLEXES AND THEIR CELLULAR IMAGING APPLICATIONS

The most widely utilized probes in cellular imaging are fluorescent and based on organic fluorescent compounds, [81] typically polyaromatic chromophores, i.e., pyrene- and perylene-containing complexes. [82] The short luminescence lifetimes of these species often limits the environmental sensitivity and their applications in fluorescence lifetime imaging. [83, 84] Compared with these systems, transition metal complexes based on metal-to-ligand charge-transfers (MLCT) mechanisms have become the best candidates for bioimaging owing to their good stability, [85-90] and their photophysical properties such as emission wavelength shifts with changes in the local environments, significant Stokes shifts for easy separation of excitation and emission, and relatively long lifetimes compared with purely organic luminophores. [91] Ruthenium complexes are particularly attractive for photoactivated biological applications, as they possess tunable photophysical properties, and they absorb strongly in the visible region ($\lambda_{max} \sim 450$ nm).

Ruthenium polypyridyl complexes have unique photophysical properties which make them potentially invaluable as probes for cellular imaging including: intense polarizing luminescence, large Stokes shifts, red emission wavelength, and good photostability. [92] They are oxygen-sensitive and do not generally exhibit the complication of dimer or excimer formation as observed for some O_2-sensitive organic probes. [93] The biological activity of ruthenium complexes was first examined by Francis Dwyer in the early 1950s, [94-97] where a family of tris(polypyridyl) complexes were shown to have bacteriostatic and antiviral activities. [94] Owing to their facile synthesis, stability in aqueous solution, and luminescence, [98] the cellular uptake properties and cytotoxicity of polypyridine complexes of ruthenium are been widely reported [98-104].

Due to their unique photophysical properties, sensitively depending on environment, a series of ruthenium-dppz complexes were synthesized by Svensson et al. [105, 106] and utilized as probes for cellular imaging with fluorescence microscopy. [107] Three complexes derivatized with alkyl ether chains of varied length as shown in figure 4, were shown to exhibit distinctly different cellular staining patterns by confocal laser scanning microscopy.

There is significant difference in the localization of the complexes where a decreased length of the alkyl ether chain results in higher emission intensity in the nucleus compared to in the cytoplasm. Co-staining with commercial RNA and membrane-specific dyes showed the least lipophilic complexes exclusively stain DNA inside the nucleus of the cell shown in figure 4 A; whereas the most lipophilic complexes preferentially stain membrane-rich portions including the endoplasmic reticulum of the cell shown in figure 4 B. Interestingly, only complexes of intermediate lipophilicity showed intense staining of the RNA-rich nucleoli [107].

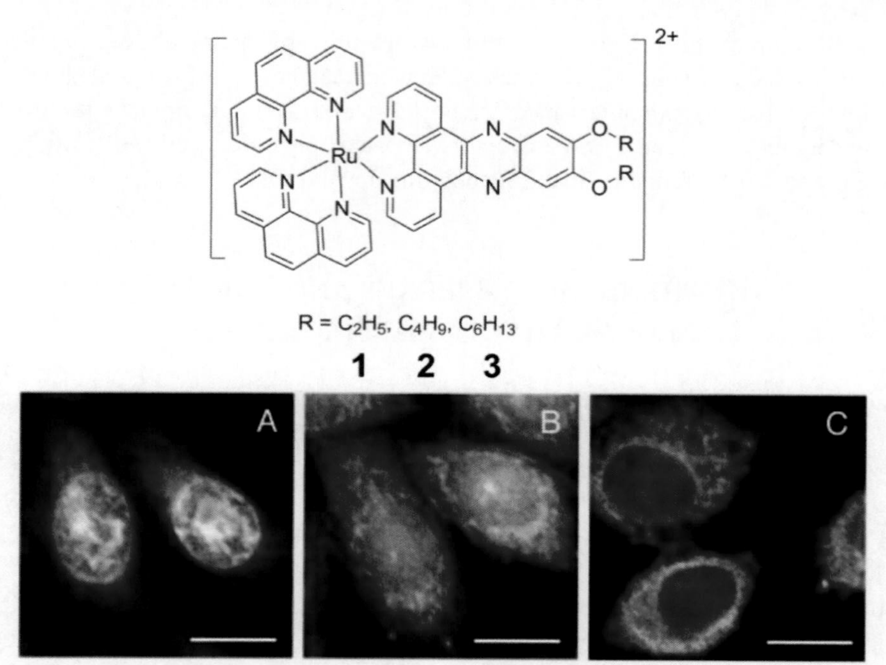

Scale bars indicate 10 μm. Reprint with permission from Svensson, F.R.; Matson, M.; Li, M.; Lincoln, P. *Biophys. Chem.* 2010, *149*, 102. Copyright 2010 American Chemical Society [108].

Figure 4. Confocal fluorescence microscopy images showing the cellular distribution of ruthenium complexes in CHO-K1 cells. **1** (A), **2** (B), and **3** (C) 10 μM excited at 488 nm.

The three lipophilic ruthenium-dppz complexes with tunable lipophilicity show major variations in binding preference comparing RNA with DNA and phospholipid membranes. The localization studies as by confocal microscopy analyses correlate with the emission spectroscopy measurements as well as *in vitro* luminescence. The different preferences as a response to small structural variation highlights the potential of ruthenium-complexes as selective and sensitive cellular and biomacromolecular probes [107].

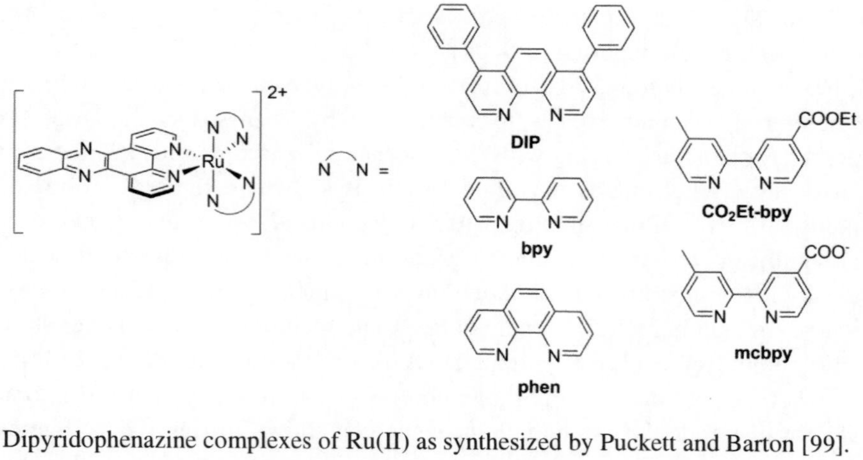

2+

N N =

DIP

CO_2Et-bpy

bpy

mcbpy

phen

Figure 5. Dipyridophenazine complexes of Ru(II) as synthesized by Puckett and Barton [99].

Figure 5 shows the structures of another series of ruthenium(II)-dppz complexes which were synthesized by Puckett and Barton for systematic comparison of the cellular uptake response of HeLa cells to variations in complex charge, size, and hydrophobicity. [99] Uptake of the different ruthenium complexes was compared using mean fluorescence values obtained following flow cytometric analysis as shown in table 3.

Table 3. Mean luminescence intensity of HeLa cells incubated with ruthenium complexes by flow cytometry

	Ancillary Ligands of $[RuL_2\text{-dppz}]^{n+}$				
[Complex]/μM	bpy	CO_2Et-bpy	mcbpy	phen	DIP
0. 5	n.d.	n.d.	n.d.	n.d.	60
1	n.d.	n.d.	n.d.	n.d.	99
5	38	45	20	52	597
10[b]	38	45	21	58	974 (571)
20[b]	48 (27)	51 (29)	26 (19)	111 (50)	n.d.

[a]cells incubated with ruthenium complex for 2 h at ambient temperature. Ruthenium complexes were excited at 488 nm, with emission observed at 600-620 nm. [b]Samples washed after incubation are shown in parentheses. n.d. = not determined.

[a]Reprint with permission from Puckett, C. A.; Barton, J. K. *J. Am. Chem. Soc.* 2006, *129*, 46. Copyright 2006 American Chemical Society [99].

Below 1 uM, $[Ru(DIP)_2(dppz)]^{2+}$ is taken up well above the background for cells, while even at higher concentrations of $[Ru(bpy)_2(dppz)]^{2+}$, $[Ru(CO_2\text{-Et-bpy})_2(dppz)]^{2+}$, and $[Ru(phen)_2(dppz)]^{2+}$ are taken up to a lesser extent. Even at concentration of 20 μM Ru little luminescence was evident for $[Ru(mcbpy)_2(dppz)]$ [99]. Confocal microscopy confirmed the intracellular transport of the complexes to the cell interior, with $[Ru(DIP)_2(dppz)]^{2+}$ displaying intense luminescence within two (2) hours as shown in figure 6, and $[Ru(bpy)_2dppz]^{2+}$ and $[Ru(phen)_2dppz]^{2+}$ showing slower uptake (>4 h) as consistent with the flow cytometric data [99].

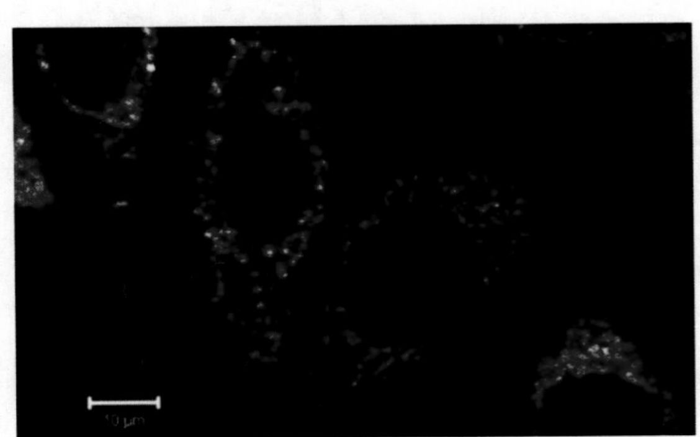

Reprint with permission from Puckett, C. A.; Barton, J. K. *J. Am. Chem. Soc.* 2006, *129*, 46. Copyright 2006 American Chemical Society [99].

Figure 6. Cellular uptake of $[Ru(DIP)_2(dppz)]^{2+}$ in HeLa cells at low incubation concentration and short time (5μM, 2 h).

These results are consistent with result reported by Svennson and co-workers as well as with cisplatin analogues, where the complexes with the greatest lipophilicity exhibit the highest cellular uptake. [109] These results establish that ruthenium complexes are stable to intracellular environment; and that flow cytometry can be rapidly applied to analyze ruthenium analogues without further specialized instrumentation. Statistics on thousands of cells treated with a wide range of metal complexes can be generated quickly.

To highlight difference that may arise from isomeric differences of complexes cellular localization, uptake, and biomolecular interactions studies of the pure enantiomers of two structural isomers (ΔΔ and ΛΛ) of [μ-bipb $(phen)_4Ru_2]^{4+}$ using confocal laser scanning microscopy, emission spectroscopy, and linear dichroism were conducted by Svensson et al. [110] Both complexes containing either *meta*-bipb ((1,3-bis(imidazo[4,5-f]-1,10-phenanthrolin-2-yl)benzene) or *para*-bipb (1,4-bis(imidazo[4,5-f]-1,10-phenanthrolin-2-yl)benzene) displayed distinct enantiomeric differences in the staining pattern of CHO-K1 cells, which arise from chiral discrimination in the binding to intracellular components. The ΔΔ enantiomers of both the meta- and para- showed intense emission inside the nucleus, while the ΛΛ enantiomers showed emission within the cytoplasm shown in Figure 7 [110].

Uptake of complexes in live cells is efficient and nontoxic at 5 μM and occurs through an apparent energy-dependent mechanism. No differences in uptake were observed between the structural isomers or the enantiomers, suggesting that the interactions triggering uptake are rather insensitive to structural variations.

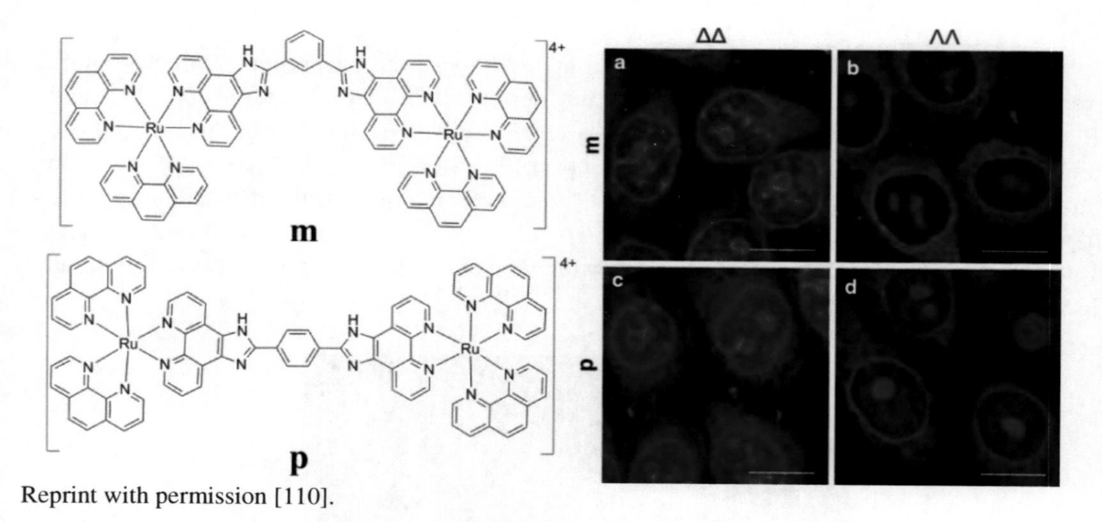

Reprint with permission [110].

Figure 7. Structures of [μ-*meta*-bipb$(phen)_4Ru_2]^{4+}$ and [μ-*para*-bipb$(phen)_4Ru_2]^{4+}$ and confocal laser scanning microscopic images of a) ΔΔ-m, b) ΛΛ-m, c) ΔΔ-p, and d) ΛΛ-p, in fixed cells.

Altogether, these findings show that the complexes studied are promising for cellular imaging probes. In addition, linear dichroism studies showed the complexes exhibit DNA-condensing properties (polyplex formation), making them interesting as potential gene delivery vectors [110].

Since the discovery of the DNA intercalation of $[Ru(bpy)_2(dppz)]^{2+}$, [111] numerous "DNA light-switch" compounds have been discovered. [112-115] $[Ru(phen)_2(tppphz)]^{2+}$ and $[(Ru(phen)_2)_2(tppphz)]^{4+}$ were examined and demonstrated luminescent light switch complex properties as a DNA imaging agent by Gill et al. [116, 117] Both complexes were internalized by cells via an non-endocytic mechanism of active transport, where they rapidly target the nuclei of MCF-7 human breast cancer cells. [116] A more lipophilic derivative ruthenium(II) complex $[(Ru(DIP)_2)_2(tpphz)]^{4+}$ was recently reported. [118] Aqueous *in vitro* binding studies indicate that this complex binds to duplex DNA with an affinity of 1.8×10^6 M^{-1} through a non-classical groove-binding interaction, however, unlike the parent complex $[(Ru(phen)_2)_2(tpphz)]^{4+}$, it also displays an increase in MLCT luminescence on addition of liposomes. [118] Confocal microscopy studies show that this lipophilic complex selectively targets the endoplasmic reticulum (ER) of eukaryotic cells, where it functions as an imaging agent for this organelle. While ER-targeting has been established for luminescent europium(III), [119] zinc(II), [120] and platinum(II) complexes, [121] along with a wide range of other metal based systems, [122-124] this is the first time that a ruthenium(II) complex has been definitively proven to be a luminescent cellular probe for this organelle.

In addition to light microscopy Ru(II) complexes as may function as contrast agents in transmission electron microscopy (TEM). TEM analysis indicated intracellular localization was strong in the nuclear membrane and ER, while not showing strong intranuclear contrast signal. These results indicate Ru(II) complexes have potential as dual-mode cellular imaging agents for uses in both light and electron microscopies [118].

DNA light switch complexes are luminescent when bound to DNA and often are utilized to confirm DNA intercalation by transition metal complexes. [111, 125-128] Contrary to this well held idea recent work conducted by Turro and co-workers with $[(bpy)_2Ru(tpphz)Ru(bpy)_2]^{4+}$ (whose structure is shown in figure 8 below) has shown that DNA intercalation is not required to obtain light-switch behavior. [129] Weak emission for the excited state in water and a red shift and forty-fold increase in intensity were observed upon addition of 100 μM $[(bpy)_2Ru(tpphz)Ru(bpy)_2]^{4+}$ to calf thymus DNA (CTDNA). However, addition of increasing concentration of $[(bpy)_2Ru(tpphz) Ru(bpy)_2]^{4+}$ to herring sperm DNA did not result in an increase in the viscosity of the solution, indicate the complex does not intercalate into DNA. [129] Several methods were utilized to try to thread the complex into DNA but were unsuccessful confirming the 'light-switch' behavior without intercalation. This work for the first time highlights the fact that light-switch behavior cannot be exclusively use to confirm intercalation of transition metal complexes into DNA. [129] More recently, Zhang et al. [130] reported on a dual activated molecular light switch complex $[Ru(phen)_2(Hcdpq)](ClO_4)_2$ which responds to both pH and DNA. The complex is capable of distinguishing CTDNA from yeast RNA with the selectivity being superior to two well-known DNA light switches ($[Ru(bpy)_2(dppz)]^{2+}$ and ethidium bromide). DNA viscosities show no change upon addition of complex indicating an intercalative binding mode is excluded; instead groove binding is the proposed main mode of action [130].

Barton and Puckett have shown that attaching a fluorescein moiety to a ruthenium-octaarginine conjugate preferentially directs the molecule to the nucleus. [100] This shows that the nature of the organic fluorophore affects the transport pathway and its subcellular localization. O'Conner et al. [101] recently reported on a new cellular imaging probe capable of imaging RNA. RuEth (as shown below in figure 9) is composed of a phenanthridine moiety covalently linked to a ruthenium(II) isothiocyanante modified complex.

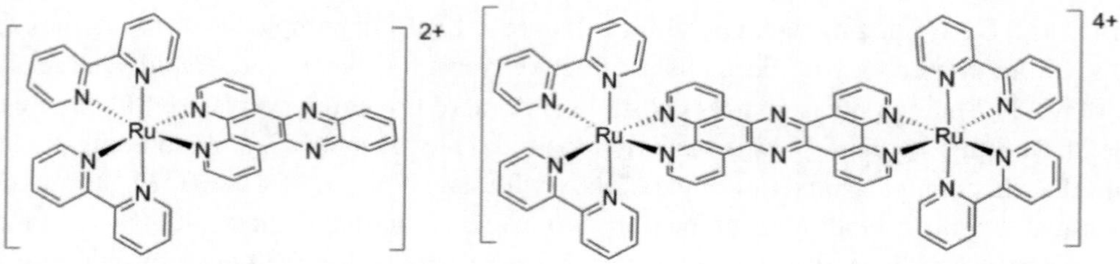

Figure 8. Structure of $[Ru(bpy)_2(dppz)]^{2+}$ and $[(bpy)_2Ru(tpphz)Ru(bpy)_2]^{4+}$ both shown to act as DNA "light-switch" complexes.

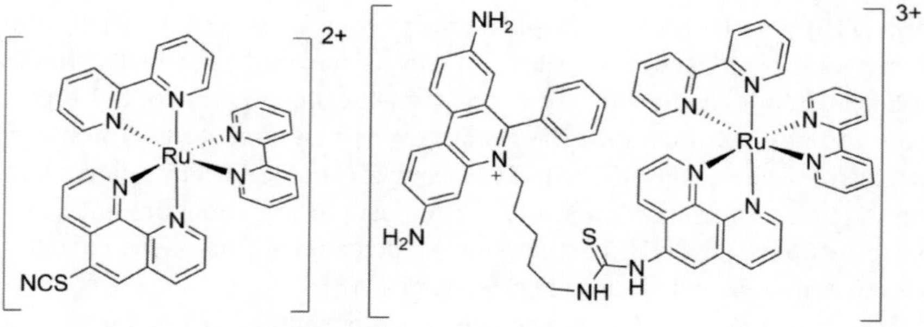

Figure 9. Structural formulas of RuITC and RuEth as by O'Conner et al. [101].

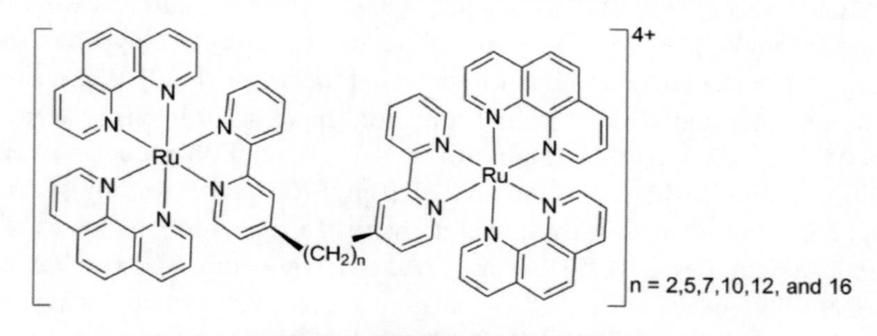

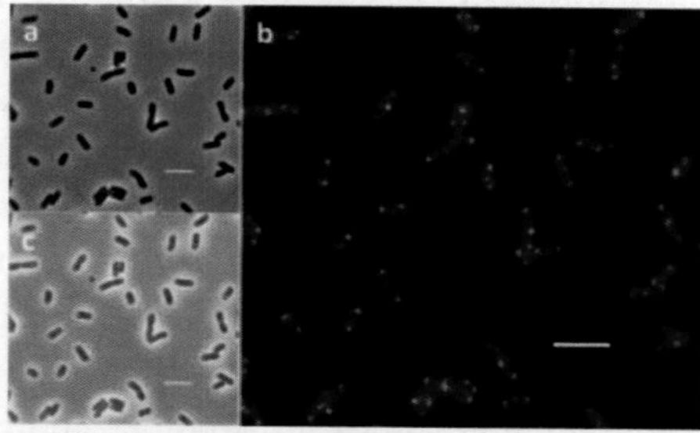

Reprinted with permission from (Li, F.; Harry, E. J.; Bottomley, A. L.; Edstein, M. D.; Birrell, G. W.; Woodward, C. E.; Keene, F. R.; Collins, J. G. *Chem. Sci.* 2014, *5*, 685). Published by The Royal Society of Chemistry [131].

Figure 10. Structure of dinuclear polypyridylruthenium(II) complexes and $Rubb_{16}$ localization in E. coli MG1665 cells at MIC – 4 mg ml^{-1}. The fluorescence microscopy images are: (a), phase-contrast; (b),phosphorescence; and (c), merged.

RuEth offers a longer fluorescence lifetime of the ruthenium bipyridine complex through a spin-forbidden resonance energy transfer (SF-RET) making the complex an excellent probe for RNA detection using time-resolved fluorescence spectroscopy. Coupling RuEth and time-resolved fluorescence spectroscopy results in a drastic increase in signal to background of when compared with steady-state fluorescence methods for cell growth medium from 3 to 13. [101] RuEth is utilized to image mammalian breast cancer cells regions rich in polyribonucleotides (cytoplasm and nucleolus) show more fluorescent intensity when compared with areas rich in DNA (nucleus) [101].

A series of dinuclear polypyridylruthenium(II) complexes $Rubb_n$, (where n = 2,5,7,10,12, and 16) as shown in figure 10 were examined using wide-field fluorescence to study the intracellular binding sites in Escherichia coli [131, 132].

Upon incubation of the complex with *E. coli* cells at the minimum inhibitory concentration (4 μg ml^{-1}), $Rubb_{16}$ localized within ribosomes with no significant DNA binding observed as shown in figure 10. [131] Localization studies suggest major accumulation generally occupy a central region of non-dividing *E. coli* cells with the poles generally devoid of DNA.

Furthermore, $Rubb_{16}$ condensed the ribosomes when they existed as polysomes.

It is postulated that the condensation of polysomes would halt protein production, and thereby inhibit bacterial growth. The results of this study indicate that the family of inert dinuclear ruthenium complexes $Rubb_n$ selectively target RNA over DNA *in vivo.* [131] Selective RNA targeting could be advantageous for the development of therapeutic agents, and because of differences in ribosome structure between bacteria and eukaryotic cells, the $Rubb_n$ complexes could be selectively toxic to bacteria.

In support of this hypothesis, the toxicity of $Rubb_{16}$ was found to be significantly less toxic to liver and kidney cell lines than against a range of bacteria [131].

Gunnlaugsson and co-workers were the first to report on modified gold nanoparticles (AuNPs) with Ru(II)-polypyridyl complexes to be utilized as luminescent cellular imaging agents. [133] Each AuNP possesses a common ligand and a covalent spacer to separate the Ru(II) polypyridyl complex from the surface of the AuNP as shown below in figure 11. High affinity for DNA binding of the functionalized AuNPs was confirmed with UV-Vis, luminescence and ethidium bromide displacement assays.

Figure 12 shows that bightfield (12 A) and fluorescence confocal laser scanning microscopic images (12 B) showed a perfect overlap and confirmed that AuNP-1 is luminescent from within the cells; with apparent localization in the cytoplasm and nucleus in HeLa cells. Co-staining the nucleus with DAPI and TEM imaging further confirmed localization in the nucleus and cytosol, as shown in figure 12C and D, respectively. No apparent toxicity was observed for the AuNPs against mesothelioma cell line (CRL5195) via the Alamar blue cytotoxicity assay. [133] These studies confirm the potential use of Ru(II) polypyridyl functionalized AuNPs as highly sensitive cellular imaging agent.

For more information on the use of ruthenium complexes as cellular imaging agents the reader is encouraged to see the work of Drs. Michael P. Coogan, Martin R. Gill, Jim A. Thomas, Frida R. Svensson, and Thorfinnur Gunnlaugsson.

Radiopharmaceutical Imaging Using Ruthenium

Metal containing radiopharmaceuticals are classified into two broad areas: (1) those that find their target by the virtue of the properties of aqua metal ions or the metal ion itself; and (2) those that localize in the desired tissues by attaching to a targeted protein or polypeptide.

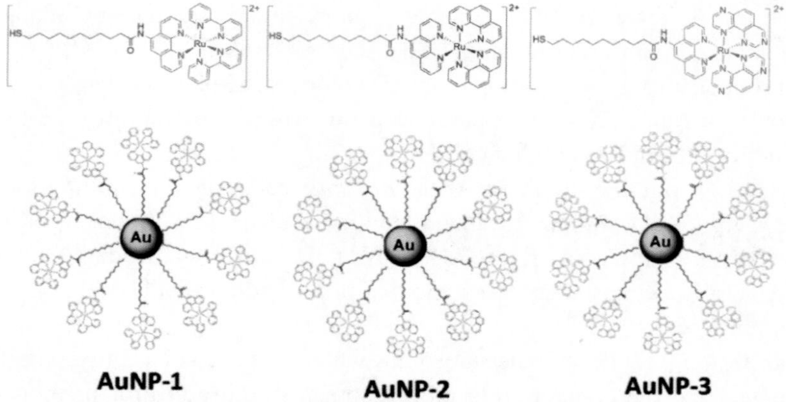

AuNP-1 AuNP-2 AuNP-3

Reprint with permission from Elmes, R. B. P.; Orange, K. N.; Cloonan, S. M.; Williams, D. C.; Gunnlaugsson, T. *J. Am. Chem. Soc.* 2011, *133*, 15862. Copyright 2011 American Chemical Society [133].

Figure 11. Structures of complexes and cartoon representation on their corresponding AuNPs systems as by Elmes et al.

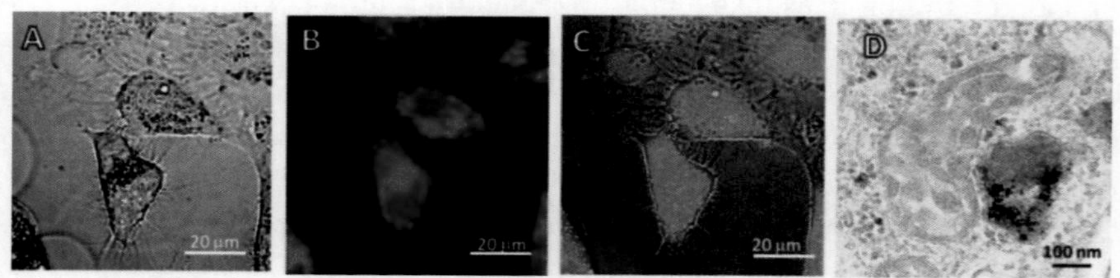

Reprint with permission from Elmes, R. B. P.; Orange, K. N.; Cloonan, S. M.; Williams, D. C.; Gunnlaugsson, T. *J. Am. Chem. Soc.* 2011, *133*, 15862. Copyright 2011 American Chemical Society [133].

Figure 12. Live cell confocal laser scanning microscopic images of AuNP-1 (~16 nM gold concentration) with HeLa cells: (A) the bright field image; (B) emission arising from 600 to 700 nm; (C) overlay of the luminescence from AuNP-1 (red), nuclear co-stain DAPI (blue), and the bright field image; (D) TEM image of AuNP-1 following incubation with HeLa cells.

Localization of α- or β-emitting radionuclides in tumor cells can be uses to the kill the cell as is done in boron-neutron capture therapy. Recently ^{99m}Tc, a γ-emitting radionucleotide, has gained much attention for it use in diagnostic organ imaging. Radioscintigraphy refers to the visualization of organs which contain concentrated γ-emitting radionucleotide. [134] The γ-rays are detected by a photodetector and allow for real time imaging of organ and its function.

^{97}Ru has radiophysical properties which are compatible with most radioscintigraphic instruments as it decays by electron capture with a half-life of 2.88 days and emits a 216 keV γ-ray [1].

Unfortunately, ^{97}Ru is not commercially available. ^{103}Ru is commercially available, but emits a 497 keV γ-ray which is only fairly useful in radioscintigraphy, and has a longer half-life of 39.55 days [1].

As per earlier discussion a large number of Ru(III) complexes are able to concentrate within tumor cells as a result of reduction and intracellular binding. However, as previously discussed ruthenium can act as an iron mimic, meaning many Ru complexes remain in the blood through binding of albumin and transferrin. $RuCl_3$ has been shown to exhibit nonspecific binding to erythrocytes [135].

Coordination of ruthenium to transferrin can lead to enhanced tumor uptake, as neoplastic cells have high requirement and display large numbers of transferrin receptors on their membrane surfaces. Srivastava, Larson et al. [136, 137] utilized this protein to localize radioruthenium in tumor cells, and showed that uptake of ^{103}Ru-labelled transferrin by EMT-6 sarcoma in mice was almost double that of widely utilized ^{67}Ga-citrate, a widely used tumor-imaging agent [136, 137].

Radioimaging has been developed using many derivatives of radioruthenium(III), for instance ^{97}Ru-PIPIDA, ^{97}Ru-BIDA, and ^{97}Ru-DISPA complexes containing iminodiacetato ligands with lipophilic groups are concentrated in the liver. [138-140] An amminerutheium(III) complex containing ^{103}Ru and amino acid β-(4-pyridyl)-α-alanine displays good uptake in the pancreas. The complex $[^{103}Ru(BLM)(NH_3)_5]$, where BLM = bleomycin, a clinically used glycopeptide antibiotic often used as an anticancer agent, yielded a tissue distribution in normal and tumor-bearing mice essentially the same as BLM itself. [141] Aside for nonspecific cause, it is likely that accumulation of ammine-ruthenium complexes occurs in two ways: (1) tumor uptake of Ru(III) prodrug which is reduced in the tumor environment; (2) transferring mediated tumor binding. The former of which is fast process in which ions are excreted through the kidneys and response rapidly decreases with time and the latter a much slower process which may occur for many days following injection [142].

Anti-Cancer Applications of Ruthenium-Containing Complexes

Cancer is a generic term for a large group of disease which can affect nearly every part of the body. The defining feature in any form of cancer is the rapid creation of abnormal cells which grow beyond normal boundaries causing them to invade adjoining body parts facilitating their spread to other organs. This is generally referred to as metastasis; metastases are a major cause of death from cancer. Despite extensive research and various treatment regimens cancer remains among the leading causes of death worldwide and is the 2nd leading cause of death in the USA, with 14.1 million new cases and 8.2 million deaths in 2012 alone. [143-145] As shown in figure 13, between the 1950s and 2006, the changes in death rates related to major disease in the USA have dropped considerably, except from those related to cancer. The global burden of disease study commissioned in 1990 (as a collaborative effort between the World Health Organization, Harvard School of Public Health, the University of Auckland, the Institute for Health Metrics and Evaluation, and the World Bank) reported updates in 2004 and 2010 which project the incidence of cancer to continue to rise over the next twenty years as shown in figure 13. [146-149] It is hard (if not impossible) to find drugs that are both effective and have low toxicity to normal human cells.

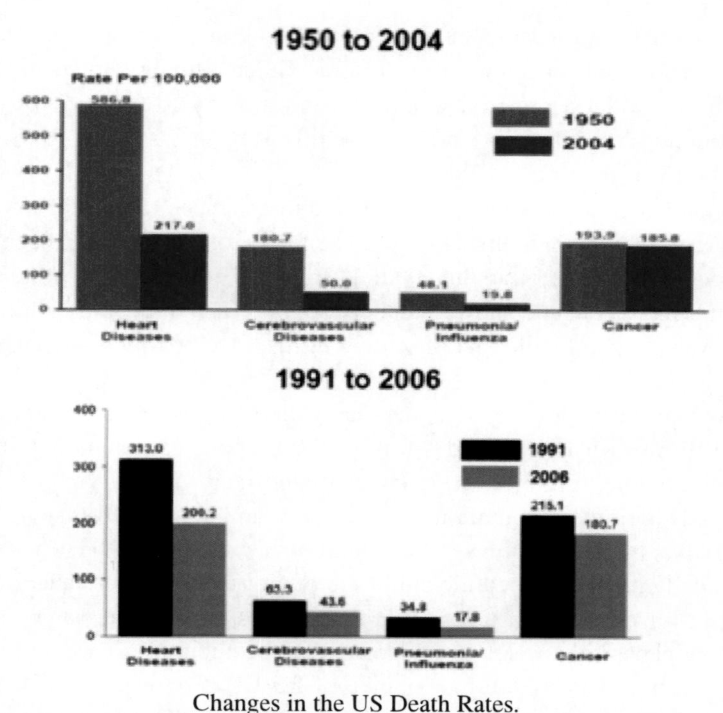

Changes in the US Death Rates.

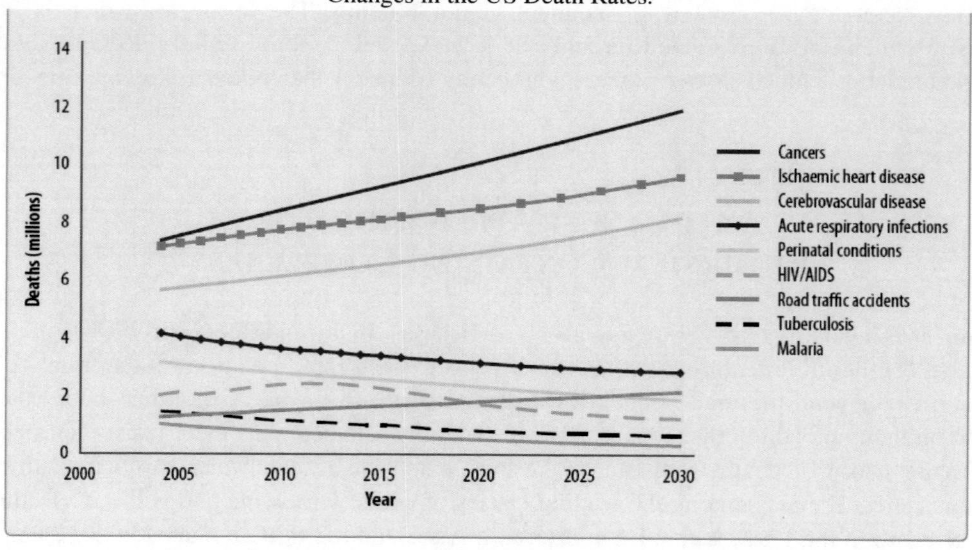

Figure 13. Projected global deaths for selected causes 2004 - 2030 [148].

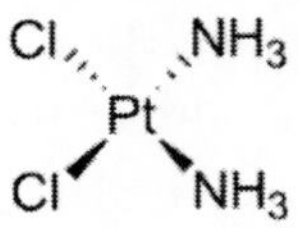

Cl,, ,NH3
Pt
Cl NH3

Cisplatin

Cisplatin (*cis*-diamminedichloroplatinumn(II)), *cis*-$[PtCl_2(NH_3)_2]$ is one of the most widely used anticancer drugs, and has shown particular promise in treatment of testicular cancer and ovarian carcinoma. [150-153] Cisplatin was approved for clinical treatment in 1978 for the treatment of genitourinary tumors and is generally combined with one or multiple organic anticancer drugs, such as 5-fluorouracil, cyclophosphamide, or gemcitabine.

While cisplatin remains one of the most active anticancer drugs to date, side effects including nephrotoxicity (kidney poisoning), ototoxicity (loss of high frequency hearing), peripheral neuropathy and the emergence of cisplatin-resistant cancer decrease its effectiveness [153-155].

Following the initial success of cisplatin, many other metal complexes have been investigated for their uses as antitumor drugs. Ruthenium compounds are arguably the best candidates to add to platinum-based drugs in cancer therapy as several ruthenium complexes have been shown to exhibit high *in vitro* and *in vivo* antitumor activity and some compounds are in advanced stages of clinical trials. Although the mechanism of action of antitumor ruthenium compounds if not fully understood to date, it is thought, that similar to platinum drugs, the chloride complex can hydrolyze, *in vivo* allowing the ruthenium to bind to nucleobases of DNA. However, despite showing generally less toxicity than platinum based drugs, ruthenium complexes are not highly selective and are specific to only certain types of cancers. Therefore, the development of more effective chemotherapeutic agents remains a very active field of research.

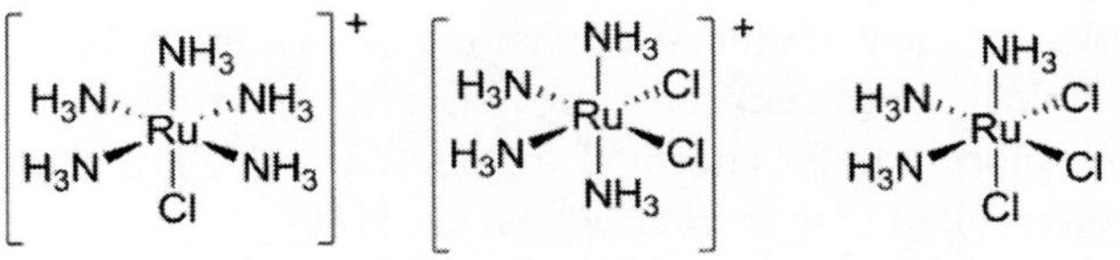

a b c

Figure 14. Chloro-ammino ruthenium derivative. (a) $[Ru^{II}(NH_3)_5Cl]^+$, (b) *cis*-$[Ru^{III}(NH_3)_4Cl_2]^+$, (c) *fac*-$[Ru^{III}(NH_3)_3Cl_3]$.

The potential anti-cancer activity of ruthenium compounds were first examined by Clarke and co-workers who studies chloro-ammino derivatives of the general formula $[Ru(NH_3)_{6-x}Cl_x]^{Y+}$. [80, 156, 157] The compounds were chosen due to similarities with cisplatin to allow for binding of the complexes with nucleic acids. $[Ru^{II}(NH_3)_5Cl]^+$ and its aqua analog $[Ru^{II}(NH_3)_5H_2O]^{2+}$ have been extensively studied and show rapid binding to DNA with an affinity constant of approximately 5000 M^{-1} (Figure 14A).

The binding product of the complex with DNA involves the loss of the chloride/aqua ligand and coordination to N^7 nitrogen of guanine in the DNA major groove. Despite strong binding to N^7 of guanine similar to cisplatin, penta-ammineruthenium complexes do not show efficient anti-cancer activity.

In contrast, *cis*-[$Ru^{III}(NH_3)_4Cl_2]^+$ and *fac*-[$Ru^{III}(NH_3)_3Cl_3$] shown in figure 14B and C, respectively, have been tested against multiple tumor cell and show comparable *in vivo* activity to cisplatin [158-160].

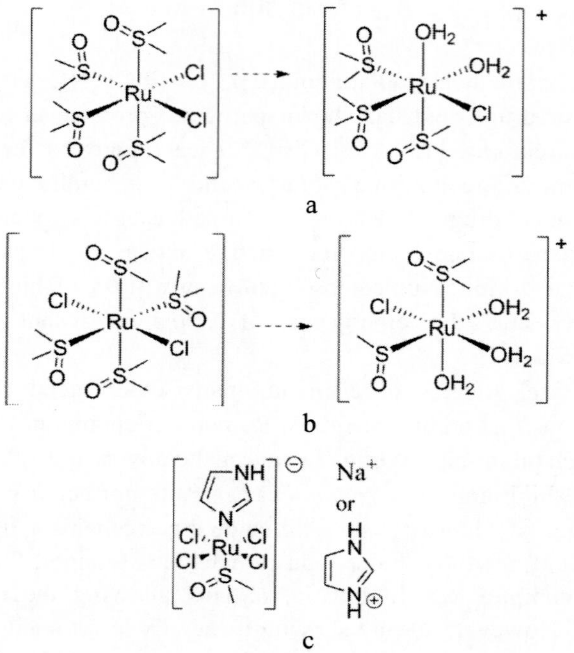

Figure 15. Dimethyl-sulfoxide complexes. (a) *cis*-[$Ru^{II}(DMSO)_4Cl_2$] and the corresponding aqua species, (b) *trans*-[$Ru^{II}(DMSO)_4Cl_2$] and the corresponding aqua species, (c) *trans*-[$Ru^{II}(DMSO)_4Cl_2$] (NAMI) and its imidazolium salt (NAMI-A).

Clarke and co-workers have rationalized that the *in vivo* tumor environment reduces the inactive Ru(III) complex to the corresponding active Ru(II) drug which is able to lose its chloro ligands much more rapidly and bind to DNA. [161] Unfortunately, many of these complexes are far too insoluble for pharmaceutical use [158].

Solubility issues can be highly improved by coordinating a DMSO molecule as opposed to the previously utilized NH_3 ligands as shown in figure 15. Mestroni, Alessio and co-workers conducted *in vitro* and *in vivo* studies on *cis*- and *trans*-[$Ru^{II}(DMSO)_4Cl_2$] complexes. [162] Monoadduct formation was observed for the *cis*-isomer, whereas the *trans*-complex, similar to cisplatin, showed the ability to form DNA biadducts leading to both intra- and inter-strand cross-links. [162] Both isomers coordinate the N^7 position of guanine residues in DNA, however the *trans* isomer has been shown bind more rapidly and is almost sixteen (16) times more active than the *cis* isomer in P388 leukemia cells [163].

The encouraging results obtained with *trans*-[$Ru^{II}(DMSO)_4Cl_2$] are at the epicenter of the search for other *trans*-DMSO ruthenium complexes as anti-cancer agents. Na[*trans*-[$Ru^{III}(DMSO)(Im)Cl_4$]] (NAMI) and its imidazolium salt NAMI-A represent the greatest achievements in this area as they were the first Ru compounds to enter clinic trials in 2000, and have since entered phase II clinical trials. [164] NAMI-A is practically noncytotoxic in common cancer cell lines but has turned out to be a specifically antimetastatic drug. The mechanism by which NAMI-A exerts its anti-metastatic activity is not yet completely elucidated. Similar to other ruthenium complexes it is thought that both of its chloride ligands are lost though aquation before it binds with biomolecules such as DNA. NAMI inhibits the actions of DNA and RNA polymerases, but does not form significant DNA interstrand cross-linking. [165] Thus, it is hypothesized that the anti-metastatic activity of NAMI arises from a mechanism different than that of cisplatin, such as protein-DNA cross-links [166]. Francis Dwyer and co-workers in early 1950s, [94-97] showed a family of tris(polypyridyl) complexes had bacteriostatic and antiviral activities (in some instance, the growth of Gram-positive bacterial was inhibited at concentration of 1mM for $[Ru(phen)_3](ClO_4)_2$ and thus it is plausible that other ruthenium complexes may have antitumor applications. [94] Figure 16 shows some of the many Ru(II) complexes of the type *cis*-$[Ru^{II}(L)_2Cl_2]$ (where L = bidentate heteroaromatic ligands) that have been prepared and are being investigated for their anti-tumor properties. One of the first studied complexes *cis*-$[Ru^{II}(bpy)_2Cl_2]$ has been tested against many cell lines but is mostly inactive as an anti-tumor agent [167].

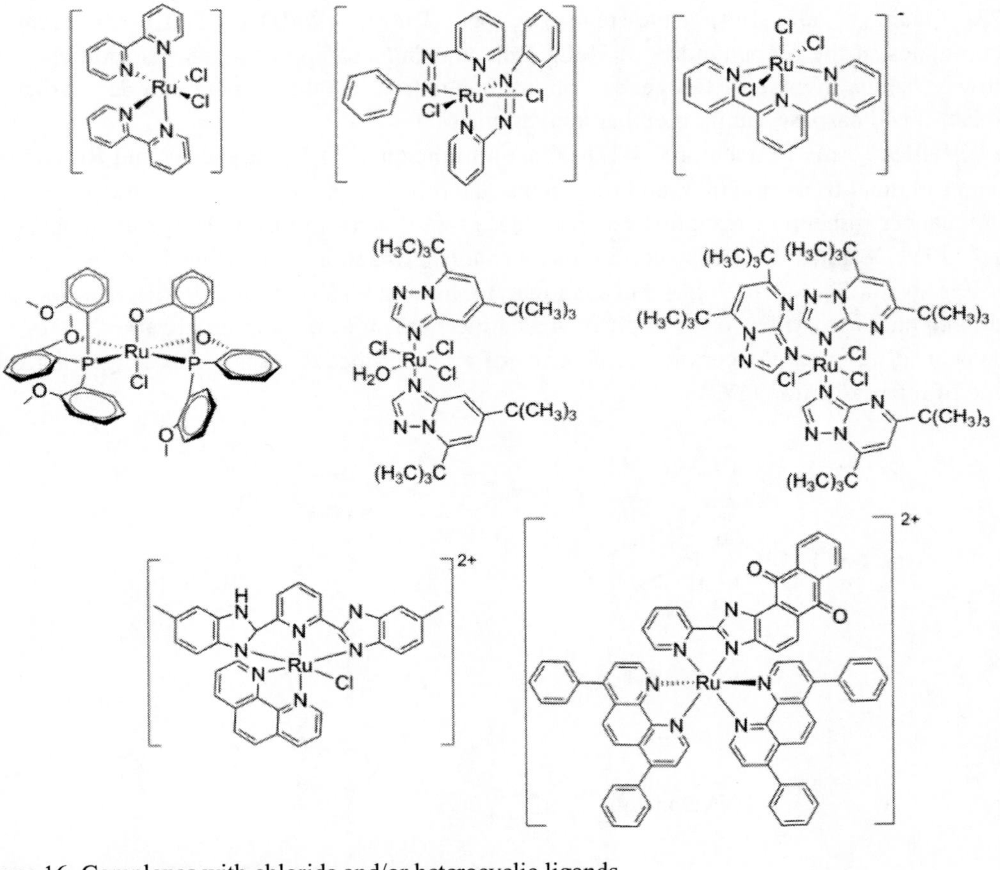

Figure 16. Complexes with chloride and/or heterocyclic ligands.

In contrast, Reedijk and co-workers have shown that one isomer of *cis*-$[Ru^{II}(azpy)_2Cl_2]$ exhibits high toxicity comparable to that of cisplatin against a series of cell lines [167-169].

Barbec and co-workers reported high cytotoxicity comparable to that of cisplatin and carboplatin with their complex *mer*-$[Ru^{II}(terpy)Cl_3]^-$ which contains a tridentate terpyridine ligand. [170] This complex similar to cisplatin was shown to form a high number of interstand cross-links. [170] Bouwan and co-workers have shown a novel complex $[Ru^{III}(PAn_3)P(An)(phenolate)_2Cl]$ shows toxicity similar to cisplatin, and enhanced toxicity in cisplatin-resistant cell lines. [171] Tan et al. [76] reported a series of ruthenium-norharman complexes which are highly cytotoxic to a variety of cancer cell lines with IC_{50} values well below those of cisplatin and NAMI-A. Lakomska et al. [172] have developed two Ru(III) complexes based on triazolopyrimidine ligands. The bulky substituents in the heterocyclic ligands significantly enhance the cytotoxicity of both complexes which is attributed to the high lipophilicity which facilitates high cellular uptake.

Both show much higher cytotoxicity than cisplatin against human lung carcinoma A-549 and T47D breast carcinoma cell lines with IC_{50} values in the range of 0.02-2.4 μM. [172] Li et al. [173] synthesized a series of Ru(II) complexes containing *bis*-benzimidazole derivatives, and introduced phenanthroline as a mixed ligand for comparison. $[Ru(bmbp)(phen)]^{2+}$ showed selective toxicity towards a series of cancerous cell lines the origin of which being overproduction of superoxide leading to caspase-dependant apoptosis. [173] Quain et al. [174] have revealed that $[Ru(dip)_2(PAIDH)](ClO_4)_2$ preferentially accumulates in the mitochondria of HeLa cells and induces apoptosis via the mitochondrial pathway, which involved ROS generation, mitochondrial membrane potential depolarization, and Bcl-2 and caspase family member activation.

KP1019, (*trans*-[tetrachlorobis(1*H*-indazole)ruthenate(III)]), was the second Ru complex to enter clinical trials, in 2003, and represents one of the most successful complexes in terms of anticancer ruthenium complexes as it reduces tumor sizes in rats and triggers apoptosis *in vitro*. [175] Despites KP1019s success, its mechanism of action remains up for debates.

For example, KP1019 has been shown to bind transferrin, and transferrin receptor-mediated endocytosis has been implicated as a mechanism of drug internalization. [176, 177] However, drug uptake occurs in the absence of KP1019-loaded transferrin, suggesting other mode of internalization [177].

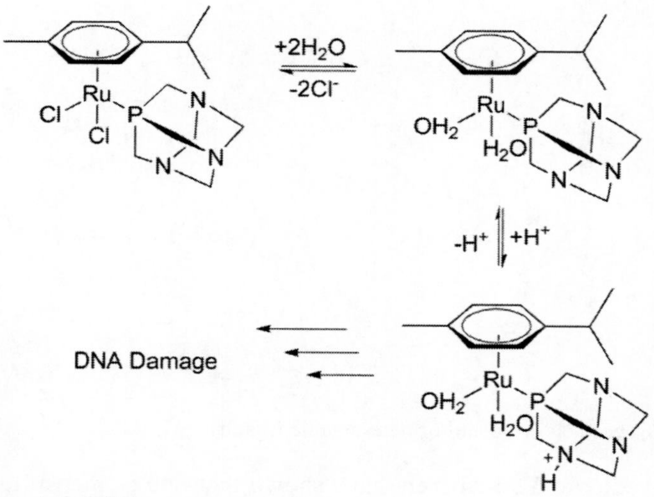

Adapted from Scolaro et al. [186].

Figure 17. Aquation and protonation of RAPTA-C complex prior to DNA damage.

Furthermore, the mechanism by which the drug exits the endosomes and gains access to intracellular targets remains unclear.

Arenes are known to stabilize ruthenium(II) and provides a hydrophobic face which may facilitate biomoelcular recognition and transportation of ruthenium through cell membranes; thus the potential uses of ruthenium-arene complexes are gaining much attention in literature. [53, 178-182] The "half-sandwich" Ru(II) mono-arene complexes often possess good aqueous stability and the arene ligand is relatively inert towards displacement under physiological conditions.

Following the entrance of an organometallic titanium(IV) complex (titanocene dichloride $[Ti(Cp)_2Cl_2]$ Cp = η^5-C_5H_5) into clinical trials as an anticancer drug, Dyson and his co-workers have conducted much work on ruthenium-arene complexes [183-186].

Dyson and co-workers reported on the synthesis of a new class of cytotoxic ruthenium compounds $[(\eta^6$-arene)Ru(pta)$(Cl)_2]$, also known as RAPTA complexes, which are water soluble compounds which exhibits pH dependent DNA damage as shown in figure 17 [183].

Protonation of the pta ligands influences the solubility properties of the complex and at physiological pH environments the predominant species carries no charge and can thus be easily transported across the lipid membrane and move freely into and within the cells [183].

Incubation of the complex with pBR322 plasmid DNA above a pH of 7.5 indicated no change in the conformation of the DNA via gel electrophoresis, however incubation at lower pH values closer to the pk_a value show retardation in the migration of DNA on the gel. [183] These results indicate selective DNA binding for this complex at lower than physiological pH values which many diseases cells possess due to metabolic changes associated with accelerated cell division [187]. *In vivo* biological screening of series of nine complexes of the generic formula $[(\eta^6$-arene)Ru(pta)$(Cl)_2]$ (arene = *p*-cymene, toluene, benzene, benzo-15-crown-5, 1-ethylbenzene-2,3-dimethylimidazolium tetrafluoroborate, ethyl benzene, hexamethylbezene) synthesized by Dyson et al. [186] failed to produce a complex with IC_{50} comparable to cisplatin, however $[(\eta^6$-arene)Ru (pta)$(Cl)_2]$ did reduce the number and weight of metastasis cells similar to NAMI-A with a higher system clearance rate [186].

Maysinger and co-workers showed the synergistic effect which can be obtained from their ruthenium-letrozole complex, shown in figure 18, which exhibits significant higher activity towards cancer cells line when compared with compounds analogous to RAPTA-C (a ruthenium drug presently in pre-clinical trials) [188].

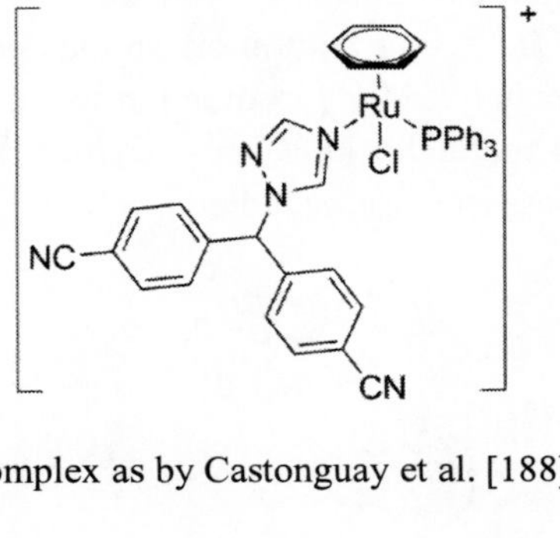

Figure 18. Ruthenium-letrozole complex as by Castonguay et al. [188].

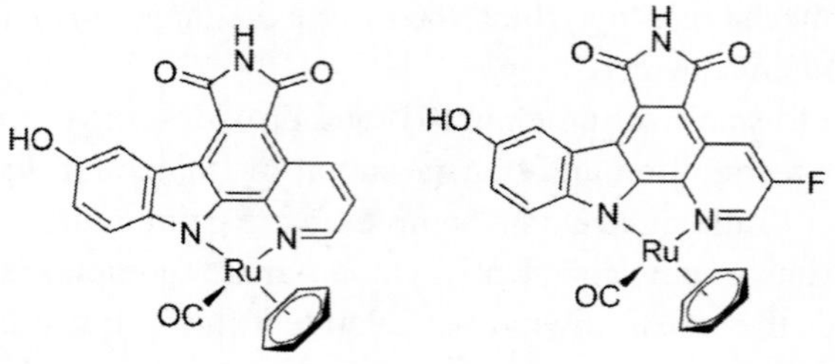

Figure 19. DW12 and NP309 a fluorinated derivative as by Meggers et al. [191].

Sadler and co-workers have pioneered work on ruthenium-arene complexes for similar applications. Cytotoxicities obtained for a series of complexes with the generic formula $[(\eta^6$-arene)Ru(en)(Cl)$]^+$ indicated that the cytotoxic behavior increased with as a function of the size of the coordinated arene (benzene < *p*-cymene < biphenyl < dihydroanthracene < tetrahydroanthracene), such that in wild and cisplatin resistant A2780 human ovarian cancer cells, the biphenyl complex showed similar toxicity to carboplatin and the tetrahydroanthracene complex showed similar toxicity to cisplatin. [189] Structure activity studies with these compounds indicated that single ligand exchange (presence of bidentate ligand) facilitates high cytotoxicity. Binding studies indicate the formation of monoadducts with N^7 of guanine similar to results observed with other ruthenium complexes. [189, 190] Meggers and co-workers have functionalized the half-sandwich motif with a kinase inhibitor staurosporine as a bidentate ligands which exert toxicity via a nontraditional mechanism which are shown in figure 19. [191] DW12 does not interact with nucleic acids and instead exerts it anticancer effects by inhibiting protein kinases; while NP309 a more cytotoxic derivative triggers kinases which activate the mitochondrial mediated apoptotic pathway. Both show promising anticancer activity in drug resistant cell lines with nanomolar activity against melanoma cell lines [191].

Coordination of carborane ligands to ruthenium-arene complexes has recently been explored for their potential utilization in boron neutron capture therapy (BNCT). [192] One such complexes is shown below in figure 20. BNCT allows for selective activation of drugs in a spatial controlled manner, in better proximity to better target cancer cells. The biological evaluations of these potential BNCT agents are still under investigation [193].

Beckford and co-workers are conducting work in the synthesis of ruthenium-arene complexes containing thiosemicarbazone (TSC) ligands. [194, 195] TSCs possess a broad range of medicinal application including antitumor, antibacterial, and antiviral properties all of which can be modified and enhanced by coordination to a metal ion. A series of complexes as shown in figure 21 of the general formula $[(\eta^6$-p-cymene)Ru(TSC)(Cl)]Cl were recently reported and their biological properties were studied [194, 195].

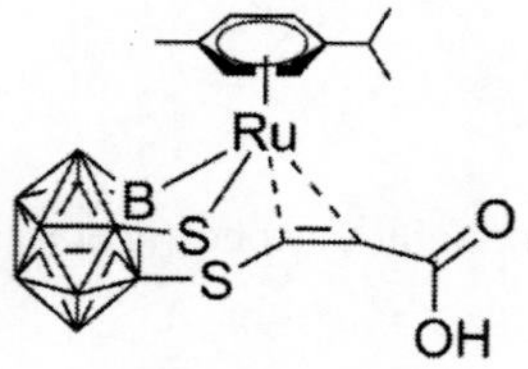

Figure 20. Carborane arene ruthenium complex [192].

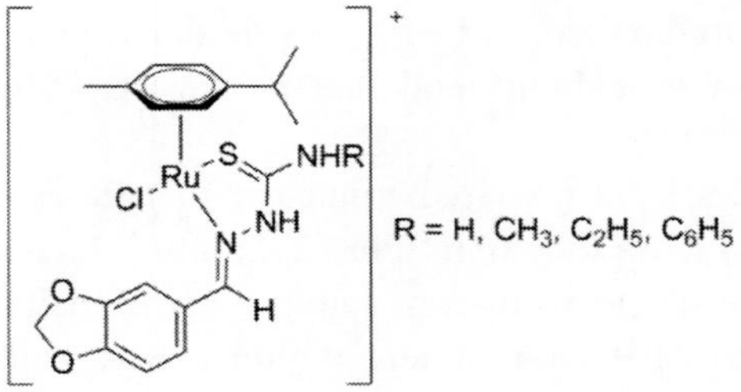

Figure 21. Structure of arene ruthenium(II)-thiosemicarbazone complexes as byBeckford et al. [194].

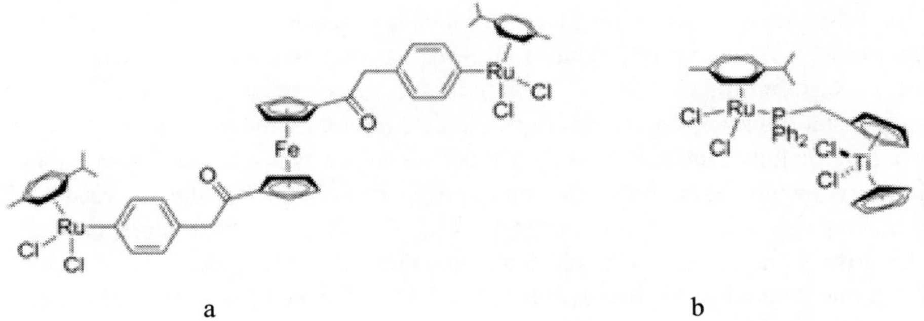

Figure 22. Heteronuclear arene ruthenium complexes containing a ferrocene (A) [196] and titanocene (B) [197] moiety.

Studies indicate *in vitro* activity as anticancer agents against human colon cancer cell line, with moderate interaction with DNA. Complexes showed comparable anticancer activity to cisplatin and other similar ruthenium-arene complexes currently under investigation; however no complex provided activity similar to etoposide (an anticancer drug belonging to the topoisomerase inhibitor class). Two of the complexes ([(η^6-*p*-cymene)Ru (pEtTSC)Cl]Cl and [(η^6-*p*-cymene)Ru(pPhTSC)Cl]Cl showed modest capability of inhibiting topoisomerase II enzymes at low concentrations which may still give these complexes application in anticancer drug development [194]. Similar to binuclear and multinuclear ruthenium complexes strategies have been employed in synthesizing multinuclear and heteronuclear ruthenium-arene complexes which modify the mode of action of the metal based drug. Two heteronuclear complexes containing ruthenium(II)-arenes with ferrocene and titanocene were recently prepared and are shown in in figure 22 [196, 197].

In vitro studies demonstrate the cytotoxicities correlate with the lipophilicity and water solubility of the complexes similar to other ruthenium(II) complexes. Dinuclear, trinuclear, tetranuclear, hexanuclear, and octanuclear systems can all be found in literature, with each system showing a different level of activity and degree of selectivity towards certain cancer cell lines.

Dinuclear complexes containing pyridone linkers have provided insight into the correlation present between the spacer length and cytotoxicity (Figure 23A), [198, 199] while the thiophenolato-bridged *p*-cymene ruthenium complex $[(p^iPrC_6H_4Me)_2Ru_2(\mu_2SC_6H_5)_3]Cl$ shows activity against human ovarian cancer cell lines in the nanamolar range (Figure 23B) [200].

A dinuclear (η^6-arene)ruthenium(II) benzaldehyde thiosemicarbazone complex as shown in figure 23C was shown to exhibit moderate *in vitro* activity (IC_{50} = 9 μM) against oesophageal cancer cells [201].

Severin and co-workers have prepared trinuclear metalla-cycles from pyridone ligands and *p*-cymene ruthenium units as shown in figure 23D [202].

The triruthenium metal-cycle facilitates delivery and remains stable under neutral pH, however, under the reduced pH environment within cancer cells the trimeric structure is concerted to the activated monomeric species [202].

Rectangular shaped metalla-cycles of the general formula $[(arene)_4Ru_4\ (OO\text{-}OO)_2(N\text{-}N)_2]^{4+}$ as shown in figure 23E (arene = p-cymene, hexamethylbenzene; OO-OO = oxalato, oxamido, 1,4-benzoquinonato-2,5-dilato, 3,6-dichloro-1,4-benzoquinonato; N-N = pyrazine, 4,4'-bipyridine, 1,2-bis(pyridyl)ethylene, 1,2-bis(4-pyridyl)ethane), have been tested against multiple cancer cell lines. [203] The activity of these metal-cycles against normal and cisplatin resistant ovarian cancer cell lines indicate moderate to excellent activity, depending on the size of the linker utilized, in some cases IC_{50} values as low as 4 μM were obtained.

Similarly, metalla-assemblies containing polypyridyl-porphyrin derivatives and dinuclear ruthenium complexes have been reported. [204] $[(p^iPrC_6H_4Me)_6Ru_6(dhnq)_3(tpeb)_3][CF_3SO_3]_6$ a metalla-prism as reported by Chi and Stang has shown excellent activity to a wide variety of cancer cell line including: SK-hep-1, HeLa, HCT-15, A549 and MDA-MB-231 [205].

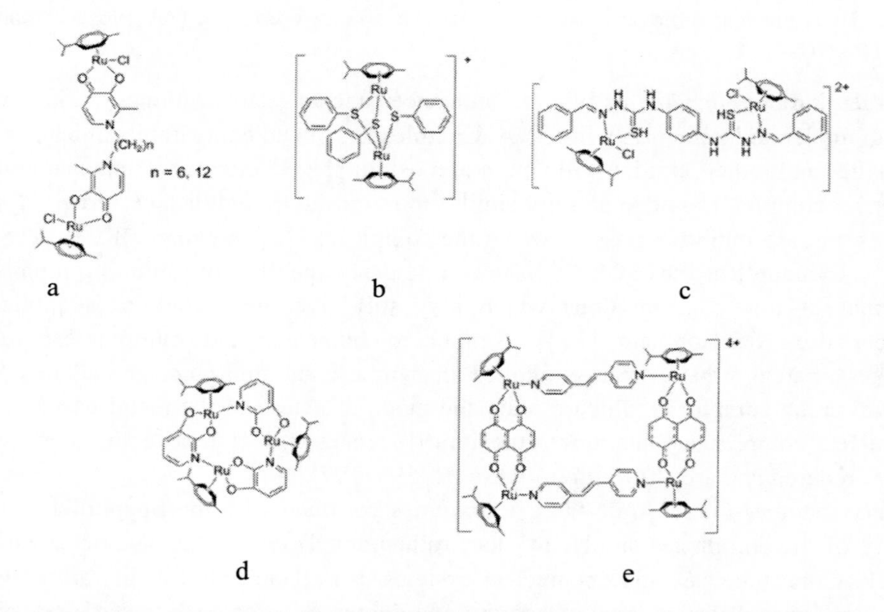

Figure 23. Dinuclear arene ruthenium complex bridged by pyridone (A), [198, 199] thiophenolato (B), [200] thiosemicarbazone (C), [201] Trinuclear metalla-cycle (D), [202] tetranuclear arene ruthenium complex (E) [203].

Larger metalla-assemblies are possible and have been assembled using tetra(pyridyl)porphyrin panels which give rise to octacationic arene ruthenium complexes. These systems generally interact with duplex and qudraplex DNA, showing slight preference for quadraplex DNA. [206] The *in vitro* activity of such complexes has been investigated and they show high cytotoxicity against A2780 and A2780cisR cancer cell lines. The porphyrin panels can be further metallated to afford even more cytotoxic agents [207].

PHOTODYNAMIC THERAPY WITH RUTHENIUM-CONTAINING COMPLEXES

Photodynamic therapy seeks to utilize nontoxic light-sensitive compounds (photosensitizer) that when selectively exposed to light, become toxic to malignant and other diseased cells. The sensitizer should preferably absorb red light (>600 nm) strongly, since longer wavelength light penetrate tissue more effectively than more energetic, short wavelength light. [208, 209] Light can be delivered internally using fiber optics, thus photodynamic therapeutics are not limited to treatment of skin conditions. This is a two- step process: (1) absorption of light by a photosensitizer, which in a second step reacts with a targeted molecule (generally O_2 or DNA) via an electron or energy transfer shown in equations 3 and 4.

$$\text{Photosensitizer}^* + \text{Target} \xrightarrow{h\nu} \text{Photosensitizer} + \text{Target}^* \quad \text{(energy transfer)} \tag{3}$$

$$\text{Photosensitizer}^* + \text{Target} \xrightarrow{h\nu} \text{Photosensitizer}^{\bullet-} + \text{Target}^{\bullet-} \quad \text{(electron transfer)} \tag{4}$$

Polyazaaromatic ruthenium(II) complexes are generally well suited for use as photosensitizers. [210] The properties of such complexes can be varied by varying the ligands chelated to the metal center as shown by their different photophysical and photochemical behaviors in the presence and absence of DNA. [210] Ruthenium(II) complexes are capable of interacting with DNA forming three distinct interaction geometries: (1) the complex can be externally associated in the electrostatic environment of the DNA double helix, (2) it can be absorbed into the DNA grooves, or (3) it can intercalate between two DNA base pairs via one of its ligands. Barton et al. [32] have confirmed many of these binding modes showing that $[Ru(bpy)_2]^{2+}$ shows weak interaction with DNA either by intercalation or electrostatic interaction; while in contrast $[Ru(phen)_3]^{2+}$ and $[Ru(DIP)_3]^{2+}$ show strong affinity for DNA.

The photophysics of most Ru(II) polypyridyl complexes can be described by the basic scheme established for the reference complex $[Ru^{II}(bpy)_3]^{2+}$ as shown in figure 24. [211, 212] First the photoabsoption populates a singlet MLCT excited state (^{1}MCLT), which deactivates via intersystem crossing (ISC) to a triplet MLCT (^{3}MCLT).

The ^{3}MLCT, in the presence of DNA, generally gives rise to the electron or energy processes necessary to facilitate DNA photocleavage. [212] The ^{3}MC state often involved populating a high energy d-orbital with antibonding characteristics weakening one or more of the Ru-N bonds which results in ligand substitution. The ‘flash-quench’ approach involves oxidizing the excited state (usually ^{3}MLCT) by adding an oxidant, such as $[(NH_3)_6Ru]^{3+}$, to prepare a more powerful ground state oxidant.

As previously stated, DNA damages arise from photoinduced electron transfer between the excited state of the PDT molecule and DNA, thereby damaging the cell’s ability to function (type I).

Alternatively, light absorption by a photosensitizing molecule can lead to an energy transfer to activate another molecule, such as the conversion of O_2 to the excited singlet state; energy transfer between the triplet excited photosensitizer and an oxygen molecule, leading the production of singlet oxygen (type II) as shown in equation 5 [213]. Guanine is the most commonly oxidized DNA base and is most commonly affected by PDT.

$$[Ru^{II}(bpy)_3]^{2+*} + {}^3O_2 \xrightarrow{h\nu} [Ru^{II}(bpy)_3]^{2+} + {}^1O_2^* \quad (5)$$

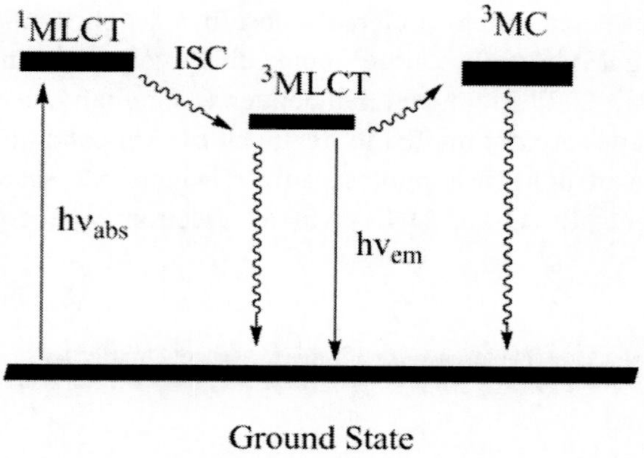

Figure 24. Photophysical scheme for $[Ru^{II}(bpy)_3]^{2+}$.

Various products can form depending on which type of reaction occurs to oxidize the base. Single electron oxidation (type I) generally leads to 2-aminoimidazolone and oxazolone, which further react with piperidine leading to DNA cleavage. Singlet oxygen is a reactive oxygen species, which may induce the formation of other oxidizing agents such as superoxide radicals ($O_2^{\bullet-}$) or hydroxyl radicals ($OH^{\bullet}$). These species are able to damage DNA, leading mainly to oxidation of the guanine moiety to 8-oxoguanine and 4-hydroxyl-8-oxoguanine eventually leading to DNA cleavages, however, other bases as well as sugar can possibly be affected. [213] These cleavages are generally demonstrated by gel electrophoresis experiments with plasmid DNA (Figure 25). Single strand breaks in a strand of the DNA double helix of a supercoiled circular form of plasmid DNA, cause the conversion into an open circular form which exhibits a different migration velocity [214-218].

Hundreds of molecules have already been shown to photosensitize singlet oxygen production, many of which are polypyridyl Ru(II) complexes due to their large absorbance spectra and long excited-state lifetimes. Barton et al. [32] have shown excitation of $[Ru^{II}(bpy)_3]^{2+}$, $[Ru^{II}(phen)_3]^{2+}$, and $[Ru^{II}(DIP)_3]^{2+}$ shown in figure 26, induces the production of singlet oxygen and DNA single strand breaks. [32] High quantum yields of singlet oxygen productions from (0.1 to 1.0 depending on the complex and solvent) have been determined for a variety of Ru(II) complexes. [219] Photoinduced ligand substitution is also possible whereby a metal complex would either release a biologically active molecule or bind to nucleic acids or protein active sites.

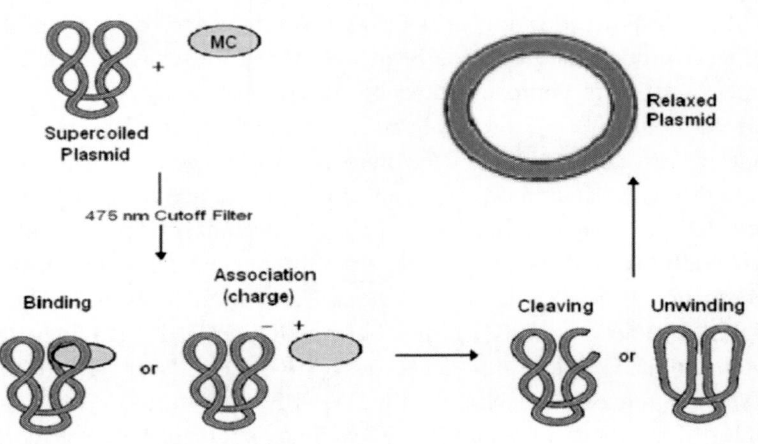

Credit Karen J. Brewer and Alvin A. Holder.

Figure 25. Proposed conversion of supercoiled DNA to relaxed form.

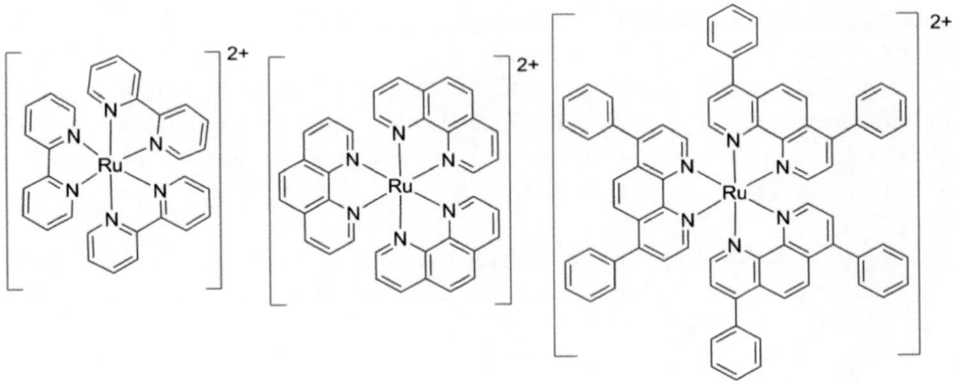

Figure 26. $[Ru^{II}(bpy)_3]^{2+}$, $[Ru^{II}(phen)_3]^{2+}$, $[Ru^{II}(DIP)_3]^{2+}$.

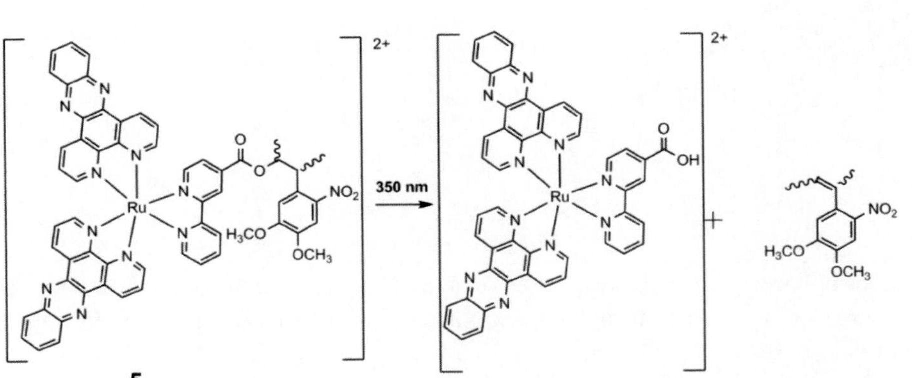

Figure 27. Photocleavage of DMNPB ester moiety to form active $[Ru(dppz)_2(CppH)]^{2+}$, as synthesize by Joshi et al., [221].

Improving the selectivity of anticancer drugs towards cancer cells is the main goal of drug optimization; a prodrug strategy has been one of the most promising. Light-triggered prodrugs provide an efficient approach for controlling cytotoxicity. Gasser and co-workers previously utilized confocal microscopy and atomic absorption spectrometry to show $[Ru(dppz)_2(CppH)]^{2+}$ (6) accumulates in the mitochondria of cells. [220] IC_{50} values were relatively close to those of cisplatin on three cancer cells lines, and the complex showed more activity on cisplatin-resistant cell lines. [220] $[Ru(dppz)_2(CppH)]^{2+}$ exerts toxicity through a mitochondria related pathway rather than the nuclear DNA mode of action as by cisplatin. Attachment of a photolabile functionality, DMNPB ester, makes the active $[Ru(dppz)_2(CppH)]^{2+}$ moiety within $[Ru(dppz)_2(Cpp\text{-}ODMPNB)]^{2+}$ (5) innocuous to both cancerous (HeLa and U2OS) and non-cancerous (MRC-5) cells ($IC_{50} > 100$ μM). [221] Irradiation at 350 nm releases the photolabile DMNPB ester forming the active complex $[Ru(dppz)_2(CppH)]^{2+}$ as shown in figure 27. IC_{50} values obtained before irradiation (> 100 μM) indicate nontoxic behavior of the complexes containing the DMNPB ester; while after irradiation values (17.5 and 17.2 μM) are comparable with those of cisplatin 12.0 and 32.6 μM in HeLa and U2OS, respectively. [221] Though still in the prototype stage, light triggered prodrugs hold potential for designing sophisticated properties well-suited for controllable cytotoxic action under physiological conditions.

Turro et al. [222] recently reported on the use of a ruthenium containing light-activated dual-action therapeutic $[Ru(tpy)(5CNU)_3]^{2+}$ (**7**). 5-fluorouracil, a structural relative of 5CNU, has been used for over 20 years in the treatment of malignancies in colorectal and breast cancers. 5CNU molecules exhibit biological activity through inhibition of pyrimidine catabolism [223].

UV-Visible and ^1H NMR spectroscopic studies show that the absorption of two photons are necessary to release two molecules of 5CNU and produce the diaqua product which is capable of interacting with DNA as shown below.

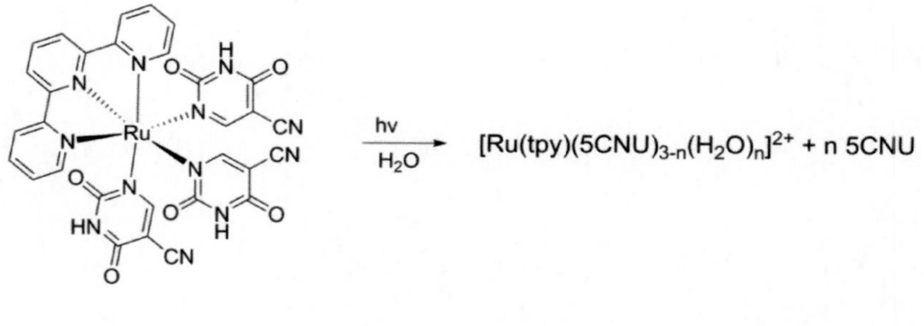

$$\mathbf{7} \xrightarrow[H_2O]{h\nu} [Ru(tpy)(5CNU)_{3-n}(H_2O)_n]^{2+} + n\ 5CNU$$

7

Gel electrophoresis shift assays, as shown in figure 28, show that linearized pUC19, mobility decreases as a function of complex concentration when irradiated with light in the presence of complex **7** [222].

In contrast, plasmid incubated in the dark or with the monoaqua species for the same amount of time shows no change in DNA mobility.

As indicated by these results, complex **7** could potentially serve as a dual action photochemotheraputic agent. Photochemical activation of drugs is now being explored in the area of nanoparticles.

Since they are nontoxic to cells and can undergo cellular uptake into liposomes via endocytosis, mesoporous silica nanoparticles (MSNPs) have recently emerged as a promising drug delivery system.

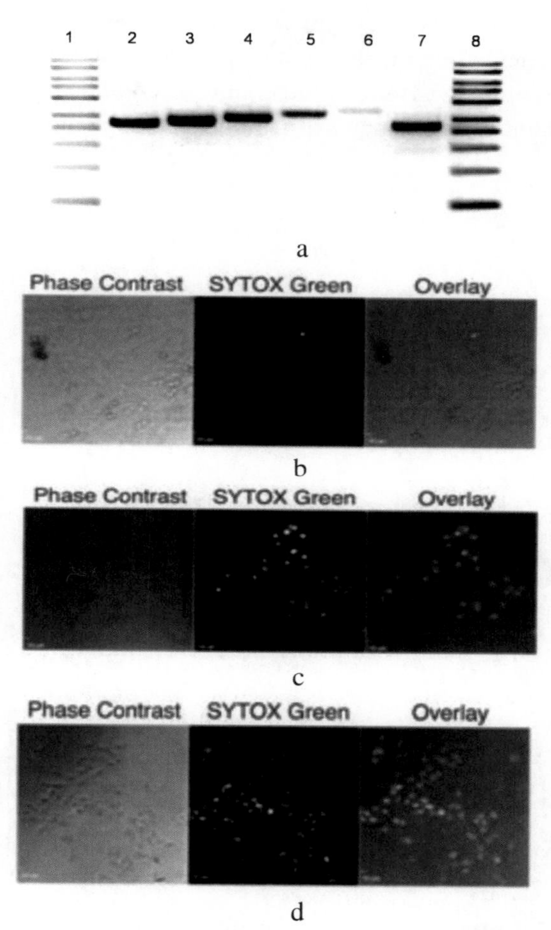

Reprint (Adapted) with permission from Sgambellone, M. A.; David, A.; Garner, R. N.; Dunbar, K. R.; Turro, C. *J. Am. Chem. Soc.* 2013, *135*, 11274. Copyright 2013 American Chemical Society [222].

Figure 28. (a) Imaged ethidium bromide stained agarose gel of 50 μM linearized pUC19 plasmid irradiated with $\lambda_{irr} \geq 395$ nm (tirr = 15 min). Lanes 3–6: 5, 10, 25, 50 μM complex **7**. Lanes 1 and 8, 1 kb DNA molecular weight standard; and lanes 2 and **7**, linearized plasmid alone. Fluorescence microscopy of HeLa cells incubated with 100 μM of 7 (b) incubated in the dark and (c) irradiated, and (d) 100 μM 5CNU alone incubated in the dark ($\lambda_{irr} > 400$ nm, tirr = 1 h; dark incubation 1 h at 25 °C).

A potential theranostic agent obtained from grafting the surface of MSNPs with a "capping" ruthenium(II) dppz complexes was recently reported. [224] Following irradiation with visible light the surface-grafted Ru(II) complex is selectively substituted by water, thereby releasing the aqua complex which is then capable of subsequently binding to DNA as shown in figure 29A. While unreactive in the dark, the ruthenium complex on the MSNP is activated by light, allowing it to form monoadducts with DNA and act as a DNA light-switching complex. UV-Visible spectroscopic and HPLC analysis reveal that when this ruthenium(II) dppz complex is selectively cleaved release, it releases an internalized drug molecule, i.e., paclitaxel (an anticancer drug) from the porous structure occurs with high release efficiency as shown in figure 29B. Cytotoxic studies against two breast cancer cells lines indicate the loaded functionalized MSNPs showed comparable cytotoxicity when compared with the parent drug molecule following light activation as shown in figure 29C-F. [224] While toxicity remained higher than the parent complex at present, this system has the potential for adaptation to employ cytotoxic ruthenium(II) complexes as the "capping" agent on the nanoparticle which may further increase its biological application.

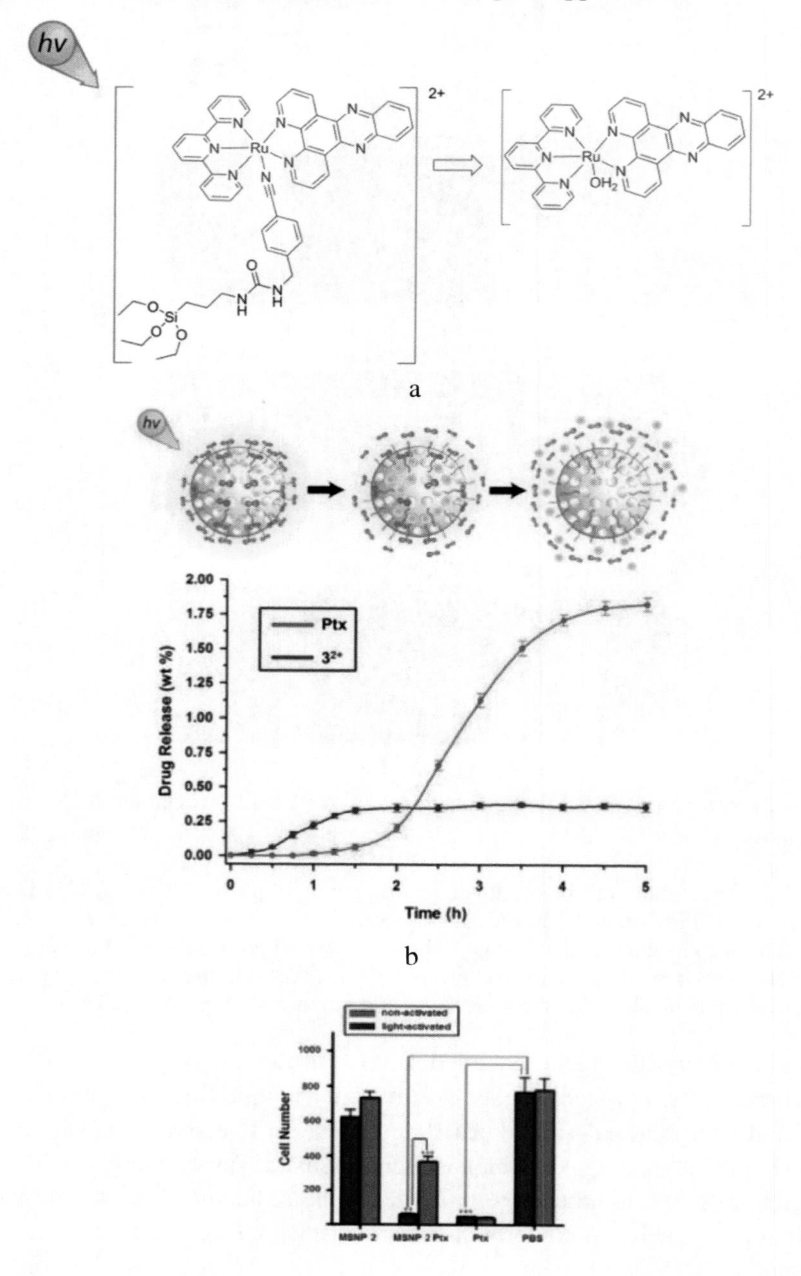

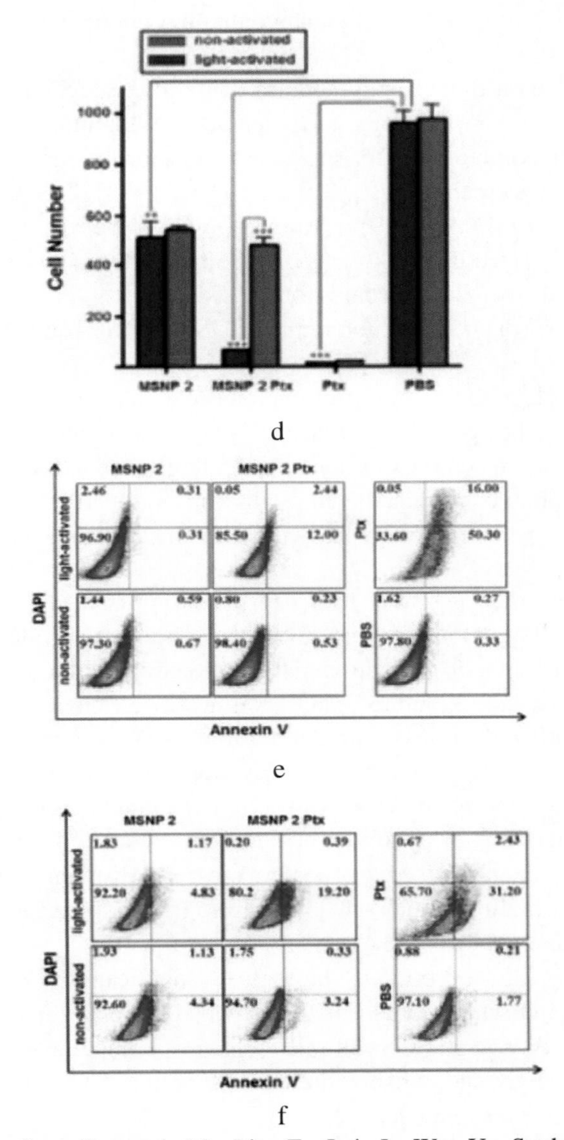

Reprinted with permission from Frasconi, M.; Liu, Z.; Lei, J.; Wu, Y.; Strekalova, E.; Malin, D.; Ambrogio, M. W.; Chen, X.; Botros, Y. Y.; Cryns, V. L.; Sauvage, J.-P.; Stoddart, J. F. *J. Am. Chem. Soc.* 2013, *135*, 11603. Copyright 2013 American Chemical Society [224].

Figure 29. (a) Photorelease of ruthenium(II) complexes following irradiation. (b) Step-by-step dual release profile of aqua ruthenium(II) complex (blue trace) and paclitaxel (Ptx) (red trace) Cell survival of MDA-MB-231 (c) and MDA-MB-468 (d) breast cancer cells treated with 5 μg mL^{-1} MSNPs 2, 5 μg mL^{-1} MSNPs 2 Ptx, 100 ng mL^{-1} free Ptx or PBS for 96 h without light activation (red bars) or with visible-light activation (blue bars). Annexin V flow cytometry assay of MDA-MB-231 (e) and MDA-MB-468 (f) breast cancer cells treated with 5 μg mL^{-1} MSNPs 2, 5 μg mL^{-1} MSNPs 2 Ptx, 100 ng mL^{-1} free Ptx or PBS for 72 h with or without visible-light activation.

As the search for adequate PDT agents continues to evolve, the systems being utilized are also constantly evolving. The above discuss describes examples of systems containing mononuclear ruthenium complexes and some containing photocleavable units which activate PDT-active complexes.

DNA interactions with dinuclear ruthenium containing species have also been reported, [225-231] however, their applications as potential DNA-binding agents remains largely unexplored. Dinuclear complexes offer increased variation in shape and size and have the potential to show greater specificity. $[\{Ru(phen)_2\}_2(l\text{-}HAT)]_4$ has been shown to strongly bind partially denatured DNA, [229] $[\{Ru(Me_2bpy)_2\}_2(l\text{-}bpm)]_4$ specifically binds DNA bulge sequences, [230] $[\{Ru(dpq)_2\}_2(phen\text{-}x\text{–}SOS\text{–}phen)]^{4+}$ (x = 3, 4, 5) exhibit high DNA affinity at 100 mM NaCl concentration. [231] Chao et al. [232] reported on $[(phen)_2Ru(mbpibH_2)Ru(phen)_2]^{4+}$ which binds to DNA by inserting the bridging moiety into adjacent base pairs.

Mixed metal dinuclear complexes offer even more advantages over ruthenium-ruthenium dinuclear complexes as the second metal utilized may possess its own biological application making for dual-application complex or enhanced biological function.

Sakai and co-workers have tethered a tris(bpy)ruthenium(II) derivative to a *cis*-$PtCl_2(amine)_2$ moiety to incorporate a known DNA intercalating unit with a known DNA binding unit.

The complex $[Ru(bpy)_2\{\mu\text{-}bpy(CONH(CH_2)_3NH_2)_2\}PtCl_2](PF_6)_2\cdot 3H_2O$ shows efficient cleavage of PBR322 DNA to nicked and linearized forms only following irradiation (λ_{irr} = 470 ± 10 nm) at atmospheric conditions. [233] Reedijk and co-workers reported on a ruthenium-copper terpyridine complex that serves as an efficient DNA cleaver. [234] The ruthenium moiety is utilized to direct the copper unit to DNA; subsequently the copper unit can cleave DNA. This is the first report of Cu(terpy) complex selectively cleaving DNA. Cleavage activity was found to increase with a higher number of copper active sites. Large fractions of linearized DNA were observed at micromolar concentrations for a complex containing two ruthenium and two copper centers most likely owing to the enhanced targeting ability associated with multiple Ru(II) metal centers. PAGE experiments indicate that DNA cleavage is non-selective [234].

Liang et al. [235] reported biological application of $[(phen)_2Ru(bpibH_2)Co(phen)_2](ClO_4)_5{\bullet}2H_2O$ which includes Ru (II)-Co(III) metal centers. During this present study this system does not show cytotoxic behavior comparable to cisplatin, however, information from this study can enhance the understanding of the mechanism for binding of metal polypyridyl complexes to nucleic acid [235].

Holder et al. [236] reported the synthesis, characterization and biological properties of two ruthenium(II)-vanadium(IV) complexes: $[Ru(pbt)_2(tpphz)\ VO(sal\text{-}L\text{-}tryp)](PF_6)_2{\bullet}6H_2O$ and $[Ru(pbt)_2(phen_2DTT)VO(sal\text{-}L\text{-}tryp)](PF_6)_2\ {\bullet}5H_2O$, the structures of which are shown in figure 30. [237] Biological screenings showed the monomer $[VO(sal\text{-}L\text{-}tryp)(phen)]{\bullet}H_2O$ and $[Ru(pbt)_2\ (tpphz)VO(sal\text{-}L\text{-}tryp)]Cl_2$ were the most active against A431 carcinoma cells with IC_{50} values comparable to those obtained for cisplatin as shown in table 4, while showing significantly less toxicity to non-cancerous HFF (human foreskin fibroblast). Figure 31 shown the dark and light toxicity studies which were conducted following irradiation of $[Ru(pbt)_2(tpphz)VO(sal\text{-}L\text{-}tryp)]Cl_2$ and $[Ru(pbt)_2(phen_2DTT)VO(sal\text{-}L\text{-}tryp)]Cl_2$ at 740 nm which show drastic differences in the morphologies of HFF and A431 cells at a concentration of 20 μM indicating a light enhanced cytopathic effect in A431 carcinoma cells. [236] This qualitative study gives indication that mixed-metal ruthenium(II)-vanadium(IV) complexes may be good PDT agents.

Supramolecular chemistry has played an important role in many new pharmaceutical therapies especially in those involved in mapping interactions of drug sites. [238-242] The extensive properties of supramolecular complexes have thus found applications in PDT. [243-245] Higgins et al. [246] reported both $[(Ph_2phen)_2Ru(dpp)PtCl_2]Cl_2$ and $[(Ph_2phen)_2Ru(dpq)PtCl_2]Cl_2$ which covalently bind and photocleave DNA through the *cis*-$PtCl_2$ bioactive site via an oxygen-dependent mechanism.

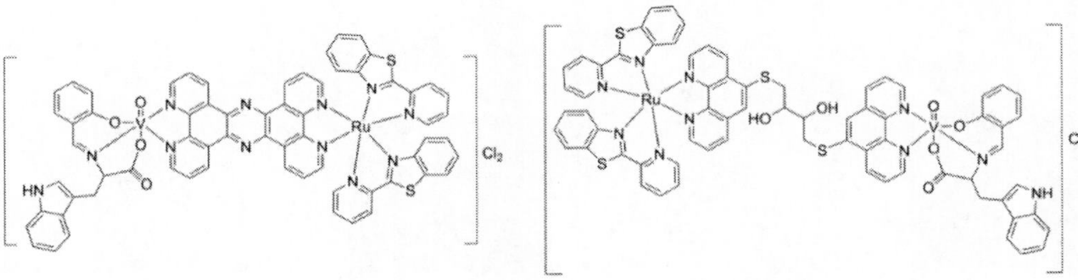

Figure 30. $[Ru(pbt)_2(tpphz)VO(sal\text{-}L\text{-}tryp)]Cl_2$ and $[Ru(pbt)_2(phen_2DTT)VO(sal\text{-}L\text{-}tryp)]Cl_2$ as synthesized by Holder et al. [236].

Table 4. Anti-proliferative data obtained for respective complexes in the presence of respective cell lines

	IC_{50} / [μM]	
Species	A431	HFF
$[Ru(pbt)_2(tpphz)VO(sal\text{-}L\text{-}tryp)]Cl_2$	41.3 ± 7.6	100.7 ± 17.7
$[Ru(pbt)_2(phen_2DTT)VO(sal\text{-}L\text{-}tryp)]Cl_2$	48.6 ± 13.1	41.3 ± 7.6
$[VO(sal\text{-}L\text{-}tryp)(phen)]{\bullet}H_2O$	41.3 ± 7.6	41.3 ± 7.6
Cisplatin	41.3 ± 7.6	41.3 ± 7.6

Data expresses as IC_{50} value in μM. Reprinted with permission [236].

Coupling the chromophore to DNA via the *cis*-$PtCl_2$ site directs the $^1O_2$ to the DNA target. Photolysis studies, exciting in the presence of plasmid DNA, show marked photoreactivity as DNA photocleaving agents over previous Ru(II)-Pt(II) systems. The complex $[(Ph_2phen)_2Ru(dpp)\text{-}PtCl_2]^{2+}$ also displays a new mechanism for DNA modifications as it photobinds through a ^{3}MLCT excited state. [247] This complex is only one of a handful of metal complexes which can be activated in the therapeutic window and was the first reported Ru(II)-Pt(II) bimetallic complex. [247-249] Varying the bridging ligand impacts the nature and localization of the reactive ^{3}MLCT state and sterics around the Pt center which may modulate photoreactivity of these systems. [246] Similarly, Mongelli et al. [250] reported on the effects of varying the terminal ligand in a series of complexes with the generic structure $[(TL)_2Ru(dpp)]Cl_2$ (where TL = 2,2'-bipyridine, 1,10-phenanthroline, or 4,7-diphenyl,1,10-phenanthroline). As shown in figure 32, pUC18 plasmid DNA was photocleaved by all three $[(TL)_2Ru(dpp)]Cl_2$ complexes in aqueous solution upon excitation with low energy visible light. Gel electrophoresis assay demonstrates the ability of these $[(TL)_2Ru(dpp)]Cl_2$ complexes to cleave supercoiled DNA through an oxygen-mediated pathway.

The efficiency of DNA photocleavage by the $[(TL)_2Ru(dpp)]Cl_2$ complexes increases from bpy to phen to Ph_2phen.

All three of these complexes share the same bridging ligand, dpp, which allows for further functionalization in supramolecular assemblies.

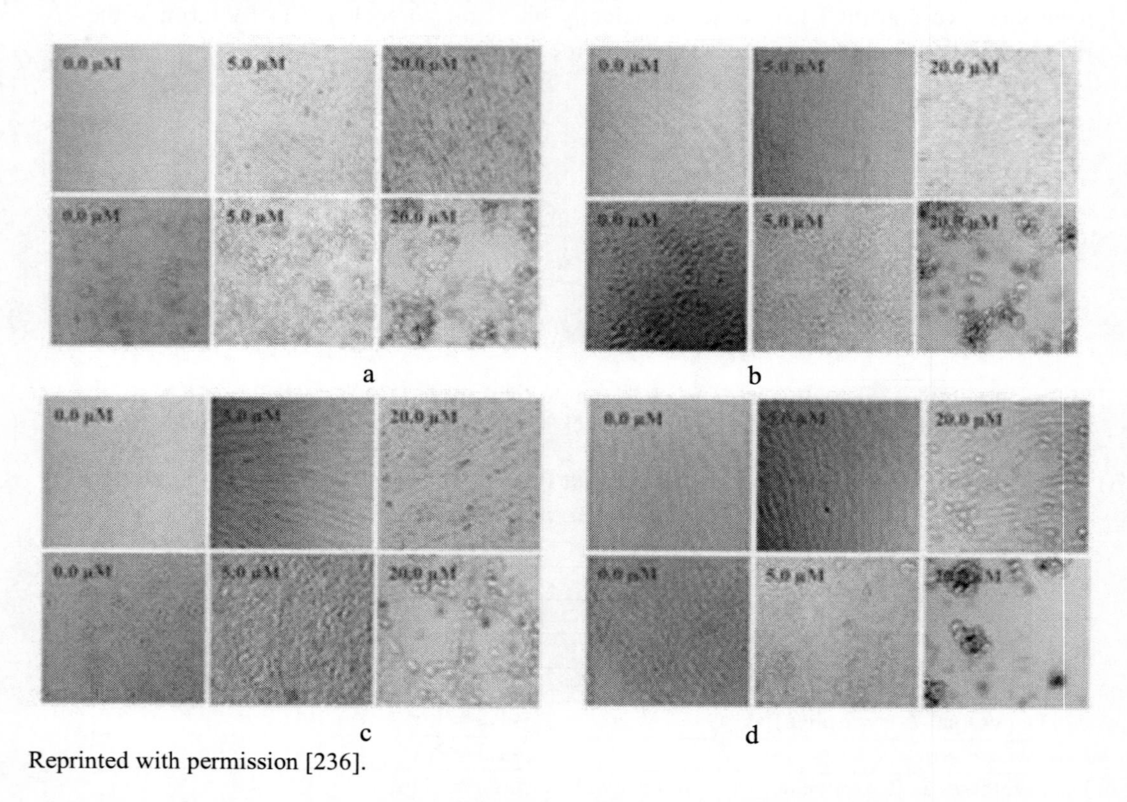

Reprinted with permission [236].

Figure 31. Phase contrast image of HFF (upper panel) and A431 cells (lower panel). (A) dark and (B) light toxicity with $[Ru(pbt)_2(tpphz)VO(sal\text{-}L\text{-}tryp)]Cl_2$; (C) dark and (D) light toxicity with $[Ru(pbt)_2(phen_2DTT)VO(sal\text{-}L\text{-}tryp)]Cl_2$.

Brewer et al. [251] reported the first photocleavage of pUC18 with a mixed metal supramolecular complex $[\{(bpy)_2Ru(dpp)\}_2RhCl_2](PF_6)_5$ (**8**) in absence of molecular oxygen as shown in figure 33.

Holder et al. [252] reported Vero cells exposed to a supramolecular complex **8** at 3.0 µM, tha were irradiated with > 460 nm light had cell growth limited to 2.7 times the initial cell population. Growth decreased rapidly as the concentration of **8** was increased from 3.0 to 12 µM ($cells_{48h}/cells_0$ = 2.7 and 0.8, respectively) [252].

Remarkably, completely normal cell growth was seen for all dark controls indicating high photocytotoxicity; indicating the promise of this compound in the development of new PDT agents of this structural motif as shown in figure 34A – E.

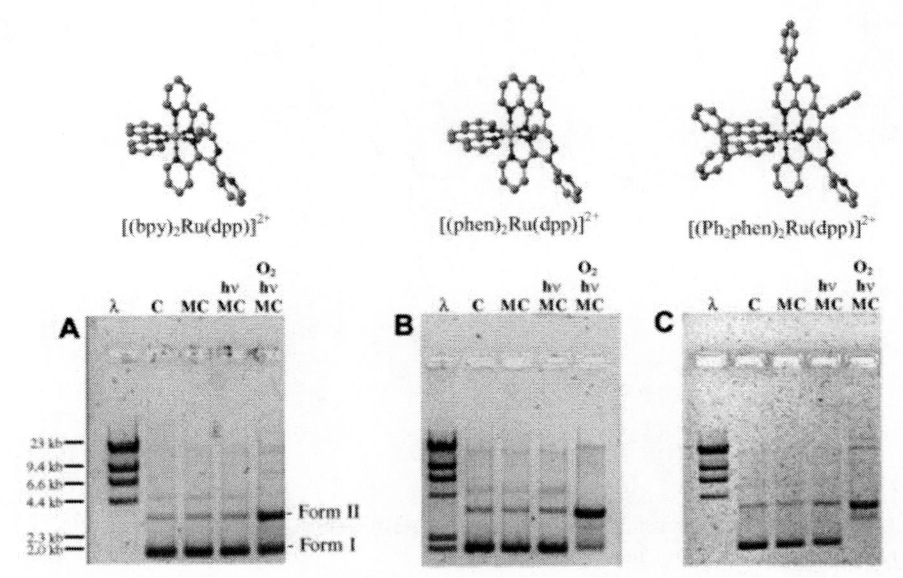

Reprint from J. Inorg. Biochem., 100, Mongelli, M. T.; Heinecke, J.; Mayfield, S.; Okyere, B.; Winkel, B. S. J.; Brewer, K. J.Variation of DNA photocleavage efficiency for [(TL)2Ru(dpp)]Cl2 complexes where TL = 2,2'-bipyridine, 1,10-phenanthroline, or 4,7-diphenyl-1,10-phenanthroline, 100, 1983-1987, Copyright (2006), with permissions from Elsevier [250].

Figure 32. DNA photocleavage assay for the complexes $[(bpy)_2Ru(dpp)]Cl_2$ (A), $[(phen)_2Ru(dpp)]Cl_2$ (B), and $[(Ph_2phen)_2Ru(dpp)]Cl_2$ (C) using pUC18 circular plasmid DNA, 0.8% agarose gel electrophoresis, imaged with ethidium bromide staining. Lane λ is the λ molecular weight standard. Lane C is the DNA control showing pUC18 occurs in primarily the supercoiled (form I) with minor nicked (form II) components. Lane MC is 5:1 base pair (BP):metal complex (MC) dark control illustrating no dark modification of pUC18 by these metal complexes. Lane MC, hν is 5:1 BP:MC photolyzed in the absence of molecular oxygen. Lane MC, hν, O_2 is 5:1 BP:MC photolyzed in the presence of molecular oxygen illustrating that all three complexes photocleave DNA through an oxygen-mediated pathway.

Brewer and co-workers have also reported a new tetrametallic supramolecular complex, $[\{(bpy)_2Ru(dpp)\}_2\text{-}Ru(dpp)PtCl_2](PF_6)_6$ (**9**), the *cis*-dichloroplatinum(II) moiety is designed to allow coordination to DNA, while the Ru polyazine units allow for sensitization of molecular oxygen leading to the cleavage of DNA [253]. Interaction of the complex with pUC18, as studied with gel electrophoresis, indicate that in the dark and with incubation at 37 °C there is retardation in the migration of the band observed indicated binding to DNA via the *cis*-dichloroplatinum(II) moiety.

Upon irradiation with light (λ_{irr} > 450 nm) at atmospheric conditions, there is significant conversion from the supercoiled to the nicked form.

In the absences of molecular oxygen, there is no conversion to the nicked form indicating the formation of singlet oxygen is necessary to facilitate DNA photocleavge [253].

Photofrin, a FDA approved porphyrin-based photosensitizer, [254-256] has been shown to generate singlet oxygen through an energy transfer upon photoexcitation in the visible region causing cell death. [254-256] While photoexcitation leads to cell death, Photofrin also suffers from dark toxicity and purification difficulties, [254-256] thus it is imperative to find alternatives to eliminate negative attributes.

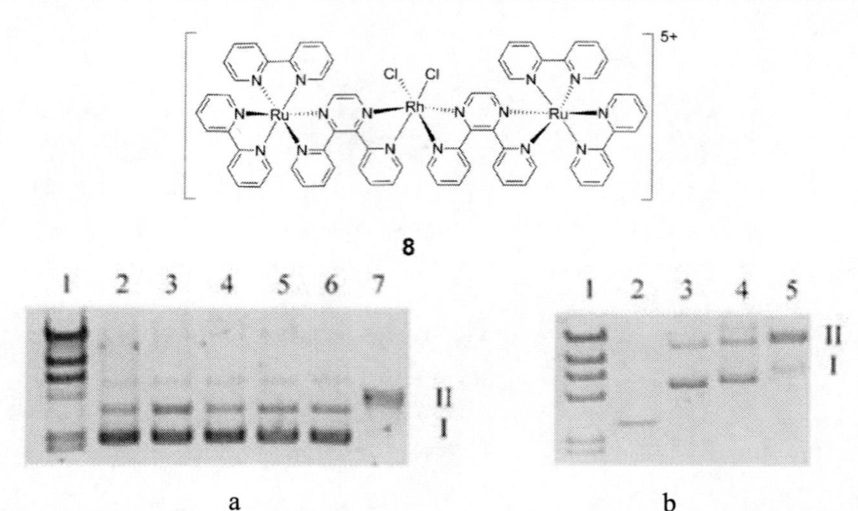

Reprint (Adapted) with permission from Swavey, S.; Brewer, K. J. *Inorg. Chem.* 2002, *41*, 6196. Copyright 2002 American Chemical Society [251].

Figure 33. (a) Photocleavage of pUC18 plasmid by **8** in the absence of molecular oxygen. Lane 1 λ molecular weight standard, lanes 2 and 3 plasmid controls, lanes 4 and 6 plasmid incubated at 37 °C (2 h) in the presence of $[(bpy)_2Ru\text{-}(dpp)]^{2+}$ and **8**, respectively (1:5 metal complex/ base pair), lanes 5 and 7 plasmid irradiated at $\lambda \geq 475$ nm for 10 min in the presence of $[(bpy)_2Ru(dpp)]^{2+}$ and **8**, respectively. (b) Imaged agarose gel showing photocleavage of pBluescript plasmid in the absence of molecular oxygen by **8**. Lane 1 is the λ molecular weight standard, lane 2 is the control linearized DNA (cut with HindIII) with no metal present, lane 3 is the control circular DNA with no metal present, lane 4 is a 1:5 metal complex/base pair mixture of the plasmid with the metal complex incubated at 37 °C (4 h), and lane 5 is a 1:5 metal complex/base pair mixture of the plasmid with the metal complex photolyzed at 520 ± 5 nm for 4 h.

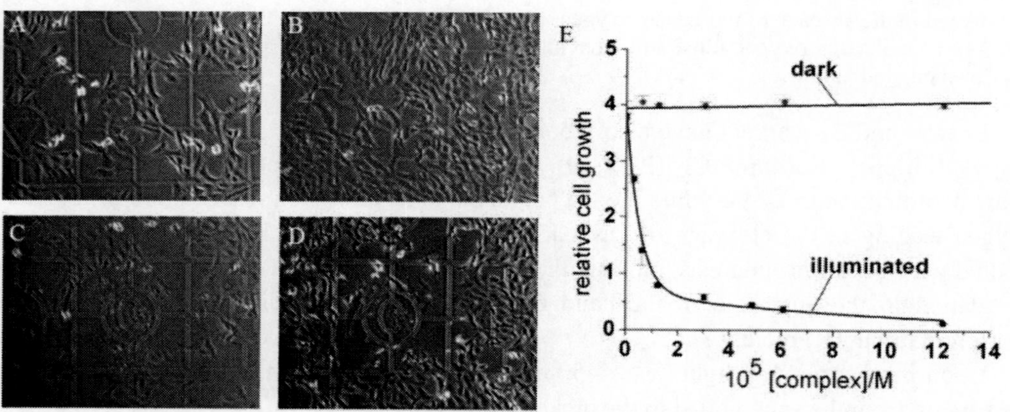

Reprinted with permission from Holder, A. A.; Zigler, D. F.; Tarrago-Trani, M. T.; Storrie, B.; Brewer, K. J. *Inorg. Chem.* 2007, *46*, 4760. Copyright 2007 American Chemical Society [252].

Figure 34. Phase contrast images of Vero cells after uptake of **8** (A) Dark, (B) Dark 48 hours, (C) Pre-illumination (0 hour), (D) Post-illumination (48 hours). (E) Inhibition of Vero cell replication by **8**.

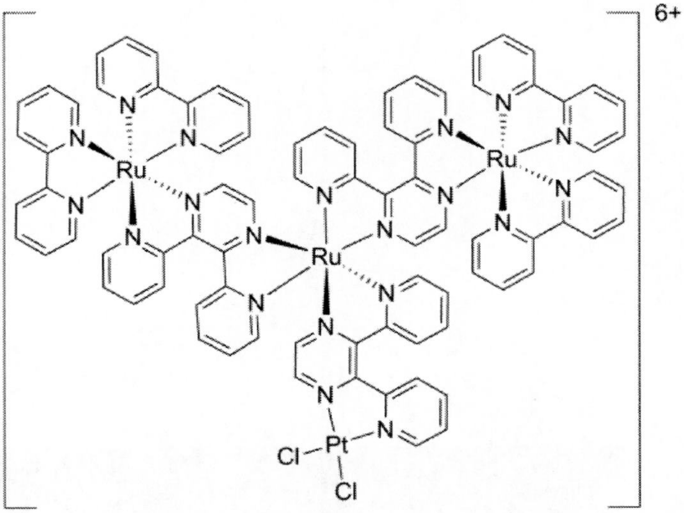

9

Masico first reported on the use of tetraruthenated porphyrins as potential photosensitizer for photodynamic therapy in the late 1990s. [257] Polypyridyl ruthenium(II) substituents, covalently linked to porphyrins, offer enhanced water solubility while maintaining the intercalation properties of the ruthenium metal center. [258, 259] Swavey and co-workers have combined the properties of fluorinated porphyins with those of ruthenium polypyridyl complexes to create highly active photosensitizers for use in photodynamic therapy.

In one report a ruthenium porphyrin complex [*cis*-H_2(DPDPFPP)Ru_2 $(bpy)_4Cl_2(PF_6)_2$] (**10**), shown in figure 35, exhibits the ability to bind and photocleave supercoiled DNA when irradiated with low-energy light. [260] Cell studies indicate a low dark toxicity of the complex towards both melanoma and normal cells, however, under visible light melanoma cells reveal extensive apoptosis, as shown in figure 36 [260].

In another study a new porphyrin 5,15-(4-pyridyl)-10,20-(pentafluorophenyl)porphyrin (H_2DPDPFPP) and its diruthenium(II) analogue ([*trans*-H_2(DPDPFPP)$Ru_2(bpy)_4Cl_2(PF_6)_2$]) were examined for their interaction with linearized pUC18 plasmid. [261] Gel electrophoresis studies showed interactions between the metallated porphyrin and DNA which was confirmed by UV-visible spectroscopic titrations with CTDNA which resulted in a binding constant of 10^5 M^{-1}.

Irradiation with a 50 W halogen lamp, again, led to the conversion of supercoiled DNA to a nicked circular form. [261] More recent studies by Swavey and co-workers have found that multi-nuclear porphyrin systems behavior similarly. A Cu/Ru/Pt complex showed complete photoclevage of pUC18 within eight minutes of irradiation. [262] Complex **13** was not as effective as complex **12** suggesting that addition of copper(II) into the porphyrin center plays a role in the mechanism of photoclevage.

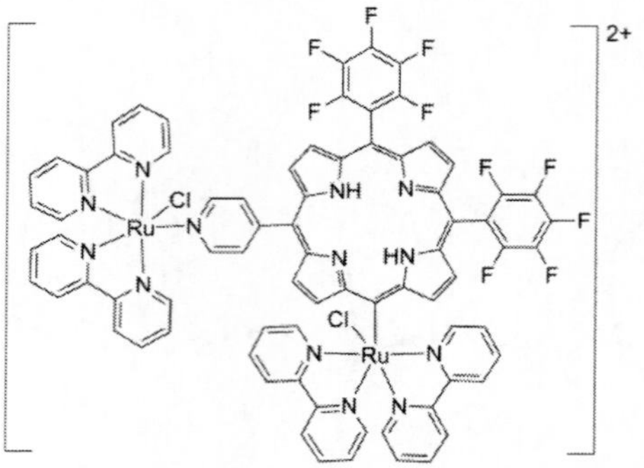

10

Reprinted with permission from Rani-Beeram, S.; Meyer, K.; McCrate, A.; Hong, Y.; Nielsen, M.; Swavey, S. *Inorg. Chem.* 2008, *47*, 11278. Copyright 2008 American Chemical Society [260].

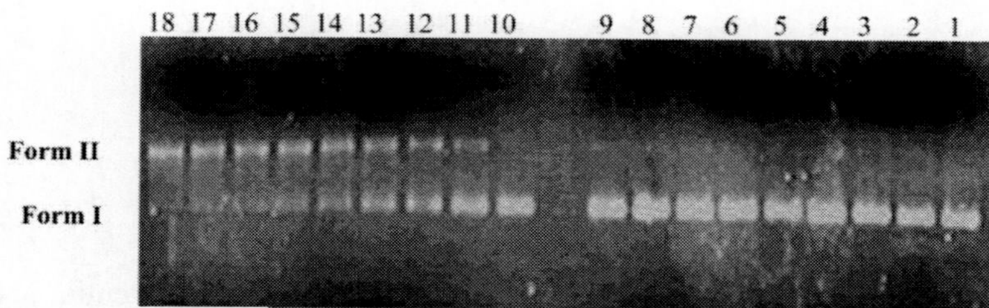

Figure 35. Gel electrophoresis of circular plasmid DNA (pUC18) in the absence (lanes 1−9) and presence (lanes 10−18) of complex **10** at a 5:1 base pair to complex ratio. Lane 1 represents pUC18 prior to irradiation, while lanes 2−9 represent pUC18 irradiated at 15 min intervals. Lane 10 represents Samples were irradiated with a 100 W mercury arc lamp equipped with a long pass filter, cutting off wavelengths below 400 nm. Samples were taken at 15 minutes intervals.

Reprinted with permission from Rani-Beeram, S.; Meyer, K.; McCrate, A.; Hong, Y.; Nielsen, M.; Swavey, S. *Inorg. Chem.* 2008, *47*, 11278. Copyright 2008 American Chemical Society [260].

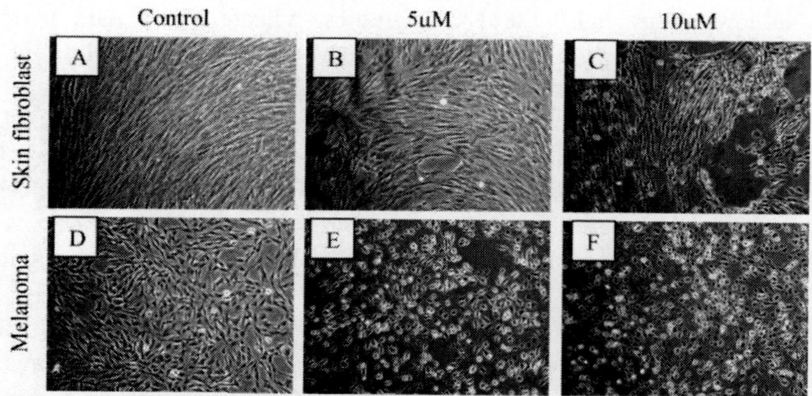

Figure 36. Phase-contrast microscope images of cells irradiated with a 60 W tungsten lamp for 30 min and then incubated for a 1 h period. Skin fibroblast cells without complex **10** (A) and with complex **10** at 5 and 10 μM concentrations (B, C) and melanoma cells under the same conditions without complex **10** (D) and with complex **10** at 5 and 10 μM concentrations (E, F).

Further studies are being conducted to discern the mechanism of DNA photocleavage of these mixed-metal multi-nuclear porphyrins.

Dyson and co-workers recently reported the first conjugation between a porphyrin and arene-ruthenium system and evaluated its biological applications against human melanoma cells. [185] Five 5,10,15,20-tetra(4-pyridyl)porphyrin (TPP) areneruthenium(II) derivatives were prepared and characterized as potential photosensitizing chemotherapeutic agents, as shown in figure 28. Cells exposed to 5 J cm^{-2} of 652 nm red light showed 60 – 80 % phototoxicity, whereas 30 J cm^{-2} of 652 nm red light was needed to induce this level of photocytotoxicity with an osmium complex and was never reached for a rhodium complex, shown in figure 38. [185] Cellular uptake and localization microscopy studies of $[Ru_4(\eta^6\text{-}C_6H_5CH_3)_4(TPP)Cl_8]$ and $[Rh_4(\eta^5\text{-}C_5Me_5)_4(TPP)Cl_8]$ revealed that they accumulated in the melanoma cell cytoplasm in granular structures different from lysosomes.

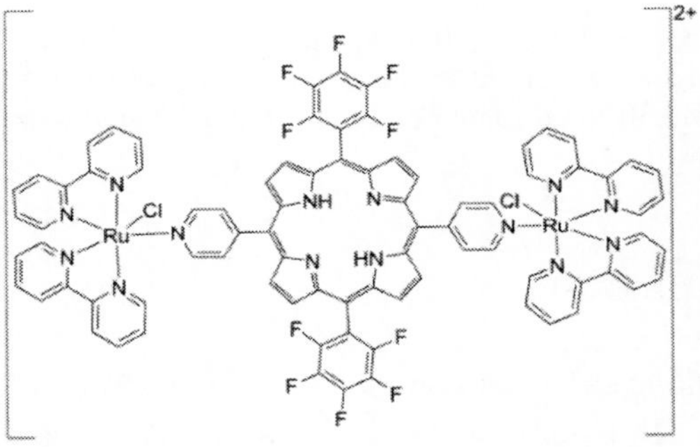

11 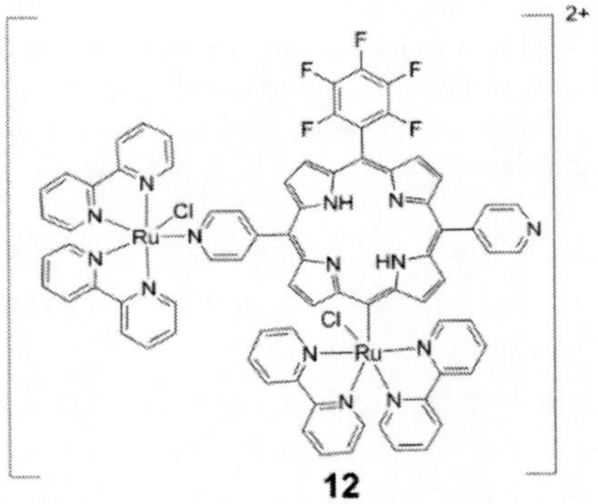 12 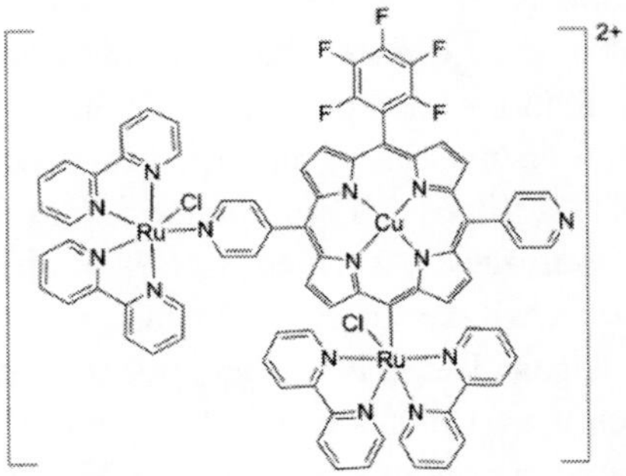 13 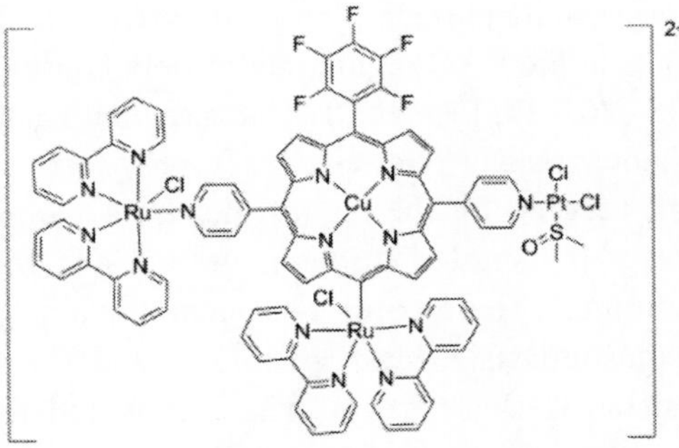 14

Figure 37. Structure of metallophorphyrin complexes as by Swavey and co-workers [261, 262].

Thus, the porphyrin areneruthenium(II) derivatives represent a promising new class of organometallic photosensitizers able to combine chemotherapeutic activity with photodynamic therapeutic treatment of cancer [185].

The reader is encouraged to read the works of Drs. Jacqueline K. Barton, Karen J. Brewer, Peter J. Sadler, Paul J. Dyson, Michael J. Clarke, Alvin A. Holder, and the textbook entitled "*Ruthenium Complexes as Photosensitizers: New Possibilities in Photodynamic Therapy*" by Shawn Swavery, Nova Science Publishers, Inc. New York, 2011, ISBN-13: 978-1-611222-963-9, for detailed information on the use of ruthenium complexes as chemotherapeutic agents.

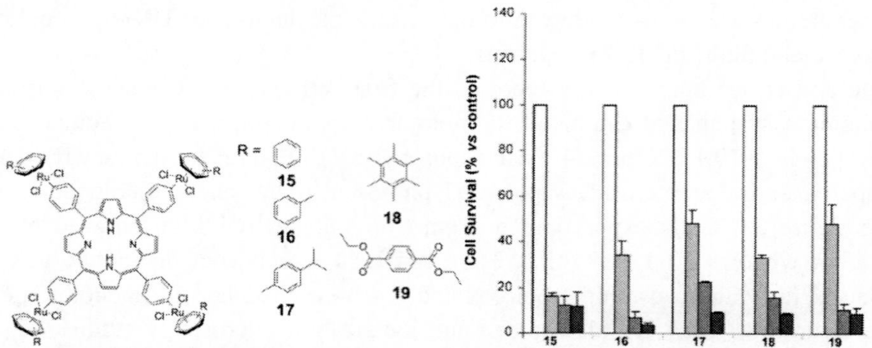

Reprint (adapted) with permission from Schmitt, F.; Govindaswamy, P.; Süss-Fink, G.; Ang, W. H.; Dyson, P. J.; Juillerat-Jeanneret, L.; Therrien, B. *J. Med. Chem.* 2008, *51*, 1811. Copyright 2008 American Chemical Society [185].

Figure 38. Photodynamic sensitivities for compounds **15–19** in Me300 melanoma cells. Survival by MTT test was assessed for cells exposed to increasing doses of light at 652 nm wavelength (0 J/cm^2 in white, 5 J/cm^2 in light gray, 15 J/cm^2 in dark gray, and 30 J/cm^2 in black). Cells were incubated with photosensitizers (10 μM) for 24 h before light treatment.

OTHER DISEASES

Neglected tropical diseases (NTDs) are among the most common condition afflicting an estimated 99 million people who live on less the US$2 per day in the Latin America and Caribbean (LAC) regions. It is estimated that almost all of the nearly 100 million living Americans in these regions suffer from at least one NTD. The NTDs cause a burden of disease in the LAC region that closely approximates or even exceeds that resulting from HIV/ AIDS [263-265]. Of the 13 parasitic and bacterial infections known as NTDs Human African Trypanosomiasis (caused by *Trypanosoma bruci*), Leishmaniasis, and Chagas disease (*T. cruzi*) account for the highest death rates among NTDs. [266] All are zoonotic vector-borne diseases transmitted through the bite and feces of various fly species: tsetse, sandfly, and triatomine. There are two main stain protozoa which infect humans in African trypanosomiasis *T. bruci gambiense* and *T. bruci*. Chagas disease is named after the Brazilian physician Carlos Chagas, who discovered the disease in 1909, and it affects about 7 to 8 million people worldwide, mostly in Latin America where the disease is endemic. [265] The life cycle of *T. cruzi* is shown in figure 39. The cost for the treatment of Chagas disease remains substantial; in Columbia alone, there annual cost of medical treatment for all patients was estimated to be $267 million USD in 2008 [264].

Sánchez-Delgado and co-workers have demonstrated over the last decade that attaching azole-type sterol biosynthesis inhibitors (SBIs), specifically clotrimazole (CTZ) or ketoconazole (KTZ), to ruthenium-containing fragments effectively enhances their activity against *T. cruzi*, while maintaining low toxicity to mammalian cells [268-272]. $[Ru^{II}(\eta^6\text{-}p\text{-cymene})Cl_2(CTZ)]$ showed large enhancements of the activity CTZ against *L. major* and *T. cruzi*, with low nanomolar and low micromolar lethal doses, respectively [269].

Similarly, a series of organometallic complexes $[Ru^{II}\text{-}\eta^6\text{-}p\text{-cymene})Cl_2\,(KTZ)]$, $[Ru^{II}\text{-}\eta^6\text{-}p\text{-cymene})(en)(KTZ)](BF_4)_2$, $[Ru^{II}\text{-}\eta^6\text{-}p\text{-cymene})(bpy)(KTZ)]\,(BF_4)_2$, shown in figure 40, exhibit marked enhancement in their activity toward promastigotes and epimastigotes of *L.*

major and *T. cruzi*, when compared with uncomplexed KTZ, or with similar ruthenium complexes not containing KTZ. Particularly, [Ru^{II}-η^{6}-*p*-cymene)Cl_2(KTZ)] showed selectivity toward leishmania and tryoanosoma parasite, in relation to human fibroblasts and osteoblasts and mouse macrophage, indicating its potential application as anti-parasitic drug [273].

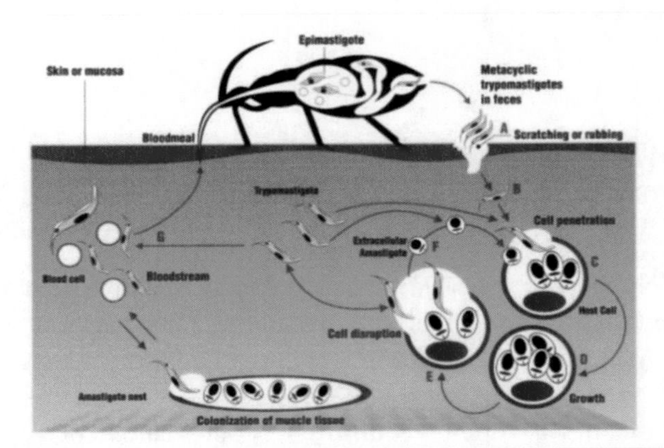

Reprint from New Biotechnology, 27/6, Lima, F. M.; Oliveira, P.; Mortara, R. A.; Silveira, J. F.; Bahia, D., The challenge of Chagas' disease: Has the human pathogen, Trypanosoma cruzi, learned how to modulate signaling events to subvert host cells?, 837-843, Copyright 2010, with permission from Elsevier [267].

Figure 39. Life cycle of *Trypanosoma cruzi*. Epimastigotes in the midgut of the triatomine hematophagous vector (above) differentiate into metacyclic trypomastigotes that are released in the feces during the blood meal. By means of scratching/rubbing, or through the mucosa (a) the infective parasite forms penetrate neighboring host cells (b). Internalized parasites reside for a few hours inside the parasitophorous vacuole from which they escape, and differentiate into the dividing amastigote that grows free in the cytoplasm (c). After approximately nine cycles, amastigotes differentiate back into trypomastigotes (d) which disrupt the infected cell and may either disseminate the infection (f) or infect another insect vector (g). Alternatively, amastigotes that are prematurely released from infected cells, or derived from the extracellular differentiation of trypomastigotes, may also invade cells and sustain an infective cycle (e, f).

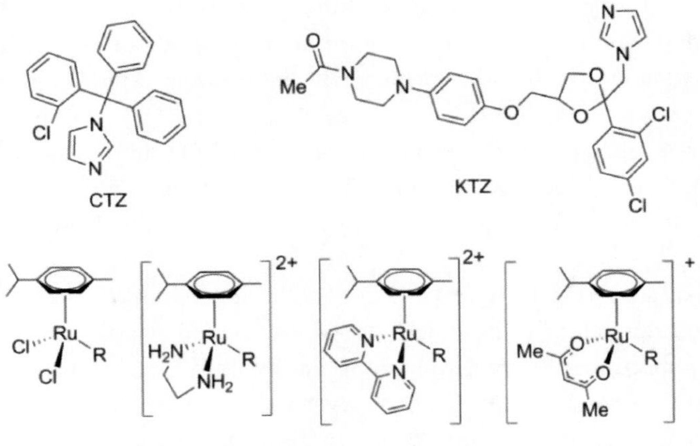

CTZ KTZ

Figure 40. CTZ (clotrimazole), KTZ (ketoconazole), Series of complexes synthesized by Sánchez-Delgado which show antimalarial behavior against *L. major* and *T. cruzi*.

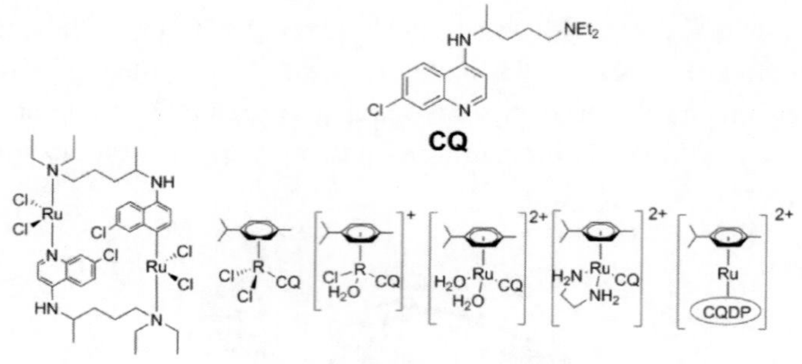

Figure 41. Chloroquine, $[RuCQCl_2]_2$, and series of Organo-Ru(II)-CQ complexes as synthesized by Rajapakse et al. [275].

Malaria is a major cause of morbidity and death in children and adults in tropical countries. An estimated 207 million malarial cases and 627,000 malarial deaths occurred in 2012, 562,000 of which were in Africa in which children under the age of five accounted for 77% [274].

Current malaria treatments often require the combination of a multiple organic compounds employed as drugs including: quinine, chlorquine, hydrochloroquine, mefloquine, primaquine, proguanil, cotrifazid, doxycycline, sulfadoxine, pyrimethamine, artemether, lumefantrine, artesunate, and amodiaquine. Of the current approved drug treatments, chloroquine (CQ) utilized as chloroquine diphosphate represents the most successful. After over twenty years of successful use, CQ-resistant malarial parasites have emerged and spread from Asia to Africa and South America and a treating to further increase morbidity and mortality [274].

Metal-drug synergism has been exploited in the treatment of malaria similar with similar success to other NTDs. Work pioneered by Sánchez-Delgado and co-workers has led to the synthesis of several metal complexes with anti-malarial activity. Ruthenium(II) chloroquine $[RuCQCl_2]_2$ (**20**) has been shown to cause inhibition of the causative agent *Plasmodium berghei* and is effective against CQ-resistant FcB1 and FcB2 *P. falciparum* strains with nanomolar concentrations of 10.5 ± 6.5 and 46.5 ± 9.0, respectively. [272, 276] Following this study, a series of organo-Ru(II)-CQ complexes (**21-25**) shown in figure 41 were synthesized and tested against several *P. falciparum* strains; all of which displayed higher activity against resistant-stains of the parasite than chloroquine diphosphate as indicated by table 5 [275].

Martinez and co-workers have recently report that Ru-CQ complexes bind to hematin in solution and inhibit aggregation of β-hematin. They suggest that inhibition of heme aggregation may be the principle target of Ru-CQ complexes which allows it to overcome the CQ resistance [276, 277].

Alzheimer's disease (AD) is a progressive neurodegenerative disorder that leads to cognitive decline and dementia in the elderly. AD is one of the most common neurological disorders and affects more than 5.2 million people in the USA as of 2014, and is predicted to triple to over 16 million by 2050. No curative AD treatments have been developed so far. Many of the attempted treatments are trying to limit the side effects such as memory impairment. [278, 279].

Those suffering from AD have buildups of senile plaques composed mainly peptides called amyloid-*β* (A*β*) specifically $A\beta_{40}$ and $A\beta_{42}$. Aβ peptides contain high affinity metal binding sites which can potentially affects peptide aggregation and toxicity, thus ongoing research efforts have focused on developing inhibitors of A*β* aggregation as a means of treatment of AD [237, 280, 281].

Table 5. Antimalarial Activity of New Ru-CQ Complexes Against *P. falciparum*; IC_{50} - 50% Inhibitory Concentration (nM)

	IC_{50}/ (nM)				
Strain	CQDP	21	22	23	25
Dd2	1184 ± 188	483 ± 110	442 ± 30	234 ± 41	19. 3 ± 2. 8
K1	1883 ± 165	600 ± 87	508 ± 84	353 ± 61	529 ± 97
W2	2155	1667	1619	906	2549

Reprinted (adapted) with permission from Rajapakse, C. S. K.; Martínez, A.; Naoulou, B.; Jarzecki, A. A.; Suárez, L.; Deregnaucourt, C.; Sinou, V.; Schrével, J.; Musi, E.; Ambrosini, G.; Schwartz, G. K.; Sánchez-Delgado, R. A. *Inorg. Chem.* 2009, *48*, 1122. Copyright 2009 American Chemical Society [275].

AD represents the most expensive condition to treat with an estimated $214 billion USD spent on care in the last year.

Ruthenium complexes have been recently proposed as a better alternative to platinum based inhibitors for selective modification of A*β* histidines as ruthenium has a strong tendency to coordinate to imidazole nitrogen atoms and generally display a favorable systematic toxicity profile. Valensin and co-workers synthesized the first ruthenium based compound, *fac*-$[Ru(CO)_3Cl_2\text{-}(N^1\text{-thz})]$ (**26**) to be used in the treatment of AD [280].

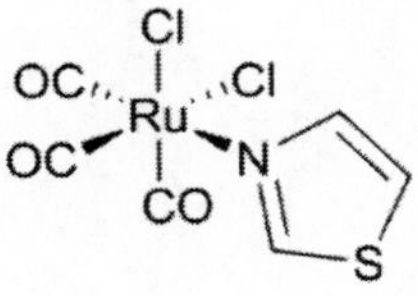

26

^1H-^1H TOCSY and NOESY spectroscopic studies coupled with ESI-MS analysis indicate that a reaction between **26** and $A\beta_{28}$ and $A\beta_{40}$ indicate the formation of a monoruthenated complex and a fast tight binging of $[Ru(CO)_3]^{2+}$ to histidine residues after the displacement of labile chloride and thz ligands. [280] NMR titration based on the modified peptide residue indicated His-13 and His-14 as primary coordination sites for ruthenium. [280] Pt/Ru binuclear complexes have been shown to selectively bind to A*β* as well. Mixed-metal complexes the same advantage of inhibition of the A*β* aggregation while providing the ability to optimize a potential secondary interaction with A*β*. Rangachari and co-workers were the first to synthesize a binuclear Ru^{II}-Pt^{II} complex $[(bpy)_2Ru^{II}\text{-}(dpp)Pt^{II}Cl_2]Cl_2$ (**27**) to be utilized for prevention of $A\beta_{40}$ and $A\beta_{42}$ aggregation [281].

27

Complex **27** was shown to inhibit $A\beta_{42}$ aggregation in a way comparable to other L-$PtCl_2$ complexes but with a distinct mode of action. Complex **27** is also able to inhibit the formation of amyloid fibrils suggesting a substantial rearrangement of the conformation of the monomeric peptide, from random coil to a more compact form as shown in figure 42 [281].

For further reading on treatment of NTDs the reader is encouraged to see the work of Drs. Roberto Sanchez-Delgato, Dinorah Gambino and Lucia Otero; and the work of Drs. Chiara Gabbiani and Luigi Messori for more information on ruthenium complexes for AD treatment.

Conclusion

Ruthenium containing complexes are particularly important in biological settings. The unique properties of this metal allow for biocompatibility and often low inherit toxicity.

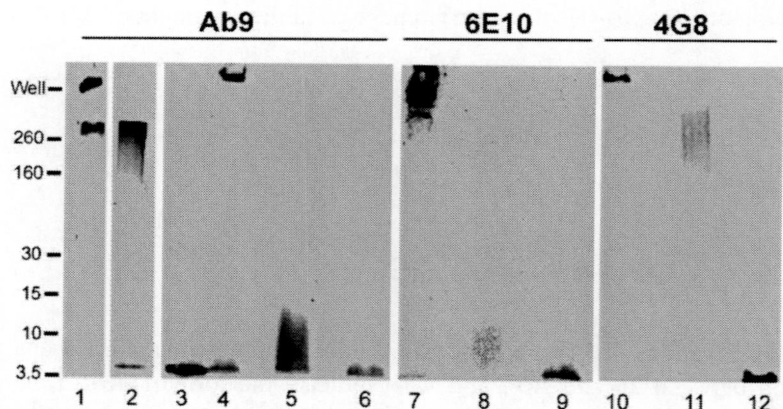

Figure 42. Immunoblots of $A\beta_{42}$ inhibition by the designed compounds. The $A\beta_{42}$ (25 μM) was incubated alone (control) or with 10-fold excess of compounds at 37 °C for 10 days. The samples (400 ng) were electrophoresed on a 12% polyacrylaminde gel followed by Western blotting and immunostaining using monoclonal antibodies Ab9, 6E10, and 4G8. Lanes 1−6, Ab9: Ru-1 (lane 1), Pt-2 (lane 2), and Aβ42 monomer (lane 3), control Aβ42 (lane 4), +Pt-1 (lane 5), +PtRu-1 (lane 6). Lanes 7−9, 6E10: control Aβ42 (lane 7), +Pt-1 (lane 8), +PtRu-1 (lane 9). Lanes 10−12, 4G8: control Aβ42 (lane 10), +Pt-1 (lane 11), and +PtRu-1 (lane 12).

These two properties make ruthenium containing complexes especially useful in cellular imaging. Selectively towards for various organelles within the cell has already been achieved; as well as the creation of many DNA "light-switch" complexes capable of binding and luminescing upon DNA binding. Further work is being conducted in employing ruthenium containing complexes as potential theranostic agents in combination with nanoparticles and lanthanide complexes.

It has been well demonstrated in cancer tissue, as well as other diseased cells, that biochemical changes within the cellular environment alter the physiological environment thereby activating ruthenium complexes allowing for selective activation in diseased tissues. Since the entrance of NAMI-A and KP1019 into clinic trials much attention has been given to ruthenium-based chemotherapeutics. Various ligands and systems can be coordinated to the ruthenium metal center thereby increasing the toxicity and specificity of the complex. While at present the mechanism by which ruthenium-based complexes exert their toxicity is not fully understood they circumvent inherently toxic platinum-based drugs with minimal side effects.

ACKNOWLEDGMENTS

AAH would like to thank the National Science Foundation (NSF) for an NSF CAREER Award. This material is based upon work partially supported by the National Science Foundation under CHE-1431172 (formerly CHE - 1151832). JLB and AAH would like to acknowledge Prof. Karen J. Brewer of Virginia Tech for the use of some of her figures and for mentoring AAH when he was a postdoctoral fellow in her laboratory from May 2002 until June 2003.

REFERENCES

[1] Lide, D. R. *CRC Handbook of Chemistry and Physics*; CRC Press: Boca Raton, FL, 2008.

[2] Emsley, J. *"Ruthenium". Nature's Building Blocks: An A-Z Guide to the Elements.*; Oxford University Press: Oxford, England UK, 2003.

[3] Osann, C. *Annalen der Physik* 1826, 84, 505.

[4] Pitchkov, V. N. *Platinum Metals Rev.* 1996, 40, 181.

[5] Abhik Bandyopadhyay, L. W., Joseph Agyin, Yuping Tang, Shu Lin, I-Tien Yeh, Keya De,; Sun, L.-Z. *Plos One* 2010, 5.

[6] Harris, D. C.; Cabri, L. J. *Can. Mineral.* 1973, 12, 104.

[7] Nyirenda, R. L.; Phiri, W. S. *Miner. Eng.* 1998, 11, 23.

[8] Charlesworth, P. *Platinum Metals Rev.* 1981, 25, 106.

[9] Gouldsmith, A. F. S.; Wilson, B. *Platinum Metals Rev.* 1963, 7, 136.

[10] Seymour, R. J.; O'Farrelly, J. I. In: *Kirk-Othmer Encyclopedia of Chemical Technology*; John Wiley and Sons, Inc.: 2000.

[11] Renner, H.; Schlamp, G.; Kleinwächter, I.; Drost, E.; Lüschow, H. M.; Tews, P.; Panster, P.; Diehl, M.; Lang, J.; Kreuzer, T.; Knödler, A.; Starz, K. A.; Dermann, K.;

Rothaut, J.; Drieselmann, R.; Peter, C.; Schiele, R. In: *Ullmann's Encyclopedia of Industrial Chemistry*; Wiley-VCH Verlag GmbH and Co. KGaA: 2000.
[12] Gilchrist, R. *Chem. Rev.* 1943, 32, 277.
[13] Tennant, S. *Philos. Trans. R. Soc. London* 1804, 94, 411.
[14] Wollaston, W. H. *Philos. Trans. R. Soc. London* 1804, 94, 419.
[15] Wollaston, W. H. *Philos. Trans. R. Soc. London* 1805, 95, 316.
[16] Hunt, L. B.; Lever, F. M. *Platinum Metals Rev.* 1969, 13, 126.
[17] Kolarik, Z.; Renard, E. V. *Platinum Metals Rev.* 2003, 47, 123.
[18] Kolarik, Z.; Renard, E. V. *Platinum Metals Rev.* 2003, 47, 74.
[19] Duraippandi Palanimuthu, A. G. S. *Inorg. Chim. Acta* 2013, 408, 152.
[20] Cotton, F. A.; Wilkinson, G.; Murillo, C. A.; Bochmann, M. *Advanced Inorganic Chemistry*; 6th ed.; Wiley-Interscience: New York, 1999.
[21] Bernhard, P.; Biner, M.; Ludi, A. *Polyhedron* 1990, 9, 1095.
[22] Aebischer, N.; Laurenczy, G.; Ludi, A.; Merbach, A. E. *Inorg. Chem.* 1993, 32, 2810.
[23] Laurenczy, G.; Merbach, A. E. *J. Chem. Soc., Chem. Commun.* 1993, 187.
[24] Karlen, T.; Ludi, A. *J. Am. Chem. Soc.* 1994, 116, 11375.
[25] Lynn, D. M.; Kanaoka, S.; Grubbs, R. H. *J. Am. Chem. Soc.* 1996, 118, 784.
[26] Patel, A.; Richens, D. T. *Inorg. Chem.* 1991, 30, 3789.
[27] Togano, T.; Nagao, N.; Tsuchida, M.; Kumakura, H.; Hisamatsu, K.; Howell, F. S.; Mukaida, M. *Inorg. Chim. Acta* 1992, 195, 221.
[28] Bardwell, D. A.; Horsburgh, L.; Jeffery, J. C.; Joulie, L. F.; Ward, M. D.; Webster, I.; Yellowlees, L. J. *J. Chem. Soc., Dalton Trans.* 1996, 2527.
[29] Ghadiri, M. R.; Soares, C.; Choi, C. *J. Am. Chem. Soc.* 1992, 114, 4000.
[30] Knowles, T. S.; Howells, M. E.; Howlin, B. J.; Smith, G. W.; Amodio, C. A. *Polyhedron* 1994, 13, 2197.
[31] Creutz, C.; Taube, H. *J. Amer. Chem. Soc.* 1969, 91, 3988.
[32] Kumar, C. V.; Barton, J. K.; Turro, N. J. *J. Am. Chem. Soc.* 1985, 107, 5518.
[33] Brewer, K.; Swavey, S.; Virginia Tech Intellectual Properties, Inc., US. 2003, p. 31 pp.
[34] Cunningham, M.; McCrate, A.; Nielsen, M.; Swavey, S. *Eur. J. Inorg. Chem.* 2009, 1521.
[35] Elmes, R. B. P.; Kitchen, J. A.; Williams, D. C.; Gunnlaugsson, T. *Dalton Trans.* 2012, 41, 6607.
[36] Elmes, R. B. P.; Orange, K. N.; Cloonan, S. M.; Williams, D. C.; Gunnlaugsson, T. *J. Am. Chem. Soc.* 2011, 133, 15862.
[37] Fang, Z.; Swavey, S.; Holder, A.; Winkel, B.; Brewer, K. J. *Inorg. Chem. Commun.* 2002, 5, 1078.
[38] Gill, M. R.; Derrat, H.; Smythe, C. G. W.; Battaglia, G.; Thomas, J. A. *ChemBioChem* 2011, 12, 877.
[39] Coe, B. J.; Meyer, T. J.; White, P. S. *Inorg. Chem.* 1995, 34, 593.
[40] Carter, F. *Ind. Eng. Chem.* 1935, 27, 751.
[41] Moss, J. R. *Platinum Metals Rev.* 1995, 39, 33.
[42] Rao, C. R. K.; Trivedi, D. C. *Coord. Chem. Rev.* 2005, 249, 613.
[43] Weisberg, A. M. *Met. Finish.* 1999, 97, 297.
[44] Predel, B. In: *Li-Mg – Nd-Zr*; Madelung, O., Ed.; Springer Berlin Heidelberg: 1997; Vol. 5H, p. 1.
[45] Gürler, R. *J. Alloys Compd.* 1999, 285, 133.

[46] Stern, M.; Wissenberg, H. *J. Electrochem. Soc.* 1959, 106, 759.
[47] Tomashov, N. D.; Altovsky, R. M.; Chernova, G. P. *J. Electrochem. Soc.* 1961, 108, 113.
[48] Pollock, T. M.; Tin, S. *J. Propul. Power* 2006, 22, 361.
[49] Tan, X. P.; Liu, J. L.; Jin, T.; Hu, Z. Q.; Hong, H. U.; Choi, B. G.; Kim, I. S.; Jo, C. Y. *Met. Mater. Int.* 2012, 18, 769.
[50] Ma, G.; Yan, H.; Shi, J.; Zong, X.; Lei, Z.; Li, C. *J. Catal.* 2008, 260, 134.
[51] Vieille-Petit, L.; Clavier, H.; Linden, A.; Blumentritt, S.; Nolan, S. P.; Dorta, R. *Organometallics* 2010, 29, 775.
[52] Ulman, M.; Grubbs, R. H. *J. Org. Chem* 1999, 64, 7202.
[53] Yan, Y. K.; Melchart, M.; Habtemariam, A.; Sadler, P. J. *Chem. Comm.* 2005, 4764.
[54] Sava, G.; Bergamo, A. *Int. J. Oncol.* 2000, 17, 353.
[55] Salas, P. F.; Herrmann, C.; Orvig, C. *Chem. Rev.* 2013, 113, 3450.
[56] Silveira-Lacerda, E. D.; Vilanova-Costa, C.; Pereira, F. D.; Hamaguchi, A.; Pavanin, L.; Goulart, L.; Homsi-Brandenburgo, M.; Soares, A.; Santos, W.; Nomizo, A. *Biol. Trace Elem. Res.* 2010, 133, 270.
[57] Ghosh, K.; Kumar, S.; Kumar, R.; Singh, U. P. *J. Organomet. Chem.* 2014, 750, 169.
[58] Fry, N. L.; Mascharak, P. K. *Acc. Chem. Res.* 2011, 44, 289.
[59] Pandrala, M.; Li, F.; Feterl, M.; Mulyana, Y.; Warner, J. M.; Wallace, L.; Keene, F. R.; Collins, J. G. *Dalton Trans.* 2013, 42, 4686.
[60] Li, F.; Feterl, M.; Mulyana, Y.; Warner, J. M.; Collins, J. G.; Keene, F. R. *J. Antimicrob. Chemother.* 2012, 67, 2686.
[61] Turel, I.; Kljun, J.; Perdih, F.; Morozova, E.; Bakulev, V.; Kasyanenko, N.; Byl, J. A. W.; Osheroff, N. *Inorg. Chem.* 2010, 49, 10750.
[62] Kljun, J.; Bytzek, A. K.; Kandioller, W.; Bartel, C.; Jakupec, M. A.; Hartinger, C. G.; Keppler, B. K.; Turel, I. *Organometallics* 2011, 30, 2506.
[63] Glans, L.; Ehnbom, A.; de Kock, C.; Martinez, A.; Estrada, J.; Smith, P. J.; Haukka, M.; Sanchez-Delgado, R. A.; Nordlander, E. *Dalton Trans.* 2012, 41, 2764.
[64] Holst, G.; Glud, R. N.; Kühl, M.; Klimant, I. *Sens. Actuators B* 1997, 38, 122.
[65] Dierichs, R. *Histochemistry* 1979, 64, 171.
[66] Laatikainen, L.; Tarkkanen, A. *Acta Ophthalmologica* 1987, 65, 148.
[67] Richards, A. D.; Rodger, A. *Chem. Soc. Rev.* 2007, 36, 471.
[68] Kuang, D.; Ito, S.; Wenger, B.; Klein, C.; Moser, J.-E.; Humphry-Baker, R.; Zakeeruddin, S. M.; Grätzel, M. *J. Am. Chem. Soc.* 2006, 128, 4146.
[69] Puodziukynaite, E.; Wang, L.; Schanze, K. S.; Papanikolas, J. M.; Reynolds, J. R. *Polym. Chem.* 2014, 5, 2363.
[70] Vasilyev, V. Y. *Russ. Microelectron.* 2011, 40, 279.
[71] Clarke, M. J. *Coord. Chem. Rev.* 2002, 232, 69.
[72] Clarke, M. J. *Coord. Chem. Rev.* 2003, 236, 209.
[73] Srivastava, S. C.; Richards, P.; Som, P.; Meinken, G.; Atkins, H. L.; Sewatkar, A.; Ku, T. H. In: *Frontiers in Nuclear Medicine*; Horst, W., Wagner, H., Jr., Buchanan, J., Eds.; Springer Berlin Heidelberg: 1980, p. 123.
[74] Antonarakis, E.; Emadi, A. *Cancer Chemother. Pharmacol.* 2010, 66, 1.
[75] Allardyce, C. S.; Dyson, P. J. *Platinum Metals Rev.* 2001, 45, 62.
[76] Tan, C.; Wu, S.; Lai, S.; Wang, M.; Chen, Y.; Zhou, L.; Zhu, Y.; Lian, W.; Peng, W.; Ji, L.; Xu, A. *Dalton Trans.* 2011, 40, 8611.

[77] Tan, C.; Lai, S.; Wu, S.; Hu, S.; Zhou, L.; Chen, Y.; Wang, M.; Zhu, Y.; Lian, W.; Peng, W.; Ji, L.; Xu, A. *J. Med. Chem.* 2010, 53, 7613.

[78] Kou, J.-F.; Qian, C.; Wang, J.-Q.; Chen, X.; Wang, L.-L.; Chao, H.; Ji, L.-N. *J. Biol. Inorg. Chem.* 2012, 17, 81.

[79] Yacoub, E.-S. A. K.; El-Kourashy, A.-G.; Al-Hajjaji, M. A. *Arabian J. Chem.* 2013, 6, 111.

[80] Clarke, M. J.; Jansen, B.; Marx, K. A.; Kruger, R. *Inorg. Chim. Acta* 1986, 124, 13.

[81] Yang, H.; Li, L.; Wan, L.; Zhou, Z.; Yang, S. *Inorg. Chem. Commun.* 2010, 13, 1387.

[82] Biner, S. M.; Häner, R. *Chem. Biodiv.* 2012, 9, 2485.

[83] Wei, Z.; Paul, U.; Mary-Ann, M. *J. Phys. D: Appl. Phys.* 2003, 36, 1689.

[84] Musatkina, E.; Amouri, H.; Lamoureux, M.; Chepurnykh, T.; Cordier, C. *J. Inorg. Biochem.* 2007, 101, 1086.

[85] Bolink, H. J.; Cappelli, L.; Coronado, E.; Grätzel, M.; Nazeeruddin, M. K. *J. Amer. Chem. Soc.* 2005, 128, 46.

[86] Wu, P.; Wong, E. L.-M.; Ma, D.-L.; Tong, G. S.-M.; Ng, K.-M.; Che, C.-M. *Chem. – Eur. J.* 2009, 15, 3652.

[87] Picot, A.; D'Aléo, A.; Baldeck, P. L.; Grichine, A.; Duperray, A.; Andraud, C.; Maury, O. *J. Am. Chem. Soc.* 2008, 130, 1532.

[88] Fu, L.-M.; Wen, X.-F.; Ai, X.-C.; Sun, Y.; Wu, Y.-S.; Zhang, J.-P.; Wang, Y. *Angew. Chem. Int. Ed.* 2005, 44, 747.

[89] Koo, C.-K.; Wong, K.-L.; Man, C. W.-Y.; Lam, Y.-W.; So, L. K.-Y.; Tam, H.-L.; Tsao, S.-W.; Cheah, K.-W.; Lau, K.-C.; Yang, Y.-Y.; Chen, J.-C.; Lam, M. H.-W. *Inorg. Chem.* 2009, 48, 872.

[90] Koo, C.-K.; Wong, K.-L.; Man, C. W.-Y.; Tam, H.-L.; Tsao, S.-W.; Cheah, K.-W.; Lam, M. H.-W. *Inorg. Chem.* 2009, 48, 7501.

[91] Carraway, E. R.; Demas, J. N.; DeGraff, B. A.; Bacon, J. R. *Anal. Chem.* 1991, 63, 337.

[92] Neugebauer, U.; Pellegrin, Y.; Devocelle, M.; Forster, R. J.; Signac, W.; Moran, N.; Keyes, T. E. *Chem. Commun.* 2008, 5307.

[93] Kaler, G. V.; Samoilenko, S. G.; Aksentsev, S. L. *J. Appl. Spectrosc.* 1997, 64, 214.

[94] Dwyer, F. P.; Gyarfas, E. C.; Rogers, W. P.; Koch, J. D. *Nature* 1952, 170, 190.

[95] Dwyer, F. P.; Gyarfas, E. C. *J. Proc. Roy. Soc. N.S.W* 1949, 83, 170.

[96] Dwyer, F. P.; Gyarfas, E. C.; O'Dwyer, M. F. *Nature* 1950, 167, 1036.

[97] Burstall, F. H.; Dwyer, F. P.; Gyarfas, E. C. *J. Chem. Soc.* 1950, 950.

[98] Puckett, C. A.; Barton, J. K. *Biochemistry* 2008, 47, 11711.

[99] Puckett, C. A.; Barton, J. K. *J. Am. Chem. Soc.* 2006, 129, 46.

[100] Puckett, C. A.; Barton, J. K. *J. Am. Chem. Soc.* 2009, 131, 8738.

[101] O'Connor, N. A.; Stevens, N.; Samaroo, D.; Solomon, M. R.; Marti, A. A.; Dyer, J.; Vishwasrao, H.; Akins, D. L.; Kandel, E. R.; Turro, N. J. *Chem. Commun.* 2009, 2640.

[102] Lo, K. K.-W.; Lee, T. K.-M.; Lau, J. S.-Y.; Poon, W.-L.; Cheng, S.-H. *Inorg. Chem.* 2007, 47, 200.

[103] Miao, R.; Mongelli, M. T.; Zigler, D. F.; Winkel, B. S. J.; Brewer, K. J. *Inorg. Chem.* 2006, 45, 10413.

[104] Rose, M. J.; Patra, A. K.; Alcid, E. A.; Olmstead, M. M.; Mascharak, P. K. *Inorg. Chem.* 2007, 46, 2328.

[105] Svensson, F. R.; Abrahamsson, M.; Strömberg, N.; Ewing, A. G.; Lincoln, P. *J. Phys. Chem. Lett.* 2011, 2, 397.

[106] Svensson, F. R.; Li, M.; Nordén, B.; Lincoln, P. *J. Phys. Chem. B.* 2008, 112, 10969.
[107] Matson, M.; Svensson, F. R.; Norden, B.; Lincoln, P. *J. Phys. Chem. B* 2011, 115, 1706.
[108] Svensson, F. R.; Matson, M.; Li, M.; Lincoln, P. *Biophys. Chem.* 2010, 149, 102.
[109] Ghezzi, A.; Aceto, M.; Cassino, C.; Gabano, E.; Osella, D. *J. Inorg. Biochem.* 2004, 98, 73.
[110] Svensson, F.; Andersson, J.; Åmand, H.; Lincoln, P. *J. Biol. Inorg. Chem.* 2012, 17, 565.
[111] Friedman, A. E.; Chambron, J. C.; Sauvage, J. P.; Turro, N. J.; Barton, J. K. *J. Am. Chem. Soc.* 1990, 112, 4960.
[112] Hartshorn, R. M.; Barton, J. K. *J. Am. Chem. Soc.* 1992, 114, 5919.
[113] Holmlin, R. E.; Barton, J. K. *Inorg. Chem.* 1995, 34, 7.
[114] Holmlin, R. E.; Tong, R. T.; Barton, J. K. *J. Am. Chem. Soc.* 1998, 120, 9724.
[115] Moucheron, C.; Kirsch-De Mesmaeker, A.; Choua, S. *Inorg. Chem.* 1997, 36, 584.
[116] Gill, M. R.; Garcia-Lara, J.; Foster, S. J.; Smythe, C.; Battaglia, G.; Thomas, J. A. *Nat. Chem.* 2009, 1, 662.
[117] Baggaley, E.; Gill, M. R.; Green, N. H.; Turton, D.; Sazanovich, I. V.; Botchway, S. W.; Smythe, C.; Haycock, J. W.; Weinstein, J. A.; Thomas, J. A. *Angew. Chem.* 2014, 126, 3435.
[118] Gill, M. R.; Cecchin, D.; Walker, M. G.; Mulla, R. S.; Battaglia, G.; Smythe, C.; Thomas, J. A. *Chem. Sci.* 2013, 4, 4512.
[119] Pandya, S.; Yu, J.; Parker, D. *Dalton Trans.* 2006, 2757.
[120] Hai, Y.; Chen, J.-J.; Zhao, P.; Lv, H.; Yu, Y.; Xu, P.; Zhang, J.-L. *Chem. Comm.* 2011, 47, 2435.
[121] Zou, T.; Lok, C.-N.; Fung, Y. M. E.; Che, C.-M. *Chem. Commun.* 2013, 49, 5423.
[122] Lau, J. S.-Y.; Lee, P.-K.; Tsang, K. H.-K.; Ng, C. H.-C.; Lam, Y.-W.; Cheng, S.-H.; Lo, K. K.-W. *Inorg. Chem.* 2008, 48, 708.
[123] Song, B.; Vandevyver, C. D. B.; Chauvin, A.-S.; Bunzli, J.-C. G. *Org. Biomol. Chem.* 2008, 6, 4125.
[124] Fernandez-Moreira, V.; Thorp-Greenwood, F. L.; Amoroso, A. J.; Cable, J.; Court, J. B.; Gray, V.; Hayes, A. J.; Jenkins, R. L.; Kariuki, B. M.; Lloyd, D.; Millet, C. O.; Williams, C. F.; Coogan, M. P. *Org. Biomol. Chem.* 2010, 8, 3888.
[125] Walker, M. G.; Gonzalez, V.; Chekmeneva, E.; Thomas, J. A. *Angew. Chem. Int. Ed.* 2012, 51, 12107.
[126] Yata, P.; Shilpa, M.; Nagababu, P.; Reddy, M. R.; Kotha, L.; Gabra, N.; Satyanarayana, S. *J. Fluoresc.* 2012, 22, 835.
[127] Yao, J.-L.; Gao, X.; Sun, W.; Shi, S.; Yao, T.-M. *Dalton Trans.* 2013, 42, 5661.
[128] Yao, J.-L.; Gao, X.; Sun, W.; Fan, X.-Z.; Shi, S.; Yao, T.-M. *Inorg. Chem.* 2012, 51, 12591.
[129] Lutterman, D. A.; Chouai, A.; Liu, Y.; Sun, Y.; Stewart, C. D.; Dunbar, K. R.; Turro, C. *J. Am. Chem. Soc.* 2008, 130, 1163.
[130] Zhang, A.-G.; Zhang, Y.-Z.; Duan, Z.-M.; Wang, K.-Z.; Wei, H.-B.; Bian, Z.-Q.; Huang, C.-H. *Inorg. Chem.* 2011, 50, 6425.
[131] Li, F.; Harry, E. J.; Bottomley, A. L.; Edstein, M. D.; Birrell, G. W.; Woodward, C. E.; Keene, F. R.; Collins, J. G. *Chem. Sci.* 2014, 5, 685.

[132] Pisani, M. J.; Weber, D. K.; Heimann, K.; Collins, J. G.; Keene, F. R. *Metallomics* 2010, 2, 393.

[133] Elmes, R. B. P.; Orange, K. N.; Cloonan, S. M.; Williams, D. C.; Gunnlaugsson, T. *J. Am. Chem. Soc.* 2011, 133, 15862.

[134] Clarke, M. J.; Podbielski, L. *Coord. Chem. Rev.* 1987, 78, 253.

[135] Marik, T.; Bibr, B.; Kselikova, M.; Petz, J.; Becicova, M. *Radiobiol. Radiother.* 1986, 27, 359.

[136] Som, P.; Oster, Z. H.; Matsui, K.; Guglielmi, G.; Persson, B. R. R.; Pellettieri, M. L.; Srivastava, S. C.; Richards, P.; Atkins, H. L.; Brill, A. B. *Eur. J. Nucl. Med.* 1983, 8, 491.

[137] Srivastava, S. C.; Mausner, L. F.; Clarke, M. J. *Prog. Clin. Biochem. Med.* 1989, 10, 111.

[138] Schachner, E. R.; Gil, M. C.; Atkins, H. L.; Som, P.; Srivastava, S. C.; Badia, J.; Sacker, D. F.; Fairchild, R. G.; Richards, P. *J. Nucl. Med.* 1981, 22, 352.

[139] Schachner, E. R.; Gil, M. C.; Som, P.; Oster, Z. H.; Atkins, H. L.; Subramanian, G.; Badia, J.; Srivastava, S. C.; Richards, P.; Treves, S. *Nucl. Med. Commun.* 1983, 4, 94.

[140] Zanzi, I.; Srivastava, S. C.; Meinken, G. E.; Robeson, W.; Mausner, L. F.; Fairchild, R. G.; Margouleff, D. *Int. J. Rad. Appl. Instrum. B.* 1989, 16, 397.

[141] Margalit, R.; Gray, H. B.; Clarke, M. J.; Podbielski, L. *Chem. Biol. Interact.* 1986, 59, 231.

[142] Srivastava, S.; Mausner, L.; Clarke, M. In: *Ruthenium and Other Non-Platinum Metal Complexes in Cancer Chemotherapy*; Baulieu, E., Forman, D., Ingelman-Sundberg, M., Jaenicke, L., Kellen, J., Nagai, Y., Springer, G., Träger, L., Will-Shahab, L., Wittliff, J., Eds.; Springer Berlin Heidelberg: 1989; Vol. 10, p. 111.

[143] Ferlay, J.; Shin, H.-R.; Bray, F.; Forman, D.; Mathers, C.; Parkin, D. M. *Int. J. Cancer* 2010, 127, 2893.

[144] Jemal, A.; Bray, F.; Center, M. M.; Ferlay, J.; Ward, E.; Forman, D. *CA Cancer J. Clin.* 2011, 61, 69.

[145] Jemal, A.; Center, M. M.; DeSantis, C.; Ward, E. M. *Cancer Epidemiol. Biomarkers and Prev.* 2010, 19, 1893.

[146] Lozano, R.; Naghavi, M.; Foreman, K.; Lim, S.; Shibuya, K.; Aboyans, V.; Abraham, J.; Adair, T.; Aggarwal, R.; Ahn, S. Y.; AlMazroa, M. A.; Alvarado, M.; Anderson, H. R.; Anderson, L. M.; Andrews, K. G.; Atkinson, C.; Baddour, L. M.; Barker-Collo, S.; Bartels, D. H.; Bell, M. L.; Benjamin, E. J.; Bennett, D.; Bhalla, K.; Bikbov, B.; Abdulhak, A. B.; Birbeck, G.; Blyth, F.; Bolliger, I.; Boufous, S.; Bucello, C.; Burch, M.; Burney, P.; Carapetis, J.; Chen, H.; Chou, D.; Chugh, S. S.; Coffeng, L. E.; Colan, S. D.; Colquhoun, S.; Colson, K. E.; Condon, J.; Connor, M. D.; Cooper, L. T.; Corriere, M.; Cortinovis, M.; de Vaccaro, K. C.; Couser, W.; Cowie, B. C.; Criqui, M. H.; Cross, M.; Dabhadkar, K. C.; Dahodwala, N.; De Leo, D.; Degenhardt, L.; Delossantos, A.; Denenberg, J.; Des Jarlais, D. C.; Dharmaratne, S. D.; Dorsey, E. R.; Driscoll, T.; Duber, H.; Ebel, B.; Erwin, P. J.; Espindola, P.; Ezzati, M.; Feigin, V.; Flaxman, A. D.; Forouzanfar, M. H.; Fowkes, F. G. R.; Franklin, R.; Fransen, M.; Freeman, M. K.; Gabriel, S. E.; Gakidou, E.; Gaspari, F.; Gillum, R. F.; Gonzalez-Medina, D.; Halasa, Y. A.; Haring, D.; Harrison, J. E.; Havmoeller, R.; Hay, R. J.; Hoen, B.; Hotez, P. J.; Hoy, D.; Jacobsen, K. H.; James, S. L.; Jasrasaria, R.; Jayaraman, S.; Johns, N.; Karthikeyan, G.; Kassebaum, N.; Keren, A.; Khoo, J.-P.;

Knowlton, L. M.; Kobusingye, O.; Koranteng, A.; Krishnamurthi, R.; Lipnick, M.; Lipshultz, S. E. *The Lancet* 2012, 380, 2095.
[147] Horton, R. *The Lancet* 2012, 380, 2053.
[148] Mathers, C.; Fat, D. M.; Boerma, J. *The global burden of disease: 2004 update*; World Health Organization, 2008.
[149] Murray, C. J. L.; Lopez, A. D. *N. Engl. J. Med.* 2013, 369, 448.
[150] Nakamura, T.; Miki, T. *Int. J. Urol.* 2010, 17, 148.
[151] Wang, D.; Lippard, S. J. *Nat. Rev. Drug. Discov.* 2005, 4, 307.
[152] Cohen, S. M.; Lippard, S. J. *Prog. Nucleic Acid. Res. Mol. Biol.* 2001, 67, 93.
[153] Siddik, Z. H. *Oncogene* 2003, 22, 7265.
[154] Pabla, N.; Dong, Z. *Kidney Int.* 2008, 73, 994.
[155] Sullivan, M. J. *Cancer* 2009, 115, 5623.
[156] Clarke, M. J.; Buchbinder, M.; Kelman, A. D. *Inorg. Chim. Acta* 1978, 27, L87.
[157] Rodriguez-Bailey, V. M.; LaChance-Galang, K. J.; Doan, P. E.; Clarke, M. J. *Inorg. Chem.* 1997, 36, 1873.
[158] Clarke, M. J.; Zhu, F.; Frasca, D. R. *Chem. Rev.* 1999, 99, 2511.
[159] Frasca, D. R.; Ciampa, J.; Emerson, J.; Umans, R. S.; Clarke, M. J. *Met. Based Drugs* 1996, 3, 197.
[160] Silveira-Lacerda, E. P.; Vilanova-Costa, C.; Hamaguchi, A.; Pavanin, L.; Goulart, L.; Homsi-Brandenburgo, M.; Santos, W.; Soares, A.; Nomizo, A. *Biol. Trace Elem. Res.* 2010, 135, 98.
[161] Clarke, M. J.; Bitler, S.; Rennert, D.; Buchbinder, M.; Kelman, A. D. *J. Inorg. Biochem.* 1980, 12, 79.
[162] Alessio, E.; Mestroni, G.; Nardin, G.; Attia, W. M.; Calligaris, M.; Sava, G.; Zorzet, S. *Inorg. Chem.* 1988, 27, 4099.
[163] Coluccia, M.; Sava, G.; Loseto, F.; Nassi, A.; Boccarelli, A.; Giordano, D.; Alessio, E.; Mestroni, G. *Eur. J. Cancer* 1993, 29A, 1873.
[164] Sava, G.; Salerno, G.; Bergamo, A.; Cocchietto, M.; Gagliardi, R.; Alessio, E.; Mestroni, G. *Met. Based Drugs* 1996, 3, 67.
[165] Gallori, E.; Vettori, C.; Alessio, E.; Vilchez, F. G.; Vilaplana, R.; Orioli, P.; Casini, A.; Messori, L. *Arch. Biochem. Biophys.* 2000, 376, 156.
[166] Barca, A.; Pani, B.; Tamaro, M.; Russo, E. *Mutation Research* 1999, 423, 171.
[167] Novakova, O.; Kasparkova, J.; Vrana, O.; van Vliet, P. M.; Reedijk, J.; Brabec, V. *Biochemistry* 1995, 34, 12369.
[168] Velders, A. H.; Kooijman, H.; Spek, A. L.; Haasnoot, J. G.; de Vos, D.; Reedijk, J. *Inorg. Chem.* 2000, 39, 2966.
[169] Hotze, A. C. G.; Velders, A. H.; Ugozzoli, F.; Biagini-Cingi, M.; Manotti-Lanfredi, A. M.; Haasnoot, J. G.; Reedijk, J. *Inorg. Chem.* 2000, 39, 3838.
[170] Van Vliet, P. M.; Toekimin, S. M. S.; Haasnoot, J. G.; Reedijk, J.; Nováková, O.; Vrána, O.; Brabec, V. *Inorg. Chim. Acta* 1995, 231, 57.
[171] Van Rijn, J. A.; Marques-Gallego, P.; Reedijk, J.; Lutz, M.; Spek, A. L.; Bouwman, E. *Dalton Trans.* 2009, 10727.
[172] Lakomska, I.; Fandzloch, M.; Muziol, T.; Lis, T.; Jezierska, J. *Dalton Trans.* 2013, 42, 6219.
[173] Li, L.; Wong, Y.-S.; Chen, T.; Fan, C.; Zheng, W. *Dalton Trans.* 2012, 41, 1138.

[174] Qian, C.; Wang, J.-Q.; Song, C.-L.; Wang, L.-L.; Ji, L.-N.; Chao, H. *Metallomics* 2013, 5, 844.

[175] Berger, M. R.; Garzon, F. T.; Keppler, B. K.; Schmal, D. *Anticancer Res.* 1989, 9, 761.

[176] Kratz, F.; Hartmann, M.; Keppler, B.; Messori, L. *J. Biol. Chem.* 1994, 269, 2581.

[177] Pongratz, M.; Schluga, P.; Jakupec, M. A.; Arion, V. B.; Hartinger, C. G.; Allmaier, G.; Keppler, B. K. *J. Anal. At. Spectrom.* 2004, 19, 46.

[178] Habtemariam, A.; Melchart, M.; Fernández, R.; Parsons, S.; Oswald, I. D. H.; Parkin, A.; Fabbiani, F. P. A.; Davidson, J. E.; Dawson, A.; Aird, R. E.; Jodrell, D. I.; Sadler, P. J. *J. Med. Chem.* 2006, 49, 6858.

[179] Clavel, C. M.; Păunescu, E.; Nowak-Sliwinska, P.; Griffioen, A. W.; Scopelliti, R.; Dyson, P. J. *J. Med. Chem.* 2014, 57, 3546.

[180] Wu, K.; Liu, S.; Luo, Q.; Hu, W.; Li, X.; Wang, F.; Zheng, R.; Cui, J.; Sadler, P. J.; Xiang, J.; Shi, Q.; Xiong, S. *Inorg. Chem.* 2013, 52, 11332.

[181] Pettinari, R.; Pettinari, C.; Marchetti, F.; Skelton, B. W.; White, A. H.; Bonfili, L.; Cuccioloni, M.; Mozzicafreddo, M.; Cecarini, V.; Angeletti, M.; Nabissi, M.; Eleuteri, A. M. *J. Med. Chem.* 2014.

[182] Chen, Y.; Lei, W.; Jiang, G.; Zhou, Q.; Hou, Y.; Li, C.; Zhang, B.; Wang, X. *Dalton Trans.* 2013, 42, 5924.

[183] Allardyce, C. S.; Dyson, P. J.; Ellis, D. J.; Heath, S. L. *Chem. Commun.* 2001, 1396.

[184] Schmitt, F.; Govindaswamy, P.; Suess-Fink, G.; Ang, W. H.; Dyson, P. J.; Juillerat-Jeanneret, L.; Therrien, B. *J. Med. Chem.* 2008, 51, 1811.

[185] Schmitt, F.; Govindaswamy, P.; Süss-Fink, G.; Ang, W. H.; Dyson, P. J.; Juillerat-Jeanneret, L.; Therrien, B. *J. Med. Chem.* 2008, 51, 1811.

[186] Scolaro, C.; Bergamo, A.; Brescacin, L.; Delfino, R.; Cocchietto, M.; Laurenczy, G.; Geldbach, T. J.; Sava, G.; Dyson, P. J. *J. Med. Chem.* 2005, 48, 4161.

[187] Martin, G. R.; Jain, R. K. *Cancer Res.* 1994, 54, 5670.

[188] Castonguay, A.; Doucet, C.; Juhas, M.; Maysinger, D. *J. Med. Chem.* 2012, 55, 8799.

[189] Morris, R. E.; Aird, R. E.; del Socorro Murdoch, P.; Chen, H.; Cummings, J.; Hughes, N. D.; Parsons, S.; Parkin, A.; Boyd, G.; Jodrell, D. I.; Sadler, P. J. *J. Med. Chem.* 2001, 44, 3616.

[190] Aird, R. E.; Cummings, J.; Ritchie, A. A.; Muir, M.; Morris, R. E.; Chen, H.; Sadler, P. J.; Jodrell, D. I. *Br. J. Cancer* 2002, 86, 1652.

[191] Meggers, E.; Atilla-Gokcumen, G. E.; Grundler, K.; Frias, C.; Prokop, A. *Dalton Trans.* 2009, 10882.

[192] Wu, C.-H.; Wu, D.-H.; Liu, X.; Guoyiqibayi, G.; Guo, D.-D.; Lv, G.; Wang, X.-M.; Yan, H.; Jiang, H.; Lu, Z.-H. *Inorg. Chem.* 2009, 48, 2352.

[193] Armstrong, A. F.; Valliant, J. F. *Dalton Trans.* 2007, 4240.

[194] Beckford, F.; Dourth, D.; Shaloski Jr, M.; Didion, J.; Thessing, J.; Woods, J.; Crowell, V.; Gerasimchuk, N.; Gonzalez-Sarrías, A.; Seeram, N. P. *J. Inorg. Biochem.* 2011, 105, 1019.

[195] Beckford, F. A.; Leblanc, G.; Thessing, J.; Shaloski Jr, M.; Frost, B. J.; Li, L.; Seeram, N. P. *Inorg. Chem. Commun.* 2009, 12, 1094.

[196] Auzias, M.; Therrien, B.; Süss-Fink, G.; Štěpnička, P.; Ang, W. H.; Dyson, P. J. *Inorg. Chem.* 2007, 47, 578.

[197] Pelletier, F. D. R.; Comte, V.; Massard, A.; Wenzel, M.; Toulot, S. P.; Richard, P.; Picquet, M.; Le Gendre, P.; Zava, O.; Edafe, F.; Casini, A.; Dyson, P. J. *J. Med. Chem.* 2010, 53, 6923.

[198] Mendoza-Ferri, M.-G.; Hartinger, C. G.; Eichinger, R. E.; Stolyarova, N.; Severin, K.; Jakupec, M. A.; Nazarov, A. A.; Keppler, B. K. *Organometallics* 2008, 27, 2405.

[199] Mendoza-Ferri, M. G.; Hartinger, C. G.; Nazarov, A. A.; Kandioller, W.; Severin, K.; Keppler, B. K. *Appl. Organomet. Chem.* 2008, 22, 326.

[200] Gras, M.; Therrien, B.; Suss-Fink, G.; Zava, O.; Dyson, P. J. *Dalton Trans.* 2010, 39, 10305.

[201] Stringer, T.; Therrien, B.; Hendricks, D. T.; Guzgay, H.; Smith, G. S. *Inorg. Chem. Commun.* 2011, 14, 956.

[202] Ang, W. H.; Grote, Z.; Scopelliti, R.; Juillerat-Jeanneret, L.; Severin, K.; Dyson, P. J. *J. Organomet. Chem.* 2009, 694, 968.

[203] Mattsson, J.; Govindaswamy, P.; Renfrew, A. K.; Dyson, P. J.; Štěpnička, P.; Süss-Fink, G.; Therrien, B. *Organometallics* 2009, 28, 4350.

[204] Barry, N. P. E.; Zava, O.; Furrer, J.; Dyson, P. J.; Therrien, B. *Dalton Trans.* 2010, 39, 5272.

[205] Vajpayee, V.; Yang, Y. J.; Kang, S. C.; Kim, H.; Kim, I. S.; Wang, M.; Stang, P. J.; Chi, K.-W. *Chem. Commun.* 2011, 47, 5184.

[206] Barry, N. P. E.; Abd Karim, N. H.; Vilar, R.; Therrien, B. *Dalton Trans.* 2009, 10717.

[207] Barry, N. P. E.; Zava, O.; Dyson, P. J.; Therrien, B. *Aus. J. Chem.* 2010, 63, 1529.

[208] Dougherty, T. J.; Gomer, C. J.; Henderson, B. W.; Jori, G.; Kessel, D.; Korbelik, M.; Moan, J.; Peng, Q. *J. Natl. Cancer Inst.* 1998, 90, 889.

[209] Lane, N. *Sci. Am.* 2003, 18, 80.

[210] Armitage, B. *Chem. Rev.* 1998, 98, 1171.

[211] Durham, B.; Caspar, J. V.; Nagle, J. K.; Meyer, T. J. *J. Am. Chem. Soc.* 1982, 104, 4803.

[212] Moucheron, C.; Kirsch-De Mesmaeker, A.; Kelly, J. M. *J. Photochem. Photobiol., B* 1997, 40, 91.

[213] Piette, J. *J. Photochem. Photobiol., B* 1991, 11, 241.

[214] Barton, J. K.; Danishefsky, A.; Goldberg, J. *J. Amer. Chem. Soc.* 1984, 106, 2172.

[215] Pyle, A. M.; Rehmann, J. P.; Meshoyrer, R.; Kumar, C. V.; Turro, N. J.; Barton, J. K. *J. Am. Chem. Soc.* 1989, 111, 3051.

[216] Jackson, B. A.; Alekseyev, V. Y.; Barton, J. K. *Biochemistry* 1999, 38, 4655.

[217] Fleisher, M. B.; Waterman, K. C.; Turro, N. J.; Barton, J. K. *Inorg. Chem.* 1986, 25, 3549.

[218] Mei, H. Y.; Barton, J. K. *Proc. Natl. Acad. Sci. US.* 1988, 85, 1339.

[219] Tanielian, C.; Wolff, C.; Esch, M. *J. Phys. Chem.* 1996, 100, 6555.

[220] Pierroz, V.; Joshi, T.; Leonidova, A.; Mari, C.; Schur, J.; Ott, I.; Spiccia, L.; Ferrari, S.; Gasser, G. *J. Am. Chem. Soc.* 2012, 134, 20376.

[221] Joshi, T.; Pierroz, V.; Mari, C.; Gemperle, L.; Ferrari, S.; Gasser, G. *Angew. Chem.* 2014, 126, 3004.

[222] Sgambellone, M. A.; David, A.; Garner, R. N.; Dunbar, K. R.; Turro, C. *J. Am. Chem. Soc.* 2013, 135, 11274.

[223] Gentry, G. A.; Morse, P. A.; Dorsett, M. T. *Cancer Res.* 1971, 31, 909.

[224] Frasconi, M.; Liu, Z.; Lei, J.; Wu, Y.; Strekalova, E.; Malin, D.; Ambrogio, M. W.; Chen, X.; Botros, Y. Y.; Cryns, V. L.; Sauvage, J.-P.; Stoddart, J. F. *J. Am. Chem. Soc.* 2013, 135, 11603.
[225] Lincoln, P.; Norden, B. *Chem. Commun.* 1996, 2145.
[226] Zou, X.-H.; Ye, B.-H.; Li, H.; Liu, J.-G.; Xiong, Y.; Ji, L.-N. *J. Chem. Soc., Dalton Trans.* 1999, 1423.
[227] O'Reill, F. M.; Kelly, J. M. *J. Phys. Chem. B* 2000, 104, 7206.
[228] Önfelt, B.; Lincoln, P.; Nordén, B. *J. Am. Chem. Soc.* 2001, 123, 3630.
[229] Brodkorb, A.; Kirsch-De Mesmaeker, A.; Rutherford, Todd, J.; Keene, F. R. *Eur. J. Inorg. Chem.* 2001, 2001, 2151.
[230] Smith, J. A.; Collins, J. G.; Patterson, B. T.; Keene, F. R. *Dalton Trans.* 2004, 1277.
[231] Aldrich-Wright, J.; Brodie, C.; Glazer, E. C.; Luedtke, N. W.; Elson-Schwab, L.; Tor, Y. *Chem. Commun.* 2004, 1018.
[232] Chao, H.; Yuan, Y.-X.; Zhou, F.; Ji, L.-N.; Zhang, J. *Transition Met. Chem.* 2006, 31, 465.
[233] Sakai, K.; Ozawa, H.; Yamada, H.; Tsubomura, T.; Hara, M.; Higuchi, A.; Haga, M.-A. *Dalton Trans.* 2006, 3300.
[234] Van der Steen, S.; de Hoog, P.; van der Schilden, K.; Gamez, P.; Pitie, M.; Kiss, R.; Reedijk, J. *Chem. Commun.* 2010, 46, 3568.
[235] Liang, X.; Zou, X.; Tan, L.; Zhu, W. *J. Inorg. Biochem.* 2010, 104, 1259.
[236] Holder, A. A.; Taylor, P.; Magnusen, A. R.; Moffett, E. T.; Meyer, K.; Hong, Y.; Ramsdale, S. E.; Gordon, M.; Stubbs, J.; Seymour, L. A.; Acharya, D.; Weber, R. T.; Smith, P. F.; Dismukes, G. C.; Ji, P.; Menocal, L.; Bai, F.; Williams, J. L.; Cropek, D. M.; Jarrett, W. L. *Dalton Trans.* 2013, 42, 11881.
[237] Valensin, D.; Gabbiani, C.; Messori, L. *Coord. Chem. Rev.* 2012, 256, 2357.
[238] Bertrand, N.; Gauthier, M. A.; Bouvet, C.; Moreau, P.; Petitjean, A.; Leroux, J.-C.; Leblond, J. *J. Control Rel.* 2011, 155, 200.
[239] Oleksi, A.; Blanco, A. G.; Boer, R.; Usón, I.; Aymamí, J.; Rodger, A.; Hannon, M. J.; Coll, M. *Angew. Chem.* 2006, 118, 1249.
[240] Rabut, G.; Doyle, V.; Ellenberg, J. *Nat. Cell Biol.* 2004, 6, 1114.
[241] Yu, H.; Wang, X.; Fu, M.; Ren, J.; Qu, X. *Nucl. Acids Res.* 2008, 36, 5695.
[242] Uerpmann, C.; Malina, J.; Pascu, M.; Clarkson, G. J.; Moreno, V.; Rodger, A.; Grandas, A.; Hannon, M. J. *Chem. – Eur. J.* 2005, 11, 1750.
[243] Sasmal, P. K.; Patra, A. K.; Nethaji, M.; Chakravarty, A. R. *Inorg. Chem.* 2007, 46, 11112.
[244] Kolárová, H.; Mosinger, J.; Lenobel, R.; Kejlová, K.; Jírová, D.; Strnad, M. *Toxicol. In Vitro* 2003, 17, 775.
[245] Nishiyama, N.; Jang, W.-D.; Kataoka, K. *New J. Chem.* 2007, 31, 1074.
[246] Higgins, S. L. H.; White, T. A.; Winkel, B. S. J.; Brewer, K. J. *Inorg. Chem.* 2010, 50, 463.
[247] Higgins, S. L. H.; Tucker, A. J.; Winkel, B. S. J.; Brewer, K. J. *Chem. Commun.* 2012, 48, 67.
[248] Sun, Y.; Joyce, L. E.; Dickson, N. M.; Turro, C. *Chem. Commun.* 2010, 46, 6759.
[249] Wang, J.; Higgins, S. L. H.; Winkel, B. S. J.; Brewer, K. J. *Chem. Commun.* 2011, 47, 9786.

[250] Mongelli, M. T.; Heinecke, J.; Mayfield, S.; Okyere, B.; Winkel, B. S. J.; Brewer, K. J. *J. Inorg. Biochem.* 2006, 100, 1983.

[251] Swavey, S.; Brewer, K. J. *Inorg. Chem.* 2002, 41, 6196.

[252] Holder, A. A.; Zigler, D. F.; Tarrago-Trani, M. T.; Storrie, B.; Brewer, K. J. *Inorg. Chem.* 2007, 46, 4760.

[253] Miao, R.; Mongelli, M. T.; Zigler, D. F.; Winkel, B. S. J.; Brewer, K. J. *Inorg. Chem.* 2006, 45, 10413.

[254] Sharman, W. M.; Allen, C. M.; van Lier, J. E. *Drug Discovery Today* 1999, 4, 507.

[255] Ackroyd, R.; Kelty, C.; Brown, N.; Reed, M. *Photochem. Photobiol.* 2001, 74, 656.

[256] Capella, M.; Capella, L. *J. Biomed. Sci.* 2003, 10, 361.

[257] Onuki, J.; Ribas, A. V.; Medeiros, M. H. G.; Araki, K.; Toma, H. E.; Catalani, L. H.; Di Mascio, P. *Photochem. Photobiol.* 1996, 63, 272.

[258] Gianferrara, T.; Bratsos, I.; Iengo, E.; Milani, B.; Ostric, A.; Spagnul, C.; Zangrando, E.; Alessio, E. *Dalton Trans.* 2009, 10742.

[259] Gianferrara, T.; Bergamo, A.; Bratsos, I.; Milani, B.; Spagnul, C.; Sava, G.; Alessio, E. *J. Med. Chem.* 2010, 53, 4678.

[260] Rani-Beeram, S.; Meyer, K.; McCrate, A.; Hong, Y.; Nielsen, M.; Swavey, S. *Inorg. Chem.* 2008, 47, 11278.

[261] Narra, M.; Elliott, P.; Swavey, S. *Inorg. Chim. Acta* 2006, 359, 2256.

[262] Xu, Z.; Swavey, S. *Dalton Trans.* 2011, 40, 7319.

[263] Hotez, P. J.; Dumonteil, E.; Heffernan, M. J.; Bottazzi, M. E. *Adv. Exp. Med. Biol.* 2013, 764, 1.

[264] Hotez, P. J.; Bottazzi, M. E.; Franco-Paredes, C.; Ault, S. K.; Periago, M. R. *PLoS Negl. Trop. Dis.* 2008, 2, e300.

[265] Hotez, P. J.; Dumonteil, E.; Woc-Colburn, L.; Serpa, J. A.; Bezek, S.; Edwards, M. S.; Hallmark, C. J.; Musselwhite, L. W.; Flink, B. J.; Bottazzi, M. E. *PLoS Negl. Trop. Dis.* 2012, 6, e1498.

[266] Hotez, P. J.; Molyneux, D. H.; Fenwick, A.; Kumaresan, J.; Sachs, S. E.; Sachs, J. D.; Savioli, L. *N. Engl. J. Med.* 2007, 357, 1018.

[267] Lima, F. M.; Oliveira, P.; Mortara, R. A.; Silveira, J. F.; Bahia, D. *New Biotechnology* 2010, 27, 837.

[268] Demoro, B.; Sarniguet, C.; Sanchez-Delgado, R.; Rossi, M.; Liebowitz, D.; Caruso, F.; Olea-Azar, C.; Moreno, V.; Medeiros, A.; Comini, M. A.; Otero, L.; Gambino, D. *Dalton Trans.* 2012, 41, 1534.

[269] Martínez, A.; Carreon, T.; Iniguez, E.; Anzellotti, A.; Sánchez, A.; Tyan, M.; Sattler, A.; Herrera, L.; Maldonado, R. A.; Sánchez-Delgado, R. A. *J. Med. Chem.* 2012, 55, 3867.

[270] Navarro, M.; Lehmann, T.; Cisneros-Fajardo, E. J.; Fuentes, A.; Sánchez-Delgado, R. A.; Silva, P.; Urbina, J. A. *Polyhedron* 2000, 19, 2319.

[271] Sánchez-Delgado, R. A.; Navarro, M.; Lazardi, K.; Atencio, R.; Capparelli, M.; Vargas, F.; Urbina, J. A.; Bouillez, A.; Noels, A. F.; Masi, D. *Inorg. Chim. Acta* 1998, 275–276, 528.

[272] Sánchez-Delgado, R. A.; Navarro, M.; Pérez, H.; Urbina, J. A. *J. Med. Chem.* 1996, 39, 1095.

[273] Iniguez, E.; Sánchez, A.; Vasquez, M.; Martínez, A.; Olivas, J.; Sattler, A.; Sánchez-Delgado, R.; Maldonado, R. *J. Biol. Inorg. Chem.* 2013, 18, 779.

[274] http://www.who.int/research/en/

[275] Rajapakse, C. S. K.; Martínez, A.; Naoulou, B.; Jarzecki, A. A.; Suárez, L.; Deregnaucourt, C.; Sinou, V.; Schrével, J.; Musi, E.; Ambrosini, G.; Schwartz, G. K.; Sánchez-Delgado, R. A. *Inorg. Chem.* 2009, 48, 1122.

[276] Martínez, A.; Rajapakse, C. K.; Naoulou, B.; Kopkalli, Y.; Davenport, L.; Sánchez-Delgado, R. *J. Biol. Inorg. Chem.* 2008, 13, 703.

[277] Martínez, A.; Rajapakse, C. K.; Jalloh, D.; Dautriche, C.; Sánchez-Delgado, R. *J. Biol. Inorg. Chem.* 2009, 14, 863.

[278] Birks, J. *Chochrane System Review* 2006, CD005593.

[279] Raschetti, R.; Albanese, E.; Vanacore, N.; Maggini, M. *PLoS Med.* 2007, 4, e338.

[280] Valensin, D.; Anzini, P.; Gaggelli, E.; Gaggelli, N.; Tamasi, G.; Cini, R.; Gabbiani, C.; Michelucci, E.; Messori, L.; Kozlowski, H.; Valensin, G. *Inorg. Chem.* 2010, 49, 4720.

[281] Kumar, A.; Moody, L.; Olaivar, J. F.; Lewis, N. A.; Khade, R. L.; Holder, A. A.; Zhang, Y.; Rangachari, V. *ACS Chem. Neurosci.* 2010, 1, 691.

In: Ruthenium
Editor: Gary P. Keeler
ISBN: 978-1-63321-657-0

Chapter 2

SOLVING SOME OF THE WORLD'S PROBLEMS WITH RUTHENIUM COMPLEXES: THEIR USE IN SOLAR ENERGY CAPTURE AND PRODUCTION OF HYDROGEN

Michael J. Celestine, Jimmie L. Bullock and Alvin A. Holder*
Department of Chemistry and Biochemistry,
Old Dominion University, Norfolk, Virginia, US

ABSTRACT

This chapter discusses the chemistry of several ruthenium-containing complexes and their roles in the conversion of solar energy into chemical and electrical energy. In this chapter, subsections will include polypyridyl ruthenium dyes which are currently being developed for their use in the manufacture of solar cells and mixed-metal and non-mixed-metal complexes for the production of hydrogen in various media.

ABBREVIATIONS

BL = bridging ligand
bpy-4-CH_3,4′-CONH(4-py) = 4-methyl-*N*-4′-pyridinyl[2,2'-bipyridine]-4-carboxamide-$\kappa N^1,\kappa N^{1'}$
COD = 1,5-cyclooctadiene
Cp^- = cyclopentadienyl
DMF = N,N-dimethylformamide
dmgBF_2 = difluoroboryldimethylglyoximato
dpp = 2,3-bis(2-pyridyl)pyrazine
dpq = 2,3-bis(2-pyridyl)quinoxaline

* Telephone: 757-683-7102 and e-mail: aholder@odu.edu.

EDTA =	ethylenediaminetetraacetic acid
H_2ase =	hydrogenase
HEC =	hydrogen evolution catalyst
L-pyr =	(4-pyridine)oxazolo[4,5-*f*]phenanthroline
Me_2bpy =	4,4'-dimethyl-2,2'-bipyridine
MLCT =	metal-to-ligand-charge-transfer
N3 =	[*cis*-di(thiocyanato)bis(2,2'-bipyridyl-4,4'-dicarboxylate) ruthenium(II)]
Ph_2phen =	4,7-diphenyl-1,10-phenanthroline
pbt =	2-(2-pyridinyl)benzothiazole
PCy_3 =	tricyclohexylphosphine
pdt =	propyldithiolate
pmcbpy =	4,4'-bis(N-(4-pyridyl)methylcarbamoyl)-2,2'-bipyridine
tbbpy =	4,4'-bis(*tert*-butyl)-2,2'-bipyridine
TEOA =	triethanolamine
tpac =	tetrapyrido[3,2-a:2',3'-c:3",2"-h:2'",3'"-j]acridine
tpphz =	tetrapyrido[3,2-a:2',3'-c:3",2"-h:2'",3'"-j] phenazine
TOF =	turnover frequency
TON =	turnover numbers

X.1. Ruthenium and Its Role in Solar Energy Capture

The World's Problem Caused by the Burning of Fossil Fuels

The rapid consumption of fossil fuels as a primary fuel source is causing major environmental problems with the potential to alter the global climate by the emission of the greenhouse gas CO_2. [1-2] Furthermore it could be inferred that the increase in the average global temperature is believed to be due to the increasing amount of greenhouse gasses that are released during the combustion of fossil fuels. Solar energy is an energy source that has been gaining much attention as a potential alternative to fossil fuels. [2] The conversion of solar-to-chemical energy via the production of hydrogen from water offers a fuel source which is clean and renewable, and could potentially reduce the amount of harmful greenhouse gases emitted through the burning of fossil fuels. [3-9] The process of splitting water into hydrogen and oxygen requires a multi-electron redox process all while overcoming the large energy barriers which can be lowered with the use of a catalyst. [10] The most effective catalysts for water splitting in order to produce hydrogen as a fuel source are rare noble metals such as platinum, palladium, and rhodium, to name a few, but the costs to produce such catalysts are extreme, making these catalysts less attractive alternatives when compared to the use of fossil fuels. [11-13] Recent major advancements and enhancements in hydrogen fuel cell technologies allows for storage in transportation, stationary and portable applications opening the door for hydrogen production. [14]

Due to the demand for fossil fuels being as high as it is currently and the dwindling amount of fossil fuels in the World's reserves, the search of alternative non-fossil fuels is expanding. As shown in figure **1** the renewable fuel energy sources such as wind, solar, tide, and wave are on the borderline of non-existence when compared to fossil fuels which makes up about 83% of the energy produced worldwide.

The world's consumption of fossil fuel through combustion is known to produce carbon dioxide, which is known as a Green House gas; a gas that is believed to be the cause of global warming and the current climate change. In the last forty decades, we have evidence to show that the World's temperatures are rising when compared to the year 1850. Figure **2** shows the temperature anomalies from 1850 to 2010 where from about 1910 on there seems to be a steady increase number of these anomalies. Figure 3 shows the carbon dioxide emissions in the U.S.A. by source, where non-fossil fuel consumption accounts for 5% of such emissions; that is alarming!! There have been many strives for alternative energy sources that are carbon-neutral or free. [16] Carbon neutral or fossil free energy sources may have the ability to steady these anomalies. Large scale use of alternative fossil fuel sources have the potential to return the average temperature to the averages seen in a pre-1910 era. One of the best routes for the development of alternative energy sources would be to expand on research involving solar energy capture and the development of cheaper catalysts to produce alternative energy sources to that of fossil fuels.

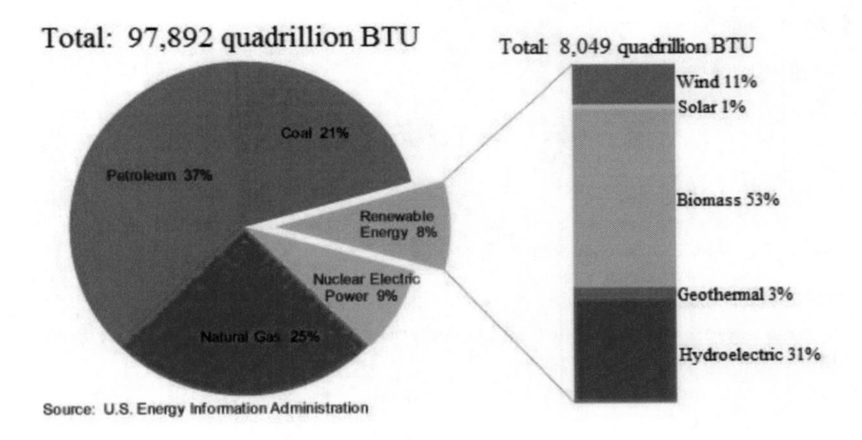

Figure 1. United States of America's energy consumption for 2010. [15]

In light of the problems, we need to discuss hydrogen's role in an uncertain energy future as energy use in this century and beyond faces deep uncertainties. There are widely conflicting opinions on the size of ultimately recoverable fossil fuel reserves, and the extent to which unconventional resources can be tapped. If, as expected in most forecasts, fossil fuel use continues to grow, the sequestration of vast amounts of CO_2 would be needed if we are to limit global warming. Large emitters such as power plants could probably only capture around a third of the amount needed, requiring the deployment of air capture, untried, and energy-intensive technology. Non-carbon sources face their own uncertainties. The future of nuclear energy depends heavily on the successful and timely development of either breeder reactors or fusion energy. Yet after nearly half a century of effort, neither is near commercialization, and fission technologies face deep public opposition. Ongoing climate change will adversely affect hydro and biomass energy expansion. The potential for intermittent renewable energy sources, wind and solar, is far greater, but is unevenly distributed spatially, and both face orders of magnitude scale-up to be major energy suppliers.

They will eventually also need conversion and storage, which will greatly raise the costs of delivered energy. For all these reasons, we have argued that a low energy future is more likely. There is a need to use ruthenium-containing complexes in solar energy capture and as photosensitizers for the production of hydrogen in various solvent media. In the following sections, we will discuss solving some of the world's problems with ruthenium complexes; through their use in solar energy capture and production of hydrogen. In the interim, the reader is encouraged to read the review entitled "Hydrogen's role in an uncertain energy future." [19]

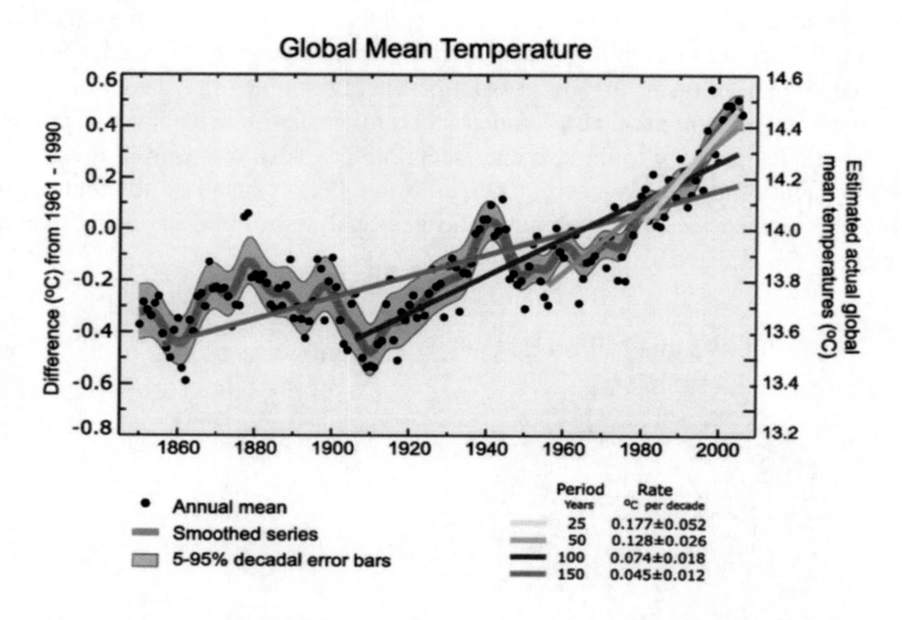

Figure 2. Global annual average temperature and carbon dioxide concentration measured over land and oceans from 1850 to 2010. [17]

X.2. Ruthenium's Role in Capture of Solar Energy

We all know that sunlight is the key source of energy on earth which has a limitless potential. [20] Photosynthetic organisms have the ability to directly convert sunlight to chemical energy through photosynthesis. [20] For many years now, ruthenium-containing complexes have been reported to be very efficient in its ability to capture solar energy. [21] Some ruthenium(II) complexes have been reported to have efficient charge separations that are comparable to that of photosynthesis where every photon that is absorbed leads to an electron being transferred in an efficient fashion. [20, 22]

For many years, ruthenium(II) polypyridyl complexes there have been many reports in the literature for their roles in the research areas of photochemistry, photocatalysis, photoelectrochemistry, and electron and energy transfer. [21] Such cases involve the production of efficient solar cells which are capable of harnessing and storing the sun's energy for future use and also have the potential to reduce the amount of greenhouse gases produced through the burning of fossil fuels. Many polypyridyl and porphyrin-based ruthenium complexes are known for their ability to be used as photocatalyst which could lead to advances in research that can involve the use of alternatives to fossil fuels. [21] A clear example is the ruthenium dye-sensitized solar cells of the type N3, as shown in figure **4**, which were first reported by O'Regan and Grätzel with the N3 photo sensitizer being unmatched by any other known sensitizer in the early 1990s. [23-24] When treated on TiO_2, the ruthenium dyes act as proficient charge-transfer sensitizers for nanocrystalline TiO_2 films. [24] As a result many ruthenium based solar cells are reported to work very efficiently in areas of low light. During photosynthesis only about 10% of the solar radiation captured by plants is converted into chemical energy, but it is reported hat porous nanocrystaline TiO_2 films that were sensitized by polypyridyl ruthenium dyes have an efficiency that exceeds 11%. [25] In 2013 work done by Nath et al. [26] reported that when the carboxylic acids of the N3 ruthenium dyes are capped with 1-methyl-3-phenylpropylamine they were able to achieve an efficiency of 15%, thus placing such ruthenium solar cells on par with some of the more expensive silicon-based solar cells.

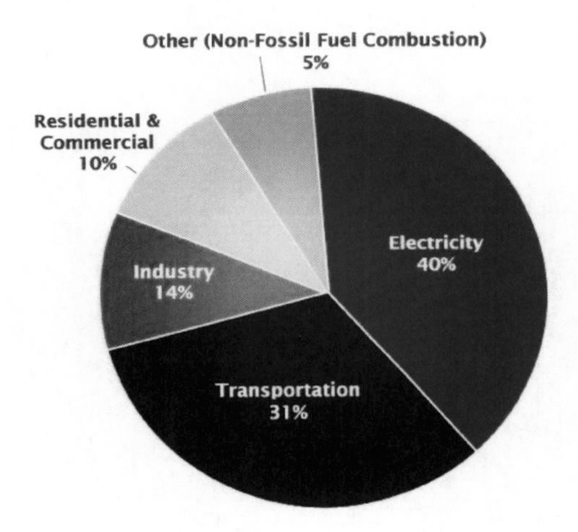

Figure 3. Carbon dioxide emissions in the U.S.A. by source. [18]

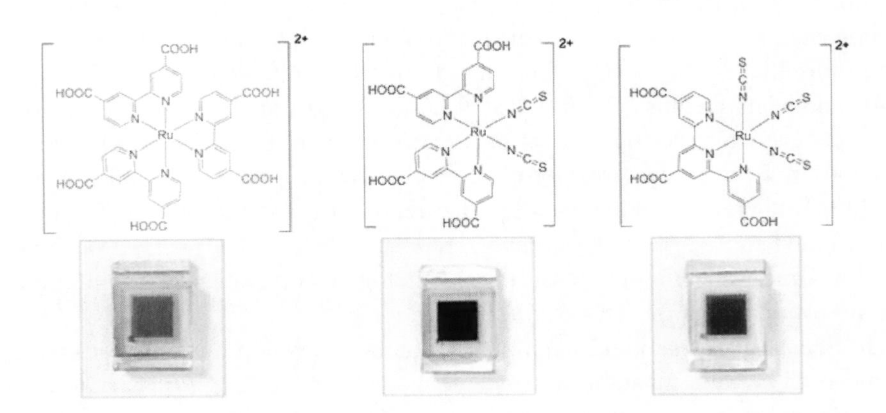

Figure 4. Solar cells coated with ruthenium dye-sensitized TiO_2. Reprinted (adapted) with permission from Grätzel, M., *Inorg. Chem.* 2005, *44* (20), 6841. Copyright 2005 American Chemical Society. [25]

The formation of the covalent Ti-O-C, Ti-O-P, or Ti-S linkages between the TiO_2 and the ligand improves binding and promotes faster charge transfer between the photoexcited photosensitizer and the nanoparticle. [27-29] A study reported by Shahroosvand et al. [30] showed that by increasing the amount of carboxylate attached to the dye, one can get better penetration of the dye into the porous TiO_2 nanostructure. It was concluded that their dyes had an efficiency of 13% for light with a wavelength of 510 nm. [30] Studies conducted on dyes with thiol functional groups binding to metal oxides showed that there was an increase in the bonding affinity and current when the thiol was deprotonated. [29] Complex **5** was shown to be an efficient solar energy converter with an efficiency of ~5.6% followed closely by complexes **2**, **1**, **3**, and **4** with efficiencies of 2.6%, 2.1%, 0.9%, and 0.3%, respectively. [28-29]

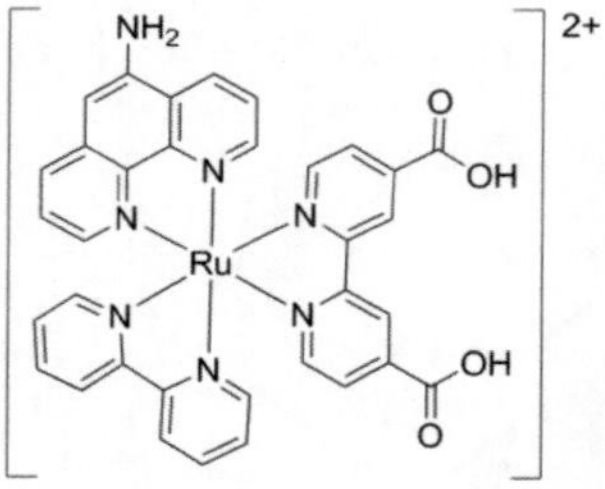

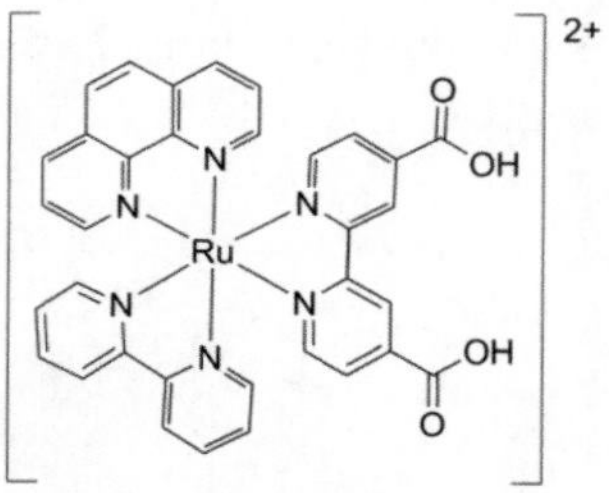

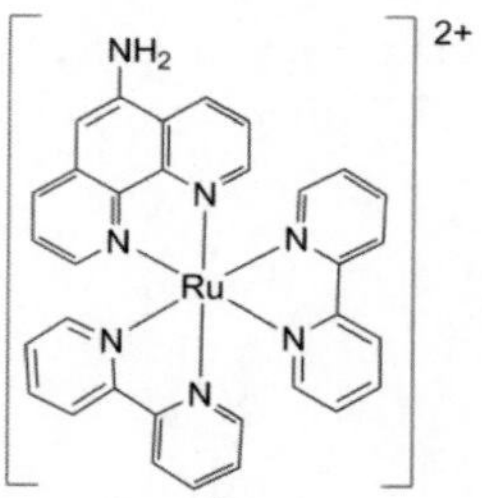

Based on mechanistic studies, photoexcitation of $[Ru(bpyR_2)_2XY]^{n+}$ (where X = Y = NCS, or a bpy analogue), occurred when an electron was excited into a MLCT transition. [21, 31] This transpired when the electron from the d-orbital of ruthenium was transferred to the π^* orbital of one of its ligands. [21, 31] The MLCT excited state of the photosensitizer was reductively quenched by sacrificial electron donors such as Et_3N and TEOA. [32] Upon photoexcitation an electron was transferred from the dye into the conductance band of the conductor. [33] Ruthenium complexes were also reported to be able to transfer an electron after it was excited to TiO_2 creating a charge separation. [22, 34] The electron donor thus reduced the oxidized ruthenium photosensitizer which generally enhanced the lifetime of the electron as it moves through the TiO_2. [35]

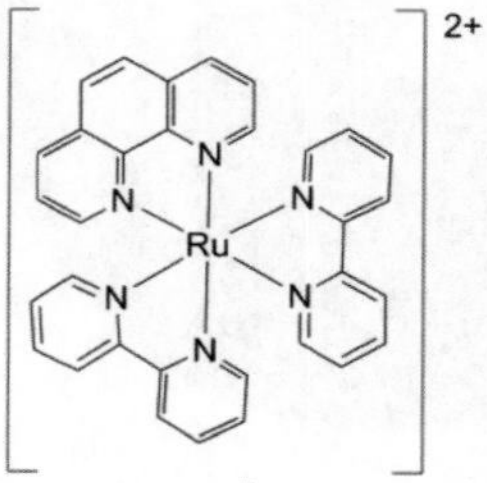

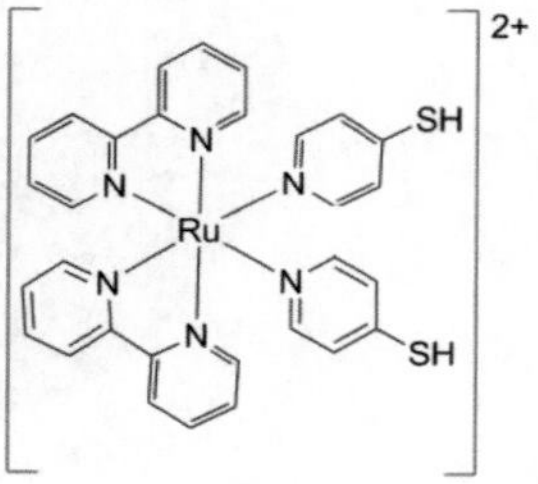

There has been an substantial amount of research to develop an effective converter of light to electricity with nanometer-sized semiconductor. [22] Polypyridyl-ruthenium complexes have been shown to very successful charge transfer sensitizers in photovoltaics. [36] Effective charge separation is important in the conversion of light to a suitable energy source similar to what is observed in photosynthesis. [22] This process occurs when the electron is transferred from the photoexcited photosensitizer to the TiO_2 nanoparticle creating a hole confined around the photosensitizer. [22] The efficiency of solar cells are dependent on the time it takes for the electron and hole recombines to return to the ground state. [22]

Complexes **6-9** were synthesized with the tridentate bipyridine-pyrazolate ancillary ligands to increase the π-conjugated of the system as well as increase the dye uptake onto the TiO_2 nanoparticles. [37] The solar energy uptake of the ruthenium dyes with the tridentate bipyridine-pyrazolate ancillary ligands was larger than that of the N3 type, with their conversion of solar energy to electricity being comparable around 6%. [37] It was believed that the increased thermal and light absorption stability could lead to an extension in the life spans of solar devices. [37]

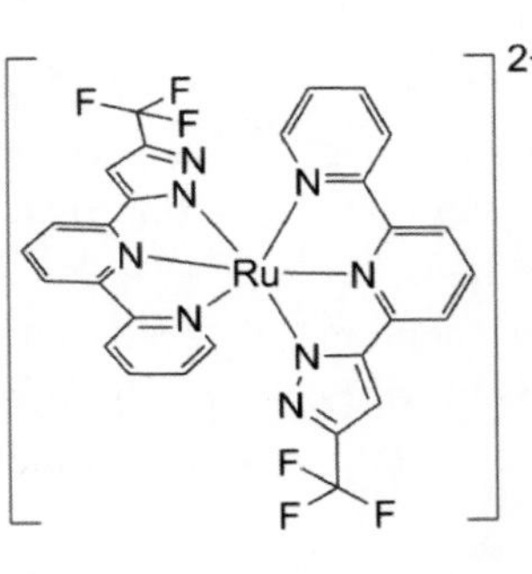

6 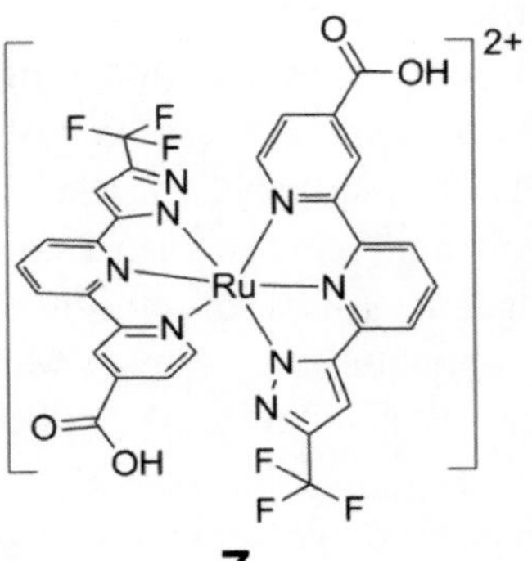 **7**

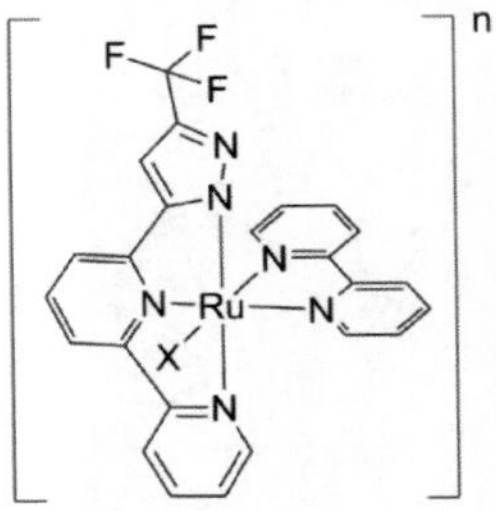

8 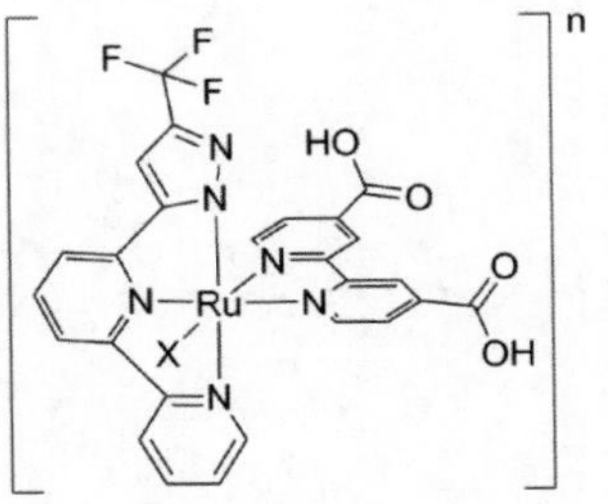 **9**

X = Cl, n = 1+
X = NCS, n = 2+

In 1993 it was reported that a device created from a simple molecular light absorber achieved a conversion efficiency comparable to that of the conventional silicon-based photovoltaic cells. [24] That is really phenomenal. We will now with the aid of figure **5** demonstrate how a solar cell with a ruthenium dye functions in the presence of light. First the ruthenium dye is excited in the presence of light and when it relaxes; an electron is transferred to the conducting glass via the nanocrystaline TiO_2 film generating a current and leaving a hole on the ruthenium dye. [38] The spent electron is returned to cathode where it reduces the mediator, in which the electrolyte mixture is normally I^-/I_3^-, which transfers an electron to reduce the ruthenium dye while taking the hole to the cathode to begin the catalytic process over again. [38] The final solar cell would resemble the cell shown in figure 6.

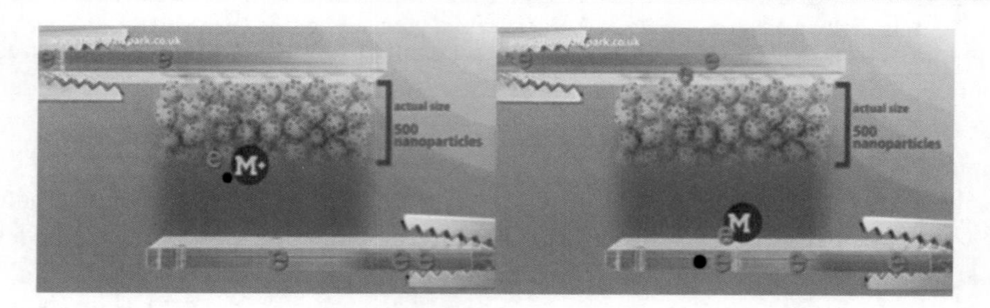

Figure 5. Cross section of a TiO_2 dye-sensitized solar cell. [38]

Dyesol™ engineered a ruthenium dye-sensitized solar panels which by their predictions should be more cost effective to produce and use versus the traditional silicon based solar panels. [39] Dyesol's panels were reported to have a lifetime of approximately 20 years with an efficiency of ~15% and can produce energy in conditions where there is limited amount light unlike silicon-based solar panels that need direct sunlight. [39] Other researchers have reported the use of ruthenium in solar energy conversion. [40-52]

For more information on Dyesol and the use of ruthenium solar cells in solar energy, please see http://www.youtube.com/watch?v=8mmYs5s2w1o. For more information on how dye-sensitized solar cells utilized, please see http://www.youtube.com/embed/95sLq3aQRMU.

The reader is encouraged to read reviews cited at this point in the chapter. [54-72]

Figure 6. A ruthenium-containing porphyrin dye sensitized solar cell. Reprinted with permission from Campbell, W. M.; Jolley, K. W.; Wagner, P.; Wagner, K.; Walsh, P. J.; Gordon, K. C.; Schmidt-Mende, L.; Nazeeruddin, M. K.; Wang, Q.; Graetzel, M.; Officer, D. L., *J. Phys. Chem. C* 2007, *111* (32), 11760. Copyright 2007 American Chemical Society. [53]

X. 3. Ruthenium and Its Role in Hydrogen Production

As mentioned earlier, polypyridyl ruthenium(II) complexes are reported for their roles in the development of efficient photocatalysts and for their ability to for electron transfer in its excited state. [21] The development of heterogeneous catalytic systems for hydrogen production from water under light irradiation has been investigated during the last three decades. Homogeneous photocatalysts however, are very attractive that their chemical and photochemical properties can be understood and tuned on molecular level. Moreover, in homogeneous systems catalysts may be covalently bound to photosensitizers, which lead to more efficient electron transfer. Molecular devices for water splitting based on such a systems are of great interest. As such, a well-written review entitled "Light-driven hydrogen production catalyzed by transition metal complexes in homogeneous systems" was presented by Wang et al. [73]

Chan et al. [74] reported a classic for the mechanism of the formation of hydrogen from the photoinduced reactions of polypyridineruthenium(II) and poylypyridinerhodium(III). Chan et al. [74] reported that irradiation of $[Ru(bpy)_3]^{2+}$, $[Rh(bpy)_3]^{3+}$ in the presence of TEOA (with 450 ± 20 nm light) produced rhodium(I) ($\Phi = 0.13 \pm 0.02$ mol einstein^{-1}) and hydrogen ($\Phi = 0.11 \pm 0.02$ mol einstein^{-1}) in the absence and presence of platinum, respectively. [74] A detailed mechanistic scheme was construed from the results gathered from continuous- and flash-photolysis experiments. [74] Upon irradiation $[Ru(bpy)_3]^{2+}$ was excited to form $[^*Ru(bpy)_3]^{2+}$ which is then oxidized by $[Rh(bpy)_3]^{3+}$ ($k = 3.9 \times 10^8$ M^{-1} s^{-1}) forming $[Ru(bpy)_3]^{3+}$ and $[Rh(bpy)_3]^{2+}$ with a cage escape yield of 0.15 ± 0.03. Back-reaction of $[Ru(bpy)_3]^{3+}$ with $[Rh(bpy)_3]^{2+}$ ($k = 3 \pm 10^9$ M^{-1} s^{-1}) is prevented by the reduction of $[Ru(bpy)_3]^{3+}$ by TEOA ($k = 0.2 \times 10^8$ M^{-1} s^{-1}).[74] The oxidized TEOA radical that was generated underwent a TEOA-promoted rearrangement ($k = 0.3 \times 10^7$ M^{-1} s^{-1}) to produce a reducing radical. [74] Rate-determining loss of a bpy ligand from $[Ru(bpy)_3]^{3+}$ ($k = 1.0 \pm 0.5$ s^{-1}) was followed by the rapid reduction of $[Rh(bpy)_2]^{2+}$ by $[Rh(bpy)_3]^{2+}$ ($k = 0.3 \times 10^9$ M^{-1} s^{-1}) yielding $[Rh(bpy)_3]^{3+}$ and Rh(I). [74] Chan et al. [74] also reported that in the presence of platinum, hydrogen was formed at the expense of Rh(I); and noted that the catalyzed the reaction of Rh(II) with water occurred before disproportionation of Rh(I) can take place. The hydrogen quantum yield in the system as reported by Chan et al. [74] was limited only by the cage escape of the primary products, the homogeneous and heterogeneous "dark reactions" being efficient.

A report which involved photolytic studies of $[Ru(bpy)_3]^{2+}$ in the presence of *L*-ascorbic acid and bpy showed that hydrogen production increased when the pH value of the reaction was decreased with the ideal pH for the catalytic process being 5.0. [75] The decreased pH value was due to the formation of dihydrobipyridine which was formed from the reaction between $[Ru(bpy)_3]^+$ and hydrobipyridine (where $[Ru(bpy)_3]^+$ was formed when the photo-excited $[Ru(bpy)_3]^{2+}$ is reduced by the *L*-ascorbic acid). [75-76] $[Ru(bpy)_3]^{2+}$ in the presence of $[Co(bpy)_3]^{2+}$ was also reported to produce H_2 in aqueous media, but the best results for the formation of hydrogen was reported when a solution mixture consisting of 50% water and 50% CH_3CN was used. [77]

In this study, upon irradiation, the photoexcited $[^*Ru(bpy)_3]^{2+}$ reduces $[Co(bpy)_3]^{2+}$ to $[Co(bpy)_3]^+$ which in an aqueous media is able to produce H_2 with the maximum quantum yield of 0.29 as reported in a 50%:50% mixture of CH_3CN:H_2O. [77] $[Ru(bpy)_3]^{3+}$ which was formed from the oxidation of $[^*Ru(bpy)_3]^{2+}$ was then reduced back to $[Ru(bpy)_3]^{2+}$ by the sacrificial electron donor TEOA. [77]

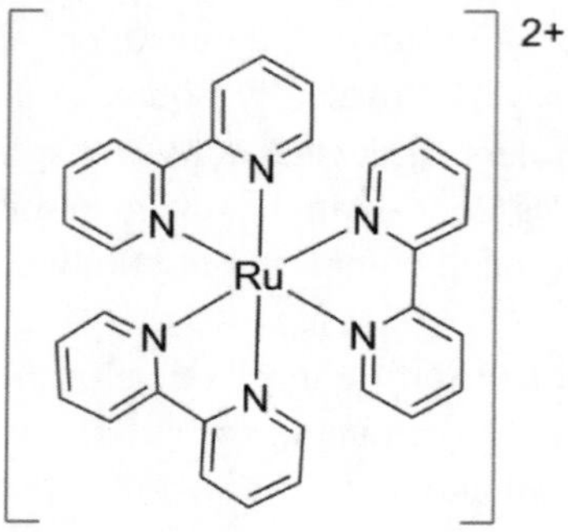

Figure 7. The structure of $[Ru(bpy)_3]^{2+}$.

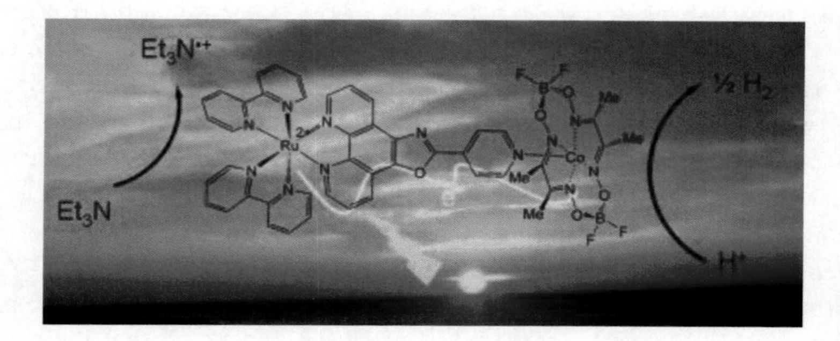

Figure 8. Photocatalytic reduction of protons through an intra-molecular electron transfer from ruthenium(II) photocenter to the cobalt(II) catalytic center via the bridging ligand in the presence of Et_3N as a sacrificial electron donor. (Reprinted with permission) [79]

Mixed-Metal Complexes with Bridged Ruthenium Photosensitizer

Recently there is an interest in the use of mixed-metal complexes (with a photoactive metal center bridged via a bridging ligand (BL) to the catalytic active subunit) for the production of hydrogen in various media. [78] In another classic piece of published research as reported by Fihri and co-workers, [79] a BL can be an electron reservoir, whereby it transfers the electron from a ruthenium(II) photoactive center to a cobalt(II) catalyst via an intra-molecular transfer process (see figure **8**). [79] In figure 8 the proton source is the $[Et_3NH]^+$ cation, and the sacrificial reductant is Et_3N. During the catalytic process, a Co(I) species is formed, followed by its reaction with protons to form H_2. [79]

Based on this brief introduction with mixed-metal complexes, we will now expand our discussion to focus on ruthenium(II)-containing complexes that consist of other metal centers.

Complexes with Ruthenium and Cobalt Metal Centers

As mentioned above, due to the fact that fossil fuel reserves are rapidly diminishing, emphasis has been placed on the use of renewable energy to meet the fuel needs of the world. Solar-to-chemical energy conversion is one of the most attractive for sustainable development; thus there is a growing need for the direct generation of molecular hydrogen from water as a result of a convenient and clean energy vector, while utilising renewable resources, for example, water and sun light. [3-8] However, splitting water into hydrogen and oxygen is a complex multi-electron redox process [10] involving high energy barriers that requires either an electric potential or a catalyst to lower energy barriers. It must be reemphasized that he splitting of water into oxygen and hydrogen has utilised catalysts that are derived from expensive and rare noble metals, for example Pt, Pd, Rh, *etc.*, [11-12] which are not competitive to fossil fuels, and unsuitable to meet global demands. [80] More recently and in the past, efforts in research have shifted from heterogeneous to the use of homogeneous catalytic processes that are based on cheaper and abundant first-row transition metals. [73, 75-76, 79, 81-85]

The entire water-to-hydrogen process first requires the oxidation of water to protons and O_2 followed by the reduction of protons to hydrogen. Success has been achieved on water oxidation, [86-88] but, however, our focus is on the latter reaction designed to produce H_2. While one approach is to mimic the core of natural hydrogenases, [89-92] there have also been reports of cobaloxime-containing complexes that are efficient electrocatalysts for hydrogen evolution. [10, 93-105] Cobaloximes are composed of a Co(II) center, two equatorial glyoxime ligands and two exchangeable axial ligands, which influence the catalytic activity. [104] Lehn and co-workers pioneered the first studies on homogeneous photogeneration of hydrogen using $[Co(dmgH)_2(OH_2)_2]$ (where dmgH = dimethylglyoximate) as a catalyst with $[Ru(bpy)_3]$ [2+] as photosensitizer and triethanolamine (TEOA) as a sacrificial electron donor in a DMF solution. [84]

Connolly et al., [94] Razavet et al., [104] and more recently, Dempsey et al. [10, 95] carried out thorough investigations of the mechanisms and kinetics of H_2 reduction by cobaloximes. Whereas three different pathways were postulated, all proceed through the same intermediate, a Co(III)-hydride (Co(III)-H) complex that possesses a high hydridic character. Depending on the relative concentrations of protons and Co(I), Co(III)-H is either protonated and releases H_2 in a heterolytic pathway or Co(III)-H is reduced by Co(I) to form Co(II)-H, followed by protonation and H_2 release. [95] The former pathway is energetically unfavourable since the formation of Co(III) involves high energy barriers. A third, homolytic and energetically more favourable pathway was suggested in which two Co(III)-H species release H_2 and form Co(II) in a reductive elimination step. [95, 104] More recently, Muckerman and Fujita [106] carried out theoretical studies of the reduction potentials of $[Co(dmgBF_2)_2(H_2O)_2]$ in an acetonitrile solution so as to shed light on its electrocatalytical mechanism for hydrogen production. Muckerman and Fujita [106] proposed three mechanisms, all of which are believed to proceed through the formation of Co(III)-H. Their results indicate that the mechanism involving a Co(II)-H intermediate is the most likely.

In an approach to couple an H_2 evolution catalyst to a photosensitizer for photocatalytic H_2 generation, Fihri et al. [79, 82] synthesized a series of supramolecular catalysts comprising a cobaloxime-based catalytic center and a Ru(II)-based photosensitizer. The coupling was performed by replacing one of the axial H_2O ligands of the cobaloxime with a pyridine-functionalized ruthenium(II)-polypyridine complex. These complexes were tested for photochemical hydrogen generation from $[Et_3NH]BF_4$, where it was found that the mixed-metal binuclear ruthenium(II)-cobalt(II) complexes were more efficient in hydrogen production than their corresponding multi-component systems under the same conditions. A complex containing a BF_2-bridged Co(II) center was found to be superior when compared to those with an H-bridged Co(III) center because the Co(II) state in the former is more easily reducible and more resistant towards side reactions, for example, acidic hydrolysis and hydrogenation. [79, 82]

Li et al. [107] also studied related mixed-metal binuclear ruthenium(II)-cobalt(II) complexes with and without linker conjugation in order to determine which of the two compounds were better photocatalysts for the generation of hydrogen under homogeneous conditions. While both complexes were more active than the corresponding multi-component systems, the non-conjugated bridge was found to exhibit higher activity for hydrogen production. [107] Over the years, our research group and others have been interested in the synthesis and characterisation of bridging and terminal ligands for the construction of mixed-metal complexes that have at least one ruthenium(II) metal center. Based on this interest, we will now discuss the use of mixed-metal complexes and non-mixed-metal for the generation of hydrogen in various solvent media.

Studies that involve the linking of cobalt HEC like cobaloximes to ruthenium photoactive catalytic complexes give rise to binuclear mixed-metal complexes such as $[Ru(pbt)_2(\mathit{L}\text{-}pyr)Co(dmgBF_2)_2(OH_2)]^{2+}$, complex 14, as reported by Cropek et al. [108] Upon irradiation, the binuclear mixed-metal complexes 10-16 in acidic acetonitrile undergo an intra-molecular electron transfer from the photoexcited ruthenium photosensitizer to the cobalt center which then leads to the production of H_2. [95] These Ru-Co mixed-metal complexes are reported to have efficiencies up to 8.5 time more than analogous systems under similar conditions. [95] Studies on complexes 15 and 16 showed that complex 16 had a higher TON when compared to complex 15 which is surprising since 15 is conjugated while 16 is not. [95, 107] Complex 14 showed that its TOF varied depending on the sacrificial electron donor, where in Et_3N the TOF was ~1 h^{-1} and in TEOA has a TOF of ~2 h^{-1} as reported in figure 9. [108] Figure 9 also shows a comparison complex 14 and the mononuclear photocatalyst in solution with the cobaloxime that there is little to no production of H_2 from the latter which could be attributed to the BL facilitating in the electron transfer process.

Two binuclear mixed-metal complexes $Ru[(bpy)_2(bpy\text{-}4\text{-}CH_3,4'\text{-}CONH(4\text{-}py))Co(dmgBF_2)_2(OH_2)](PF_6)_2$ 15 and $[(bpy)_2Ru(bpy\text{-}4\text{-}CH_3,4'\text{-}CONHCH_2(4\text{-}py)Co(dmgBF_2)_2(OH_2)](PF_6)_2$ 16 were synthesized with a polypyridyl ruthenium photosensitizer and the cobaloxime catalyst connected by a BL that was either conjugated or unconjugated. [107] Complexes 15 and 16 were tested for their ability to produce H_2. The maximum TON for hydrogen evolution were 38 for complex 15, and 48 for complex 16 in the presence of both Et_3N, a sacrificial electron donor, and $[Et_3NH][BF_4]$, a proton source, in acetone for eight hours of irradiation under visible light. [107] Complex 16 with the unconjugated BL was reported to generate H_2 more efficiently when compared to complex 15. [107]

As reported by Cropek and co-workers, [108] photocatalytic studies involving complex 14 were carried out in acidified acetonitrile revealed that H_2 was continuously produced longer than 42 hours and was detected by gas chromatography. Cropek et al. [108] proposed a mechanism for hydrogen production with binuclear mixed-metal Ru(II)-BL-Co(II) complexes, where the initial step is the photoexcitation of the ruthenium photosensitizer, followed by the intra-molecular transfer of an electron to the cobalt metal center thus forming the reactive Co(I) species. The Co(I) metal center then reacts with a proton to form a Co(III) species which transfers two electrons to the proton to form a hydride that reacts with another proton. The Co(III)-H bond cleaves through heterolytic fission. The two electrons are then replaced by Et_2N allowing the cycle to be repeated. Time resolved spectroscopic measurements performed on complex **14** confirmed that an intramolecular electron transfer from the excited Ru(II) metal center to the Co(II) metal center via the bridging L-pyr ligand. [108] The formation of the cobalt(I)-containing species is vital for the production of H_2 in the presence of H^+ ions. A proposed mechanism for the generation of hydrogen is shown in scheme **1**.

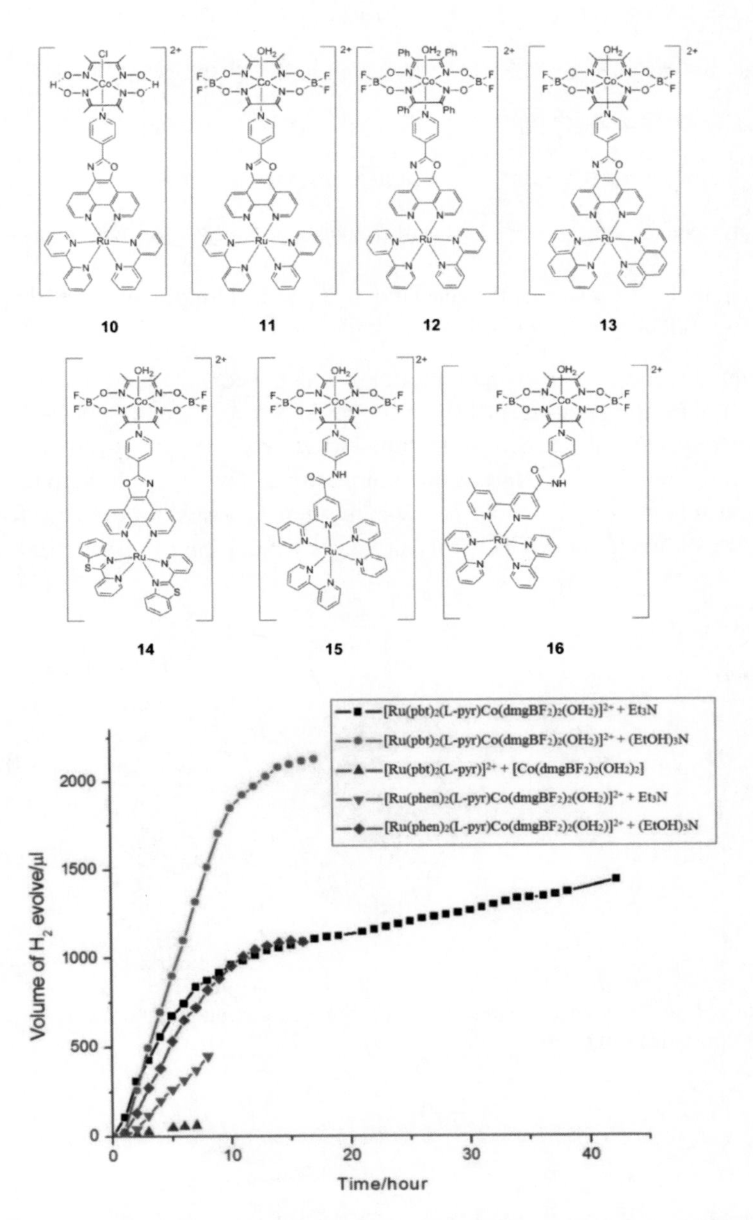

Figure 9. Photocatalytic H_2 production in acidic acetonitrile. Cropek, D. M.; Metz, A.; Mueller, A. M.; Gray, H. B.; Horne, T.; Horton, D. C.; Poluektov, O.; Tiede, D. M.; Weber, R. T.; Jarrett, W. L.; Phillips, J. D.; Holder, A. A., *Dalton Trans.* **2012,** *41* (42), 13060. Reproduced by permission of The Royal Society of Chemistry. [108]

$$[Ru^{II}(pbt)_2(L\text{-}pyr)Co^{II}(dmgBF_2)_2(H_2O)]^{2+} + h\nu \rightarrow [{}^*Ru^{II}(pbt)_2(L\text{-}pyr)Co^{II}(dmgBF_2)_2(H_2O)]^{2+} \quad (1)$$

$$[{}^*Ru^{II}(pbt)_2(L\text{-}pyr)Co^{II}(dmgBF_2)_2(H_2O)]^{2+} \rightleftharpoons [Ru^{III}(pbt)_2(L\text{-}pyr)Co^{I}(dmgBF_2)_2(H_2O)]^{2+} \quad (2)$$

$$[Ru^{III}(pbt)_2(L\text{-}pyr)Co^{I}(dmgBF_2)_2(H_2O)]^{2+} + H \rightleftharpoons [Ru^{III}(pbt)_2(L\text{-}pyr)Co^{III}H(dmgBF_2)_2(H_2O)]^{3+} \quad (3)$$

$$[Ru^{III}(pbt)_2(L\text{-}pyr)Co^{III}H(dmgBF_2)_2(H_2O)]^{3+} + H \rightleftharpoons [Ru^{III}(pbt)_2(L\text{-}pyr)Co^{III}(dmgBF_2)_2(H_2O)]^{4+} + H_2 \quad (4)$$

$$[Ru^{III}(pbt)_2(L\text{-}pyr)Co^{III}(dmgBF_2)_2(H_2O)]^{4+} + Et_3N \rightleftharpoons [Ru^{II}(pbt)_2(L\text{-}pyr)Co^{III}(dmgBF_2)_2(H_2O)]^{3+} + Et_3N^{\bullet+} \quad (5)$$

$$[Ru^{II}(pbt)_2(L\text{-}pyr)Co^{III}(dmgBF_2)_2(H_2O)]^{3+} + h\nu \rightarrow [{}^*Ru^{II}(pbt)_2(L\text{-}pyr)Co^{III}(dmgBF_2)_2(H_2O)]^{3+} \quad (6)$$

$$[{}^*Ru^{II}(pbt)_2(L\text{-}pyr)Co^{III}(dmgBF_2)_2(H_2O)]^{3+} \rightleftharpoons [Ru^{III}(pbt)_2(L\text{-}pyr)Co^{II}(dmgBF_2)_2(H_2O)]^{3+} \quad (7)$$

$$[Ru^{III}(pbt)_2(L\text{-}pyr)Co^{II}(dmgBF_2)_2(H_2O)]^{3+} + Et_3N \rightleftharpoons [Ru^{II}(pbt)_2(L\text{-}pyr)Co^{II}(dmgBF_2)_2(H_2O)]^{2+} + Et_2N^{\bullet+} \quad (8)$$

Scheme 1. The proposed mechanism for the generation of hydrogen from acidified media. Reproduced by permission of The Royal Society of Chemistry. [108]

A cobaloxime anchored to TiO_2 nanoparticles was tested for its ability to produce H_2 as an alternative to a platinum catalyst. [109] As shown in figure **10**, upon photoexcitation of the ruthenium photosensitizer, the electron is transferred from the π^* transition state of the photosensitizer to the conduction band of the nanoparticle. The electron were then transferred from the nanoparticle to the cobaloximes which then reduces protons to form H_2. The nanoparticles were shown to have a TON of 100 under irradiation of visible light. [109-110]

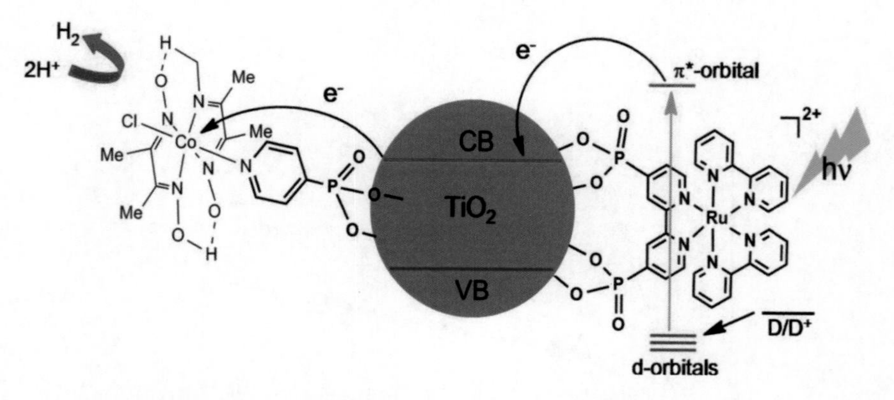

Figure 10. Structure of the TiO_2-based material for H_2 photoproduction using cobaloxime as catalyst. (Reprinted with permission) [109-110]

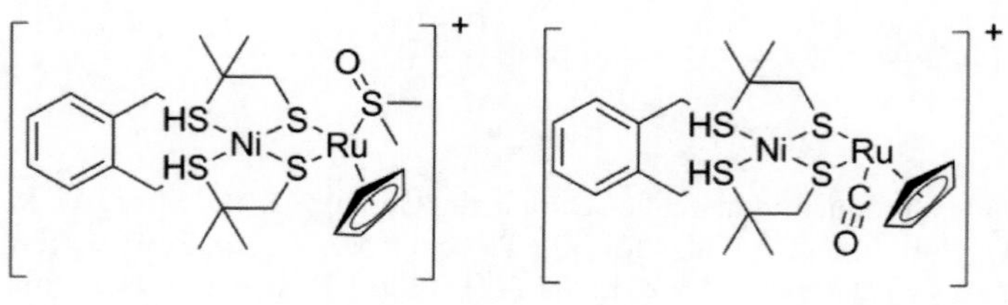

17 **18**

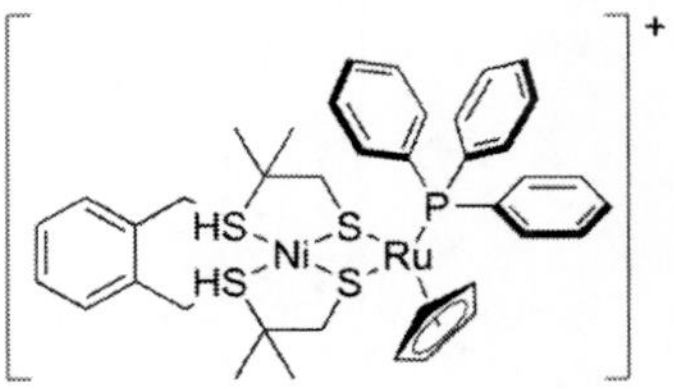

19 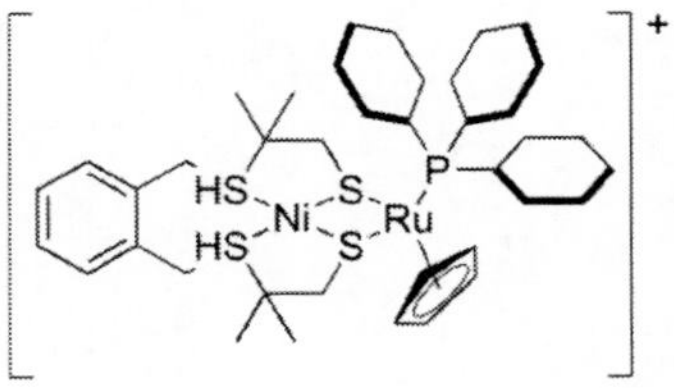 20

Complexes with Ruthenium and Nickel Metal Centers

The binuclear mixed-metal nickel–ruthenium complexes [Ni(xbsms)Ru(Cp)(L)]PF_6 (where L = DMSO (**17**), CO (**18**), PPh_3 (**19**), and PCy_3 (**20**)) were designed to mimic the active site of NiFe hydrogenases. [111] From the experiments, it was concluded that there is an increase in the electron density around the metal centers, which allowed complexes like [Ni(xbsms)Ru(Cp)(DMSO)]PF_6 **17** to be able to produce hydrogen in DMF with $[Et_3NH]^+$ as a proton source. [111] It was reported that the complexes overpotential are reduced by 180 mV compared to previous NiRu complexes making them efficient NiFe hydrogenase mimics. [111] DFT calculations were used to propose a mechanism which involved a possible bridging hydride that is formed after a two electron reduction of a proton. [112]

Complexes with Ruthenium and Rhodium Metal Centers

The binuclear mixed metal complexes, $[(bpy)_2Ru(dpp)Rh(COD)](PF_6)_3$ and $[(Me_2bpy)_2Ru(dpp)Rh(COD)](PF_6)_2(BF_4)$, were reported to produce H_2 when compared to the sterically hindered complex **23**. [113] Steric hindrance played an important role in the production of H_2 in the binuclear complexes during photoreduction, where complexes such **23** can dimerize and impede contact with the substrates. [113] It was reported that by tuning the sterics and electronics of the binuclear complexes through the terminal ligands to the point where complexes **21** and **22** were able to produce H_2 from H_2O. [113-114] Ruthenium-rhodium-ruthenium trinuclear mixed-metal complexes such as complex **24** were recognized for their ability to reduce H_2O to form H_2 through a photoreduction process, whereas the binuclear mixed-metal ruthenium-rhodium complexes were shown not to be able to catalyze H_2O reduction to form H_2. [114]

Complexes with Ruthenium and Palladium Metal Centers

A study with a complex such as $[(tbbpy)_2Ru(tpphz)Pd]^{2+}$ (shown in scheme **2**) showed that the electron-transfer process in the tpphz ligand was potentially from the possibility of water forming hydrogen bonds with the phenazine's nitrogen, followed by a reduction when the phenazine was replaced by the acridine unit. [115] It was reported that $[(tbbpy)_2Ru(tpac)Pd]^{2+}$ had a TON of 0.15, but in the presence of water, TON of 139 and 238 were reported for $[(tbbpy)_2Ru(tpac)Pd]^{2+}$ and $[(tbbpy)_2Rut(pphz)Pd]^{2+}$, respectively. [115-116]

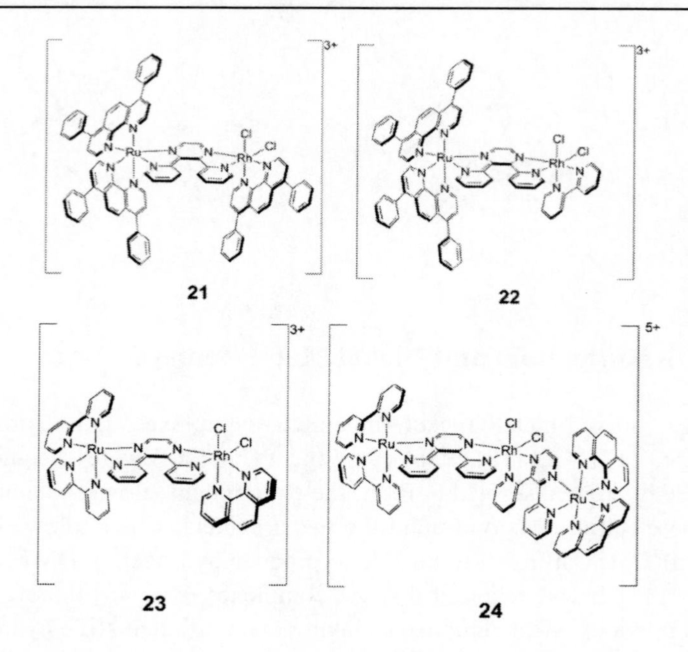

Complex **25** was reported to have a TON of 400 in the presence of water. [117] It is reported that water plays a major role in the production of hydrogen. [117] Vos et al. [117] deduced that water had three functions which are as follows (i) being a proton source, (ii) enable in proton transfer, and (iii) stabilize any polar intermediate that may be formed throughout the catalytic process.

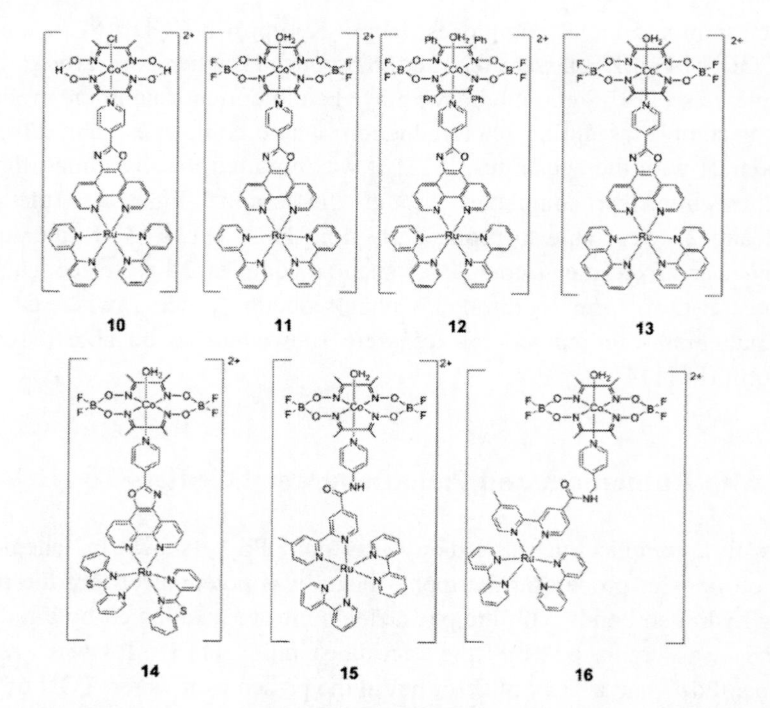

Scheme 2. Intra-molecular electron transfer from the photoactive Ru(II) center to the catalytic Pd(II) metal center. [78]

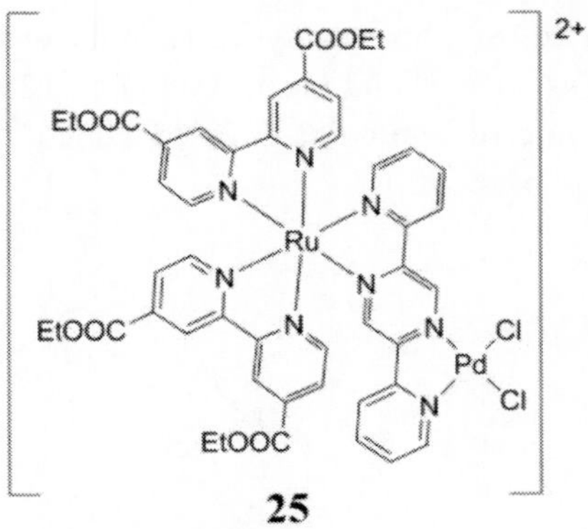

25

It is noted that when complex **26** is photo-excited the palladium metal center is reduced from Pd(II) to Pd(0). [118] The Pd(0) then dissociates from the ligand to form colloid nanoparticles in solution that becomes the site for hydrogen evolution. [118]

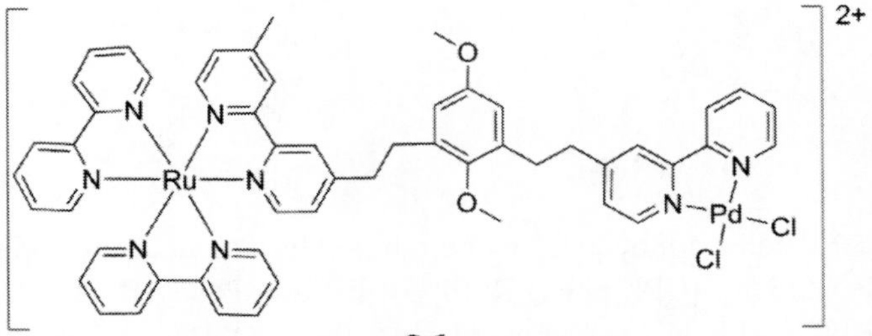

26

Complexes with Ruthenium and Platinum Metal Centers

The photocatalytic activities of two binuclear mixed-metal ruthenium(II)-platinum(II) complexes, $[(bpy)_2Ru(dpp)PtCl_2]^{2+}$ (**27**) and $[(bpy)_2Ru(pmcbpy)PtCl_2]^{2+}$ (**28**), were tested for their ability to produce H_2 in the presence of $[Ru(bpy)_3]^{2+}$ and methylviologen. [119] Complexes **27** and **28** were reported to only be able to produce H_2. [119]

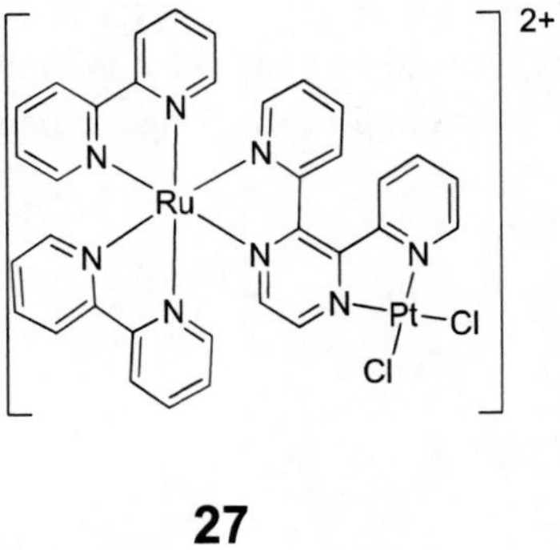

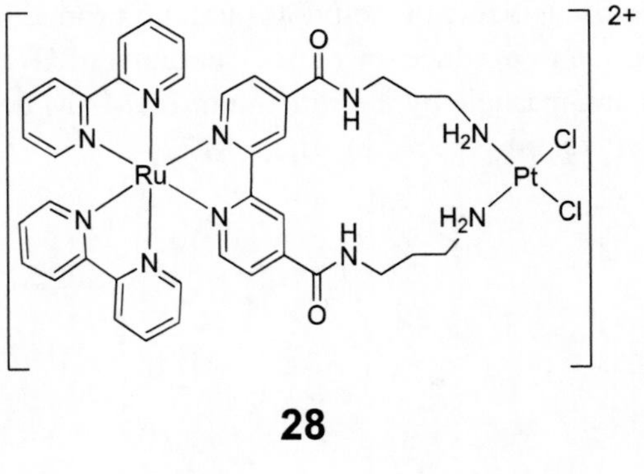

27 **28**

Complex **29** was reported to photocatalytically reduce protons to hydrogen in the presence of light and EDTA as a sacrificial electron donor. [120] When **29** was compared to **30**, it was reported that the rate of reduction doubled which could be due to the covalent linkage between the two complexes. [120]

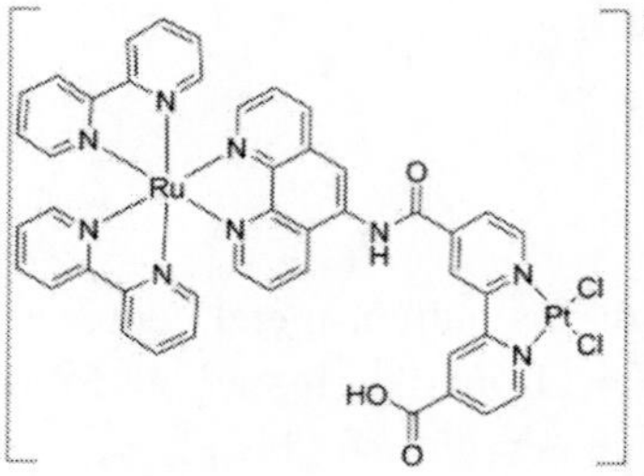

29 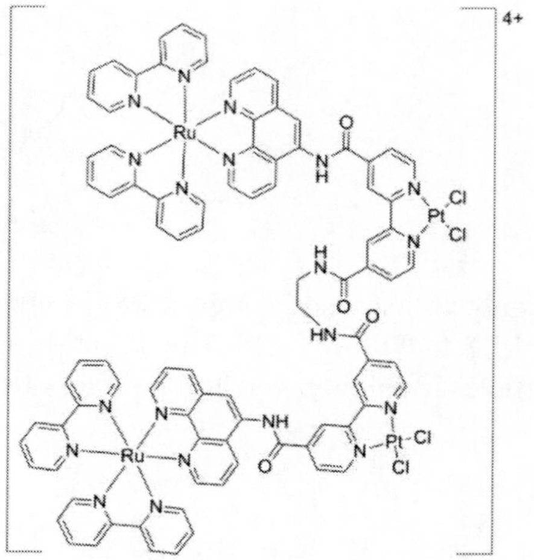 30

Electrochemical studies conducted on the tetranuclear complexes, $[((Ph_2phen)_2Ru(dpp))_2Ru(dpp)PtCl_2](PF_6)_6$ (**31**), $[((Ph_2phen)_2Ru(dpp))_2Ru(dpq)PtCl_2](PF_6)_6$ (**32**), and $[((phen)_2Ru(dpp))_2Ru(dpq)PtCl_2](PF_6)_6$ (**34**) showed that the HOMO orbitals are based on the terminal ligands and the LUMO orbitals are based on the BL. [121] The tetranuclear complexes were reported as active photocatalysts and are able to produce H_2 from H_2O, with complex **32** having the largest TON of 94 in 10 hours. [121] The environment produced by the BL has a significant impact on the catalytic activity, whereas the terminal ligands affect the wavelength of light that is absorbed. [121]

Studies conducted on platinum nanoparticles inside the cavities of a PAMAM dendrimer where $[Ru(bpy)_3]^{2+}$ are anchored to the dendrimer was tested for its ability to produce H_2 from H_2O. [122] The ruthenium complexes are used as indicating units of the Pt^{2+} complexation in the dendritic architecture through quenching of the phosphorescence and to act as photosensitizers in the photocatalytic production of H_2 from H_2O. [122] The complexes were reported to produce only small amounts of H_2 which could be caused by shielding of the platinum nanoparticle by the ruthenium PAMAM dendrimers and of the distance between the photosensitizer and the nanoparticle. [122]

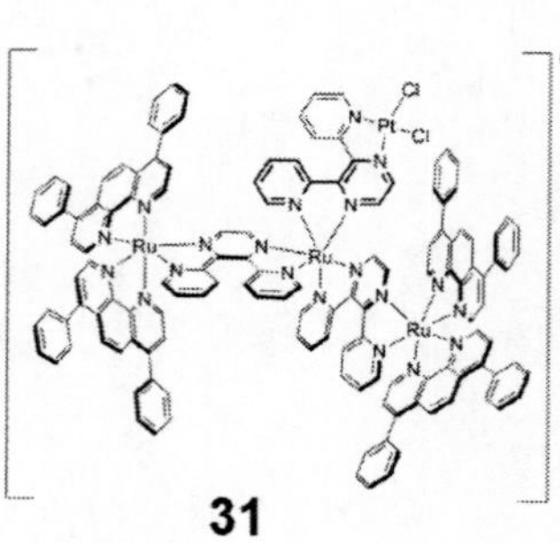

31 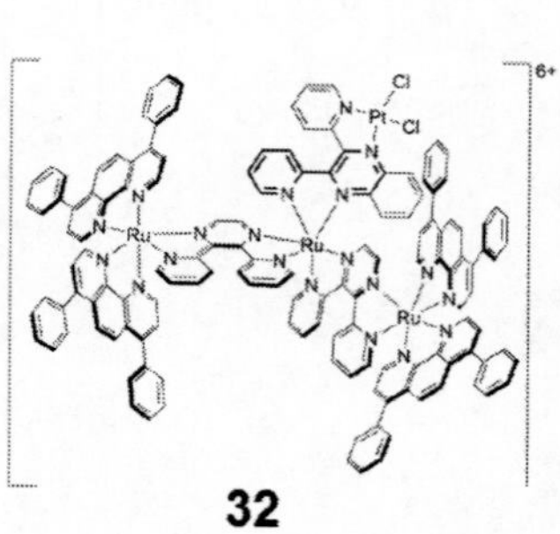 32

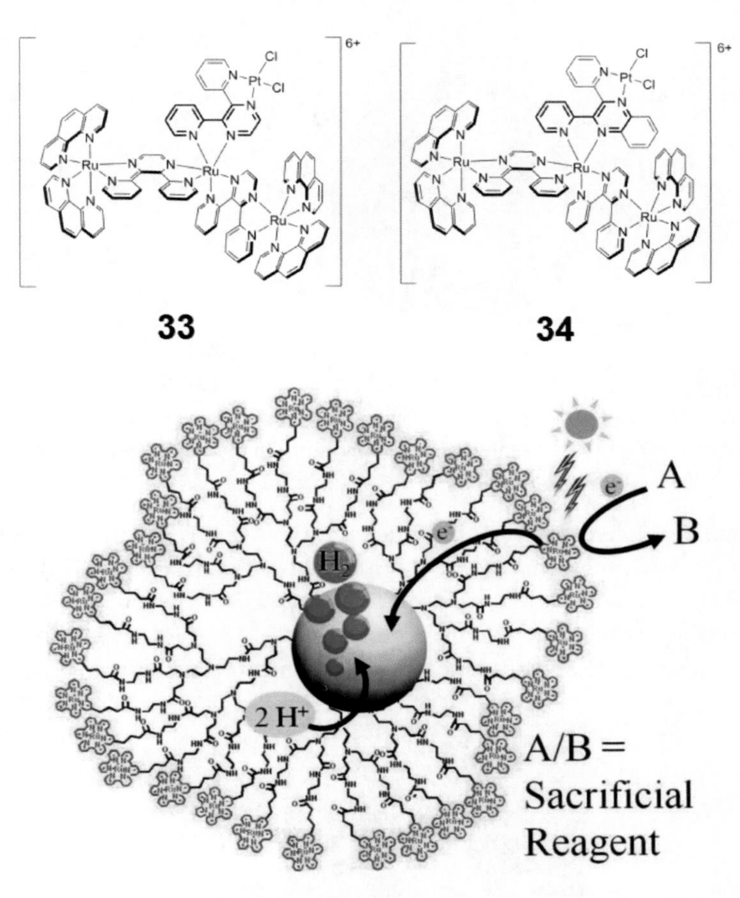

Figure 11. Dendritic ruthenium photosensitizer units complexed with Pt^{2+} nanoparticles for the production of hydrogen. Reprinted with permission Ravotto, L.; Mazzaro, R.; Natali, M.; Ortolani, L.; Morandi, V.; Ceroni, P.; Bergamini, G., *J. Phys. Chem. Lett.* 2014, *5* (5), 798. Copyright 2014 American Chemical Society. [122]

Complexes with Ruthenium and Hydrogenase

Bio-hybrid mimics of hydrogenases attached to ruthenium complexes could become very popular in the field of hydrogen production. The photoexcited ruthenium complex is oxidized by the hydrogenase active site forming the reduced form of the active site. [123] The reduced active site is then oxidize when reducing protons to hydrogen. [123] When the hydrogenase enzyme from *D. baculatum*, [NiFeSe], was attached to a ruthenium dye-sensitized TiO_2 nanoparticle, in the presence of a sacrificial electron donor, it was reported to be able to produce hydrogen in both aerobic and anaerobic conditions. [27] The ruthenium complex reported in figure **12** has a 98% adsorption onto the surface of TiO_2 and an efficiency of ~6.69% which is due in part to the phosphate group, thus enhancing charge transfer and hydrogen production. [27] When irradiated with visible light, the complex was reported to have a TON of 10,000. [27, 124]

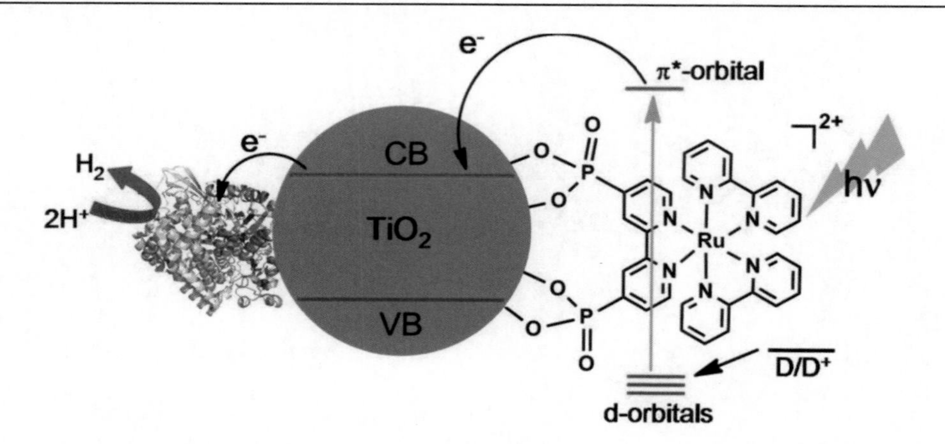

Figure 12. Structure of the TiO_2-based material for H_2 photoproduction using surface-immobilized hydrogenase as catalyst. (Reprinted with permission) [27, 124]

Another example of a hydrogenase that is able to produce H_2 in aerobic conditions is the [NiFe] H_2ase from *T. roseopersicina* where the ruthenium photosensitizer is directly attached to the enzyme. [31] Figure **13** shows a gel of *T. roseopersicina* where in lanes 2 and 3 the H_2ase had been reacted with a ruthenium photosensitizer. [31] At 30 kDa one can see the ruthenium bound H_2ase before and after the filtering of the unreacted photosensitizer. [31]

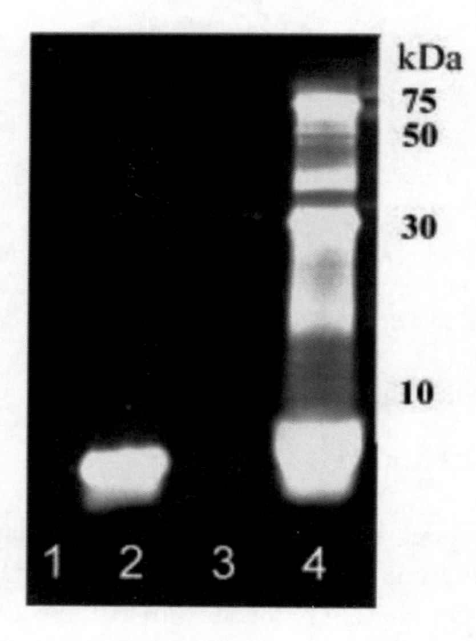

Figure 13. Fluorescent image of a gel with T. roseopersicina hydrogenase. (Reprinted with permission) [31]

The transfer of an electron from $[^*Ru(bpy)_3]^{2+}$ to the hydrogenase mimic was positive and thus thermodynamically unfavorable. [125] The hydrogenascorbate (HA^-) anion was reported to be able to reduce the excited $[^*Ru(bpy)_3]^{2+}$ to form $[Ru(bpy)_3]^+$ which then transfers an electron to the hydrogenase mimic. [125-127] Control experiments conducted in the absence of *L*-ascorbic acid showed a reduction in the lifetime of the Ru(I) species. [128] The solution was also shown to affect the efficiency of the system, where H_2O had the highest TON which was almost double that of solutions of CH_3CN/H_2O or CH_3OH. [125] The same effect was also reported when comparing the solution mixture of H_2O with hdrogenascorbate to a mixture of CH_3CN with acetic acid. [125] In water the TON was more than 88 which is higher than what was observed from CH_3CN. [125]

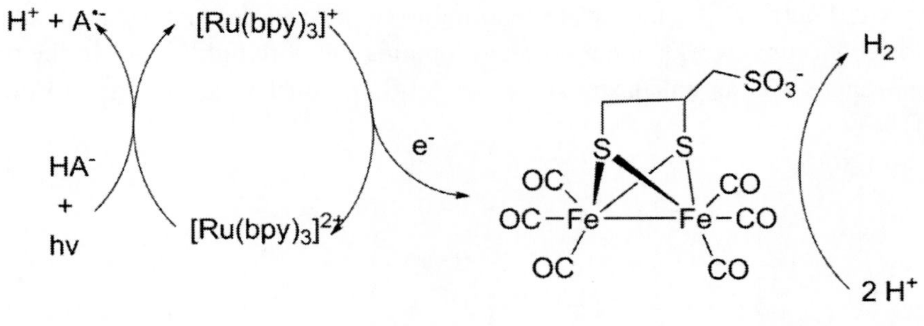

Scheme 3. The photocatalytic pathway for H_2 evolution by [FeFe]-H_2ases mimic with $[Ru(bpy)_3]^{2+}$ and *L*-ascorbic acid.

A diiron carbonyl cluster bound to Cys14 and Cys17 of a cytochrome c sequence in the presence of $[Ru(bpy)_3]^{2+}$ was reported to be an efficient HEC at a pH of 4.7 with a TON of ~80 over a two hour time period. [129] When the ruthenium photosensitizer was attached to the peptide sequence through a histidine residue was the TON was reduced to ~9 at a higher pH value (8.5) was utilized to hydrogen production. [130]

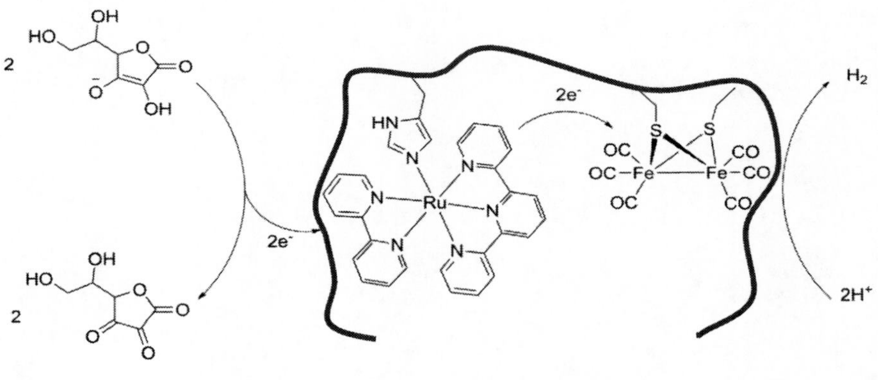

Scheme 4. Proposed catalytic cycle of peptide bound ruthenium photosensitizer in the presence of the sacrificial electron donor, hydrogenascorbate. [130]

The first [2Fe] complex linked to a ruthenium photosensitizer through a phosphate group that mimics the active [2Fe] site of hydrogenase was reported to be $[(\mu\text{-pdt})Fe_2(CO)_5(PPh_2(C_6H_4CCbpy))Ru(bpy)_2]^{2+}$ **37**. [131] The light-induced MLCT excited state of the ruthenium(II) photosensitizer on complex **37** was localized towards the potential diiron acceptor unit. [131] Complex **38** had a relatively mild potential required for the reduction of the acetylenic bipyridine, which then lead to reductive quenching of the excited state forming a transiently oxidized diiron entity. [131] Unfortunately, complexes **35** to **38** were unable to produce hydrogen. [123, 131-134]

Another route in the production of hydrogen was the use of chalcogels that incorporated [4Fe4S] clusters into its frame work as well as ruthenium photosensitizers, figure **14**. [135-

136] Most complexes that mimic H_2ase for the production of H_2 are molecular units that lack the protection of a protein's tertiary structure. [136] Therefore there have been many synthesized superstructures to protect the catalytic unit and to also drive the catalytic process forward. [136] Chalcogels have porous structures with a high surface area and when sensitized with $[Ru(bpy)_3]^{2+}$, they were reported to be able to produce H_2 in mixed aqueous solution for about three weeks under constant illumination with light. [136] In the production of hydrogen there was an enhancement if the $[Sn_4S_{10}]^{4-}$ clusters are bridged to the [4Fe4S] clusters. [135]

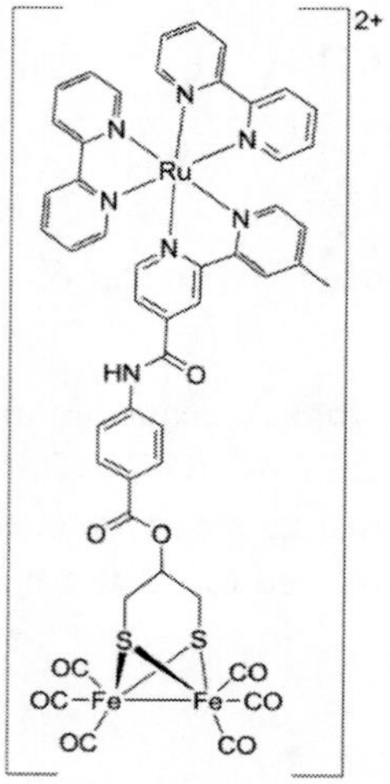

35

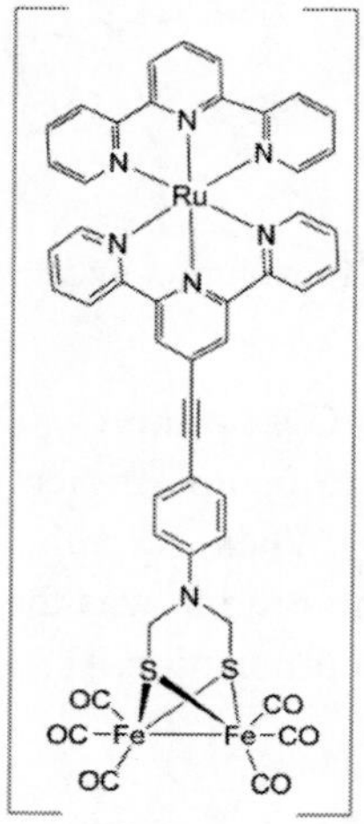

36

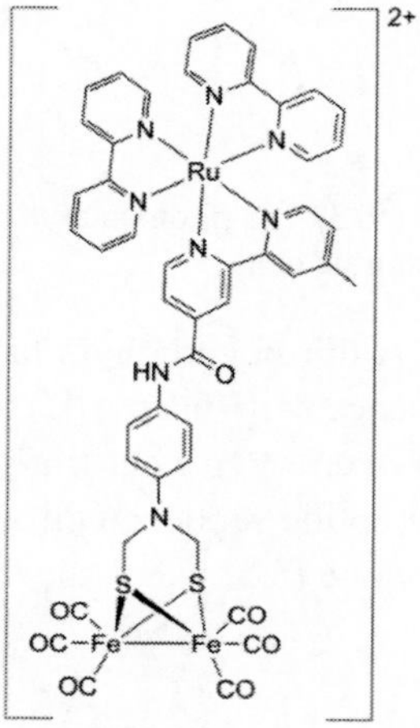

37

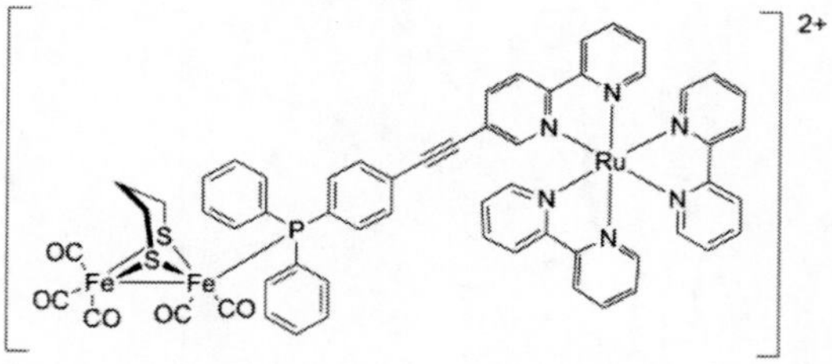

38

At this point, the reader is encouraged to read the reviews cited here for further information on the topic of hydrogen production with the use of ruthenium-based complexes. [101, 137-156]

For a more in-depth reading into renewable energy formation with the use of ruthenium and other transition metals, the reader is encouraged to read articles that are based upon the research findings of the following researchers: Harry B. Gray, Karen J. Brewer, Felix Castellano, Thomas Meyer, Nate Lewis, Richard Eisenberg, Johannes Vos, Frederick MacDonnell, Daniel G. Nocera, David Tiede, Fraser Armstrong, Randolph Thummel, Vincent Artero, Licheng Sun, Norman Sutin, Carol Creutz, and Russell Schmehl.

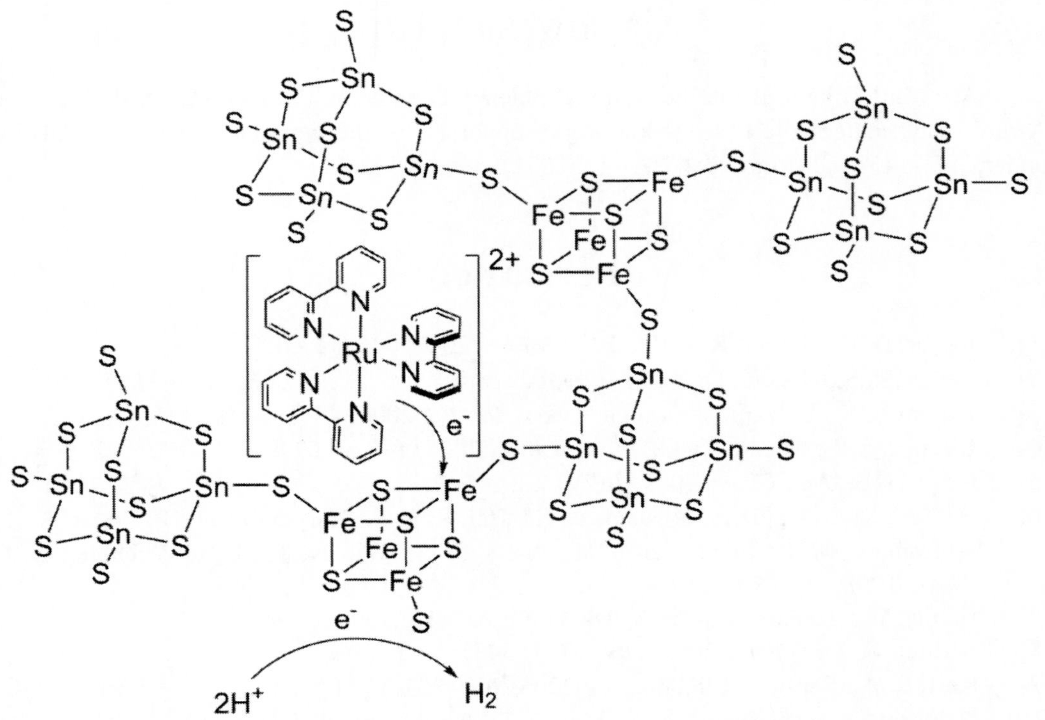

Figure 14. Ruthenium sensitized chalcogel. [135]

CONCLUSION

It can be concluded that there have been many reports on the development of ruthenium dyes to be used in solar cells for the conversion of sunlight into electricity. Since the first mention of the ruthenium dyes in the early 1990s there have been many improvements in the stability and efficiency of these complexes. As a result ruthenium dyes are reported to have solar energy conversion efficiency above 10%. [25-26]

The use of ruthenium in hydrogen evolution catalyst from mononuclear complexes in the presence of a ruthenium photocatalyst to photosensitizers anchored to hydrogenases has shown that they are able to produce copious amounts of H_2 within hours. [27, 31, 130] Studies are continuing in the creation of more stable complexes and the use of cheaper first row transition metal catalytic centers. Some of the major breakthroughs would be on the works conducted on the hydrogenases from D. baculatum and T. roseopersicina which are reported to be stable in aerobic conditions. 42, 47 With these studies, the future appears to be very bright for development of ruthenium-containing complexes for solar energy capture and for the generation of hydrogen in acidic aqueous media. Powering the planet with Harry Gray's ideas in http://www.youtube.com/watch?v=_ghJgJaJs7I and Dan Nocera's "Artificial leaf" in http://www.youtube.com/watch?v=J556uXwrjII and http://focusforwardfilms.com/contest/100/the-artificial-leaf-jared-p-scott-kelly-nyks will become a reality. The future looks good!

ACKNOWLEDGMENTS

AAH would like to thank the National Science Foundation (NSF) for an NSF CAREER Award. This material is based upon work supported by the National Science Foundation under CHE-1431172 (formerly CHE - 1151832).

REFERENCES

[1] Royer, D. L.; Berner, R. A.; Park, J., *Nature* 2007, *446* (7135),530.
[2] Lewis, N. S.; Nocera, D. G., *Proc. Natl. Acad. Sci. U. S. A.* 2006, *103* (43),15729.
[3] Armaroli, N.; Balzani, V., *Angew. Chem. Int. Ed.* 2007, *46* (1+2),52.
[4] Eisenberg, R.; Nocera, D. G., *Inorg. Chem.* 2005, *44* (20),6799.
[5] Gray, H. B., *Nat. Chem.* 2009, *1* (2),112.
[6] Hoffert, M. I.; Caldeira, K.; Jain, A. K.; Haites, E. F.; Harvey, L. D. D.; Potter, S. D.; Schlesinger, M. E.; Schneider, S. H.; Watts, R. G.; Wigley, T. M. L.; Wuebbles, D. J., *Nature* 1998, *395* (6705),881.
[7] Lubitz, W.; Tumas, W., *Chem. Rev.* 2007, *107* (10),3900.
[8] Service, R. F., *Science* 2005, *309* (5734),548.
[9] Kerr, R. A.; Service, R. F., *Science* 2005, *309* (5731),101.
[10] Dempsey, J. L.; Esswein, A. J.; Manke, D. R.; Rosenthal, J.; Soper, J. D.; Nocera, D. G., *Inorg. Chem.* 2005, *44* (20),6879.
[11] Du, P.; Knowles, K.; Eisenberg, R., *J. Am.Chem. Soc.* 2008, *130* (38),12576.
[12] Esswein, A. J.; Nocera, D. G., *Chem. Rev.* 2007, *107* (10),4022.
[13] Gordon, M. A.; Zhang, W.; Lenz, H.-J., *Curr. Pharmacogenomics* 2006, *4* (4),277.
[14] Baykara, S. Z., *Int. J. Hydrogen Energy* 2005, *30* (5),545.
[15] http://www.eia.gov/renewable/annual/preliminary/
[16] Karkas, M. D.; Johnston, E. V.; Verho, O.; Akermark, B., *Acc. Chem. Res.* 2014, *47* (1),100.
[17] www.ipcc.ch/publications_and_data/ar4/wg1/en/faq-3-1.html
[18] http://www.epa.gov/climatechange/ghgemissions/gases/co2.html
[19] Moriarty, P.; Honnery, D., *Int. J. Hydrogen Energy* 2009, *34* (1),31.
[20] Baranoff, E.; Collin, J.-P.; Flamigni, L.; Sauvage, J.-P., *Chem. Soc. Rev.* 2004, *33* (3),147.
[21] Juris, A.; Balzani, V.; Barigelletti, F.; Campagna, S.; Belser, P.; von Zelewsky, A., *Coord. Chem. Rev.* 1988, *84* (0),85.
[22] Argazzi, R.; Bignozzi, C. A.; Heimer, T. A.; Castellano, F. N.; Meyer, G. J., *J. Am.Chem. Soc.* 1995, *117* (47),11815.
[23] O'regan, B.; Grfitzeli, M., *Nature* 1991, *353*,737.
[24] Nazeeruddin, M.; Kay, A.; Rodicio, I.; Humphry-Baker, R.; Mueller, E.; Liska, P.; Vlachopoulos, N.; Graetzel, M., *J. Am.Chem. Soc.* 1993,6382.
[25] Grätzel, M., *Inorg. Chem.* 2005, *44* (20),6841.
[26] Nath, N. C. D.; Kim, J. C.; Kim, K. P.; Yim, S.; Lee, J.-J., *J. Mater. Chem. A* 2013, *1* (43),13439.

[27] Reisner, E.; Powell, D.; Cavazza, C.; Fontecilla-Camps, J.; Armstrong, F., *J. Am.Chem. Soc.* 2009, *131* (51),18457.
[28] Kim, Y. G.; Mosurkal, R.; Li, L.; Walker, J.; He, J.; Samuelson, L. A.; Kumar, J., *J. Macromol. Sci., Part A* 2007, *44* (12),1255.
[29] Ohlsson, J.; Wolpher, H.; Hagfeldt, A.; Grennberg, H., *J. Photochem. Photobiol., A* 2002, *148* (1–3),41.
[30] Shahroosvand, H.; Nasouti, F.; Sousaraei, A., *Dalton Trans.* 2014, *43* (13),5158.
[31] Zadvornyy, O.; Lucon, J.; Gerlach, R.; Zorin, N.; Douglas, T.; Elgren, T.; Peters, J., *J. Inorg. Biochem.* 2012, *106* (1),151.
[32] Summers, P. A.; Dawson, J.; Ghiotto, F.; Hanson-Heine, M. W. D.; Vuong, K. Q.; Stephen Davies, E.; Sun, X.-Z.; Besley, N. A.; McMaster, J.; George, M. W.; Schroder, M., *Inorg. Chem.* 2014, *53* (9),4430.
[33] Tennakone, K.; Kumara, G.; Kottegoda, I.; Wijayantha, K.; Perera, V., *J. Phys. D: Appl. Phys.* 1998,1492.
[34] Neupane, L. N.; Han, S. Y.; Lee, K.-H., *Chem. Commun.* 2014, *50* (44),5854.
[35] Argazzi, R.; Bignozzi, C.; Heimer, T.; Castellano, F.; Meyer, G., *J. Phys. Chem. B* 1997,2591.
[36] Humphry-Baker, R.; Grätzel, M.; Murrer, B., *Chem. Comm.* 1998,719.
[37] Chen, K.-S.; Liu, W.-H.; Wang, Y.-H.; Lai, C.-H.; Chou, P.-T.; Lee, G.-H.; Chen, K.; Chen, H.-Y.; Chi, Y.; Tung, F.-C., *Adv. Funct. Mater.* 2007, *17* (15),2964.
[38] http://www.thesolarspark.co.uk/videos/animations/
[39] www.dysol.com/about-dsc
[40] Brewster, T. P.; Konezny, S. J.; Sheehan, S. W.; Martini, L. A.; Schmuttenmaer, C. A.; Batista, V. S.; Crabtree, R. H., *Inorg. Chem.* 2013, *52* (11),6752.
[41] Chitra, S.; Somasundaram, N.; Easwaramoorthy, D., *Arch. Appl. Sci. Res.* 2013, *5* (1),112.
[42] Giribabu, L.; Kanaparthi, R. K., *Curr. Sci.* 2013, *104* (7),847.
[43] Gonzalez-Pedro, V.; Zarazua, I.; Barea, E. M.; Fabregat-Santiago, F.; de la Rosa, E.; Mora-Sero, I.; Gimenez, S., *J. Phys. Chem. C* 2014, *118* (2),891.
[44] Honda, M.; Yanagida, M.; Han, L., *AIP Adv.* 2013, *3* (7),072113/1.
[45] Hou, Y.; Chen, Z. P.; Wang, D.; Zhang, B.; Yang, S.; Wang, H. F.; Hu, P.; Zhao, H. J.; Yang, H. G., *Small* 2014, *10* (3),484.
[46] Kim, Y.-H.; Lee, I.-K.; Song, Y.-S.; Lee, M.-H.; Kim, B.-Y.; Cho, N.-I.; Lee, D. Y., *Electron. Mater. Lett.* 2014, *10* (2),445.
[47] Kley, C. S.; Dette, C.; Rinke, G.; Patrick, C. E.; Cechal, J.; Jung, S. J.; Baur, M.; Duerr, M.; Rauschenbach, S.; Giustino, F.; Stepanow, S.; Kern, K., *Nano Lett.* 2014, *14* (2),563.
[48] Krysova, H.; Zukal, A.; Trckova-Barakova, J.; Chandiran, A. K.; Nazeeruddin, M. K.; Gratzel, M.; Kavan, L., *Chimia* 2013, *67* (3),149.
[49] Noh, Y.; Song, O., *Electron. Mater. Lett.* 2014, *10* (1),263.
[50] Noh, Y.; Song, O., *Electron. Mater. Lett.* 2014, *10* (1),271.
[51] Singh, V. K.; Kanaparthi, R. K.; Giribabu, L., *RSC Adv.* 2014, *4* (14),6970.
[52] Tang, G.; Li, R.; Kou, S.; Tang, T.; Zhang, Y.; Wang, Y., *Opt. Spectrosc.* 2014, *116* (2),263.

[53] Campbell, W. M.; Jolley, K. W.; Wagner, P.; Wagner, K.; Walsh, P. J.; Gordon, K. C.; Schmidt-Mende, L.; Nazeeruddin, M. K.; Wang, Q.; Graetzel, M.; Officer, D. L., *J. Phys. Chem. C* 2007, *111* (32),11760.
[54] Abbotto, A.; Manfredi, N., *Dalton Trans.* 2011, *40* (46),12421.
[55] Amornpitoksuk, P.; Leesakul, N., *Songklanakarin J. Sci. Technol.* 2003, *25* (4),535.
[56] Bomben, P. G.; Robson, K. C. D.; Koivisto, B. D.; Berlinguette, C. P., *Coord. Chem. Rev.* 2012, *256* (15-16),1438.
[57] Clifford, J. N.; Planells, M.; Palomares, E., *J. Mater. Chem.* 2012, *22* (46),24195.
[58] Freeman, G. R.; Williams, J. A. G., *Top. Organomet. Chem.* 2013, *40*,89.
[59] Giribabu, L.; Kanaparthi, R. K.; Velkannan, V., *Chem. Rec.* 2012, *12* (3),306.
[60] Inoue, Y., *Energy Environ. Sci.* 2009, *2* (4),364.
[61] Islam, A.; Sugihara, H.; Arakawa, H., *J. Photochem. Photobiol., A* 2003, *158* (2-3),131.
[62] Kaneko, M., *Prog. Polym. Sci.* 2001, *26* (7),1101.
[63] Nishikitani, Y.; Kubo, T., *J. Jpn. Pet. Inst.* 2011, *54* (3),168.
[64] Ozawa, H.; Arakawa, H., *J. Jpn. Inst. Energy* 2012, *91* (5),369.
[65] Ragoussi, M.-E.; Ince, M.; Torres, T., *Eur. J. Org. Chem.* 2013, *2013* (29),6475.
[66] Rawling, T.; McDonagh, A., *Coord. Chem. Rev.* 2007, *251* (9+10),1128.
[67] Ryan, M., *Platinum Met. Rev.* 2009, *53* (4),216.
[68] Sekar, N.; Gehlot, V. Y., *Reson.* 2010, *15* (9),819.
[69] Stafford, N., *Chem. World* 2007, *4* (2),14.
[70] Uddin, T.; Nicolas, Y.; Olivier, C.; Toupance, T., *ACS Symp. Ser.* 2013, *1140*,143.
[71] Veerakumar, P.; Ramdass, A.; Rajagopal, S., *J. Nanosci. Nanotechnol.* 2013, *13* (7),4761.
[72] Zhou, Y.; Xu, Z.; Hu, Q.; Wang, S., *Guangzhou Huagong* 2012, *40* (7),11.
[73] Wang, M.; Na, Y.; Gorlov, M.; Sun, L., *Dalton Trans.* 2009, (33),6458.
[74] Chan, S. F.; Chou, M.; Creutz, C.; Matsubara, T.; Sutin, N., *J. Am.Chem. Soc.*1981, *103* (2),369.
[75] Krishnan, C. V.; Sutin, N., *J. Am.Chem. Soc.* 1981, *103* (8),2141.
[76] Brown, G. M.; Brunschwig, B. S.; Creutz, C.; Endicott, J. F.; Sutin, N., *J. Am.Chem. Soc.* 1979, *101* (5),1298.
[77] Krishnan, C.; Brunschwig, B. S.; Creutz, C.; Sutin, N., *J. Am.Chem. Soc.* 1985, *107* (7),2005.
[78] Tschierlei, S.; Presselt, M.; Kuhnt, C.; Yartsev, A.; Pascher, T.; Sundström, V.; Karnahl, M.; Schwalbe, M.; Schäfer, B.; Rau, S.; Schmitt, M.; Dietzek, B.; Popp, J., *Chem. Eur. J.* 2009, *15* (31),7678.
[79] Fihri, A.; Artero, V.; Razavet, M.; Baffert, C.; Leibl, W.; Fontecave, M., *Angew. Chem., Int. Ed.* 2008, *47* (3),564.
[80] Gordon, R. B.; Bertram, M.; Graedel, T. E., *Proc. Natl. Acad. Sci. USA* 2006, *103* (5),1209.
[81] Elvington, M.; Brown, J.; Arachchige, S. M.; Brewer, K. J., *J. Am.Chem. Soc.* 2007, *129* (35),10644.
[82] Fihri, A.; Artero, V.; Pereira, A.; Fontecave, M., *Dalton Trans.* 2008, (41),5567.
[83] Fisher, J. R.; Cole-Hamilton, D. J., *J. Chem. Soc., Dalton Trans.* 1984, (5),809.
[84] Hawecker, J.; Lehn, J. M.; Ziessel, R., *Nouveau J. Chimie* 1983, *7* (5),271.
[85] Krishnan, C. V.; Brunschwig, B. S.; Creutz, C.; Sutin, N., *J. Am.Chem. Soc.* 1985, *107* (7),2005.

[86] Huang, Z.; Luo, Z.; Geletii, Y. V.; Vickers, J. W.; Yin, Q.; Wu, D.; Hou, Y.; Ding, Y.; Song, J.; Musaev, D. G.; Hill, C. L.; Lian, T., *J. Am.Chem. Soc.* 2011, *133* (7),2068.
[87] McCool, N. S.; Robinson, D. M.; Sheats, J. E.; Dismukes, G. C., *J. Am.Chem. Soc.* 2011, *133* (30),11446.
[88] Reece, S. Y.; Hamel, J. A.; Sung, K.; Jarvi, T. D.; Esswein, A. J.; Pijpers, J. J. H.; Nocera, D. G., *Science* 2011, *334* (6056),645.
[89] Li, X.; Wang, M.; Zhang, S.; Pan, J.; Na, Y.; Liu, J.; Aakermark, B.; Sun, L., *J. Phys. Chem. B* 2008, *112* (27),8198.
[90] Na, Y.; Pan, J.; Wang, M.; Sun, L., *Inorg. Chem.* 2007, *46* (10),3813.
[91] Na, Y.; Wang, M.; Pan, J.; Zhang, P.; Akermark, B.; Sun, L., *Inorg. Chem.* 2008, *47* (7),2805.
[92] Barton, B. E.; Olsen, M. T.; Rauchfuss, T. B., *Curr. Opin. Biotechnol.* 2010, *21* (3),292.
[93] Baffert, C.; Artero, V.; Fontecave, M., *Inorg. Chem.* 2007, *46* (5),1817.
[94] Connolly, P.; Espenson, J. H., *Inorg. Chem.* 1986, *25* (16),2684.
[95] Dempsey, J. L.; Brunschwig, B. S.; Winkler, J. R.; Gray, H. B., *Acc. Chem. Res.* 2009, *42* (12),1995.
[96] Dempsey, J. L.; Winkler, J. R.; Gray, H. B., *J. Am.Chem. Soc.* 2010, *132* (47),16774.
[97] Dempsey, J. L.; Winkler, J. R.; Gray, H. B., *J. Am.Chem. Soc.* 2010, *132* (3),1060.
[98] Gong, L.; Wang, J.; Li, H.; Wang, L.; Zhao, J.; Zhu, Z., *Catal. Commun.* 2011, *12* (12),1099.
[99] Hu, X.; Cossairt, B. M.; Brunschwig, B. S.; Lewis, N. S.; Peters, J. C., *Chem. Commun.* 2005, (37),4723.
[100] Hu, X. L.; Brunschwig, B. S.; Peters, J. C., *J. Am.Chem. Soc.* 2007, *129* (29),8988.
[101] Losse, S.; Vos, J. G.; Rau, S., *Coord. Chem. Rev.* 2010, *254* (21-22),2492.
[102] Pantani, O.; Anxolabehere-Mallart, E.; Aukauloo, A.; Millet, P., *Electrochem. Commun.* 2006, *9* (1),54.
[103] Probst, B.; Kolano, C.; Hamm, P.; Alberto, R., *Inorg. Chem.* 2009, *48* (5),1836.
[104] Razavet, M.; Artero, V.; Fontecave, M., *Inorg. Chem.* 2005, *44* (13),4786.
[105] Zhang, P.; Wang, M.; Li, C.; Li, X.; Dong, J.; Sun, L., *Chem. Commun.* 2010, *46* (46),8806.
[106] Muckerman, J. T.; Fujita, E., *Chem. Commun.* 2011, *47* (46),12456.
[107] Li, C.; Wang, M.; Pan, J.; Zhang, P.; Zhang, R.; Sun, L., *J. Organomet. Chem.* 2009, *694* (17),2814.
[108] Cropek, D. M.; Metz, A.; Mueller, A. M.; Gray, H. B.; Horne, T.; Horton, D. C.; Poluektov, O.; Tiede, D. M.; Weber, R. T.; Jarrett, W. L.; Phillips, J. D.; Holder, A. A., *Dalton Trans.* 2012, *41* (42),13060.
[109] Lakadamyali, F.; Reisner, E., *Chem. Commun.* 2011, *47* (6),1695.
[110] Artero, V.; Fontecave, M., *C. R. Chim.* 2011, *14* (9),799.
[111] Canaguier, S.; Vaccaro, L.; Artero, V.; Ostermann, R.; Pécaut, J.; Field, M. J.; Fontecave, M., *Chem.-Eur. J.* 2009, *15* (37),9350.
[112] Vaccaro, L.; Artero, V.; Canaguier, S.; Fontecave, M.; Field, M. J., *Dalton Trans.* 2010, *39* (12),3043.
[113] Zhou, R.; Sedai, B.; Manbeck, G. F.; Brewer, K. J., *Inorg. Chem.* 2013, *52* (23),13314.
[114] White, T. A.; Whitaker, B. N.; Brewer, K. J., *J. Am.Chem. Soc.* 2011, *133* (39),15332.

[115] Karnahl, M.; Kuhnt, C.; Heinemann, F. W.; Schmitt, M.; Rau, S.; Popp, J.; Dietzek, B., *Chem. Phys.* 2012, *393* (1),65.
[116] Rau, S.; Schäfer, B.; Gleich, D.; Anders, E.; Rudolph, M.; Friedrich, M.; Görls, H.; Henry, W.; Vos, J. G., *Angew. Chem. Int. Ed.* 2006, *45* (37),6215.
[117] Singh Bindra, G.; Schulz, M.; Paul, A.; Soman, S.; Groarke, R.; Inglis, J.; Pryce, M. T.; Browne, W. R.; Rau, S.; Maclean, B. J.; Vos, J. G., *Dalton Trans.* 2011, *40* (41),10812.
[118] Lei, P.; Hedlund, M.; Lomoth, R.; Rensmo, H.; Johansson, O.; Hammarstroem, L., *J. Am.Chem. Soc.* 2008, *130* (1),26.
[119] Ozawa, H.; Yokoyama, Y.; Haga, M.-a.; Sakai, K., *Dalton Trans.* 2007, (12),1197.
[120] Ozawa, H.; Kobayashi, M.; Balan, B.; Masaoka, S.; Sakai, K., *Chem. - Asian J.* 2010, *5* (8),1860.
[121] Knoll, J. D.; Higgins, S. L. H.; White, T. A.; Brewer, K. J., *Inorg. Chem.* 2013, *52* (17),9749.
[122] Ravotto, L.; Mazzaro, R.; Natali, M.; Ortolani, L.; Morandi, V.; Ceroni, P.; Bergamini, G., *J. Phys. Chem. Lett.* 2014, *5* (5),798.
[123] Ott, S.; Kritikos, M.; Akermark, B.; Sun, L., *Angew. Chem.* 2003, *42* (28),3285.
[124] Reisner, E.; Fontecilla-Camps, J. C.; Armstrong, F. A., *Chem. Comm.* 2009, (5),550.
[125] Cao, W.-N.; Wang, F.; Wang, H.-Y.; Chen, B.; Feng, K.; Tung, C.-H.; Wu, L.-Z., *Chem. Comm.* 2012, *48* (65),8081.
[126] Fisher, J. R.; Cole-Hamilton, D. J., *Dalton Trans.* 1984, (5),809.
[127] Streich, D.; Astuti, Y.; Orlandi, M.; Schwartz, L.; Lomoth, R.; Hammarström, L.; Ott, S., *Chem. Eur. J.* 2010, *16* (1),60.
[128] Hammarström, L.; Styring, S., *Nature* 2009, *1* (3),185.
[129] Sano, Y.; Onoda, A.; Hayashi, T., *Chem. Commun.* 2011, *47* (29),8229.
[130] Sano, Y.; Onoda, A.; Hayashi, T., *J. Inorg. Biochem.* 2012, *108* (1),159.
[131] Ekström, J.; Abrahamsson, M.; Olson, C.; Bergquist, J.; Kaynak, F. B.; Eriksson, L.; Sun, L.; Becker, H.-C.; Åkermark, B.; Hammarström, L., *Dalton Trans.* 2006, (38),4599.
[132] Wolpher, H.; Borgstrom, M.; Hammarstrom, L.; Bergquist, J.; Sundstrom, V.; Styring, S.; Sun, L.; Akermark, B., *Inorg. Chem. Commun.* 2003, *6* (8),989.
[133] Eckenhoff, W. T.; Eisenberg, R., *Dalton Trans.* 2012, *41* (42),13004.
[134] Ott, S.; Borgström, M.; Kritikos, M.; Lomoth, R.; Bergquist, J.; Åkermark, B.; Hammarström, L.; Sun, L., *Inorg. Chem.* 2004, *43* (15),4683.
[135] Shim, Y.; Yuhas, B. D.; Dyar, S. M.; Smeigh, A. L.; Douvalis, A. P.; Wasielewski, M. R.; Kanatzidis, M. G., *J. Am.Chem. Soc.* 2013, *135* (6),2330.
[136] Yuhas, B. D.; Smeigh, A. L.; Douvalis, A. P.; Wasielewski, M. R.; Kanatzidis, M. G., *J. Am.Chem. Soc.* 2012, *134* (25),10353.
[137] Fukuzumi, S.; Hong, D.; Yamada, Y., *J. Phys. Chem. Lett.* 2013, *4* (20),3458.
[138] Yang, J.; Wang, D.; Han, H.; Li, C., *Acc. Chem. Res.* 2013, *46* (8),1900.
[139] Manbeck, G. F.; Brewer, K. J., *Coord. Chem. Rev.* 2013, *257* (9-10),1660.
[140] Fukuzumi, S.; Yamada, Y., *J. Mater. Chem.* 2012, *22* (46),24284.
[141] Maeda, K., *Nenryo Denchi* 2011, *10* (3),59.
[142] Parida, K. M.; Martha, S.; Das, D. P.; Biswal, N., *J. Mater. Chem.* 2010, *20* (34),7144.
[143] Saito, N., *ENEOS Tech. Rev.* 2008, *50* (2),56.
[144] Fukuzumi, S., *Eur. J. Inorg. Chem.* 2008, (9),1351.
[145] Domen, K., *Oyo Butsuri* 2008, *77* (2),160.

[146] Zheng, X.; Fu, Y.; Wei, L.; Xu, P.; Xie, B.; Wei, M., *Henan Huagong* 2007, *24* (2),8.
[147] Rau, S.; Schwalbe, M.; Schmitt, M.; Popp, J., *Nachr. Chem.* 2007, *55* (10),970.
[148] Gole, J.; Burda, C.; Fedorov, A.; White, M., *Rev. Adv. Mater. Sci.* 2003, *5* (4),265.
[149] Schmehl, R., *Spectrum* 2000, *13* (2),17.
[150] Kudo, A., *J. Ceram. Soc. Jpn.* 2001, *109* (June),581.
[151] Takata, T.; Tanaka, A.; Hara, M.; Kondo, J. N.; Domen, K., *Catal. Today* 1998, *44* (1-4),17.
[152] Sobczynski, A.; Sobczynska, A., *Pol. J. Appl. Chem.* 1997, *40* (4),339.
[153] Sutin, N.; Creutz, C.; Fujita, E., *Comments Inorg. Chem.* 1997, *19* (2),67.
[154] Inoue, Y., *Kikan Kagaku Sosetsu* 1994, *23*,113.
[155] Yanagida, S.; Wada, Y., *Kikan Kagaku Sosetsu* 1994, *23*,86.
[156] McEvoy, A. J., *Mater. Chem. Phys.* 1986, *14* (2),113.

In: Ruthenium
Editor: Gary P. Keeler
ISBN: 978-1-63321-657-0

Chapter 3

ADVANCES IN THE USE OF RUTHENIUM COMPLEXES FOR MEDICINAL APPLICATIONS

Sarah Weisner and Shawn Swavey
University of Dayton, Dayton, Ohio, US

I. ABSTRACT

Transition metals and transition metal complexes have been of great value to medicine for half a century. For example, cisplatin, cis-diaminedichloroplatinum(II), has been a key chemotherapy drug since its FDA approval in 1978. Vanadium, chromium, and magnesium have been proposed for many years in the treatment of diabetes. Ruthenium complexes have been extensively studied as potential photodynamic chemotherapy drugs over the past decade. In this chapter, we will review the roles played by ruthenium coordination complexes and ruthenium organometallic complexes in the treatment of a variety of illnesses, including uses as antimalarial, antimicrobial, and anticancer agents.

II. INTRODUCTION

In the late 1800's, the first inclination of metals involved in enzymatic systems was proposed. In the mid-1900's, scientists were beginning to identify active metal sites in enzymes. As the technology matured and the ability to detect trace metal ions in biological systems became easier, the field of bioinorganic chemistry was born. By the late 1960's and early 1970's, the field of bioinorganic chemistry was firmly established with myriad examples of transition metal active sites in what are now referred to as metalloproteins and metalloenzymes; however, the use of metals in the field of medicine had yet to be an area of interest. Although an arsenic compound (Arsphenamine) had, prior to the development of penicillin, been used for decades for the treatment of syphilis and gold salts had been used for the treatment of rheumatoid arthritis, it was not until the discovery by Rosenburg and colleagues in 1965 of the effects of *cis*-diaminedichloroplatinum(II) (cisplatin) on sarcomas in rats that the scientific community began looking more seriously at the potential use of metal complexes in medicine. From mid-1970 until now, cisplatin and some newer platinum analogs have represented the first line of treatment for numerous types of cancer. Stemming from the excitement generated by platinum compounds in the field of medicine, numerous second and third row transition metal compounds have been studied for their medicinal properties. This chapter describes some of the most recent research related to Ru(II) and Ru(III) compounds and their potential applications in the field of medicine.

III. RUTHENIUM(II) ARENE COMPLEXES

Ruthenium (II) arene complexes exhibit many beneficial properties that make them valuable as potential pharmacological agents. The bond between the ruthenium metal center and the arene ligand is very stable, and the addition of other ligands is easily achieved. The arene ligand itself is hydrophobic but the addition of a hydrophilic metal center provides desirable cytotoxic effects as it disrupts transport and targeting by the cell [1]. Simple hydrolysis of the ruthenium-ligand bond allows for direct binding to targets, a property which makes these complexes especially useful in the enhancement of ligand pharmacological activity [2].

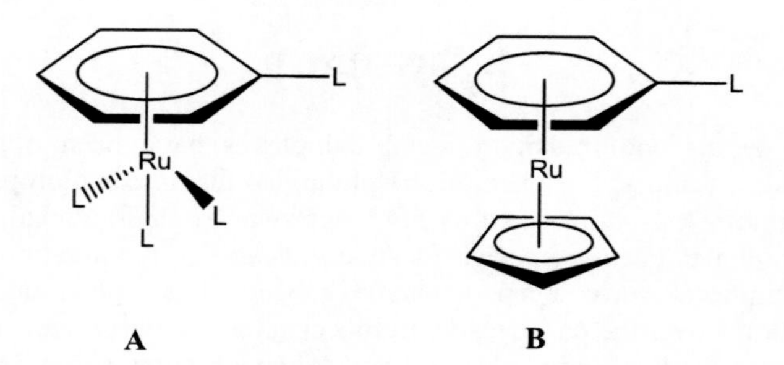

Figure 1. The structure of ruthenium(II) organometallic complexes showing the characteristic half-sandwich form **A** which can be modified into a full-sandwich form **B**.

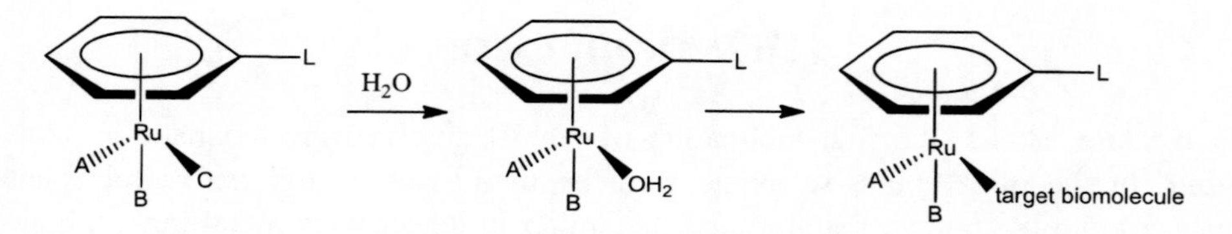

Scheme 1. Hydrolysis of half-sandwich Ru(II) arene complexes allows binding to target molecules and activation under biological conditions [4].

The most commonly used Ru(II)-arene complexes are those with the general "half-sandwich" or "piano stool" form (Figure 1A). In these complexes, the ruthenium metal is bound to an arene at three sites, leaving the remaining three sites open for coordination to various ligands, one of which must be able to be hydrolyzed as a leaving group. The three-coordinate arene, which is a π-acceptor, acts to stabilize the reduced form of the metal and is relatively inert to biological reactions [3]. One of the "leg" ligands acts as the leaving group under biological conditions, allowing for activation via hydrolysis and leaving an empty coordination site that can easily be bound by target biomolecules (Scheme 1) [4]. For some compounds, the leaving group is actually the active part of the compound, and the ruthenium complex simply acts to deliver it to the target area.

The size and nature of the ligands influences the degree of activity shown by the compound. For example, Pizarro and Sadler (2009) report that toxicity against cancer cells increases as the size of the arene ligand increases if there is a chelating ligand such as ethylenediamine and if the ligand acting as the leaving group is chlorine. Similarly, changing the nature of the chelating agent can change the activity of the compound, perhaps resulting in reduced biological activity. This can occur if the replacement ligand(s) is also a good leaving group because the complex can become activated too early and fail to bind the desired biomolecule [4]. Flexibility in ligand type and placement makes half-sandwich ruthenium arene complexes ideal for drug development because they can be easily modified to target specific compounds. Full-sandwich complexes are less commonly used and include ruthenium bound to just two ligands, an arene as seen in half-sandwich complexes and another tridentate ligand, usually a cyclopentadienyl ring (Figure 1B) [3].

Ruthenium(II)-arene complexes have been proven effective in the treatment of a wide variety of diseases, from cancer to bacterial infections. Their versatility stems from the ease with which ligands can be coordinated to the metal center. As in the case of anti-cancer complexes, these ligands can target DNA function or act as enzyme inhibitors. They may also be proven drugs in their own right and show enhanced activity when coordinated to ruthenium, as in the case of anti-bacterial complexes. The function of Ru(II)-arene complexes as anti-cancer agents will be discussed first.

It was originally thought that the low impact of ruthenium on normal cells was due to pH-dependent activation of Ru-complexes in tumor cells. The complex can travel through the body in its oxidized and inactive form and, once taken up by a cancer cell, Ru(III) would be reduced to its activated Ru(II) form due to decreased pH inside the cell. (Cancer cells grow and divide quickly and therefore establish poorly-ordered systems for blood flow and oxygenation, thus forcing cancer cells to rely on glycolytic pathways that lower pH.) Because the activated drug is only present inside cancer cells, risk to healthy cells is minimized and doses can be increased. As will be discussed later, some Ru(III) compounds do become activated and exhibit anti-cancer properties in this manner. However, the development of organoruthenium anti-cancer compounds has shown that reduced Ru(II) demonstrates low toxicity to normal cells, as well.

Ruthenium-organo complexes are used widely in the treatment of cancer and can target cancer cells in a variety of ways. Unlike the platinum compounds that have been the dominate metal-based cancer treatment for several decades; ruthenium (II) complexes can interact with DNA in multiple ways, including hydrogen bonding, insertion between bases, and via direct coordination. And, unlike cisplatin, Ru(II) complexes do not induce damaging side effects like nausea, kidney failure, and cancer cell immunity [4].

One anti-cancer mechanism depends on the ability of half-sandwich Ru(II) compounds to bind the DNA of cancer cells and trigger cell death. The compound $[Ru(\eta^6\text{-arene})(en)Cl]^+$ (Figure 2A) binds DNA at its guanine bases, a bond which is strengthened by the intermolecular attraction via hydrogen binding between the nitrogen groups of ethylenediamine and the oxygen groups of guanine [2]. The binding of Ru^{2+} complexes to the guanine bases of DNA changes the conformation of the nucleotide and induces unwinding of its supercoiled structure. This binding is further enhanced by interaction with the hydrophobic arene ligand, which can participate in base stacking and minor groove binding. The complex $[\{(\eta^6\text{-biphenyl})RuCl(ethylenediamine)\}_2 (CH_2)_6]^{2+}$ (Figure 2B), for example, causes a large degree of unwinding in DNA, perhaps due to the ability of its phenyl rings to base stack with DNA bases and disrupt base pairing [4].

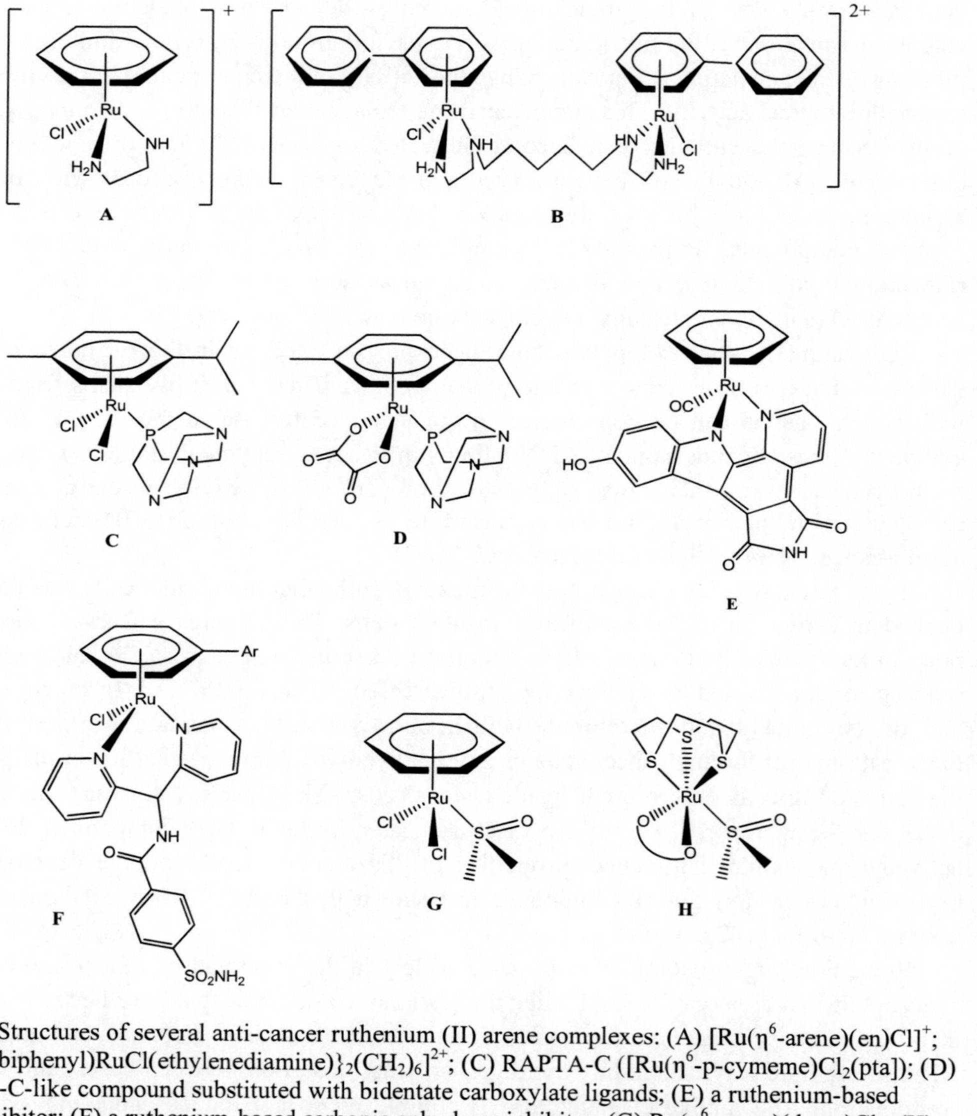

Figure 2. Structures of several anti-cancer ruthenium (II) arene complexes: (A) $[Ru(\eta^6\text{-arene})(en)Cl]^+$; (B) $[\{(\eta^6\text{-biphenyl})RuCl(ethylenediamine)\}_2(CH_2)_6]^{2+}$; (C) RAPTA-C ($[Ru(\eta^6\text{-p-cymeme})Cl_2(pta)]$); (D) a RAPTA-C-like compound substituted with bidentate carboxylate ligands; (E) a ruthenium-based kinase inhibitor; (F) a ruthenium-based carbonic anhydrase inhibitor; (G) $Ru(\eta^6\text{-arene})(dsmo)Cl_2$; (H) a ruthenium-based topoisomerase inhibitor.

Cisplatin is taken up by cancer cells by strongly targeting their sulfur-containing molecules, including amino acids such as methionine and cysteine, as well as to sulfur-containing proteins. It is this property of platinum compounds that may cause many of their harmful side effects. A study by Wang (2005) compared the sulfur affinity of ruthenium(II)-arene complexes to that of cisplatin. It was found that ruthenium has a low affinity for sulfur-containing biomolecules and will bind them weakly, which may allow Ru^{2+} to be taken up by cells. Ruthenium also has a weak affinity for histidine and cytochrome c. The difference in the two metals lies in their relative affinities for sulfur-containing amino acids and proteins and may explain the large differences in their impact on healthy cells [5].

A class of anti-cancer ruthenium(II) arenes currently undergoing clinical trials, the RAPTA compounds contain indazole derivatives such as PTA (1,3,5-triaza-7-phosphaadamantane) ligands that bind the iron-carrying protein transferrin. Rapidly growing and dividing tumor cells require more iron than healthy cells and therefore express more transferrin. Transferrin can be taken up by cells from the blood and, when bound to RAPTA-C ([Ru(η^6-p-cymeme)Cl_2(pta)]) (Figure 2C), triggers the expression of kinase inhibitor p21, terminating DNA synthesis and cell division, and ultimately leading to cell death. Ruthenium is able to bind the histidine residues at the active binding site of transferrin usually occupied by iron. This ability of ruthenium to mimic iron is thought to explain its low toxicity toward healthy cells. Ru(II)-arene complexes containing PTA have proven successful in treating metastatic tumors but are less effective against primary tumors due to the rapid hydrolysis of the chloride ligands [6, 7]. The replacement of chlorine with bidentate carboxylate ligands (Figure 2D) stabilizes the ruthenium center, increases solubility, and decreases hydrolysis rates. This substitution also makes the complex more stable in the low pH environment of cancer cells, thus amplifying its anti-cancer activity [8].

Other ruthenium-arene half-sandwich complexes act to inhibit enzymes associated with cancer proliferation and growth. One class of these drugs act as kinase inhibitors. These drugs interrupt ATP binding by blocking the active sites of the enzyme and preventing the dephosphorylation of ATP. These complexes can be modified to fit in the catalytic sites of specific kinases, thus reducing their toxicity to normal mammalian cells while maximizing their detrimental impact on cancer cell growth [2]. An example of a kinase inhibitor that mimics the apoptosis-inducing compound staurosporine is shown in Figure 2E.

Another class of ruthenium-based anti-cancer complexes includes carbonic anhydrase inhibitors which block the enzyme at its zinc catalytic center [2]. The role of carbonic anhydrases in cancer cells is to catalyze the conversion of carbon dioxide into bicarbonate and hydrogen ions. This is especially important in cancer cells that are actively undergoing metabolic changes and adaptations, such as occurs in metastatic cells with greatly reduced oxygen supplies. These adapting cells must maintain a delicate pH balance on both sides of their membranes. As the conversion of CO_2 is taking place in the extracellular space, bicarbonate is pumped into the cancer cell and neutralizes the intercellular environment. Carbonic anhydrase inhibitors can be tailored to target these hypoxic cells, prevent their conversion of carbon dioxide, and therefore disrupt cell growth and adaptation as the cells move through the body [9]. Sulfonamides are effective inhibitors of carbonic anhydrase activity and, when coordinated to ruthenium-arene complexes (Figure 2F), can be made to target specific CA enzymes [2].

Other half-sandwich complexes such as Ru(η^6-arene)(dsmo)Cl_2 (Figure 2G) are topoisomerase II inhibitors. Topoisomerase enzymes control the supercoiling of DNA in the nucleus and their inhibition prevents cancer cell division [10]. Kljun et al. (2013) report that the replacement of the arene ligand with other 6 electron systems; such as crown thioethers, does not impact the anti-cancer activity of the complex. This research also shows that quinolonato ligands, when coordinated to the ruthenium (II) center (Figure 2H), dissociate under physiological conditions and cause topoisomerase inhibition, preventing cell division, and resulting in tumor cell death [10].

Ruthenium (II) compounds demonstrate biological activity beyond targeting cancer cells. Ruthenium complexes are emerging as important anti-malarial agents, as well, mainly due to their low toxicity and the ease with which they withstand ligand exchange. The antimalarial drug chloroquinine (CQ), for example, readily coordinates to Ru(II) to form the complex $[RuCl_2CQ]_2$ (Figure 3A). The widespread use of CQ has led to resistance by the malarial *Plasmodium*. However, when introduced as part of a ruthenium complex, CQ is allowed to accumulate in the *Plasmodium* cell. *Plasmodium* organisms digest the heme found aggregated in their hosts' red blood cells and do so under hydrophobic conditions. The destruction of the parasite's immunity is due to a combination of ruthenium-based factors: increased lipophilicity, prevention of heme aggregation in red blood cells, and changed CQ structure caused by coordination with the metal [1]. The half-sandwich Ru(II) complexes [Ru(η^6-p-cymene)Cl_2(CQ] (Figure 3B) and [Ru(η^6-p-benzene)Cl_2(CQ] also demonstrate enhanced CQ activity.

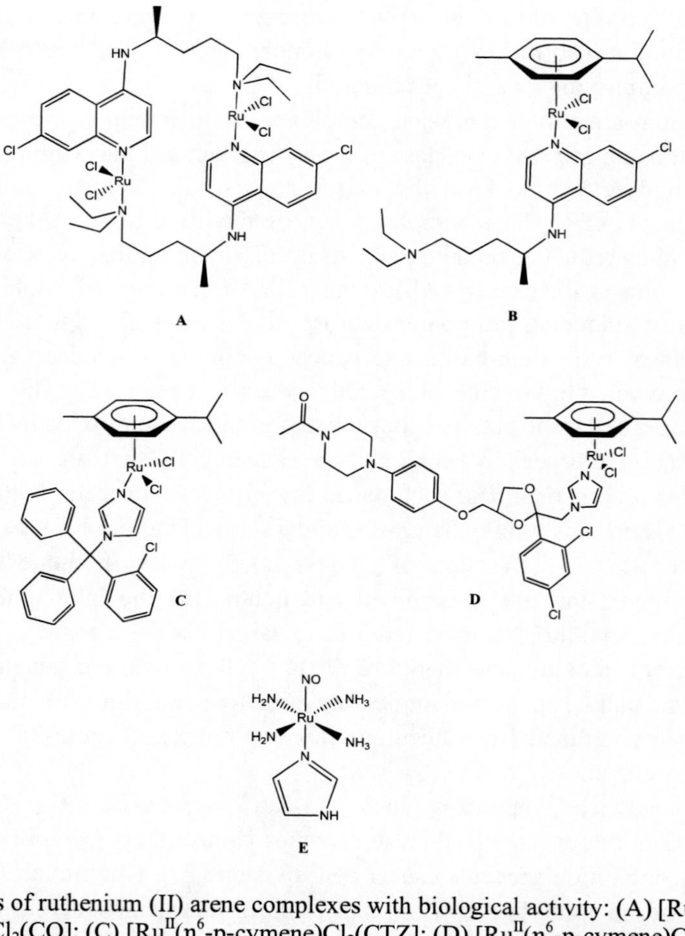

Figure 3. Structures of ruthenium (II) arene complexes with biological activity: (A) $[RuCl_2(CQ]_2$; (B) [Ru(η^6-p-cymene)Cl_2(CQ]; (C) [Ru^{II}(η^6-p-cymene)Cl_2(CTZ]; (D) [Ru^{II}(η^6-p-cymene)Cl_2(KTZ]; (E) *trans*-[Ru(-NO)$(NH_3)_4$(N-imidazole]$^{n+}$.

In addition to their use as antimalarial agents, ruthenium complexes can also be synthesized to have antifungal properties and have been shown especially effective against Chagas disease, sleeping sickness (caused by members of the *Trypanosoma* genus), and Leishmaniasis, caused by *Leishmaniasis major,* a flagellated protozoan. These parasites are all transmitted through insect bites and occur mainly in tropical environs. Leishmaniasis often weakens the immune system and therefore is sometimes seen as an infection in HIV-AIDS patients [1, 11].

The ruthenium (II)-based complex of most interest in the treatment of these parasitic disorders is $[Ru^{II}(\eta^6\text{-p-cymene})Cl_2(CTZ)]$ (Figure 3C). CTZ (clotrimazole) is an antifungal drug whose activity, which inhibits the formation of sterols, is boosted through its coordination to the ruthenium center. Hydrolysis of the chlorine ligands results in formation of a cationic center and allows for dissociation of the activated CTZ. This compound has been reported as being ten times more active than uncoordinated CTZ and is much less toxic to healthy human cells. Additionally, the complex is highly selective toward *Trypanosoma* and *Leishmaniasis* species and can have multiple targets due to the ability of Ru to bind DNA. CTZ coordinated to Ru(III) and octahedral Ru(II) similarly results in increased activity but has been shown to be less effective in combating disease than when bound to Ru(II) arene complexes. Ketoconazole (KTZ) arene complexes such as $[Ru^{II}(\eta^6\text{-p-cymene})Cl_2(KTZ]$ (Figure 3D), have also been used and show similar activity to those with CTZ ligands [1, 11, 12]. The NO donor *trans*-$[Ru(\text{-}NO)(NH_3)_4(N\text{-imidazole}]^{n+}$ (Figure 3E) also targets these tropical parasites. This complex is easily reduced under biological conditions, effecting the release of NO which inhibits the growth and spread of these disease-causing organisms [1].

IV. RUTHENIUM(III) COMPLEXES

Ruthenium (II) compounds have been the focus of recent research centered on metal-based pharmaceuticals, but it is oxidized ruthenium complexes that have shown the most stability and activity in clinical applications. Ruthenium (III) coordination compounds have been shown to be extremely stable in the body until they reach a reductive environment, such as that encountered in tumor cells, or when they become reduced by mitochondrial proteins. Under these biological conditions, Ru(III) is reduced to Ru(II) and becomes active. Recently, however, it has been argued that these complexes are truly activated only when a leaving group (usually chlorine) is hydrolyzed [7]. As described in the ruthenium-arene section of this chapter, the low toxicity of ruthenium (III) complexes arises from their low activity in the system prior to activation, allowing for greater targeting of molecules and reduced symptoms in the patient.

One way ruthenium (III) compounds act in the body is as anti-cancer treatments and immune system modulators. Simply by changing the concentration (dosage) of the compound *cis*-$[RuCl_2(NH_3)_4]Cl$ (Figure 4A), for example, one can trigger very different immune responses. Silveira-Lacerda et al. (2010) show that an increase in this compound's concentration can directly stimulate apoptosis in tumor cells while simultaneously suppressing immune response. Decreasing its dosage, however, leads to stimulation of the immune system and proliferation of cancer-fighting T cells. Ruthenium red (Figure 4B) is another Ru(III) complex that impacts immune response. It displays anti-tumor activity through action as a calcium blocker in the mitochondria [13].

Perhaps one of the most widely-studied Ru coordination compounds is *trans*-[tetrachloridobis (1*H*-indazole)ruthenate(III], commonly referred to as KP1019 (Figure 4C). This compound binds to the serum proteins human serum albumin and transferrin and demonstrates selective uptake by tumor cells. This selectivity is due to the increased expression of transferrin receptors in cancer cells compared to normal cells. Exploiting the ability of ruthenium to mimic iron, KP1019 binds competitively to transferrin as previously seen with the Ru(II)-arene complex RAPTA. KP1019 is therefore able to accumulate in the tumor cells as their need for iron increases and can bind DNA [14]. KP1019 targets the guanosine and adenosine bases of DNA and leads to interruption of transcription and tumor cell death [15]. Another drug that works in a similar fashion and, like KP1019, is currently undergoing clinical trials is [imidazoleH]*trans*-[$RuCl_4$(dmso-S)(imidazole)], or NAMI-A (Figure 4D) [10, 14]. Both of these compounds are selective toward tumor cells due to the comparatively acidic environment they afford which allows for easy reduction of Ru(III) to Ru(II), the activated forms of the drugs [16]. Cancer cells have lower pH than healthy cells due to their rapid growth and low oxygenation, leading to an increase in glycolysis [7]. Nagy et al. (2012) postulate that the reductive environment generated by low oxygen cancer cells may lead to cell apoptosis due to oxidation of biomolecules [14].

NAMI-A was the first ruthenium anticancer drug to be tested in clinical trials as has been found effective against solid state lung tumors as well as metastatic tumor cells. NAMI-A-type complexes have antitumor capabilities because they interrupt the tumor cell cycle at the G_2-M phase, cause changes in the structure and morphology of cell membranes, and significantly reduce the ability of metastatic cells to invade other tissues. Arrest during the G_2-M phase of the cell cycle signals DNA damage and forces the tumor cell to attempt DNA repair or, if repair is futile, to trigger cellular death. The power of these sulfoxide ruthenium complexes lies in their basic structure, including the four chloride ligands in one plane and the flexible, heterocyclic nitrogen ligand lying trans to a sulfoxide group. Altering the nitrogen donor ligand can change the activity of the complex, while the sulfoxide group (dmso, in the case of NAMI-A) acts as a π-acceptor and stabilizes the reduced Ru(II) center that forms under biological conditions. This reduction occurs as a result of hydrolysis of the chloride ligands and is thought to activate the complex [17].

NAMI-A is administered in aqueous solution, which allows for both the *in vivo* activating hydrolysis of the chloride ligands and for the subsequent hydrolysis of dmso at pH 7.4. At lower pH, as found in tumor cells, dmso hydrolysis is greatly reduced and the complex is much less stable. Alessio et al. (2004) found that increasing the basicity of the heterocyclic nitrogen ligand decreases the rate of dmso hydrolysis and makes the complex less stable in aqueous solution. Replacement of imidazole with less basic groups such as pyrazine and thiazole therefore stabilizes the NAMI-A-like complex in aqueous solution and appears to have no effect on its activity under physiological conditions [17].

Dinuclear complexes with the basic structure shown in Figure 4E have been shown to reduce the invasive properties of tumor cells more effectively than NAMI-A. These compounds have been synthesized with a variety of heterocyclic bridging N-N ligands, including 4,4′-bipyridine, pyrimidine, and pyrazine. It is hypothesized that molecules with two ruthenium centers are more active than NAMI-A, because they accumulate in tissues in greater concentrations [17]. This is due to the stability of heavy metal centers such as ruthenium and platinum which have slow ligand exchange rates. Because they do not dissociate quickly, complexes with ruthenium center can reach their target molecules or tissues before becoming activated [18].

Another promising variation on the original NAMI-A structure is the addition of a nitrosyl group (NO) in place of the heterocyclic nitrogen ligand (Figure 4F). Ruthenium has a high affinity for NO, which acts as a strong π acceptor, thus effecting a change from dmso bound at sulfur to binding at oxygen. Controlled release of nitric oxide radicals from ruthenium-nitrosyl complexes is achieved through a one-electron reduction under physiological conditions and can also be accomplished via photolysis. These NO radicals are toxic to tumor cells [17].

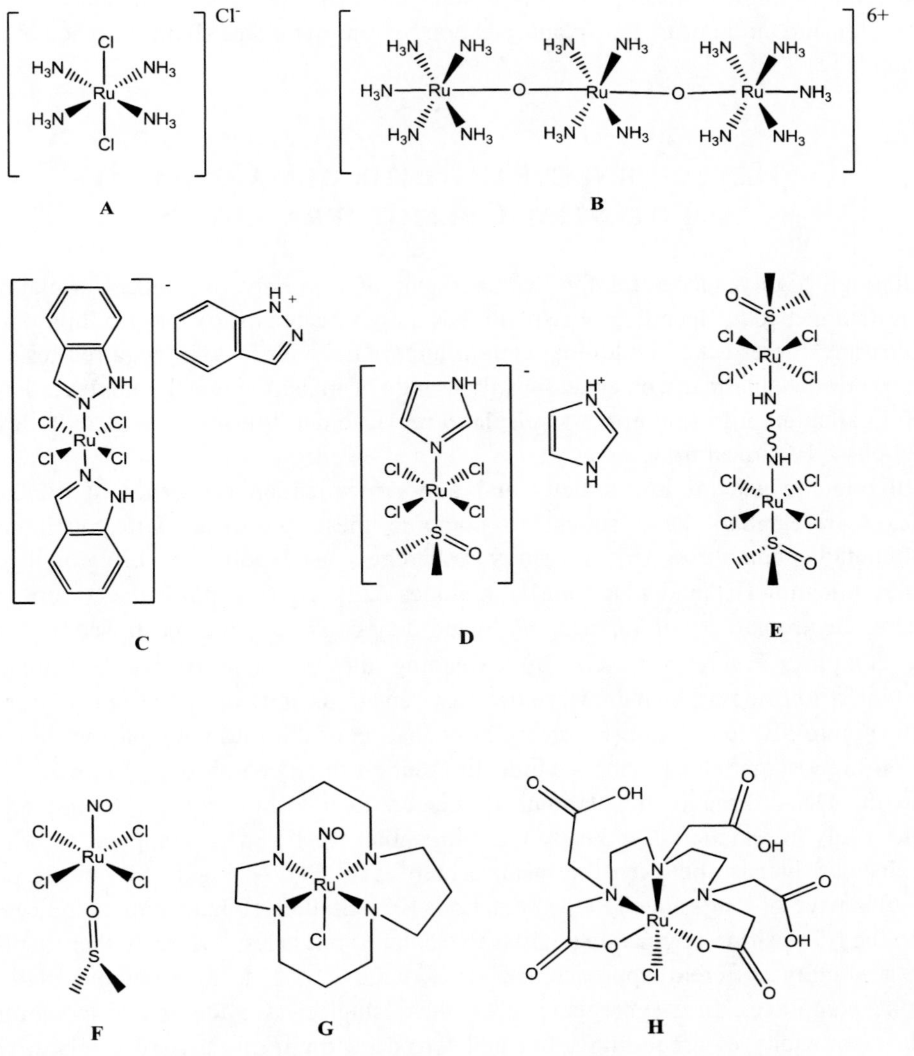

Figure 4. Structures of ruthenium (III) complexes with pharmaceutical application: (A) *cis*-$[RuCl_2(NH_3)_4]Cl$; (B) ruthenium red; (C) KP1019; (D) NAMI-A14; (E) dinuclear ruthenium complex; (F) NAMI-A-like structure with NO-donor activity; (G) *trans*-$[RuCl([15]aneN_4)NO]^{2+}$; (H) AMD6221.

In addition to targeting tumor cells; NO plays other important physiological roles in the body. It can exist *in* vivo as NO radicals and as nitroxyl (NO^-) and nitrosonium (NO^+) ions and is key in controlling vascular and blood pressures. NO causes vascular relaxation by decreasing calcium and activation of potassium channels, leading to the hyperpolarization of cell membranes. Nitroglycerin, the traditionally used NO donor treatment for vascular disease, has short-lived effects and can lead to drug immunity. Therefore, ruthenium-based drugs such as *trans*-$[RuCl([15]aneN_4)NO]^{2+}$ (Figure 4G) offer an alternative that has low toxicity and which is water-soluble [19]. Other possible Ru-nitrosyl NO donor applications include treatment of stroke, arthritis, epilepsy, and diabetes [20].

Ruthenium-nitrosyl complexes can also be used as NO scavengers, as in the case of the drug AMD6221 (Figure 4H). Harmful NO radicals in the body attack the tyrosine residues of proteins, for example, causing oxidative damage. AMD6221 has been shown to reverse hypertension and aid in heart transplant rejection by removing these harmful reactive nitrogen compounds [21].

V. Heterodinuclear Ruthenium Complexes as Potential Chemotherapeutics

Although highly successful for the treatment of a variety of cancers cisplatin is not without its drawbacks. Specifically cisplatin has a high degree of toxicity leading to a variety of unpleasant side effects; in addition, certain tumors have intrinsic or acquired resistance to cisplatin. For this and many other reasons thousands of transition metal complexes have been studied in an attempt to find effective cisplatin replacement drugs, however, only three have reached phase II clinical trials.

Utilizing the general low toxicity and tumor localization properties of ruthenium(II) complexes, researchers have sought to combine these properties with platinum(II) in heterobimetallic complexes. In one study researchers used polyazine bridging ligands to combine ruthenium(II) and platinum(II) moieties [22]. In this study they found that by increasing the aromaticity of the bridging ligand they could tune the spectroscopic properties of the complex, Figure 5 (A-C). By extending the π-system of the bridging ligand, ruthenium(II) to bridging ligand charge transfer transitions shift from 544 nm (Figure 5A) to 632 nm (Figure 5B) to 682 nm (Figure 5C). Incubation of the Ru/Pt complexes with plasmid DNA followed by gel electrophoresis indicates that all three complexes (Figure 5A, 5B, 5C) bind to the DNA through the platinum(II) center, in a fashion similar to cisplatin. In a separate study researchers synthesized a bimetallic Ru(II)/Pt(II) complex in which the intramolecular distance between the metal centers is 14.547 Å, Figure 5D, in the hopes of taking advantage of long-range DNA interactions [23]. Studies of this complex indicate that it binds to the N7 position of guanine (similar to cisplatin) but is less cytotoxic than cisplatin.

In a slightly different approach, researchers have sought to eliminate platinum in bimetallic complexes. In a synergistic effort these studies have focused on combining the specific cytotoxicity of arene-ruthenium and ferrocene fragments toward cisplatin resistant cancer cell lines [24]. Ferrocene ligands containing pyridyl and imidazole groups were first synthesized followed by coordination of the arene-ruthenium fragments, Figure 6 A and B. The ruthenium/iron bimetallic complexes were tested *in vitro* on cisplatin resistant ovarian cancer cell lines A2780 by monitoring mitochondrial dehydrogenase activity. Relatively low cytotoxicity toward this cell line was observed for both complexes, however, slight differences in the cytotoxicity of 6A and 6B allowed for some insight into structure function relationships. For instance, it was noted that when the R group was hexamethyl the complex was more cytotoxic which was attributed to greater hydrophobicity leading to greater transport into the cancer cells. In addition the imidazole bridged complexes were more cytotoxic than the pyridyl bridged complexes related to the difference in coordination strength to the ruthenium centers.

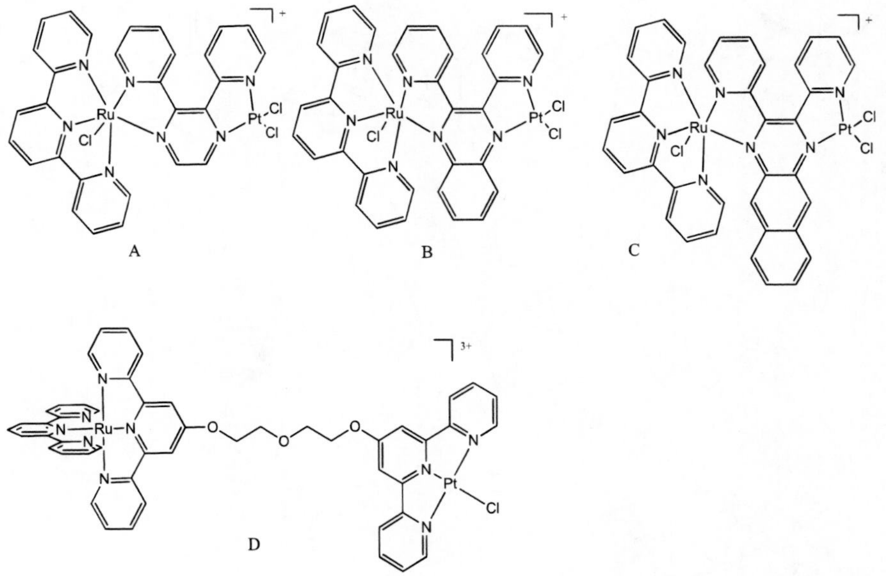

Figure 5. Sturctures of bimetallic ruthenium(II)/platinum(II) complexes.

It is interesting to note that these researchers had found greater cytotoxicity to this cancer cell line using ruthenium/iron organometallic complexes similar to 6A and 6B but with shorter linker chains between the metal centers [25].

Based on the promising studies of mononuclear ruthenium complexes as anti-tumor agents, recent work on combining two ruthenium groups together to achieve added cytotoxicity toward cancer cell lines has been evaluated. Water soluble bis-ruthenium complexes with varying distance between the ruthenium centers has been achieved, Figure 6C [26]. In this study it was determined that 50% inhibitory concentrations decreased significantly as the chain length of the bridging ligand was increased when tested on colon cancer cell lines, SW480, with the longest chain length (12 CH_2) showing one order of magnitude greater toxicity than cisplatin. Although the increased chain length decreases the water solubility of the bis-ruthenium complexes this is more than made up for by the increased ability of the longer, more hydrophobic, complex to cross the cell membrane.

One of only three non-platinum complexes to enter into phase II trials as an anticancer agent is the mononuclear titanocene dichloride, unfortunately it ultimately failed these trials. In an effort to revive this promising drug, studies have begun on a series of bridged titanocene dichloride arene ruthenium complexes, Figure 6D [27].

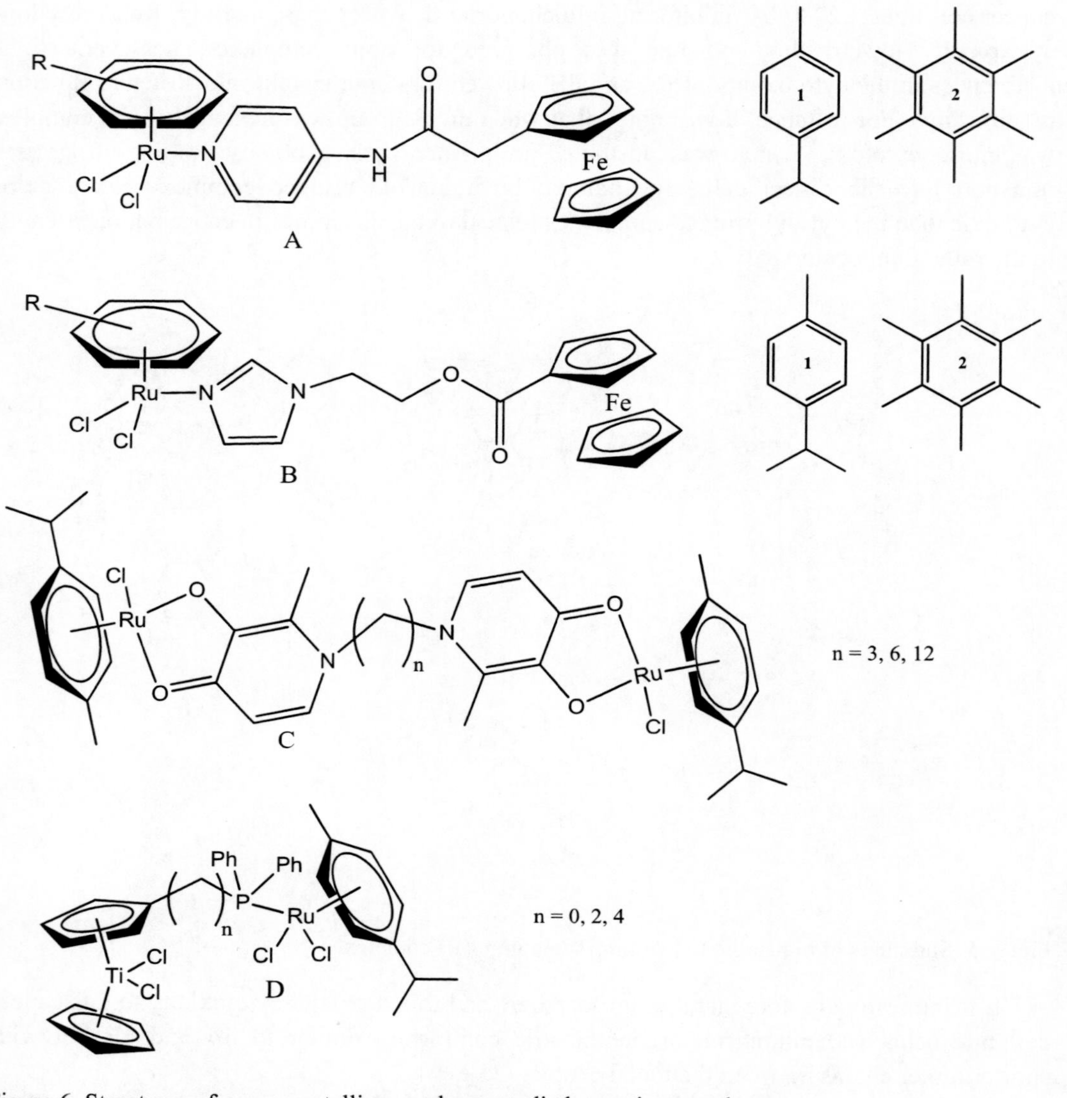

Figure 6. Structures of organometallic complexes studied as anti-tumor drugs.

These complexes were studied in human ovarian cancer cell lines (A2780) and the cisplatin resistant variant (A2780cisR). In all cases the bimetallic complexes performed better than the monometallic titanocene dichloride and arene ruthenium complexes alone. In addition the bimetallic complexes were more cytotoxic than cisplatin in the variant cell lines. It was suggested that the cytotoxic effects stem from inhibition of cathepsin B resulting from binding of the ruthenium center to the active cysteine site. The longer bridging ligand complex showed greater cytotoxicity than the shorter bridging ligands due, as suggested by the authors, to the ability of the longer chain to penetrate into the protein to reach the active site.

REFERENCES

[1] Gambino, D; Otero, L. Perspectives on what ruthenium-based compounds could offer in the development of potential antiparasitic drugs, *Inorg. Chim. Acta*, 2012, 103-114.

[2] Nazarov, AA; Hartinger, CG; Dyson, PJ. Opening the lid on piano-stool complexes: an account of ruthenium(II)-arene complexes with medicinal applications, *J. Organomet. Chem.*, 2014, 251-260.

[3] Pettinari, C; Pettinari, R; Di Niccola, C. Half-sandwich rhodium(III), iridium(III), and ruthenium (II) complexes with ancillary pyrazole-based ligands, *Advances in Organometallic Chemistry and Catalysis: The Silver/Gold Jubilee International Conference on Organometallic Chemistry Celebratory Book*, ed. A.J.L. Ponbeiro, John Wiley and Sons, 2014, 269-284.

[4] Pizarro, AM; Sadler, PJ. Unusual DNA binding modes for metal anticancer complexes, *Biochemie*, 2009, 1198-1211.

[5] Wang, F; Bella, J; Parkinson, JA; Sadler, PJ. Competitive reactions of a ruthenium arene anticancer complex with histidine, cytochrome c, and an oligonucleotide, *J. Biol. Inorg. Chem.*, 2005, 147-155.

[6] Chatterjee, S; Kunda, S; Bhattacharyya, A; Hartinger, CG; Dyson, PJ. The ruthenium(II)-arene compound RAPTA-C induces apoptosis in EAC cells through mitochondrial and p53-JNK pathways, *J. Biol. Inorg. Chem.*, 2008, 13, 1149-1155.

[7] Bergamo, A; Sava, G. Ruthenium anticancer compounds: myths and realities of the emerging metal-based drugs, *Dalton Trans.*, 2011, 40, 7817-7823.

[8] Ang, WH; Daldini, E; Scolaro, C; Scopelliti, R; Juillerat-Jeannerat, L; Dyson, PJ. Development of organometallic ruthenium-arene anticancer drugs that resist hydrolysis, *Inorg. Chem.*, 2006, 45, 9006-9013.

[9] Pastorekova, S; Zatovicova, M; Pastorek, J. Cancer-associated carbonic anhydrases and their inhibition, *Curr. Pharm. Des.*, 2008, 14, 685-698.

[10] Kljun, J; Bratsos, I; Alessio, E; Psomas, G; Repnik, U; Butinar, M; Turk, B; Turel, I. New uses for old drugs: attempts to convert quinolone antibacterials into potential anticancer agents containing ruthenium, *Inorg. Chem.*, 2013, 52, 9039-9052.

[11] Iniguez, E. et al. Metal-drug synergy: new ruthenium(II) complexes of ketoconazole are highly active against Leishmania major and Trypanosoma cruzi and nontoxic to human or murine normal cells, *J. Biol. Inorg. Chem.*, 18, 779-790.

[12] Martinez, A; Carreon, T; Iniguez, E; Anzellotti, A; Sanchez, A; Tyan, M; Sattler, A; Herrera, L; Maldonado, RA; Sanchez-Delgado, RA. Searching for new chemotherapies for tropical diseases: ruthenium-clotrimazole complexes display high in vitro activity against Leishmania major and Trypanosoma cruzi and low toxicity toward normal mammalian cells, *J. Med. Chem.,* 2012, 55, 3867-3877.

[13] De Paulo Silveira-Lacerda, E et al. The ruthenium complex *cis*-(dichloro) tetraammineruthenium(III) chloride presents immune stimulatory activity on human peripheral blood mononuclear cells, *Biol. Trace Elem. Res.*, 2010, 270-283.

[14] Nagy, EM; Pettenuzzo, A; Boscutti, G.; Marchio, L; Dalla Via, L; Fregona, D. Ruthenium(II/III)-based compounds with encouraging antiproliferative activity against non-small-cell lung cancer, *Chem. Eur. J.*, 2012, 18, 14464-14472.

[15] Hartinger, CG; Jakupec, MA; Zorbas-Seigfried, S; Groessl, M; Egger, A; Berger, W; Zorbas, H; Dyson, PJ; Keppler, BK. KP1019, a new redox-active anticancer agent – preclinical development and results of a clinical phase I study in tumor patients, *Chem. Biodiversity*, 2008, 5, 2140-2154.
[16] Domotor, O; Hartinger, CG; Bytzek, AK; Keppler, BK; Enyedy, EA. Characterization of the binding sites of the anticancer ruthenium(III) complexes KP1019 and KP1339 on human serum albumin via competition studies, *J. Biol. Inorg. Chem.*, 2013, 18, 9-17.
[17] Alessio, E; Mestroni, G; Bergamo, A; Sava, G. Ruthenium antimetastatic agents, *Curr. Trends Med. Chem.*, 2004, 4, 1525-2535.
[18] Reedijk, J. Metal-ligand exchange kinetics in platinum and ruthenium complexes: significance for effectiveness as anticancer drugs, *Platinum Metals Rev.*, 2008, 52, 2-11.
[19] Bonaventura, D; Oliveira, FS; Lunardi, CN; Vercesi, JA; da Silva, RS; Bendhack, LM. Characterization of the mechanisms of action and nitric oxide species involved in the relaxation induced by the ruthenium complex, *Nitric Oxide*, 387-394.
[20] Jurek, SC; Hirano-Kobayashi, M; Chiang, H; Kohane, DS; Matthews, BD. Prevention of ventilator-induced lung edema by inhalation of nanoparticles releasing ruthenium red, *Am. J. Respir. Cell Mol. Biol.*, 2014, 50.
[21] Hutchings, SR; Song, D; Fricker, SP; Pang, CCY. The ruthenium-based nitric oxide scavenger, AMD6221, augments cardiovascular responsiveness to noradrenaline in rats with streptozotocin-induced diabetes, *Eur. J. Parmacol.*, 2005, 132-136.
[22] Williams, RL; Toft, HN; Winkel, B; Brewer, KJ. Synthesis, characterization, and DNA binding properties of a series of Ru, Pt mixed-metal complexes, *Inorg. Chem.*, 2003, 42, 4394-4400.
[23] van der Schilden, K; Garcia, F; Kooijman, H; Spek, AL; Haasnoot, JG; Reedijk, J. A highly flexible dinuclear ruthenium(II)-platinum(II) complex: crystal structure and binding to 9-ethylguanine, *Angew. Chem. Int. Ed.*, 2004, 43, 5668-5670.
[24] Auzias, M; Gueniat, J; Therien, B; Süss-Fink, G; Renfrew, AK; Dyson, PJ, Arene-ruthenium complexes with ferrocene-derived ligands: synthesis and characterization of complexes of the type [Ru(η^6-arene)($NC_5H_4CH_2NHOC$-$C_5H_4FeC_5H_5$)Cl_2] and [Ru(η^6-arene)(NC_3H_3 $(CH_2)_2O_2C$-$C_5H_4FeC_5H_5$)Cl_2], *J. Organomet. Chem.*, 2009, 694, 855-861.
[25] Auzias, M; Therrien, B; Süss-Fink, G; Štěpnička, P; Ang, WH; Dyaon, PJ. Ferrocenoyl pyridine arene ruthenium complexes with anticancer properties: synthesis, structure, electrochemistry, and cytotoxicity, *Inorg. Chem.*, 2008, 47, 578-583.
[26] Mendoza-Ferri, M-G; Hartinger, CG; Eichinger, RE; Stolyarova, N; Severin, K; Jakupec, MA; Nazarov, AA; Keppler, BK, Influence of the spacer length on the *in Vitro* anticancer activity of dinuclear ruthenium-arene compounds, *Organometallics*, 2008, 27, 2405-2407.
[27] Pelletier, F; Comte, V; Massard, A; Wenzel, M; Toulot, S; Richard, P; Picquet, M; Le Gendre, P; Zava, O; Edafe, F; Casini, A; Dyson, PJ, Development of bimetallic titanocene-ruthenium-arene complexes as anticancer agents: relationships between structural and biological properties, *J. Med. Chem.*, 2010, 53, 6923-6933.

In: Ruthenium
Editor: Gary P. Keeler
ISBN: 978-1-63321-657-0

Chapter 4

"RuCp" A VERSATILE MOIETY: FROM NLO TO ANTITUMOR PROPERTIES

***Tiago J. L. Silva*[1], *Paulo J. Mendes*[2,*], *Tânia S. Morais*[1], *Andreia Valente*[1], *M. Paula Robalo*[3,4] *and M. Helena Garcia*[1,*]**

[1]Centro de Ciências Moleculares e Materiais,
Faculdade de Ciências da Universidade de Lisboa,
Campo Grande, Lisboa, Portugal
[2]Centro de Química de Évora, Departamento de Química,
Escola de Ciências e Tecnologia, Universidade de Évora,
R. Romão Ramalho, Évora, Portugal
[3]Área Departamental de Engenharia Química,
Instituto Superior de Engenharia de Lisboa, Lisboa, Portugal
[4]Centro de Química Estrutural, Instituto Superior Técnico,
Universidade de Lisboa, Lisboa, Portugal

ABSTRACT

Organometallic chemistry and particularly organotransition metal complexes have been an intensive area of research which growth was mainly motivated by the impressive achievements in the field of homogeneous catalysis. In fact, the development of catalysis served as foundation for many important industrial processes. Moreover, the fascinating properties of organometallic compounds encouraged the development of its chemistry for several other applications, ranging from material chemistry, where several technological applications were found (integrated optics, molecular switches, dye-sensitized solar cells (DSSCs), organic light emitting diodes (OLED's), to bioinorganic chemistry where they appear as potential drugs for several diseases (cancer, diabetes, malaria, etc.).

In this frame, ruthenium organometallic complexes have revealed a prominent role in all these areas due to their great scope in molecular engineering. The vast diversity of frameworks and structures, associated with their stability in several oxidation states, bonding modes and electronic features place ruthenium compounds among the most successful organotransition metal complexes studied to date. In particular, η^5-monocyclopentadienylruthenium derivatives ("RuCp") have been thoroughly studied due to the promising results in the field of nonlinear optics. More recently, the "RuCp" fragment emerged in the new fascinating bioorganometallic subject, displaying important results in the area of potential agents for cancer therapy.

These apparent greatly incongruent endeavors might find some common explanation in the unique characteristics of this versatile metal fragment. This chapter presents an overview of the work published during the last two decades in the fields of nonlinear optics and bioorganometallic chemistry concerning the "RuCp" scaffold. An outlook of the synthetic methods involved and the relevant properties for each purpose is also discussed. It will be shown the versatility of the "RuCp" on the design of different organometallic environments, with structural features aiming a particular application.

1. PREAMBLE

Nonlinear optical (NLO) properties arise from the interaction of strong electromagnetic fields, such as the ones of laser beams, with matter. These interactions give rise to the modification of the electromagnetic field components of the incident light beam and the production of new components (differing in phase, frequency, amplitude, etc.). The effects arising from these properties are of great technological importance for optical devices, with potential applications in laser technologies, optical signal processing, data storage and microscopy, for example. [1-6]

Due to the need for materials with exceptional NLO properties and fast response times in combination with mechanical and thermal stability and ease of processing, intense research activity has been carried out in second- and third-order nonlinear optical materials in the last decades. The research on NLO properties was initially focused on crystalline inorganic salts and glasses, that currently dominate the market for second- and third-order NLO applications, respectively, but there are shortcomings with aspects of their performance, namely the trade-off problem between response time and magnitude of the optical nonlinearities. Later, organic systems have received much interest due to their low cost, fast and large NLO response, high optical damage thresholds, chemical versatility and tailor ability for particular end-uses such as in form of thin films, fibers or liquid crystals. Nevertheless, the drawbacks of these organic materials arise from the trade-off between nonlinear efficiency and optical transparency, low thermal stability and mechanical weakness. During the last two decades coordination and organometallic complexes have increasingly occupied a relevant role in this field since the discovery of the second-harmonic generation (SHG) for a ferrocenyl compound. [7] In fact, coordination and organometallic complexes have the potential to combine the advantages of organics (such as fast response, ease of processing, and significant design flexibility) with the benefits that arise from incorporation of a metal center. The worth of these systems is mainly due to the presence of various ICT processes, i.e., metal–ligand charge-transfer (MLCT), ligand-to-metal charge-transfer (LMCT), and metal-to-metal/intervalence charge-transfer (MM/IVCT), usually at relatively low energy and of high intensity. These ICT processes can be tunable leading to a strong enhancement of the NLO properties by virtue of the nature, oxidation state, and coordination geometries of the metal centre.

Various classes of metal complexes have systematically been explored in terms of new and optimized NLO materials, in particular for second-order NLO, with the large amount of review papers published in the last years indicating the breadth of the active research in this field. [8-23] Dipolar (1D), and octupolar (2D and 3D) frameworks have been extensively studied, most of them within the categorized following groups of compounds: (1) metallocenyl derivatives, (2) η^5-monocyclopentadienyl/indenyl and η^5-pentamethylcyclopentadienyl metal derivatives, (3) metal-carbonyl complexes, (4) metal complexes possessing only metal-ligand σ bonds and (5) bimetallic complexes. Among these compounds, ruthenium organometallic complexes revealed a prominent role due to its main structural features associated with stability in several oxidation states and bonding modes that lead to a diversity of frameworks and structures. In particular, η^5-monocyclopentadienylruthenium derivatives ("RuCp") have been fully studied in this field due to its promising results. The success of this ruthenium unit, as scaffold in the building of different structures, can find a possible explanation on its strong stability found by studies of fragmentation pathways and energetics, carried out by electrospray ionization mass spectrometry. For all the studied compounds, it was not possible to find any bond dissociation energy for the $[RuCp]^+$ remaining fragment [24].

This contribution surveys the "RuCp" complexes, where the metal center, bonded to a polarizable organic conjugated backbone (chromophore), acts as an electron releasing group and reviews the ongoing efforts to design, characterize and optimize the NLO properties of this class of compounds. Ruthenocenes, η^5-pentamethylcyclopentadienyl and indenyl ruthenium derivatives have also been extensively studied but are not considered in this review. As can be seen in several reviewing data on these complexes, replacing the cyclopentadienyl by the indenyl or η^5-pentamethylcyclopentadienyl ligand generally results in increased nonlinearities due to an improved electron donor ability of the metal center whereas ruthenocene derivatives have lower NLO responses due to less favorable electronic coupling between the metal center and the polarizable organic conjugated backbone. [10, 11, 13, 15-17, 20, 21, 23] A basic description of NLO effects, the structural requirements for high nonlinearities, the relation between molecular and macroscopic NLO properties and the current methods for the determination of the second- and third-order NLO properties of the compounds are presented in Sections 2.1 and 2.2. Sections 2.3-2.6 are dedicated to an overview of the reported properties of "RuCp" compounds, both at molecular level from solution studies, with the aim to understand the relationships between structure and NLO properties, and in bulk materials.

The versatility of the fragment "RuCp" has been also revealed by the new families of compounds emerging in the last years with potentiality as cytotoxic agents against cancer cells and thus promising future as anticancer agents. The relevance of these findings comes from the urgency to find an alternative for chemotherapy treatments that can overcome the noxious effect of platinum based drugs, the only metallodrugs in clinical use. On Section 3 different structural approaches on the synthesis of "RuCp" based compounds are presented in view to a potential interest in medicinal chemistry. As mentioned for NLO properties, ruthenocene derived compounds are not considered in this review. Relevant information concerning this family of compounds can be find in the literature particularly for the anticancer properties of a series of ruthenocene compounds (analogues of ferrocifens which structure is based on tamoxifen) [25, 26], ruthenocene-containing β-diketones [27], or mixed ruthenocenes RuCp(η^6-arene) [28], to give some examples. Section 3.1 reports a new family of compounds using "RuCp" fragment as inert scaffold in the building of enzyme inhibitor structures. The main role of this organometallic fragment is to allow a spatial organization of substituents around the metal center in order to mimic the effect of staurosporine, a strong kinase inhibitor. Section 3.2 presents a wide family of compounds with important anticancer properties where the "RuCp" fragment plays an important role. It was found that these properties come from the whole molecule since the separated components, say RuCp(phosphane)Cl starting material, free phosphane and heteroaromatic ligands present, by their own, very weak cytotoxic properties. These "RuCp" complexes were used as a foundation for the new family of compounds presented on Section 3.3 where a new approach for the design of macromolecules for targeting therapy is presented. The main idea is to create macromolecular drugs that selectively accumulate in the cancer tissues with the advantage of decreasing the severe side effects of chemotherapy. This section includes a brief description of a new approach on the design of zero generation of metallodendrimers appending four "RuCp" units in their arms. This reported study is still in a very early stage but might constitute another promising area for the search of ruthenium drugs.

2. NLO Properties

2.1. Basic Concepts and Structural Requirements

This brief introductory description of the nature and origin of second- and third-order NLO properties and structural requirements should give the readers a starting point for understanding the structure-properties relationships from a chemical point of view. Major details for the principles of nonlinear optics and structural requirements can be found elsewhere. [1-3, 29-32]

Nonlinear optical phenomena arise from the interaction of matter with strong electromagnetic fields. Within these interactions, the electromagnetic field components of the incident light beam are modified and new components (differing in phase, frequency, amplitude, etc.) produced. When a light beam, via its associated electric field $\boldsymbol{E}$, interacts with the polarizable electrons of a molecule, it generates a distortion in the electron density distribution, resulting in an induced dipole moment, $\boldsymbol{\mu}$, which can be expressed by a power series of $\boldsymbol{E}$, according to Eq. (1):

$$\boldsymbol{\mu} = \boldsymbol{\mu}_0 + \alpha \boldsymbol{E} + \beta \boldsymbol{EE} + \gamma \boldsymbol{EEE} + \ldots \qquad (1)$$

where $\boldsymbol{\mu}_0$ is the intrinsic dipole moment, α is the polarizability and β and γ are, respectively, the second-order (SO) and third-order (TO) polarizabilities (or the quadratic and cubic hyperpolarizabilities) of the molecule. As $\boldsymbol{\mu}$ and $\boldsymbol{E}$ are vectors, the polarizabilities are tensors of the appropriate ranks: α is a second-rank tensor, β is a third-rank tensor, and γ is a fourth-rank tensor. The quadratic coefficient β is associated with second-order NLO phenomena, whereas third-order NLO phenomena are related to the cubic coefficient γ. The terms $\beta\boldsymbol{EE}$ and $\gamma\boldsymbol{EEE}$ of the series only become significant for electric fields comparable in strength to the internal electric fields of the molecule (such as with lasers). In that case the molecular dipole moment becomes a non-linear function of the applied electric field.

Eq. (1) is an oversimplification, being only strictly correct for a static field. Optical fields are time-dependent, containing an oscillatory term at a frequency ω:

$$E(t) = E_0 \cos(\omega t) + \frac{E_0}{2}\left[\exp(\mathrm{i}\omega t) + \exp(-\mathrm{i}\omega t)\right] \tag{2}$$

Substituting the equation of the electric field into Eq. (1) and expanding using trigonometric relations one obtains:

$$\mu = \mu_0 + \frac{1}{2}\alpha E_0 \exp(\mathrm{i}\omega t) + \frac{1}{2}\beta E_0^2 + \frac{1}{4}\beta E_0^2 \exp(2\mathrm{i}\omega t) + \frac{3}{8}\gamma E_0^3 \exp(i\omega t) + \frac{1}{8}\gamma E_0^3 \exp(3i\omega t) + \text{c.c.} + \ldots \tag{3}$$

with c.c. denoting complex conjugate terms. It is evident from the equation above that the presence of higher-order terms leads to generation of new frequencies of molecular dipole oscillation. The "β term'' causes the appearance of frequency doubling (2ω) while the "γ term" gives frequency tripling (3ω). In addition, the second-order term generates a time-independent contribution to the dipole (called "optical rectification") and the third-order term generates a contribution oscillating at the frequency ω (related to optical Kerr effect). If instead of an individual molecule, the applied electromagnetic field is interacting with a bulk material, an analogous power series of the dipole moment can be written for the polarization P, as expressed by Eq. (4):

$$P = P_0 + \chi^{(1)} E + \chi^{(2)} EE + \chi^{(3)} EEE + \tag{4}$$

where $\chi^{(1)}$ is the linear susceptibility and $\chi^{(2)}$ and $\chi^{(3)}$ are, respectively, the second- and third-order nonlinear susceptibilities, corresponding to the non-linear responses of the bulk material. Also, similar expansion using trigonometric relations can be achieved for polarization as obtained for dipole moment.

As can be seen from the previous equations, the tensors β and $\chi^{(2)}$ and γ and $\chi^{(3)}$ are complex, with real and imaginary parts. For second-order NLO effects only the real part is important but for third-order NLO effects both real and imaginary parts have to be taken into account. Symmetry considerations [33] imply that both β and $\chi^{(2)}$, as all even-order parameters, vanish in a centrosymmetric structural environment so that, to have a second-order NLO emission, the acentricity requirement must be fulfilled. This means that β is only nonzero for non-centrosymmetric molecules, this being a basic criterion for the design of SO NLO molecules. Moreover to obtain a material with $\chi^{(2)} \neq 0$, these molecules must assemble in a macroscopic non-centrosymmetric arrangement so that their individual contributions do not sum up to zero. This situation is found in measurements in solution due to the randomly orientation of the NLO chromophores, but in the solid state, crystallization in an acentric space group is required. This has been a limitation for solid state NLO measurements (see below). Therefore, the design of high β molecules and the control of their macroscopic assembly are key factors in the development of molecular SO NLO materials. This symmetry requirement is not required for odd-order tensors, such as γ and $\chi^{(3)}$, thus leading that all materials can exhibit third-order NLO effects.

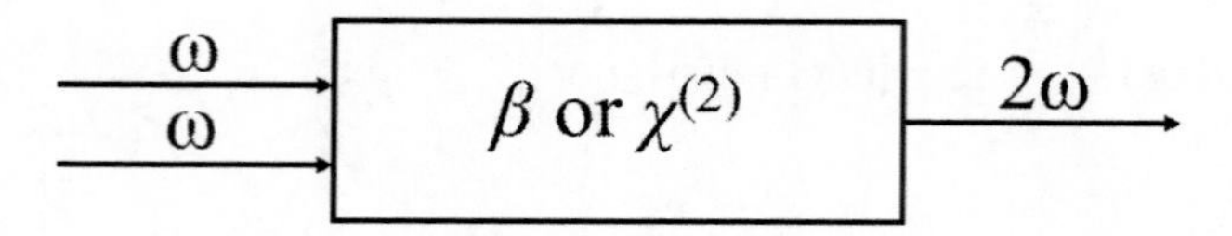

Figure 1. Second-Harmonic Generation (SHG).

A plethora of NLO effects appears when one considers that electromagnetic fields can contain several components with different frequencies and also propagating in different directions in space with consequent several potential technological applications. The major technological applications of second-order NLO effects are related to the modulation of the phase, frequency and path of light beams. The Pockels or linear electro-optic effect is the modification of the refractive index of an optical medium when exposed to a static (or varying) electric field. The applications of the effect are the modulation of the amplitude, phase and path of a light beam, usually to enable it to carry binary information. Sum frequency generation (SFG) and difference frequency generation (DFG) are processes in which two signals at frequencies ω_1 and ω_2 originate signals at ω_3 ($\omega_1 + \omega_2$) and ω_3 ($\omega_1 - \omega_2$, assuming $\omega_1 > \omega_2$), respectively. A special case of SFG, and also the most common, is second-harmonic generation (SHG). This effect results from the interaction of two incident waves with ω frequency with the molecule or the bulk material, characterized by a given value of quadratic hyperpolarizability, β, or of the second-order susceptibility $\chi^{(2)}$, to produce a new wave, or SH, with frequency 2ω (Figure 1). SHG has been mostly used for the conversion of infrared radiation into visible light or visible into ultraviolet light. Parametric generation, in which a signal at frequency ω_1 is split into two signals at frequencies ω_2 and ω_3 can be considered as the reverse phenomenon of SFG. This effect is widely used for the generation of infrared laser beams from visible or near-infrared beams.

There are also numerous third-order NLO effects and, as is the case of second-order counterparts, they depend on the frequency of the incident light beam. At a given wavelength, third-order NLO properties are related to the cubic coefficient γ. As indicated above, γ is a complex number and can be divided into its real and imaginary parts:

$$\gamma = \left(\gamma_{real}^2 + \gamma_{imag}^2\right)^{1/2} \tag{5}$$

The real part is responsible for the modification of the refractive properties of the molecule while modifications of the absorptive properties are related to the imaginary part of γ. Some of the third-order NLO effects constitute valuable tools for nonlinear spectroscopy, while others have a greater technological importance, namely the Kerr effect and two-photon absorption. The Kerr effect (or quadratic electro-optic effect) is based on the same principle as the Pockels effect and it is its third-order equivalent. Compared to the linear electro-optic effect the variation of the refractive index of the medium is a function of the square of the applied electric field instead of varying linearly with the electric field. The applications of this effect are to instantaneously modify the path of the light beam through a material (e.g., to encrypt information onto a light beam). Two-photon absorption (TPA) corresponds to the simultaneous absorption of two photons by a compound. This process is suitable for optical limiting (attenuation of high power beams occurs because their high photon density permits TPA). The presence of γ in any substance means that all materials are susceptible to third-harmonic generation (THG). This effect can be viewed as a result from the interaction of three incident waves with ω frequency with the molecule or the bulk material, characterized by a given value of cubic hyperpolarizability, γ, or of the third-order susceptibility $\chi^{(3)}$, to produce a new wave, or TH, with frequency 3ω (Figure 2). Several other third-order processes exist as can be found in the above-cited references.

Two unit systems are commonly employed in describing NLO properties: the SI (MKS) and the Gaussian (cgs) systems. In most cases, the cgs system is used being the values of the tensors β, $\chi^{(2)}$, γ and $\chi^{(3)}$ expressed in electrostatic units (esu). It should be point out that many equations have a different form when written in these two systems of units [12], and that conversion between these two systems is frequently puzzling. One should also be aware that definitions of hyperpolarizabilities and susceptibilities may differ between different authors because of the lack of general agreement whether the complex field amplitude in Eq. (2) should include a factor of 1/2 and whether the multiplying factors, such as those in Eq. (3), should be included in the hyperpolarizabilities.

Materials displaying significant second-order NLO effects must necessarily have high values of the molecular quadratic hyperpolarizability, β. Several synthetic strategies, through an appropriate molecular design, and computational studies using quantum theory afforded useful insights concerning the molecular structural requirements necessary to produce efficient second-order molecular NLO chromophores. In 1977, Oudar and Chemla developed a theoretical interpretation of the electronic origin of β and, therefore, of the electronic factors responsible for SHG, providing a simple model for the design of second-order NLO molecular materials, the so-called Two Level Model (TLM)[34]. Because NLO properties are related to the polarizability of the electrons under the effect of the electric field E of the incident light, second-order NLO properties are mostly dependent on electronic transitions with higher charge-transfer (CT) character. Oudar and Chemla assumed that, in asymmetric dipolar 1D organic NLO chromophores, the second-order NLO response is dominated mainly by one major charge-transfer process, so that it is possible to assume that:

$$\beta_{zzz} = \frac{3}{2h^2c^2} \frac{(\nu_{eg})^2(r_{eg})^2\Delta\mu_{eg}}{((\nu_{eg})^2 - (\nu_L)^2)((\nu_{eg})^2 - 4(\nu_L)^2)} \tag{6}$$

where z is the direction of the charge-transfer, ν_{eg} (cm^{-1}) the frequency of the charge-transfer transition, r_{eg} its transition dipole moment, μ_{eg} its difference between the excited and ground state molecular dipole moment (μ_e-μ_g) and ν_L is the frequency of the incident radiation.

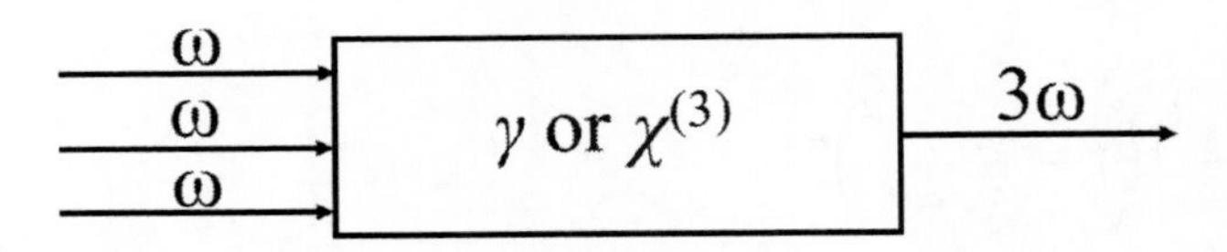

Figure 2. Third-Harmonic Generation (THG).

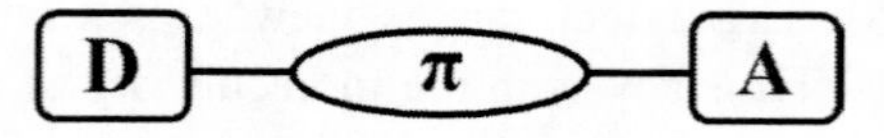

Figure 3. Scheme of a dipolar (1D) chromophore.

The TLM allows the evaluation of the necessary electronic requirements that a molecule must fulfill in order to show a significant second-order NLO response. Such molecules must: (i) be non-centrosymmetric, (ii) have a low energy transition for the ground state to first excited-state, and (iii) have a strong intramolecular charge transfer for this lowest energy transition. The strategy to obtain these features have been mostly devoted to the synthesis of compounds with a general framework involving a highly polarizable molecular structure (e.g., a π-conjugated pathway) having an asymmetric charge distribution (e.g., with donor and/or acceptor group substituents) to form a typical dipolar 1D donor-π conjugated bridge-acceptor (D-π-A) or push-pull system (Figure 3). In this specific case, the charge-transfer process occurs between the donor and the acceptor group through the polarizable π system, thus producing large $\Delta\mu_{eg}$ and r_{eg} values being the λ_{max} value controlled by the polarizability of the π system and the strength of donor and acceptor groups.

To this category of molecular compounds belong most conjugated organic species and metallo-organic compounds. In the latter compounds, the metal center can behave either as acceptor or donor group by simply varying the metal and/or its oxidation state. In addition to dipolar molecules, octupolar species have also been studied for NLO but are not under the scope of this review. These are non-dipolar species whose second-order NLO response is related to multidirectional charge transfer excitations, rather than to dipolar unidirectional excitations. The theoretical description of nonlinearity of such systems implies, even in the simplest case, a three-level approach instead of the two level approximation.

The TLM is a simple way to estimate, from spectroscopic data, the frequency dependent quadratic hyperpolarizability β_{zzz} or β_{CT}, when a single charge-transfer dominates the NLO response. Extrapolation to zero frequency (ν_L =0.0 eV; $\lambda = \infty$) allows estimation of the static quadratic hyperpolarizability, β_0, which, being independent of the laser incident radiation, is useful to evaluate the second-order NLO properties of a molecular material. β_0 is the intrinsic response in the absence of any resonance, especially relevant to practical applications where light absorption must be avoided. Values of β_0 are essential for ascertaining molecular structure-activity relationships and, thus, for comparisons of the second-order NLO molecular responses within a set of compounds. In practice, the results obtained experimentally can be corrected for resonance enhancement via the two-state model, Eq. (7), which is a reasonable approximation for dipolar molecules for which β is largely associated with a single ICT excitation:

$$\beta_0 = \beta\left(\frac{2\lambda_{max}}{\lambda_{fund}}\right)\left(1-\left(\frac{\lambda_{max}}{\lambda_{fund}}\right)^2\right) \tag{7}$$

where λ_{fund} is the wavelength of the laser fundamental beam and λ_{max} is the wavelength of the ICT excitation. Generally speaking, β_0 values derived from experimental measurements become more reliable as the laser fundamental and second-harmonic wavelength are further removed from absorption bands.

In contrast to second-order nonlinearities, for which considerable success in the finding structure-property relationships were achieved, less is known about the optimization of third-order effects. The study of theoretical models [1, 3] and experimental values of γ, obtained for different molecular structures, showed that the magnitude of the third-order NLO response depends essentially on the extension of the conjugated electronic π system. These molecular structures do not have to be asymmetric because, as stated above, γ (and $\chi^{(3)}$) are odd-order parameters. Conjugated polymers provide a molecular frame for higher degree of conjugation and have emerged as the most widely studied group of organic materials. Small organic oligomers have been also studied and, as for β, γ values also depend on the presence of substituents in the conjugated π system. In particular, the presence of donor and acceptor groups in oligomeric systems can be effective to obtain enhanced third-order NLO responses.

Third-order optical nonlinearities of organometallic/coordination complexes were first reported in the mid-1980s. To date, several classes of active structures have been studied. They possess the same characteristics: polarizable π-electrons and low-energy intramolecular charge transfer, but differ in the nature of their multi-polar charge distributions. In a recent review, these classes were categorized in three main groups of compounds [23]: (i) those with the same dipolar (1D) structure exhibited by many efficient second-order NLO-active compounds: a donor and an acceptor group linked together by an unsaturated bridge possessing polarizable π-electrons (Figure 3); (ii) those with quadrupolar composition consisting of two acceptor or donor groups linked by an unsaturated π-delocalized bridge (variations exist with the intercalation of a donor group between the two terminal acceptor groups and vice versa); (iii) those possessing octupolar geometries (Td, D3h). Most of the "RuCp" complexes, subject of this review, studied so far for third-order NLO properties have dipolar (1D) structures as for second-order NLO-active compounds.

2.2. Evaluation of NLO Properties

A number of experimental techniques and computational methods have been used for the evaluation of second- and third-order NLO properties of organometallic molecules. The most popular are briefly described below. A more complete description of these and other used techniques can be found elsewhere [1, 3, 12, 13, 15, 29, 31, 32] and in the references cited below for each technique.

Two main experimental techniques - the electric field induced second-harmonic generation (EFISH) and hyper-Rayleigh scattering (HRS, also termed harmonic light scattering method) - are used to measure, in solution, the experimental value of the quadratic hyperpolarizability of molecular NLO chromophores.

In the EFISH method [35, 36] the quadratic hyperpolarizability, β, is determined by measuring the second-harmonic of laser radiation generated by a system that has been made macroscopically noncentrosymmetric by application of an external electric field. In this technique, together with the incident polarized laser beam of frequency ω, a strong static electric field, E, is applied to a cell containing a solution of the sample, which is placed perpendicularly to the incoming laser beam. The molecules of the medium align according to the electric field, hence breaking the centrosymmetry of the medium, and allowing second-order nonlinear properties to be obtained. EFISH is formally a third-order nonlinear process described by the susceptibility $\chi^{(3)}$(-2ω; ω, ω, 0), so all materials will produce an EFISH signal. There are two contributions to this susceptibility, one arising from the sum of the orientationally-averaged third-order hyperpolarizabilities γ(-2ω; ω, ω, 0) of the medium, and another due to the vectorial sum of the components of the second-order hyperpolarizabilities. Molecules with a permanent dipole μ partially align with the dc-field. The net second-order effect is dependent on the $\boldsymbol{\mu} \cdot \boldsymbol{\beta}_{vec}$ product ($\boldsymbol{\mu}$ is the dipole moment of the molecule and $\boldsymbol{\beta}_{vec}$ is the vectorial component of the second-order hyperpolarizability). In general, the directions of $\boldsymbol{\mu}$ and $\boldsymbol{\beta}_{vec}$ are not coincident. The effective hyperpolarizability measured by this technique, β_{EFISH}, is given by $\boldsymbol{\mu} \cdot \boldsymbol{\beta}_{vec} = \mu\beta_{EFISH}$. β_{EFISH} is, thus, the projection along the dipole moment axis of β_{vec} working with an incident frequency ω of a pulsed laser. For dipolar molecules containing strong electron donor and acceptor groups, β_{CT} (the hyperpolarizability along the charge-transfer axis) usually accounts for most of β_{EFISH}. The EFISH-derived third-order susceptibility $\chi^{(3)}$ is related to the molecular cubic hyperpolarizability γ_{EFISH} by local field factors and the molecule number density, and β_{EFISH} can then be obtained from:

$$\gamma_{EFISH} = \gamma(-2\omega;\ \omega,\omega,0) + \frac{\mu\beta_{EFISH}}{5K_bT} \tag{8}$$

where γ_{EFISH} is the effective cubic hyperpolarizability, γ(-2ω; ω, ω, 0) is the intrinsic cubic hyperpolarizability (consisting of electronic and vibrational contribution) which is negligible for many molecules with a limited electronic polarizability, k_b is Boltzmann's constant and T is the temperature in K. The term $\mu\beta_{EFISH}/5k_bT$ represents the dipolar orientational contribution of the quadratic hyperpolarizability. To obtain the value of β_{EFISH} it is thus necessary to know the value of the ground state dipole moment μ of the molecule. Comparison against a reference, usually a pure solvent of well-known nonlinear optical properties, enables β_{EFISH} values to be determined. One of the major drawbacks of the EFISHG technique becomes clear from the previous equation since several other quantities may be required for the interpretation of the results, namely the dielectric constant of the solvent, the permanent dipole moment and the intrinsic quadratic hyperpolarizability of the solute. The EFISH technique is only suitable for neutral molecules since the presence of ionic species unable the possibility to apply high electric fields to a solution. Thus this technique has been widely used in the study of organic molecules and a variety of neutral organometallic compounds. However, much of the work in the domain of organometallic complexes has shifted to the more widely applicable hyper-Rayleigh scattering (HRS) technique.

Hyper-Rayleigh scattering [37-39] is currently the most used technique to estimate quadratic molecular nonlinearities, β. HRS is based on the detection of the incoherently scattered second-harmonic light generated from an isotropic solution when crossed by a laser beam. An isotropic solution is normally thought to be a random collection of molecules with no preferred orientation, and therefore having all tensor components of $\chi^{(2)}$ equal to zero (with the obvious exception of a liquid containing chiral molecules); it is thus unable to generate a coherent second-harmonic beam. However, orientational fluctuations of unsymmetrical molecules in solution do result in local asymmetry and give rise to scattering of light at the second-harmonic frequency. The HRS signal is originated by the individual nonlinear scatterers, and hence is related with the individual molecular hyperpolarizability. The intensity of the harmonic light is a sum of the contributions of all molecules interacting with the laser radiation and it is proportional to the square of the fundamental light beam and $\langle\beta^2_{HRS}\rangle$, which is the orientation averaging of the molecular quadratic hyperpolarizability constituted by horizontal and vertical components denoted by $\langle\beta^2_{ZZZ}\rangle$ and $\langle\beta^2_{XZZ}\rangle$. The relationship between $\langle\beta^2_{HRS}\rangle$ and the molecular tensor components of the second-order molecular hyperpolarizability, β_{ijk}, where the indexes i, j and k represent the molecular coordinate system, depends on the polarization of the fundamental and the harmonic-scattered light. Usually, a 90-degree geometry is adopted, where the fundamental light propagates in the X-axis and it is polarized in the Z-axis direction and the scattered light propagates in the Y-axis direction. In such geometry, a relation between $\langle\beta^2_{HRS}\rangle$ and β_{ijk} was proposed by Cyvin et al. [40], and it's given by:

$$\langle\beta^2_{ZZZ}\rangle = \frac{1}{7}\sum_i \beta^2_{iii} + \frac{6}{35}\sum_{i\neq j} \beta_{iii}\beta_{ijj} + \frac{9}{35}\sum_{i\neq j} \beta^2_{iij} + \frac{6}{35}\sum_{ijk,cyclic} \beta_{iij}\beta_{jkk} + \frac{12}{35}\beta^2_{ijk} \quad (9)$$

$$\langle\beta^2_{XZZ}\rangle = \frac{1}{35}\sum_i \beta^2_{iii} - \frac{2}{105}\sum_{i\neq j} \beta_{iii}\beta_{ijj} + \frac{11}{105}\sum_{i\neq j} \beta^2_{iij} - \frac{2}{105}\sum_{ijk,cyclic} \beta_{iij}\beta_{jkk} + \frac{8}{35}\beta^2_{ijk} \quad (10)$$

$$\langle\beta^2_{HRS}\rangle = \langle\beta^2_{ZZZ}\rangle + \langle\beta^2_{XZZ}\rangle \quad (11)$$

The HRS experiment consists in recording the scattered light intensity at the second-harmonic wavelength as a function of the incident laser light intensity. The solute concentration is proportional to the square the nonlinearity of all species in solution, and so varying the concentration of the solutes allow β^2 to be extracted. The same procedure is followed for a standard with well-known nonlinear optical properties, like for example *p*-nitroaniline or Disperse Red 1. The molecular hyperpolarizability is thus easily obtained using the relation:

$$\beta_{HRS}(sample) = \sqrt{\frac{S_{sample}}{S_{standard}}}\beta_{HRS}(standard) \quad (12)$$

where S_{sample} and $S_{standard}$ are the slopes obtained for the plot of the intensity of the second-harmonic light *vs.* the square of the fundamental light intensity. HRS has a number of advantages over EFISH: it is simpler (no static electric fields are required nor the knowledge of μ and γ), and it is possible to perform measurements on both octupolar and ionic species, the latter being of particular importance to organometallic complexes, many of which possess multiple accessible oxidation states. The major drawback of the HRS technique is the fact that high-energy laser pulses are need and which often results in stimulated Raman or Brillouin scattering, self-focusing, or dielectric breakdown. Moreover additional multi-photon absorption followed by fluorescence emission processes can occur at the frequency-doubled wavelength. These additional fluorescence phenomena can lead to an overestimation of the molecular quadratic hyperpolarizability and lead to unreliable results.

In the case of bulk materials second-order susceptibility values, $\chi^{(2)}$ can be obtained by means of the investigation of the SHG effect. The Kurtz-Perry powder technique [41] is often used to compare the intensity of the SHG of a powder sample with that of a reference sample of known $\chi^{(2)}$ such as urea, quartz, or dihydrogenophosphate salts, like ammonium or potassium dihydrogenophosphate (ADP or KDP):

$$\frac{I_{2\omega}(sample)}{I_{2\omega}(standard)} \alpha \left(\frac{d_{ef}(sample)}{d_{ef}(standard)}\right)^2 \quad (13)$$

where, d_{ef}, is the nonlinear optical coefficient, that is proportional to $\chi^{(2)}$. Despite the simplicity of the experimental laser setup, the interpretation of the results is not straightforward. A sample with well determined grain size is required. Indeed, the generated second-harmonic intensity depends not only on $\chi^{(2)}$, but also on phase-matching properties, optical absorption, grain size distribution, etc. Also, given that the relation between β and $\chi^{(2)}$ depends on crystal packing, this technique is not applicable to compounds crystallizing in centrosymmetric space groups, this being the case of most of the compounds possessing large dipole moments. Moreover, re-absorption of the harmonic light can also occur, in particular if the samples have absorption bands nearby the second-harmonic wavelength. Optical degradation upon irradiation with the laser beam cannot be also excluded. For all these reasons, Kurtz-Perry powder technique results do not have a quantitative significance, and are used only qualitatively to establish the magnitude of generation of second-harmonic light of a solid towards a known reference. Although this technique is limited, it is a simple and rapid method for screening a large number of powder materials.

Degenerate four-wave mixing (DFWM) [42] is a technique for determining cubic nonlinearities in various materials in solution and has been used to measure molecular cubic nonlinearities of organometallic complexes. The principle of DFWM is the interaction of three laser beams at the same frequency ω to generate a fourth beam at the same frequency which intensity depends on the quadratic of the absolute value of the third-order susceptibility, $|\chi^{(3)}|$. DFWM has several advantages: i) one can measure all of the independent $\chi^{(3)}$ tensor components of an isotropic medium by using various combinations of polarizations for the four beams employed in the experiment; ii) absolute and relative measurements of $\chi^{(3)}$ are possible and iii) the time dependence of the nonlinear response can be studied. The major drawback of DFWM is that, in order to distinguish between contributions from the real and imaginary part of the third-order susceptibility, it must be performed concentration dependence studies in a non-absorbing solvent. The concentration dependence of the DFWM signal is given by:

$$I_{DFWM} \propto |\chi^{(3)}|^2 \propto [N_{solv}\gamma_{solv} + N_{solute}Re(\gamma_{solute})]^2 + [N_{solute}Im(\gamma_{solute})]^2 \quad (14)$$

where it is assumed that the solvent contributes only to the real part of the solution susceptibility, whereas the solute can contribute to both the real and the imaginary components. The concentration dependence is thus, in general, nonlinear, complicating the derivation of the molecular hyperpolarizabilities from the experimental data. This technique was used to measure molecular cubic nonlinearities of metal complexes in early studies, but it is now much less popular than the experimentally simpler Z-scan technique (see below). Despite the experimental complexity, DFWM is very useful as a technique complementary to Z-scan since it can be used to verify that the origin of the observed nonlinearity is electronic.

The Z-Scan Technique [43] is among the most sensitive and simple technique for the determination of nonlinear refractive indexes and nonlinear coefficients of materials and has been used for the measurement of cubic NLO properties of the majority of organometallic complexes to date. Z-scan experiments are usually carried out in cells containing solutions of the complexes in common solvents. The analysis of data must take into account the fact that the effect observed for such samples incorporates contributions from the cell walls and from the solvent, in addition to those from the solute. The obtained data are usually analyzed using equations derived by Sheikh-Bahae et al. [43] and the sample nonlinearity is determined as a function of its concentration. The concentration dependence is then used to derive the extrapolated nonlinear parameters of the pure solute: they can be expressed as the real and imaginary part of $\chi^{(3)}$, the components the complex hyperpolarizability γ, or the macroscopic nonlinear refractive index parameter n_2 (related to $\chi^{(3)}$). The main advantages in the use of the Z-scan technique for the determination of the third-order NLO properties is that the sign and the magnitude of the nonlinear refractive index can be determined and both the real and the imaginary parts of $\chi^{(3)}$ are obtained. Also the single-beam configuration results in simplicity when compared to DFWM. The main difficulty is that Z-scan provides data that often lead to uncertainties about the origin of nonlinear effects. Additional experiments are often needed to establish the microscopic mechanism of the NLO effects.

Third-harmonic generation (THG) is a NLO process occurring in all materials and depending on the $\chi^{(3)}(-3\omega; \omega, \omega, \omega)$ susceptibility. The experiment is usually carried out by recording the intensity of the third-harmonic generated by a beam from an infrared laser. THG measurements can be performed on solid samples (e.g., thin films) and on solutions and the experiment is similar to that of second-harmonic generation (SHG) with a similar consideration of the complications arising from the nonlinear interaction being non-phase matched. Since all materials exhibit THG, including any glass used for a sample cell, or even air, this experiment is technically difficult. One can avoid some problems by placing the sample in a vacuum-sealed cell inside a vacuum chamber, but a simpler method involves using thick glass windows, permitting the contribution from air to be ignored; in this procedure, though, the third-order susceptibility of the glass and solvent must be known. Because of the many uncertainties related to the details of the generation of the third-harmonic, an often-adopted version of the experiment is carried out with a pulsed laser beam impinging on thin film sample deposited on a glass plate, the intensity of the beam generated at the third-harmonic usually being monitored as a function of the angle of inclination of the glass plate with respect to that of the plane perpendicular to the laser beam, which leads to the formation of Maker fringes. [44] The fringe pattern thus obtained can be compared with one obtained for the glass plate alone. The interference between the signals is used to evaluate both the amplitude and phase of $\chi^{(3)}(-3\omega; \omega, \omega, \omega)$ for the thin film sample, which lead to resolving the real and imaginary contributions of $\chi^{(3)}$ or the corresponding molecular hyperpolarizabilities. A major limitation for organometallic and coordination complexes is that needs to be chosen to avoid material resonances at ω, 2ω and 3ω which is difficult for molecules absorbing in the visible region.

The evaluation of NLO response of a material is still a great challenge for theoretical and computational chemists, since the problem relies on describing multi-photon absorption processes in the presence of a highly intense external field. Therefore, the computational effort is much more demanding than for simple linear absorption responses. However, recent advances in modern computational techniques allowed the development of several methodologies for the estimation and prediction of the NLO properties of molecules. By means of these methodologies, time-consuming synthesis can be avoided, and numerous structural variations can be probed for screening the most promising molecules for NLO purposes. One of the major drawbacks of all the computational procedures is a direct comparison to experimental techniques, and therefore results are predominantly concerning the individual microscopic or molecular hyperpolarizabilities, rather than macroscopic bulk response. Various quantum mechanical methods allow the calculation of the molecular hyperpolarizabilities. Among them, the "sum over states" (SOS) approach also gives a useful way to define the electronic origin of the NLO response. For quadratic hyperpolarizabilities, this approach describes the tensor β_{ijk} in terms of all the electronic states interacting with the perturbing electric field, as an infinite expansion over a complete set of unperturbed excited states. A simplification of this approach is the two-state model (Eq. 6) described above. During the last decades, the most used computational methods for the estimation of nonlinear hyperpolarizabilities of organometallic complexes have been Hartree-Fock (HF), Density Functional Theory (DFT) [45, 46] and Intermediate Neglect of Differential Overlap (INDO) in particular as modified by Zerner et al., ZINDO. [45, 46] Each of these methods have proved to be very useful, and a comprehensive comparison between them was made recently by Isbon et al. [47] Within these, DFT and time-dependent DFT (TD-DFT) or time-dependent HF (TD-HF) calculations are the best theoretical methods. [48-50] ZINDO and DFT have been used to evaluate the NLO merit and to rationalize the experimental observations on linear optical and quadratic nonlinear optical properties of the organometallic complexes subject of this review. Thus only these two computational methods are briefly introduced.

ZINDO is a semi-empirical intermediate neglect of differential overlap/spectroscopy (INDO/S)-based routine that uses a sum over excited particle hole states (SOS) method to calculate second-order nonlinear optical coefficients and is parameterized to accommodate transition metal calculations thus being suitable for calculation on organometallic compounds. To achieve computational efficiency, some terms of the theory equations are replaced by empirical data or neglected. The SOS treatment is then used with the so called mono-excited state configuration interaction (MECI) approximation. [51, 52] The values reported in this review are β_{vec}, the value of β that lies along the dipolar axis which is the value obtained by EFISH technique.

At present, DFT and time-dependent DFT (TD-DFT) provide a more satisfactory molecular orbital description of processes involving electronic transitions. DFT is a quantum method based on the electronic density. DFT is somewhat similar to the HF approach, in the sense that the computed electron density is expressed as a linear combination of basis functions. The great advantage of using the electron density is that it makes DFT methods much faster than most *ab initio* methods. Several studies have indicated that the calculated hyperpolarizabilities using the TD-DFT approach could match very well with experimental trends if adequate functionals are chosen and this method has been increasingly used to accurately calculate quadratic hyperpolarizabilities of organometallic complexes. Nevertheless, the majority is lack in the considerations of the environment effects, namely the solvation interactions that in some cases are critical for obtaining quantitatively satisfactory results of both the electronic excitations and the quadratic hyperpolarizabilities in comparison with the experimental results. In fact, it is well known that the solvent polarity influences both the structure and optical properties of conjugated organic molecules and metal complexes and, therefore, their NLO properties. In recent years, however, this subject is attracting increasing attention and several publications have been devoted to the study of solvation effects on the hyperpolarizabilities of organic molecules and organometallic complexes. Within this method the calculated quadratic hyperpolarizability is usually expressed as the total static quadratic hyperpolarizability, β_{tot}, obtained from the relation:

$$\beta_{tot} = \sqrt{\beta_x^2 + \beta_y^2 + \beta_z^2} \tag{15}$$

upon calculating the individual static components

$$\beta_i = \beta_{iii} + \frac{1}{3}\sum_{i \neq j}\left(\beta_{ijj} + \beta_{jij} + \beta_{jji}\right) \tag{16}$$

Due to the Kleinman symmetry [33] one finally obtains the equation that is employed:

$$\beta_{tot} = \left[\left(\beta_{xxx} + \beta_{xyy} + \beta_{xzz}\right)^2 + \left(\beta_{yyy} + \beta_{yzz} + \beta_{yxx}\right)^2 + \left(\beta_{zzz} + \beta_{zxx} + \beta_{zyy}\right)^2\right]^{1/2} \tag{17}$$

The calculated β can also be expressed as a function of the β_{ijk} components that are associated to any particular experimental measurement method. For example, for a direct comparison with experimental quadratic hyperpolarizabilities measured by HRS method, calculated β_{HRS} can be obtained according to the Eq. (11), after the summations given by Eq. (9) and Eq. (10).

2.3. Experimental Molecular Quadratic Hyperpolarizabilities

Small organic molecules structured as donor group- π spacer- acceptor group (so called D-π-A, dipolar 1D or push-pull systems) are known to possess high values of quadratic hyperpolarizabilities, β. "RuCp" complexes, with a coordinated (π-A) structure-type ligand, can be considered to have structural features similar to efficient organic molecules, in which the donor group is the organometallic moiety of the type $[RuCp(LL)]^{n+}$ (n= 0, 1), as depicted in Figure 4.

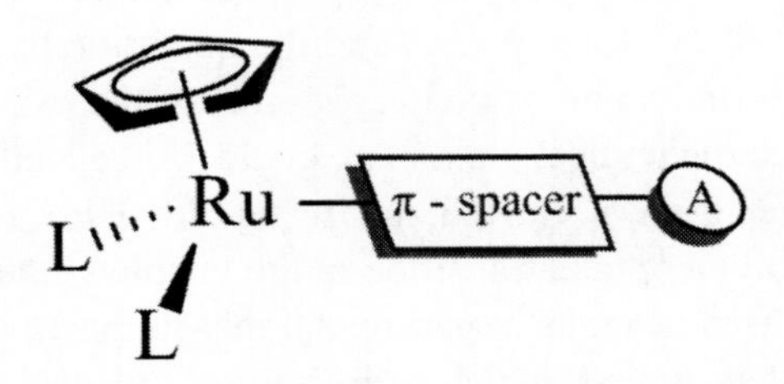

Figure 4. Molecular scheme for an organometallic dipolar (1D) system.

This type of structure, presenting the metal center in the same plane of the organic π system was anticipated to promote a favorable coupling between the metal center and the organic ligand and, therefore, to get better second-order hyperpolarizabilities than the first studied ferrocenyl complexes. [53] With these structural features, the SO NLO properties can be tuned by changing the donor ability of the organometallic fragment (playing with the L ligands) and/or changing the organic ligand (different π spacers and/or acceptor groups). Furthermore, for applications in the solid state, optimization of the crystal packing can be obtained by introducing chiral ligands and by varying the counter ion as well, which itself can additionally introduce chirality.

Systematic studies were made by our group and others on these type of systems, including also iron and nickel complexes, mostly presenting benzene- or thiophene-based conjugated chains as π spacers, coordinated to the metal centers through nitrile or acetylide linkages (see tables below). The correlation of SO NLO properties with spectroscopic FTIR, NMR and UV data has been addressed. Electrochemical data, obtained by cyclic voltammetry, was also important to understand the effect of structural differences on the electronic density at the metal center and chromophores. HOMO-LUMO gaps, expressed by the difference between the first oxidation and reduction potentials, were also found useful to predict and clarify trends in the structure-nonlinearity relationship. [54, 55] Also, computational data obtained by quantum methods, namely ZINDO and DFT, has been used to complement these studies.

The overall data has shown that $[RuCp(LL)]^{n+}$ organometallic moiety is a very efficient donor group, creating the required asymmetry to obtain a nonzero second-order NLO response, in particular when coupled with strong electron acceptors like the nitro group. This behavior is related with the presence of low-lying, intense absorption bands, in the visible spectral region, attributed to metal to ligand charge-transfer (MLCT). These bands exhibit, in general, a positive solvatochromic behavior, *i.e.,* they become red-shifted by increase of the solvent polarity, thus raising the dipole moment upon photo-excitation ($\Delta\mu > 0$). According to the two-level model cited above, the existence of low-lying, intense absorption bands and large variation of the dipole moment upon excitation contributes to the enhanced second-order hyperpolarizabilities.

Two major classes of “RuCp” complexes emerged with relevance for their SO NLO properties: cationic nitrile complexes, in which the coordination of the chromophore is made by a N≡C unit (Ru^+—N≡CR) and neutral alkynyl complexes, with the metal center and the chromophore linked by a C≡C unit (Ru—C≡CR). Also, some studies have been made on vinylidene (Ru^+—C=CR(R’)) complexes. Since several structural variation studies have been carried out within these families of complexes and the quadratic hyperpolarizability β values obtained, it was possible to find some behavior patterns on the experimental IR, NMR, UV-vis. spectroscopic and electrochemical data that could be related with high values of β. Almost all the measurements were carried out using the HRS technique. Because these compounds generally exhibit an optical transition in the visible range, the β values at 1064 nm (wavelength of the mostly used lasers in experimental measurements) can be strongly affected by two-photon resonant enhancement, which is difficult to quantify. The two-level correction can be employed to calculate frequency-independent nonlinearities (see above; eq. (6)) but it is expected to become unacceptable close to resonance as it ignores any kind of line-broadening mechanisms (for a discussion concerning the application of the TLM to coordination complexes, see ref. [56]). This model assumes that the lowest energy CT transition yields the dominant contribution to β, diverges whenever the (laser or) second-harmonic wavelength approaches the transition wavelength. This can lead to a strong overestimation of the resonance effect and hence a significant underestimation of the static quadratic hyperpolarizability, disabling the formulation of reliable relations between molecular structure and NLO properties. In the recent years, experimental measurements have been carried out at higher wavelengths of the fundamental laser beam (for example, 1500 or 1550 nm) to avoid superposition of the UV-Vis absorptions and the second-harmonic signal, this leading to more reasonable results according to the TLM analysis.

The synthesis of the cationic nitrile complexes, usually in high yields, is accomplished by halide abstraction of the parent neutral complex [RuCp(LL)Cl] with a salt of the adequate counter-ion, in the presence of the corresponding nitrile ligand (Figure 5). Results for quadratic NLO properties of these complexes are presented in Table 1 and some representative structures are depicted in Figure 6.

The first series of studied compounds were 4-nitrophenyl derivatives. [57, 58] The extension of the π system from phenyl to biphenyl in complexes $[RuCp(k^2\text{-dppe})(N{\equiv}CC_6H_4\text{-}4\text{-}NO_2)]^+$ (1) ($\beta = 126 \times 10^{-30}$ esu; $\beta_0 = 35 \times 10^{-30}$ esu) and $[RuCp(k^2\text{-dppe})(N{\equiv}CC_6H_4\text{-}C_6H_4\text{-}4\text{-}NO_2)]^+$ (2) ($\beta = 85 \times 10^{-30}$ esu; $\beta_0 = 31 \times 10^{-30}$ esu) was found to lead to a decrease in β as consequence of the loss of donor-acceptor conjugation along the chromophore, possibly due to the significant torsion angles between both phenyl rings. However, the corrected values using the TLM, β_0, are very similar. Structural modifications on the bridging backbone have a similar impact to that observed in purely organic systems: replacing the benzene ring with a thienyl (Th) spacer, to proceed from $[RuCp(k^2\text{-dppe})(N{\equiv}CC_6H_4\text{-}4\text{-}NO_2)]^+$ (1) to $[RuCp(k^2\text{-dppe})(N{\equiv}C\text{-}2\text{-}Th\text{-}5\text{-}NO_2)]^+$ (5) or $[RuCp(k^2\text{-dppe})(N{\equiv}CC_6H_4\text{-}C_6H_4\text{-}4\text{-}NO_2)]^+$ (2) to $[RuCp(k^2\text{-dppe})(N{\equiv}C\text{-}2\text{-}\{Th\}_2\text{-}5\text{-}NO_2)]^+$ (6) provides an increase in β_0 value. Thiophene groups are known to provide a higher level of electronic coupling than benzenoid based structures because of their more effective conjugation, thus yielding expected high second-order NLO responses. Contrary to that found for benzenoid-based compounds, quadratic hyperpolarizabilities were found to increase with the chain-lengthening of the π-bridge in the series of thienyl derivatives $[RuCp(k^2\text{-dppe})(N{\equiv}C\text{-}2\text{-}\{Th\}_n\text{-}5\text{-}NO_2)]^+$ (n=1-3). However, only a slight increasing effect is observed when considering β_0 values. This behaviour is very similar to that found for parent iron derivatives [54] and can be explained in terms of a competition between the growing conjugation length, which tends to raise β, and a decrease of the CT efficiency having a β lowering effect. The constancy on the quadratic hyperpolarizability response due to the insertion of a vinylene unit proceeding from $[RuCp(k^2\text{-dppe})(N{\equiv}C\text{-}2\text{-}\{Th\}_2\text{-}5\text{-}NO_2)]^+$ (6) ($\beta = 114 \times 10^{-30}$ esu; $\beta_0 = 78 \times 10^{-30}$ esu) to $[RuCp(k^2\text{-dppe})(N{\equiv}C\text{-}2\text{-}Th\text{-}5\text{-}(E)\text{-}CH{=}CH\text{-}Th\text{-}5\text{-}NO_2)]^+$ (8) ($\beta = 112 \times 10^{-30}$ esu; $\beta_0 = 74 \times 10^{-30}$ esu) further supports this assumption.

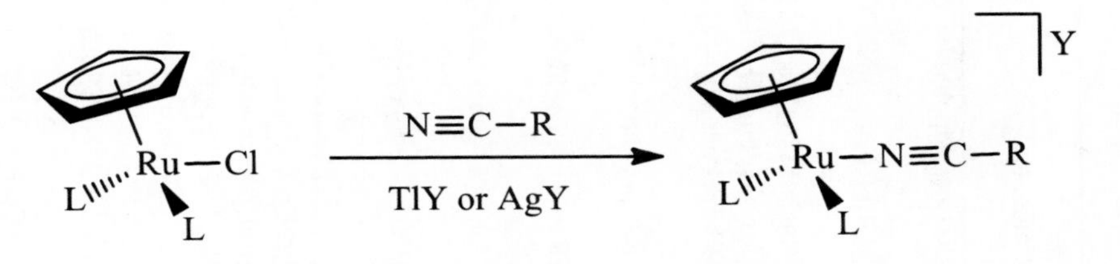

Figure 5. General reaction scheme for the synthesis of nitrile complexes.

Table 1. Molecular quadratic NLO measurements for "RuCp" nitrile complexes

Compound	λ max (nm)	β (10^{-30} esu)	β_0 (10^{-30} esu)	Technique	Solvent	Fund. (nm)	Ref.
$[RuCp(k^2\text{-dppe})(N{\equiv}CC_6H_4\text{-4-}NO_2)]PF_6$ (1)	435	138	38[a]	HRS	MeOH	1064	[57, 58]
	435	126	35[a]	HRS	$CHCl_3$	1064	[58]
$[RuCp(k^2\text{-dppe})(N{\equiv}CC_6H_4\text{-4-}C_6H_4\text{-4-}NO_2)]PF_6$ (2)	401	96	36[a]	HRS	MeOH	1064	[57, 58]
	401	85	31[a]	HRS	$CHCl_3$	1064	[58]
$[RuCp(PPh_3)_2(N{\equiv}CC_6H_4\text{-4-}Bu^n)]PF_6$ (3)	374	95	65	HRS	$CHCl_3$	1500	[59]
$[RuCp((PPh_3)_2N{\equiv}CC_6H_4\text{-3-}NH(C{=}O)H)]PF_6$ (4)	315	264	212	HRS	$CHCl_3$	1500	[59]
$[RuCp(k^2\text{-dppe})(N{\equiv}C\text{-2-Th-5-}NO_2)]PF_6$ (5)	460	340	72	HRS	$CHCl_3$	1072	[60, 61]
	460	122	72	HRS	$CHCl_3$	1550	[59]
$[RuCp(k^2\text{-dppe})(N{\equiv}C\text{-2-}\{Th\}_2\text{-5-}NO_2)]PF_6$ (6)	404	361	134	HRS	$CHCl_3$	1072	[60, 61]
	404	114	78	HRS	$CHCl_3$	1550	[59]
$[RuCp(k^2\text{-dppe})(N{\equiv}C\text{-2-}\{Th\}_3\text{-5-}NO_2)]PF_6$ (7)	443	570	150	HRS	$CHCl_3$	1072	[60, 61]
	443	141	88	HRS	$CHCl_3$	1550	[59]
$[RuCp(k^2\text{-dppe})(N{\equiv}C\text{-2-Th-5-}(E)\text{-}CH{=}CH\text{-Th-5-}NO_2)]PF_6$ (8)	422	450	145	HRS	$CHCl_3$	1072	[55, 61]
	422	112	74	HRS	$CHCl_3$	1550	[55, 61]
$[RuCp(k^2\text{-dppe})(N{\equiv}C\text{-2-Th-5-BcT-5-}C_4H_3S)]PF_6$[a] (9)	475	147	80	HRS	$CHCl_3$	1500	[62]
$[RuCp(PPh_3)_2(N{\equiv}C\text{-2-Th-5-BcT-5-}C_4H_3S)]PF_6$[b] (10)	473	105	57	HRS	$CHCl_3$	1500	[62]
$[RuCp(k^2\text{-dppe})(N{\equiv}C\text{-BDT})]PF_6$ (11)	336[a]	negligible	-	HRS	$CHCl_3$	1550	[63]
$[RuCp(k^2\text{-dppe})(N{\equiv}CC_6H_4\text{-4-}C{\equiv}C\text{-}(\{\eta^6\text{-}C_6H_5\}Cr(CO)_3))]PF_6$ (12)	376	42	18[a]	HRS	$CHCl_3$	1064	[64]
$[RuCp(k^2\text{-dppe})(N{\equiv}C\text{-2-}C_4H_2S\text{-5-}C{\equiv}C\text{-}(\{\eta^6\text{-}C_6H_5\}Cr(CO)_3))]PF_6$ (13)	414	83	28[a]	HRS	$CHCl_3$	1064	[64]
$[RuCp(k^2\text{-dppe})(N{\equiv}C\text{-2-}\{C_4H_2S\}_2\text{-5-}C{\equiv}C\text{-}(\{\eta^6\text{-}C_6H_5\}Cr(CO)_3)]PF_6$ (14)	426	143	43[a]	HRS	$CHCl_3$	1064	[64]
$[Fc\{(E)\text{-}CH{=}CH\text{-4-}C_6H_4C{\equiv}NRuCp(PPh_3)_2\}]PF_6$ (15)	485	186	25	HRS	$CHCl_3$	1064	[65]
$[Fc\{(E)\text{-}CH{=}CH\text{-4-}C_6H_4C{\equiv}NRuCp(PPh_3)_2\}]BF_4$ (16)	484	325	44	HRS	$CHCl_3$	1064	[65]
$[(NH_3)_5RuN{\equiv}CRuCp(PPh_3)_2\}(CF_3SO_3)_3$ (17)	720	1080		HRS	H_2O	1064	[66]
	716	157	69	HRS	$MeNO_2$	1064	[11, 67]
$[RuCp(PPh_3)_2\{C{\equiv}NOs(NH_3)_5\}](CF_3SO_3)_3$ (18)	440	65	16	HRS	DMSO	1064	[67]

[a]not calculated in the refs.; Th- thiophene backbone (C_4H_2S); BcT-benzo[c]thiophene backbone (C_8H_6S); BDT- benzo[1,2-*b*:4,3*b*']dithiophene ($C_{10}H_5S_2$);

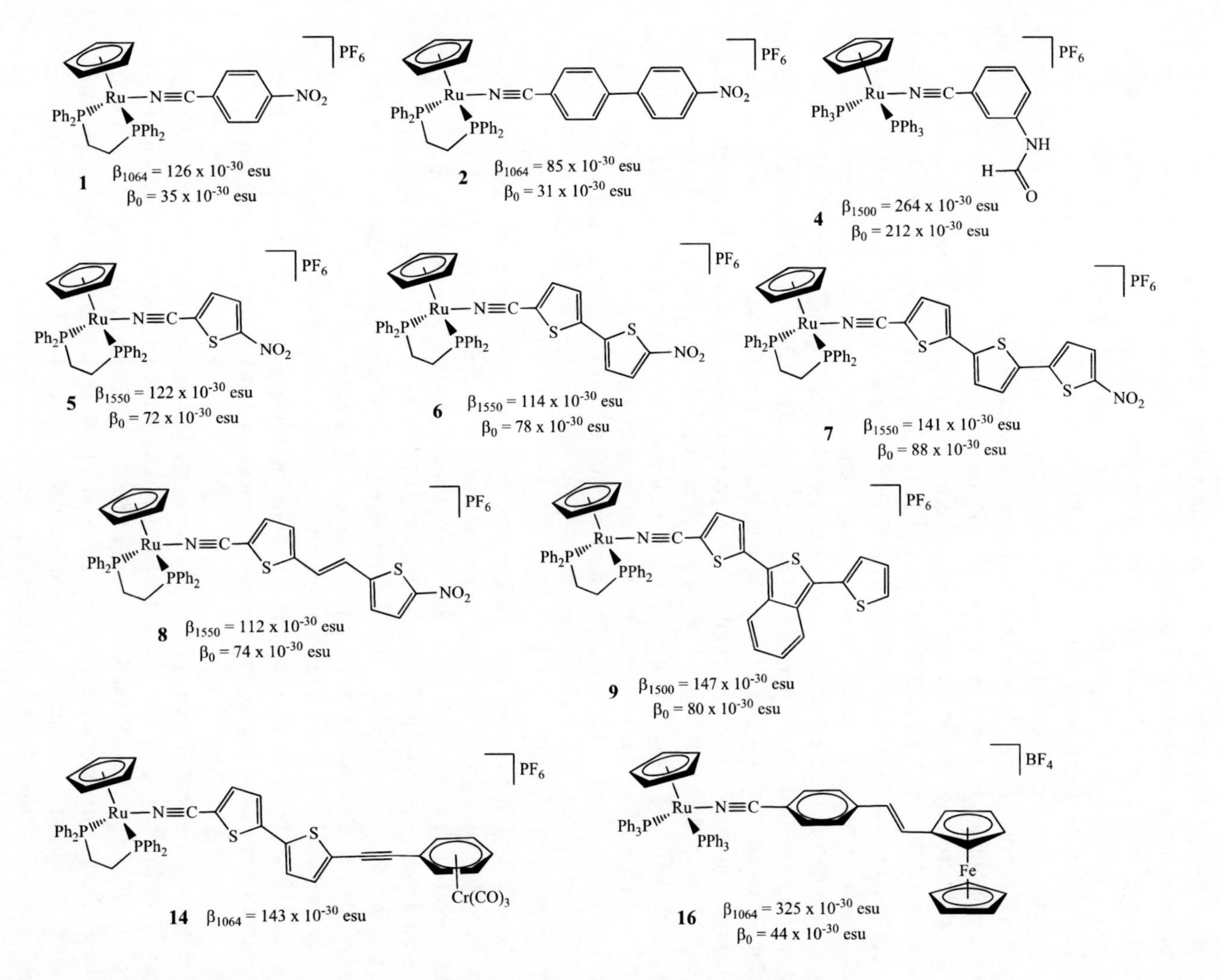

Figure 6. Selected "RuCp" nitrile complexes showing the most representative structures for SO NLO properties.

Keeping in mind that the exploitation of promising thiophene based ligands for NLO purposes should not be limited to the chain lengthening alternative, the potentialities of the benzo[1,2-*b*:4,3*b*']dithiophene (BDT) based chromophores were explored. The fused rings structure guarantees the rigidity of the ligand to be coordinated on the same plan of the metal centre, in a family of "RuCp" (and iron) derivatives. [63] Preliminary results showed, however, that quadratic hyperpolarizability for $[RuCp(k^2\text{-dppe})(N{\equiv}C\text{-BDT})]^+$ (11) is negligible due to weak π-backbonding effect which barely compensates the ligand σ-coordination, as suggested by the spectroscopic and electrochemical data. Also benzo[c]thiophene (BcT) based chromophores were studied since its unique electronic behavior originated by their low HOMO–LUMO energy gaps [68] could be potentially on the basis of interesting NLO effects. The experimental quadratic hyperpolarizabilities for $[RuCp(k^2\text{-dppe})(N{\equiv}C\text{-2-Th-5-BcT-5-}C_4H_3S)]^+$ (9) ($\beta = 147 \times 10^{-30}$ esu; $\beta_0 = 80 \times 10^{-30}$ esu) and $[RuCp(PPh_3)_2(N{\equiv}C\text{-2-Th-5-BcT-5-}C_4H_3S)]^+$ (10) ($\beta = 105 \times 10^{-30}$ esu; $\beta_0 = 57 \times 10^{-30}$ esu) [62] were found to be very similar (within the experimental error) to that observed for the oligothiophene derivative with similar conjugated length $[RuCp(k^2\text{-dppe})(N{\equiv}C\text{-2-}\{Th\}_3\text{-5-}NO_2)]^+$ (7) ($\beta = 141 \times 10^{-30}$ esu; $\beta_0 = 88 \times 10^{-30}$ esu). The effect of different co-ligands on quadratic hyperpolarizabilities of benzo[c]thiophene derivatives has been also studied since co-ligands can modify donor strength of the organometallic moieties and hence the second-order NLO responses. Replacing k^2-dppe phosphane by 2 x PPh_3 results in a decrease of both β (k^2-dppe: 147×10^{-30} esu; 2 PPh_3: 105×10^{-30} esu) and β_0 (k^2-dppe: 80×10^{-30} esu; 2 PPh_3: 57×10^{-30} esu). This behavior was explained on the basis of a poorer π-backdonation interaction, based on spectroscopic FTIR and NMR data, and a less charge transfer efficiency during the electronic excitation, based on computational DFT studies for $[RuCp(PPh_3)_2(N{\equiv}C\text{-2-Th-5-BcT-5-}C_4H_3S)]^+$ (10). [62]

The effect of different acceptor end groups has been studied. Recently, the well-known good acceptor nitro group, the most common in NLO studies for "RuCp" complexes, has been replaced by the less classical chromophore N-(3-cyanophenyl)formamide. The compound $[RuCp(PPh_3)_2(N{\equiv}CC_6H_4\text{-3-NH(C=O)H})]PF_6$ (4) gave a value of $\beta_0 = 212 \times 10^{-30}$ esu placing this compound in the best range of values reported in the literature for an organometallic. [59] Also, the electron acceptor chromium tricarbonyl moiety was used in the series of bimetallic compounds $[RuCp(k^2\text{-dppe})(N{\equiv}C\text{-}(\pi\text{-spacer})\text{-}C{\equiv}C\text{-}(\{\eta^6\text{-}C_6H_5\}Cr(CO)_3)][PF_6]$, showing enhanced nonlinearities relatively to the parent monometallic chromium compounds, but lower than similar compounds with the nitro group as acceptor. [64]

Other hetero-bimetallic complexes presenting the ferrocenyl moiety, $[Fc\{(E)\text{-CH=CH-4-}C_6H_4C{\equiv}NRuCp(PPh_3)_2\}]X$ (X= PF_6 (15), BF_4 (16)) have shown counter-ion dependent NLO responses. [65] The higher β (and β_0) observed for the compound with BF_4^- was attributed to the lack of centre of symmetry of this anion, which leads to an enhanced contribution of the nonlinear optical response. Mixed-valence Ru(II)/Ru(III) and Ru(II)/Os(III) complexes with the formula $[RuCp(PPh_3)_2\{C{\equiv}NM(NH_3)_5\}](CF_3SO_3)_3$ (M= Ru, Os) were also reported with moderate SO NLO responses. [66, 67] The complex $[RuCp(PPh_3)_2\{C{\equiv}NRu(NH_3)_5\}](CF_3SO_3)_3$ (17) was originally reported to have a very large β value [66] but it was subsequently found to have a significant fluorescence contribution, drawing attention to the problems associated with this phenomenon. [69]

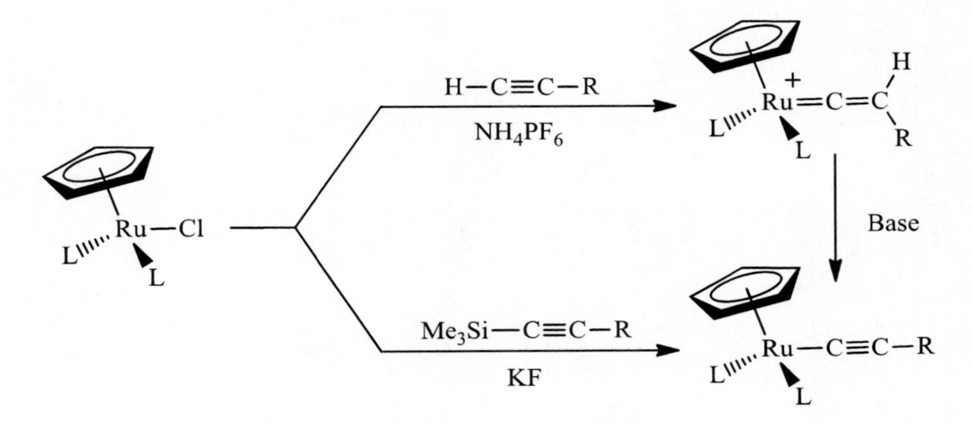

Figure 7. General reaction scheme for the synthesis of alkynyl complexes.

Alkynyls for NLO properties have been prepared in good yields by two main synthetic procedures (Figure 7). In the so-called vinylidene route, an ammonium salt (e.g., NH_4PF_6) reacts with [RuCp(LL)Cl], in the presence of the appropriated alkynyl, to afford the vinylidene complexes which are subsequently deprotonated to give the alkynyl products. An alternative method involves the use of protected alkynes, which reaction with [RuCp(LL)Cl] in the presence of a fluorinated salt (e.g., KF), gives, in a single step, the ruthenium alkynyl compounds.

The NLO properties of these complexes have been extensively reviewed. [13, 15, 16, 21, 23] The results for molecular quadratic NLO properties of these complexes are presented in Table 2 and representative structures are depicted in Figure 8. Quadratic nonlinearities at 1064 nm are, in most cases, dispersion-enhanced as can be seen for several examples in which the determined β and β_0 values differ from an order of magnitude. This observation along with the uncertainty on the magnitude of resonance enhancement, which can be significant, as demonstrated for [RuCp(PPh_3)$_2$(C≡CC_6H_4-4-(*E*)-CH=CHC_6H_4-4-NO_2)] (24) (β_{1064} = 1455 x 10^{-30} esu and $\beta_{0,1064}$ = 232 x 10^{-30} esu [70, 71]; β_{1560} = 186 x 10^{-30} esu and $\beta_{0,1560}$ = 105 x 10^{-30} esu [72]), shows how careful one must be in interpreting the results here in discussion.

In general, both β (experimental) and β_0 (two-level-corrected) values, in many cases, mimic those found for organic molecules. The data for bis(triphenylphosphine)ruthenium complexes are consistent with an increase in second-order NLO response upon increasing π-bridge lengthening: $\beta(C_6H_4) < \beta(C_6H_4C_6H_4) < \beta(C_6H_4C{\equiv}CC_6H_4) < \beta((E)\text{-}C_6H_4CH{=}CHC_6H_4)$. This trend can be rationalized attending to π-bridge lengthening, torsion effects at the phenyl–phenyl linkage, on the case of biphenyl compound, as examined theoretically for comparable Ru complexes [73] and, for the diphenylacetylene compound, to energy mismatch of the sp-hybridized π-orbitals of the acetylenic carbons with orbitals of sp^2 hybridized phenyl carbons [71]. The change in the phenyl rings linkage, from (*E*)-CH=CH to (*E*)-N=N or (*E*)-N=C, resulted in a decrease on the second-order NLO response, the imino linkage being the less effective. The same effect of the chain lengthening on the quadratic hyperpolarizability can be also seen in the series of thienyl derivatives [RuCp(LL)(C≡C-2-{Th}$_n$-5-NO_2)] (LL = 2 PPh_3, k^2-dppe; n = 1,2) [74].

Table 2. Molecular quadratic NLO measurements for "RuCp" alkynyl complexes

Compound	λ max (nm)	B (10^{-30} esu)	β_0 (10^{-30} esu)	Technique	Solvent	Fund. (nm)	Ref.
[RuCp(PPh$_3$)$_2$(C≡CPh)] (19)	310	89	45	HRS	THF	1064	[70, 75]
[RuCp(PPh$_3$)$_2$(C≡CC$_6$H$_4$-4-NO$_2$)] (20)	460	468	96	HRS	THF	1064	[70, 71, 75]
[RuCp(PMe$_3$)$_2$(C≡CC$_6$H$_4$-4-NO$_2$)] (21)	477	248	39	HRS	THF	1064	[70, 71, 75]
[RuCp(PPh$_3$)$_2$(C≡CC$_6$H$_4$-4-C$_6$H$_4$-4-NO$_2$)] (22)	448	560	134	HRS	THF	1064	[70, 75]
[RuCp(PPh$_3$)$_2$(C≡CC$_6$H$_4$-4-C≡CC$_6$H$_4$-4-NO$_2$)] (23)	446	865	212	HRS	THF	1064	[70, 75]
[RuCp(PPh$_3$)$_2$(C≡CC$_6$H$_4$-4-(*E*)-CH=CHC$_6$H$_4$-4-NO$_2$)] (24)	476	1455	232	HRS	THF	1064	[70, 71]
	476	1464	234	EFISH	THF	1064	[70, 71]
	484	2270	310	HRS	CHCl$_3$	1064	[76]
	478	186	105	HRS	CH$_2$Cl$_2$	1560	[72]
[RuCp(PPh$_3$)$_2$(C≡CC$_6$H$_4$-4-N=CHC$_6$H$_4$-4-NO$_2$)] (25)	496	840	86	HRS	THF	1064	[70, 71]
	496	760	78	EFISH	THF	1064	[70, 71]
[RuCp(PPh$_3$)$_2$(C≡CC$_6$H$_4$-4-(*E*)-CH=CH-2-Th-5-NO$_2$)] (26)	533	294	138	HRS	CH$_2$Cl$_2$	1560	[72]
[RuCp(PPh$_3$)$_2$(C≡C-2-Th-5-(*E*)-CH=CHC$_6$H$_4$-4-NO$_2$)] (27)	522	333	163	HRS	CH$_2$Cl$_2$	1560	[72]
[RuCp(PPh$_3$)$_2$(C≡CC$_6$H$_4$-4-C≡C-2-Th-5-NO$_2$)] (28)	505	210	109	HRS	CH$_2$Cl$_2$	1560	[72]
[RuCp(PPh$_3$)$_2$(C≡C-2-Th-5-{(*E*)-CH=CH-2-Th}$_2$C$_6$H$_4$-4-NO$_2$)] (29)	536	419	195	HRS	CH$_2$Cl$_2$	1560	[72]
[RuCp(PPh$_3$)$_2$(C≡CC$_6$H$_4$-4-N=CH-2-Th-5-NO$_2$)] (30)	562	308	129	HRS	CH$_2$Cl$_2$	1560	[72]
[RuCp(PPh$_3$)$_2${C≡CC$_6$H$_4$-(*E*)-4-N=NC$_6$H$_4$-4-NO$_2$)] (31)	565	1627	149	HRS	THF	1064	[77]
[RuCp(PPh$_3$)$_2${C≡CC$_6$H$_4$N=(CCH=C(Bu^t)C(O)C(Bu^t)=CH}] (32)	622	658	159	HRS	THF	1064	[78]
[RuCp(CO)$_2$(C≡CC$_6$H$_4$-4-NO$_2$)] (33)	364	58	27	HRS	THF	1064	[79]
[RuCp(k^2-dppe)(C≡CC$_6$H$_4$-4-NO$_2$)] (34)	447	664	161	HRS	THF	1064	[79]
[RuCp(PPh$_3$)$_2$(C≡CC$_6$H$_4$-4-CH{OC(O)Me}$_2$] (35)	326	68	38	HRS	THF	1064	[80]
[RuCp(PPh$_3$)$_2$(C≡CC$_6$H$_4$-4-CHO)] (36)	400	120	45	HRS	THF	1064	[80]
[RuCp(dppf)(C≡CC$_6$H$_5$)] (37)	311	120	72	HRS	THF	1064	[81]
[RuCp(dppf)(C≡CC$_6$H$_4$-4-NO$_2$)] (38)	469	770	165	HRS	THF	1064	[81]
[RuCp(PPh$_3$)$_2$(C≡C-2-C$_5$H$_4$N)] (39)	331	18	10	HRS	THF	1064	[82]
[RuCp(PPh$_3$)$_2$(C≡C-2-C$_5$H$_3$N-5-NO$_2$)] (40)	468	622	113	HRS	THF	1064	[82]
[RuCp(PPh$_3$)$_2$(C≡C-4-C$_5$H$_4$NMe)][PF$_6$] (41)	460	80	16	HRS	CH$_2$Cl$_2$	1064	[83]
[RuCp(PPh$_3$)$_2$(C≡CC$_6$H$_4$-4-(*E*)-CH=CH-4-C$_5$H$_4$NMe)][PF$_6$] (42)	582	1600	154	HRS	CH$_2$Cl$_2$	1064	[83]
[RuCp(PPh$_3$)$_2$(C≡CC$_6$H$_4$-4-C≡C-4-C$_5$H$_4$NMe)][PF$_6$] (43)	558	1400	102	HRS	CH$_2$Cl$_2$	1064	[83]
[RuCp(k^2-dppe)(C≡C-2-Th-5-NO$_2$)] (44)	517	326	151	HRS	CHCl$_3$	1500	[74]
[RuCp(k^2-dppe)(C≡C-2-{Th}$_2$-5-NO$_2$)] (45)	566	506	187	HRS	CHCl$_3$	1500	[74]
[RuCp(PPh$_3$)$_2$(C≡C-2-Th-5-NO$_2$)] (46)	536	192	82	HRS	CHCl$_3$	1500	[74]
	531	89	42	HRS	CH$_2$Cl$_2$	1560	[72]
[RuCp(PPh$_3$)$_2$(C≡C-2-{Th}$_2$-5-NO$_2$)] (47)	580	655	224	HRS	CHCl$_3$	1500	[74]

Th- thiophene backbone (C$_4$H$_2$S).

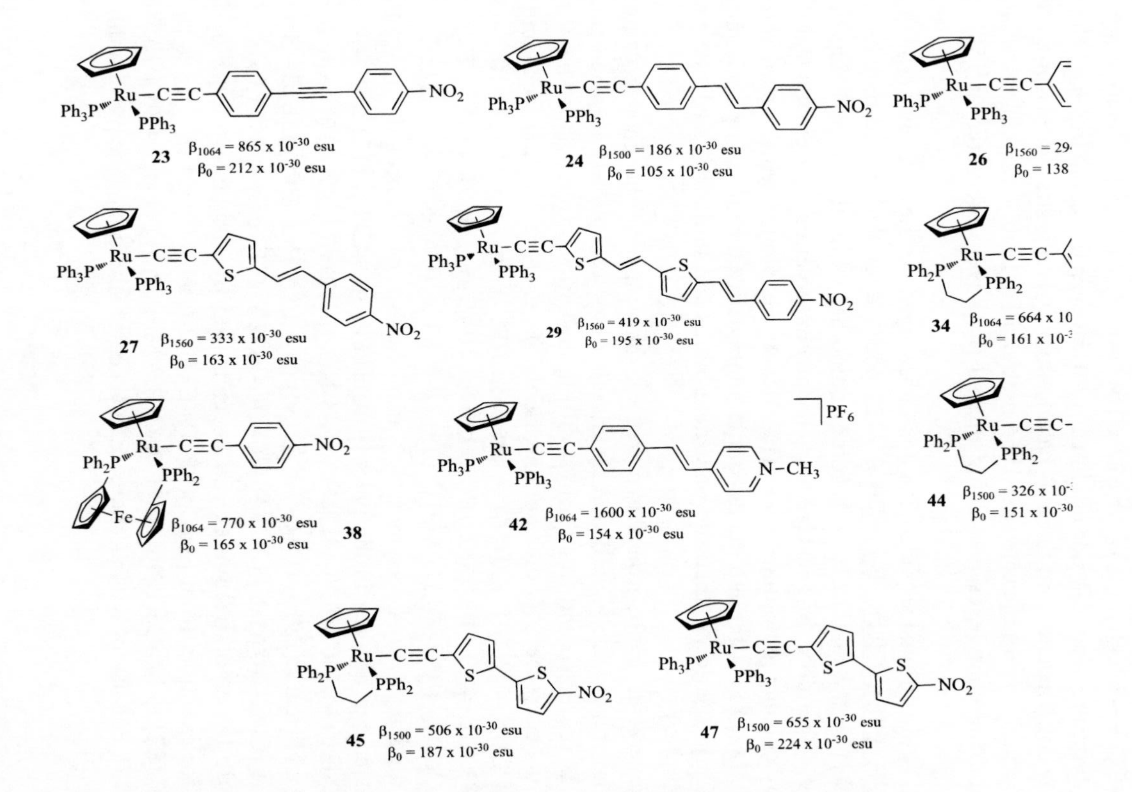

Figure 8. Selected "RuCp" alkynyl complexes showing the most representative structures for SO NLO properties.

Structural modifications to the bridging backbone have a similar impact to that observed in purely organic systems. On replacing phenyl by heterocyclic rings one could expect enhanced nonlinearities due to the lower π-electronic delocalization energies of the heterocyclic moiety. This can be seen replacing the phenyl ring in $[RuCp(PPh_3)_2(C{\equiv}CC_6H_4\text{-}4\text{-}NO_2)]$ (20) (β = 468 x 10^{-30} esu; β_0 = 96 x 10^{-30} esu) by pyridyl derivative $[RuCp(PPh_3)_2(C{\equiv}CC_5H_3\text{-}5\text{-}NO_2)]$ (40) (β = 622 x 10^{-30} esu; β_0= 113 x 10^{-30} esu) which results in a slight increase on the second-order nonlinearity. However the comparison of the results obtained for a series of benzene- and thienyl- based alkynyls is not straightforward due to the fact that phenylacetylides were measured at 1064 nm (and are highly dispersion-enhanced as denoted above) and the complexes presenting thienyl rings were measured at 1500 or1560 nm.

The use of indoanilinoacetylide ligands has been examined in $[RuCp(PPh_3)_2\{C{\equiv}CC_6H_4N{=}\underline{(CCH{=}C(Bu^t)C(O)C(Bu^t){=}C}H\}]$ (32) because in the charge-transfer excited state the ring closest to the metal center becomes quinoidal while the second ring becomes aromatic (Figure 9). Therefore, this feature leads to the conservation of aromatic stabilization energy and thereby enhancing nonlinearities. This idea was exploited with organic molecules by S. Marder et al. [84, 85] Although the quadratic nonlinearity for this complex is large (β_0= 159 x 10^{-30} esu) [78], it is lower than the ones determined for similarly sized two-ring ene- and azo-linked complexes.

Despite the several acceptor groups explored on the π spacer, the good acceptor nitro group has been the most widely used across this series of complexes. Replacement with weaker groups (e.g., protected and free formyl) [80] in the series of phenylacetylenes results, as expected, in a decrease of the nonlinearities as can be seen proceeding from $[RuCp(PPh_3)_2(C{\equiv}CC_6H_4\text{-}4\text{-}NO_2)]$ (20) (β = 468 x 10^{-30} esu; β_0 = 96 x 10^{-30} esu) to $[RuCp(PPh_3)_2(C{\equiv}CC_6H_4\text{-}4\text{-}CHO)]$ (36) (β = 120 x 10^{-30} esu; β_0 = 45 x 10^{-30} esu) or $[RuCp(PPh_3)_2(C{\equiv}CC_6H_4\text{-}4\text{-}CH\{OC(O)Me\}_2]$ (35) (β = 68 x 10^{-30} esu; β_0 = 38 x 10^{-30} esu). Increasing the dipolar D-π-A asymmetry also leads, as expected, to enhanced hyperpolarizabities as can be seen in the pairs $[RuCp(PPh_3)_2(C{\equiv}CPh)]$ (19) (β = 468 x 10^{-30} esu; β_0= 96 x 10^{-30} esu) / $[RuCp(PPh_3)_2(C{\equiv}CC_6H_4\text{-}4\text{-}NO_2)]$ (20) (β = 89 x 10^{-30} esu; β_0= 45 x 10^{-30} esu) [52, 53] and $[RuCp(PPh_3)_2(C{\equiv}C\text{-}2\text{-}C_5H_4N)]$ (39) (β = 18 x 10^{-30} esu; β_0= 10 x 10^{-30} esu) / $[RuCp(PPh_3)_2(C{\equiv}C\text{-}2\text{-}C_5H_3N\text{-}5\text{-}NO_2)]$ (40) (β = 622 x 10^{-30} esu; β_0= 113 x 10^{-30} esu). [82] Also, quadratic hyperpolarizabilities can be enhanced by alkylation of the pyridyl N atom proceeding, for example, from $[RuCp(PPh_3)_2(C{\equiv}C\text{-}2\text{-}C_5H_4N)]$ (39) (β = 18 x 10^{-30} esu; β_0= 10 x 10^{-30} esu) [82] to $[RuCp(PPh_3)_2(C{\equiv}C\text{-}4\text{-}C_5H_4NMe)][PF_6]$ (41) (β = 80 x 10^{-30} esu; β_0 = 16 x 10^{-30} esu) [83], consistent with an increase in acceptor strength of the pyridinium unit.

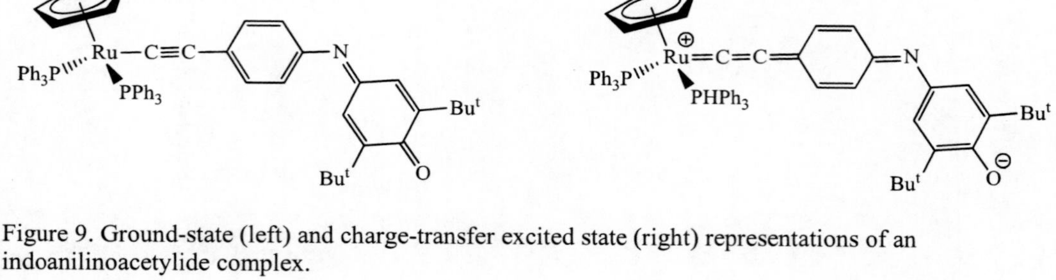

Figure 9. Ground-state (left) and charge-transfer excited state (right) representations of an indoanilinoacetylide complex.

The possibility of tuning the NLO response by co-ligand modification is a major advantage of organometallic complexes over organic compounds. Substituting phosphanes or diphosphanes with strong electron-withdrawing carbonyl ligands results in a significant decrease in electron density at the metal donor unit in the series of [RuCp(LL)(C≡CC$_6$H$_4$-4-NO$_2$)] (LL = 2 CO, 2 PPh$_3$, 2 PMe$_3$, k^2-dppe) and a corresponding decrease in molecular hyperpolarizability. Interestingly, replacing triphenylphosphine by the stronger base trimethylphosphine for the complexes [RuCp(LL)(C≡CC$_6$H$_4$-4-NO$_2$)] (LL = 2 PPh$_3$, 2 PMe$_3$) results in a decrease in hyperpolarizability, suggesting that greater π-delocalization through the phenyl groups of the former is more important for quadratic NLO merit than the greater basicity of PMe$_3$. More subtle behavior is found by replacing two phosphanes by chelating diphosphane co-ligands. Replacing triphenylphoshine by k^2-dppe for the series of complexes [RuCp(LL)(C≡C-π spacer-NO$_2$)] (LL = 2 PPh$_3$, k^2-dppe; π spacer = C$_6$H$_4$, C$_4$H$_2$S) results in a great increase in hyperpolarizability. However, for thienyl complexes presenting large π-spacer length [RuCp(LL)(C≡C-2-{Th}$_2$-5-NO$_2$)] (LL = 2 PPh$_3$, k^2-dppe), replacing triphenylphoshine by k^2-dppe results in a decrease in hyperpolarizability. Theoretical DFT calculations on model complexes have predicted a better charge transfer efficiency upon photoexcitation for the complex with 2 PPh$_3$ which contributes for the enhanced quadratic hyperpolarizabity when compared to the complex with k^2-dppe. [74] Remarkably, [RuCp(PPh$_3$)$_2$(C≡C-2-{Th}$_2$-5-NO$_2$)] (47) presents a value of static hyperpolarizability (β_0 = 224 x 10^{-30} esu) that places this complex in the range found for the best values of β_0 reported in the literature for an organometallic compound. Note that this is more impressive since the quadratic hyperpolarizability for this compound was measured at a fundamental wavelength 1500 nm, in which the second-harmonic signal (750 nm) is far from the UV-Vis absorption (λ_{max} = 580 nm), this leading to more reasonable results according to the TLM analysis.

Fundamental research on metal alkynyl complexes envisaging NLO properties have been mostly devoted to the preparation of compounds with large optical nonlinearities. Recently, the use of these properties in view to the molecular switching has attracted a considerable interest. Group 8 metal alkynyl complexes have been studied as potential redox switchable NLO systems [20] since they often possess a reversible redox process (M^{II}/M^{III}), allowing the interconversion of the complexes between the two oxidation states. If the two redox states have different NLO properties, this affords a "redox switching" for the NLO response. The replacement of k^2-dppe by the redox-active ligand such as 1,1'-bis(diphenylphosphino)ferrocene (dppf) results in a little measurable difference in quadratic hyperpolarizabilites when progressing from [RuCp(k^2-dppe)(C≡CC$_6$H$_4$-4-NO$_2$)] (34) (β = 664 x 10^{-30} esu; β_0 = 161 x 10^{-30} esu) [79] to [RuCp(dppf)(C≡CC$_6$H$_4$-4-NO$_2$)] (38) (β = 770 x 10^{-30} esu; β_0 = 165 x 10^{-30} esu) [81]. However, introduction of such a redox-active iron center does impart potentially useful additional functionality of these compounds envisaging the redox NLO switching. [81]

$$[M]-C\equiv C-R \underset{\text{base}}{\overset{+\,H^+}{\rightleftharpoons}} [M]^{+}=C=C(H)(R)$$

Figure 10. Switching of second-order NLO response in the acetylide/vinylidene pairs upon protonation/deprotonation sequences.

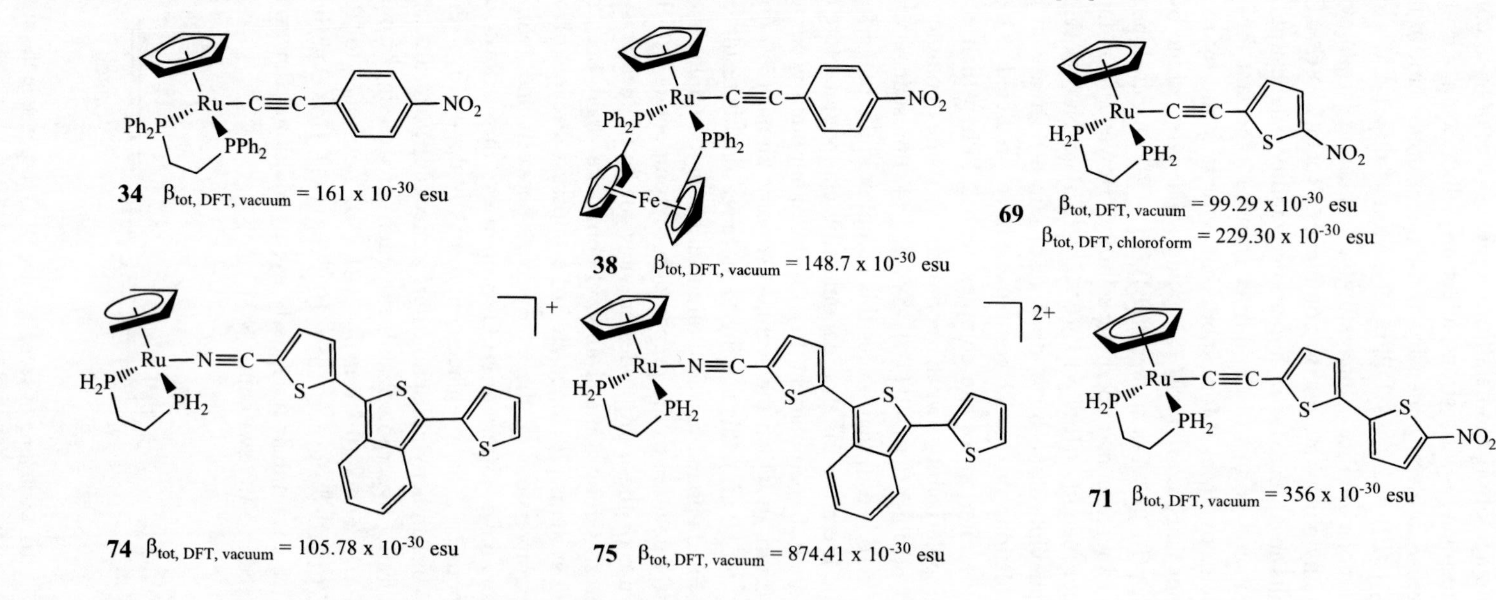

Figure 11. Selected "RuCp" vinylidene complexes showing the most representative structures for SO NLO properties

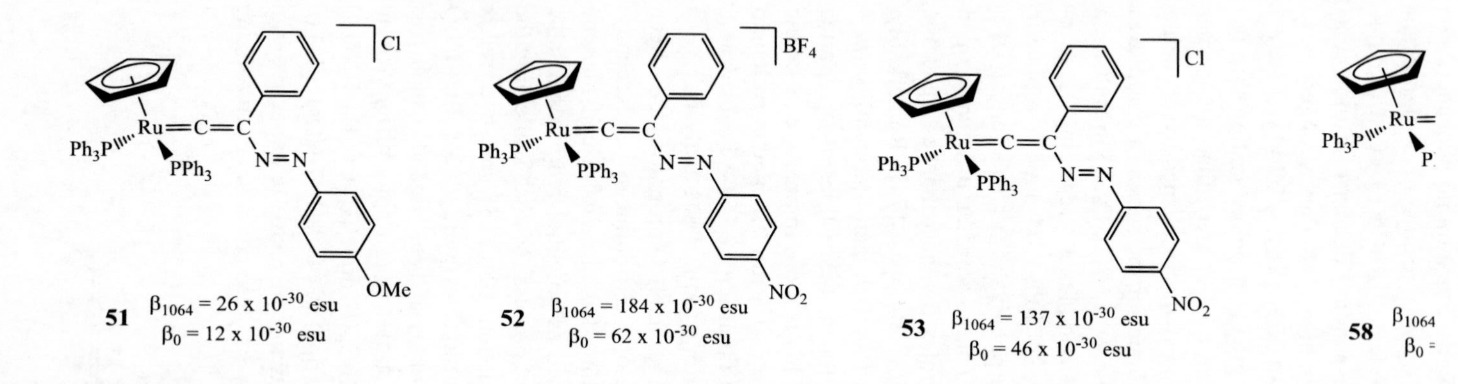

Figure 12. Selected "RuCp" complexes showing the most representative structures for SO NLO properties by computational methods.

Table 3. Molecular quadratic NLO measurements for "RuCp" vinylidene complexes

Compound	λ max (nm)	β (10^{-30} esu)	$β_0$ (10^{-30} esu)	Technique	Solvent	Fund. (nm)	Ref.
$[RuCp(PPh_3)_2(C{=}CPhN{=}NPh)]BF_4$ (48)	363	14	6.6	HRS	Acetone	1064	[86]
$[RuCp(PPh_3)_2(C{=}CPhN{=}NC_6H_4\text{-2-OMe})]Cl$ (49)	373	22	10	HRS	Acetone	1064	[86]
$[RuCp(PPh_3)_2(C{=}CPhN{=}NC_6H_4\text{-3-OMe})]BF_4$ (50)	382	23	10	HRS	Acetone	1064	[86]
$[RuCp(PPh_3)_2(C{=}CPhN{=}NC_6H_4\text{-4-OMe})]Cl$ (51)	370	26	12	HRS	Acetone	1064	[86]
$[RuCp(PPh_3)_2(C{=}CPhN{=}NC_6H_4\text{-4-}NO_2)]BF_4$ (52)	413	184	62	HRS	CH_2Cl_2	1064	[86]
$[RuCp(PPh_3)_2(C{=}CPhN{=}NC_6H_4\text{-4-}NO_2)]Cl$ (53)	413	137	46	HRS	CH_2Cl_2	1064	[86]
$[RuCp(PPh_3)_2(C{=}CPhN{=}NC_6H_4\text{-4-}NO_2)]Br$ (54)	413	136	45	HRS	CH_2Cl_2	1064	[86]
$[RuCp(PPh_3)_2(C{=}CPhN{=}NC_6H_4\text{-4-}NO_2)]I$ (55)	417	150	48	HRS	Acetone	1064	[86]
	415	101	33	HRS	THF	1064	[86]
	413	134	45	HRS	CH_2Cl_2	1064	[86]
$[RuCp(PPh_3)_2(C{=}CPhN{=}NC_6H_4\text{-4-}NO_2)](4\text{-}MeC_6H_4SO_3)$ (56)	413	164	55	HRS	CH_2Cl_2	1064	[86]
$[RuCp(PPh_3)_2(C{=}CPhN{=}NC_6H_4\text{-4-}NO_2)]NO_3$ (57)	413	181	61	HRS	CH_2Cl_2	1064	[86]
$[RuCp(PPh_3)_2(C{=}CPhN{=}N\text{-}C_6H_3\text{-3,5-}(NO_2)_2)]Cl$ (58)	395	33	13	HRS	Acetone	1064	[86]

Table 4. Computationally-derived molecular quadratic NLO properties for "RuCp" complexes[a]

Compound	β_{tot} (10^{-30} esu)	Method	Solvent	Ref.
[RuCp(PPh$_3$)$_2$(C≡CPh)] (19)	2[b]	ZINDO	Gas phase	[75, 87]
[RuCp(k^2-dppe)(C≡CPh)] (59)	19	DFT	Gas phase	[81]
[RuCp(PMe$_3$)$_2$(C≡CPh)] (60)	5[b]	ZINDO	Gas phase	[75, 87]
[RuCp(PPh$_3$)$_2$(C≡CC$_6$H$_4$-4-NO$_2$)] (20)	29[b]	ZINDO	Gas phase	[75, 87]
[RuCp(k^2-dppe)(C≡CC$_6$H$_4$-4-NO$_2$)] (34)	161	DFT	Gas phase	[81]
[RuCp(PMe$_3$)$_2$(C≡CC$_6$H$_4$-4-NO$_2$)] (21)	31[b]	ZINDO	Gas phase	[75, 87]
[RuCp(PPh$_3$)$_2$(C≡CC$_6$H$_4$-4-C$_6$H$_4$-4-NO$_2$)] (22)	36[b]	ZINDO	Gas phase	[75, 87]
[RuCp(PPh$_3$)$_2$(C≡CC$_6$H$_4$-4-C≡CC$_6$H$_4$-4-NO$_2$)] (23)	36[b]	ZINDO	Gas phase	[75, 87]
[RuCp(PPh$_3$)$_2$(C≡CC$_6$H$_4$-4-(*E*)-CH=CHC$_6$H$_4$-4-NO$_2$)] (24)	45[b]	ZINDO	Gas phase	[75, 87]
[RuCp(PPh$_3$)$_2$(C≡CC$_6$H$_4$-4-N=CHC$_6$H$_4$-4-NO$_2$)] (25)	55[b]	ZINDO	Gas phase	[75, 87]
[RuCp(PPh$_3$)$_2$(C≡CC$_6$H$_4$-4-CH=NC$_6$H$_4$-4-NO$_2$)] (61)	52[b]	ZINDO	Gas phase	[71]
[RuCp(PPh$_3$)$_2$(C≡CC$_6$H$_4$-4-N=NC$_6$H$_4$-4-NO$_2$)] (62)	89[b]	ZINDO	Gas phase	[71]
[RuCp(dppf)(C≡CPh)] (63)	13.8	DFT	Gas phase	[81]
[RuCp(dppf)(C≡CC$_6$H$_4$-4-NO$_2$)] (38)	148.7	DFT	Gas phase	[81]
[RuCp(H$_2$PCH$_2$CH$_2$PH$_2$)(C≡C-2-Th-5-NMe$_2$)] (64)	4.66	DFT	Gas phase	[88]
[RuCp(H$_2$PCH$_2$CH$_2$PH$_2$)(C≡C-2-Th-5-NH$_2$)] (65)	5.35	DFT	Gas phase	[88]
[RuCp(H$_2$PCH$_2$CH$_2$PH$_2$)(C≡C-2-Th-5-OMe)] (66)	9.62	DFT	Gas phase	[88]
[RuCp(H$_2$PCH$_2$CH$_2$PH$_2$)(C≡C-2-C$_4$H$_3$S)] (67)	17.22	DFT	Gas phase	[88]
[RuCp(H$_2$PCH$_2$CH$_2$PH$_2$)(C≡C-2-Th-5-CN)] (68)	48.68	DFT	Gas phase	[88]
[RuCp(H$_2$PCH$_2$CH$_2$PH$_2$)(C≡C-2-Th-5-CHO)] (69)	65.89	DFT	Gas phase	[88]
[RuCp(H$_2$PCH$_2$CH$_2$PH$_2$)(C≡C-2-Th-5-NO$_2$)] (70)	99.29	DFT	Gas phase	[74, 88]
	229.30	DFT	CHCl$_3$	[88]
	290.28	DFT	Acetone	[88]
	298.81	DFT	MeOH	[88]
[RuCp(H$_2$PCH$_2$CH$_2$PH$_2$)(C≡C-2-{Th}$_2$-5-NO$_2$)] (71)	356	DFT	Gas phase	[74]
[RuCp(PH$_3$)$_2$(C≡C-2-Th-5-NO$_2$)] (72)	96	DFT	Gas phase	[74]
[RuCp(PH$_3$)$_2$(C≡C-2-{Th}$_2$-5-NO$_2$)] (73)	321	DFT	Gas phase	[74]
[RuCp(H$_2$PCH$_2$CH$_2$PH$_2$)(N≡C-2-Th-5-BcT-5-C$_4$H$_3$S)]$^+$ (74)	105.78	DFT	Gas phase	[89]
	24.72[c]	DFT	CHCl$_3$	[62]
[RuCp(H$_2$PCH$_2$CH$_2$PH$_2$)(N≡C-2-Th-5-BcT-5-C$_4$H$_3$S)]$^{2+}$ (75)	874.41	DFT	Gas phase	[89]
[RuCp(H$_2$PCH$_2$CH$_2$PH$_2$)(N≡C-2-Th-5-BcT-5-C$_4$H$_3$S)] (76)	45.06	DFT	Gas phase	[89]
[RuCp(PH$_3$)$_2$(N≡C-2-Th-5-BcT-5-C$_4$H$_3$S)]$^+$ (77)	29.43[c]	DFT	CHCl$_3$	[62]
[RuCp(*k*^{2}-dppe)(N≡C-2-Th-5-BcT-5-C$_4$H$_3$S)]$^+$ (78)	24.73[c]	DFT	CHCl$_3$	[62]
[RuCp(PPh$_3$)$_2$(N≡C-2-Th-5-BcT-5-C$_4$H$_3$S)]$^+$ (10)	26.36[c]	DFT	CHCl$_3$	[62]

[a] β_{tot} calculated from eq. (17) (Section 2.2) except where otherwise indicated; [b] β_{vec}, calculated at 1910 nm;
[c] β_{HRS} calculated using Eqs.(9)-(11) (Section 2.2); Th- thiophene backbone (C_4H_2S); BcT-benzo[c]thiophene backbone (C_8H_6S);

Compared to the alkynyls, the study of the quadratic NLO properties of vinylidene complexes is comparatively recent; their SO NLO response is generally lower. [13] Their interest is mostly related to the possibility of switching the NLO properties by virtue of the facile interconvertibility of acetylide (high β values: "on" form) and protonated vinylidene (lower β values: "off" form) pairs via protonation/deprotonation sequences (Figure 10). So far SO NLO studies of "RuCp" vinylidene complexes are limited to aryldiazovinylidene derivatives (Table 3) being the representative structures depicted in Figure 11.

On this frame, vinylidene complexes were not designed to have large quadratic NLO responses and, as expected, the nonlinearities for the aryldiazovinylidene derivatives are low. In general the observed values mimic the trends observed for any dipolar 1D molecule. Thus, higher SO NLO responses are observed with the introduction of polarizing substituents leading to more asymmetric systems, as can be seen proceeding from $[RuCp(PPh_3)_2(C{=}CPhN{=}NPh)]BF_4$ (48) (β = 14 x 10^{-30} esu; β_0 = 6.6 x 10^{-30} esu) to $[RuCp(PPh_3)_2(C{=}CPhN{=}NC_6H_4\text{-}4\text{-}NO_2)]BF_4$ (52) (β = 184 x 10^{-30} esu; β_0 = 62 x 10^{-30} esu) and from $[RuCp(PPh_3)_2(C{=}CPhN{=}NC_6H_4\text{-}4\text{-}OMe)]Cl$ (51) (β = 26 x 10^{-30} esu; β_0 = 12 x 10^{-30} esu) to $[RuCp(PPh_3)_2(C{=}CPhN{=}NC_6H_4\text{-}4\text{-}NO_2)]Cl$ (53) (β = 137 x 10^{-30} esu; β_0 = 46 x 10^{-30} esu) due to the presence of an effective electron-acceptor group or from $[RuCp(PPh_3)_2(C{=}CPhN{=}N\text{-}C_6H_3\text{-}3,5\text{-}(NO_2)_2)]Cl$ (58) (β = 33 x 10^{-30} esu; β_0 = 13 x 10^{-30} esu) to $[RuCp(PPh_3)_2(C{=}CPhN{=}NC_6H_4\text{-}4\text{-}NO_2)]Cl$ (53) (β = 137 x 10^{-30} esu; β_0 = 46 x 10^{-30} esu) due to the position of the nitro group. [86] Complex $[RuCp(PPh_3)_2(C{=}CPhN{=}NC_6H_4\text{-}4\text{-}NO_2)]I$ (55) was studied in three different solvents, nonlinearities varying as β(acetone) = $\beta(CH_2Cl_2)$ > β(THF). The effect of different counter ions was studied for $[RuCp(PPh_3)_2(C{=}CPhN{=}NC_6H_4\text{-}4\text{-}NO_2)]^+$. Quadratic optical nonlinearities for the halide salts are equivalent within experimental error and for those with remaining anions, which are expected to contribute to the observed nonlinearity, the SO NLO responses are larger.

2.4. Computational Derived Molecular Quadratic Hyperpolarizabilities

Computational data obtained by quantum methods, namely ZINDO and DFT, has been used to evaluate the NLO merit and to rationalize the experimental observations on linear optical and quadratic nonlinear optical properties of some of the studied "RuCp" complexes. The results are collected in Table 4 and representative structures are depicted in Figure 12.

The first extended survey on the structure-SO NLO properties relationship of "RuCp" alkynyl complexes was assessed by the semi-empirical ZINDO method which has been used before to evaluate the NLO merit of ferrocenyl derivatives. [90] For these complexes, ZINDO gives small quadratic hyperpolarizability responses thus not reproducing the experimental data which are significantly larger and with important resonance enhancement (Table 2). Although unreliable in reproducing the magnitude, ZINDO calculations proved useful in reproducing some trends in experimental data. For instance, computational values of β_{vec} increase with the acceptor strength of the aryl substituent as can be seen proceeding from $[RuCp(LL)(C{\equiv}CPh)]$ to $[RuCp(PPh_3)_2(C{\equiv}CC_6H_4\text{-}4\text{-}NO_2)]$ (LL = PPh_3 (20), PMe_3 (21)), consistent with experimental data. The effect of chain lengthening leads to an increase in calculated nonlinear response as can be seen in the sequence $[RuCp(PPh_3)_2(C{\equiv}CC_6H_4\text{-}4\text{-}NO_2)]$ (20) (β_{vec} = 29 x 10^{-30} esu) < $[RuCp(PPh_3)_2(C{\equiv}CC_6H_4\text{-}4\text{-}C_6H_4\text{-}4\text{-}NO_2)]$ (22) (β_{vec} = 36 x 10^{-30} esu) < $[RuCp(PPh_3)_2(C{\equiv}CC_6H_4\text{-}4\text{-}(E)\text{-}CH{=}CHC_6H_4\text{-}4\text{-}NO_2)]$ (24) (β_{vec} = 45 x 10^{-30} esu) thus also reproducing experimental data. [52, 71, 81] Despite the small increase on replacing one CH by N, there is a dramatic increase on the second substitution, with the computed response for the azo-linked complex [Ru(PPh$_3$)$_2${C≡CC$_6$H$_4$-(*E*)-4-N=NC$_6$H$_4$-4-NO$_2$)] (31) (β_{vec} = 89 x 10^{-30} esu) almost double that of [RuCp(PPh$_3$)$_2$(C≡CC$_6$H$_4$-4-(*E*)-CH=CHC$_6$H$_4$-4-NO$_2$)] (24) (β_{vec} = 45 x 10^{-30} esu). The relative experimental magnitude of the complex with azo-group when compared to those with ene- and imino-group is well reproduced by the theoretical data but, in contrast, the calculated β_{vec} of the imino derivative is higher than that of ene derivative, the opposite trend to that observed experimentally. Computationally derived molecular quadratic hyperpolarizabilities increase on increasing the donor strength of the co-ligand (proceeding from PPh$_3$ to PMe$_3$), also the opposite trend to that observed experimentally. Although unreliable in reproducing some experimental trends, ZINDO calculations proved useful in assessing structural variations difficult or impossible to evaluate experimentally. For instance, the effect on quadratic NLO properties of M–C bond length modification and dependence on orientation of the acetylide aryl group was studied using this method (Figure 13). The results suggest that NLO response should increase with decreasing M–C distance and little dependence on orientation of the acetylide aryl group is predicted. [87]

In a continuous effort to get a better understanding on the electronic factors that may dictate the SO NLO properties, density functional theory (DFT) calculations were employed to investigate these properties on the thienyl acetylide model complexes [RuCp(H$_2$PCH$_2$CH$_2$PH$_2$)(C≡C-2-Th-5-Y)] (Y=NMe$_2$ (64), NH$_2$ (65), OMe (66), H (67), CN (68), CHO (69), NO$_2$ (70)). [88] Both electron-acceptor and electron-donor groups in the acetylide thienyl moiety was considered in order to verify the ability of these ligands to act as hyperpolarizable chromophores when interacting with the good electron-donor organometallic “RuCp” group. The results have shown that the traditional qualitative arguments for enhancing second-order nonlinear optical responses were applicable on these complexes, thus leading to the prediction of higher hyperpolarizabilities for [RuCp(H$_2$PCH$_2$CH$_2$PH$_2$)(C≡C-2-Th-5-NO$_2$)] (70), in which the strong electron donor organometallic fragment was combined with the better acceptor group NO$_2$. The effect on quadratic NLO properties of M–C bond length modification of this complex have shown that a maximum of β is obtained for *ca* 2.00 Å, a value that corresponds to the Ru-C1 bond length for the optimized structure (Figure 14). The solvation effects were also taken into account on the calculated quadratic hyperpolarizabilities for [RuCp(H$_2$PCH$_2$CH$_2$PH$_2$)(C≡C-2-Th-5-NO$_2$)] (70). The better SO NLO properties of this compound in solvated media when compared to that found in gas-phase was related to both lower energies and better charge-transfer efficiencies arising from the ruthenium moiety to the thienyl ligand. This was explained as a result of a suitable electronic reorganization that takes place in solvated media, which produces important changes in the optical properties. The magnitude of β_{tot} was found to increase with the solvent polarity. It is interesting to note a linear dependence of β_{tot} values with BLA (Bond Length Alternation), defined as the difference between the average carbon–carbon adjacent bond lengths along a conjugated backbone, in different media for this compound (Figure 15) which reveal that the degree of charge delocalization in the ground state can be important concerning the SO NLO properties of the studied compound.

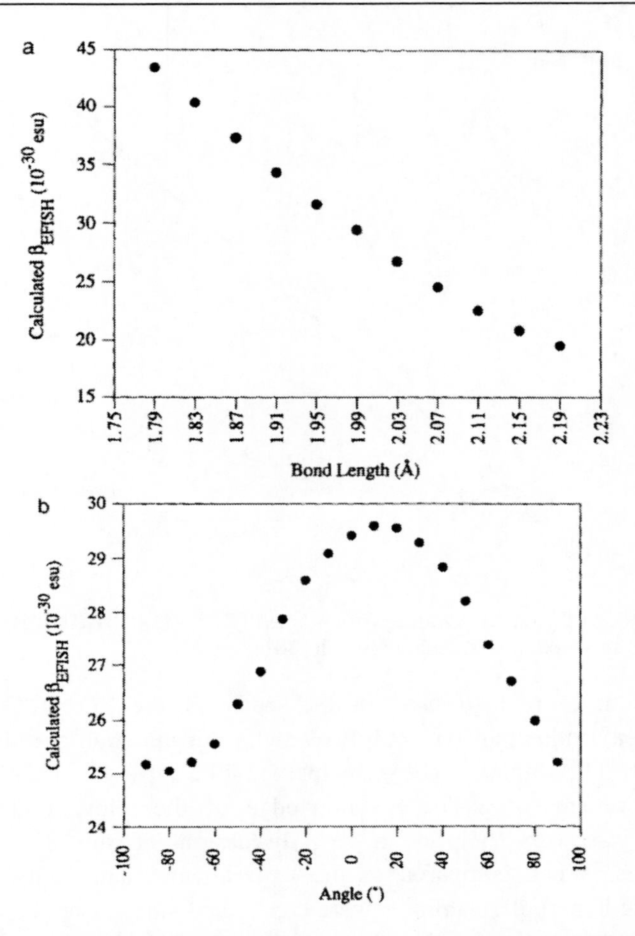

Figure 13. ZINDO-derived β_{vec} for [RuCp(PMe$_3$)$_2$(C≡CC$_6$H$_4$-4-NO$_2$)] (21) showing (a) the effect of Ru-C bond length variation and (b) the effect of acetylide phenyl ring rotation [87].

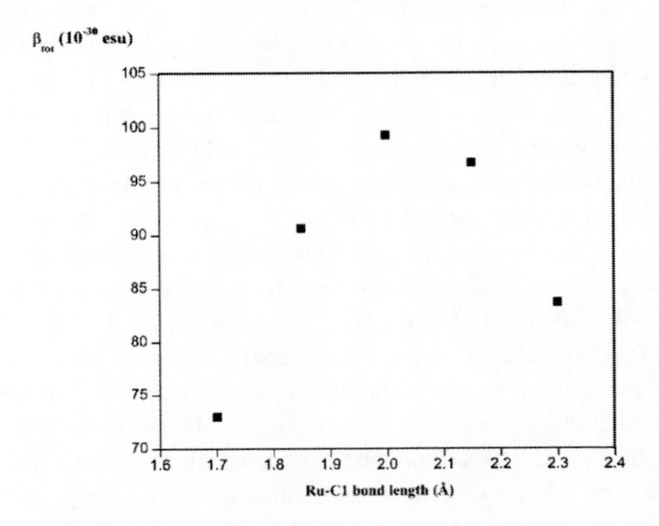

Figure 14. Effect of the Ru-C1 bond length on the quadratic hyperpolarizability for compound [RuCp(H$_2$PCH$_2$CH$_2$PH$_2$)(C≡C-2-Th-5-NO$_2$)] (70). Adapted from [88].

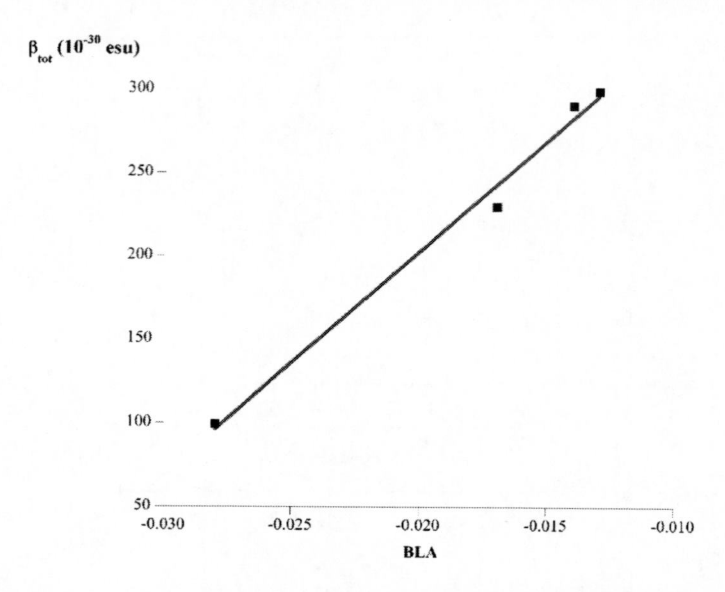

Figure 15. Dependence of β_{tot} on BLA values for complex [RuCp($H_2PCH_2CH_2PH_2$)(C≡C-2-Th-5-NO_2)] (70) in gas phase and solvated media. Adapted from [88].

DFT calculations were also used in the study of the SO NLO properties of η^5-monocyclopentadienylruthenium(II) complexes with nitrothienyl acetylide chromophores, [RuCp(LL)(C≡C-2-{Th}$_n$-5-NO_2)] (LL= k^2-dppe, 2 PPh_3; n= 1, 2). [74] Theoretical data allowed the achievement of a deeper knowledge of the relevant electronic transitions involved, which was very helpful in the discussion of the experimental quadratic hyperpolarizabilities. When compared to the experimental data, only the trends on the calculated quadratic hyperpolarizabilities were considered since several approximations were used for theoretical studies (model phosphane co-ligands, isolated molecules in the gas phase c.f. experimental data obtained in solution, calculated static-frequency quadratic hyperpolarizability, β_0, vs. experimental β_{1500}). The results show that calculated β_0 overestimates the experimental β_0 values in most cases (only for [RuCp(k^2-dppe)(C≡C-2-Th-5-NO_2)] (44) an underestimation was observed). It was difficult to compare the trend found experimentally to the one observed from computed values due to the fact that several compounds have experimental quadratic hyperpolarizabilities falling within the experimental error. However, chain lengthening clearly leads to an increase in calculated nonlinear response, thus reproducing experimental data.

DFT calculations were also employed to rationalize the second-order nonlinear optical properties of 5-(3-(thiophen-2-yl)benzo[c]thiophen-1-yl)thiophene-2-carbonitrile complexes, [RuCp(LL)(N≡C-2-Th-5-BcT-5-C_4H_3S)]$^+$ (LL = k^2-dppe (9), 2 PPh_3 (10)). [62] Model ($H_2PCH_2CH_2PH_2$, PH_3) and real (k^2-dppe, PPh_3) phosphanes were used in the calculations, in order to evaluate the use of model phosphanes to describe the behavior found for real molecules. Also, calculations were carried out in solvated media in order to obtain quantitatively satisfactory results of both the calculated electronic excitations and quadratic hyperpolarizabilities in comparison with experimental data. Very good results on the calculated λ_{max} were obtained in comparison with experimental data, either using model or real phosphanes in the calculations. However, some underestimation of the DFT β_{HRS}, in the range of 24.72 - 29.43 x 10^{-30} esu, was observed when compared to the experimental two-level model corrected values, β_0. The substitution of the model phosphanes by k^2-dppe and PPh_3 originates small differences (up to ~10%) on the corresponding calculated β_{HRS}. However, the results show that the use of real phosphanes in DFT calculations can be important to give an additional insight relating to the differences on the experimental quadratic hyperpolarizabilities of the studied complexes. DFT calculations has also used in the same model complexes in view to evaluate their potentiality for application as SO NLO switches. [89] The results showed that these complexes could be good candidate materials acting by redox means since an increase of the quadratic hyperpolarizability up to 8.3 times was predicted upon oxidation, as can be seen proceeding from $[RuCp(H_2PCH_2CH_2PH_2)(N{\equiv}C\text{-}2\text{-}Th\text{-}5\text{-}BcT\text{-}5\text{-}C_4H_3S)]^+$ (74) (β_{tot} = 105.78 x 10^{-30} esu) to $[RuCp(H_2PCH_2CH_2PH_2)(N{\equiv}C\text{-}2\text{-}Th\text{-}5\text{-}BcT\text{-}5\text{-}C_4H_3S)]^{2+}$ (75) (β_{tot} = 874.41 x 10^{-30} esu).

Recently linear optical and quadratic NLO properties of [RuCp(LL)(C≡CPh)] and $[RuCp(LL)(C{\equiv}CC_6H_4\text{-}4\text{-}NO_2)]$ (LL = k^2-dppe (59) and (34); dppf (63) and (38)) were rationalized by DFT calculations. [81] The introduction of the nitro group results in a red-shift of the main lowest energy band in the calculated spectra and also in calculated β_{tot} as can be seen in the pairs [RuCp(LL)(C≡CPh)] (k^2-dppe (59): 19 x 10^{-30} esu; dppf (63): β_{tot} = 13.8 x 10^{-30} esu) and $[RuCp(LL)(C{\equiv}CC_6H_4\text{-}4\text{-}NO_2)]$ (k^2-dppe (34): 161 x 10^{-30} esu; dppf (38): β_{tot} = 148.7 x 10^{-30} esu;). Replacing dppe ligand by dppf has only a minor effect. The overall results have shown to reproduce quite well the experimental data.

2.5. Bulk Second-Order Measurements

The motivation for the study of the NLO properties in solid state has been certainly the variety of applications in the photonic and optoelectronic technologies. In particular, NLO frequency conversion materials have an important impact on laser technology, optical communication and optical data storage. Although a large number of NLO materials have been reported, most materials fail to fulfill the requirements for practical applications since, besides high optical nonlinearity, materials must present mechanical strength, thermal stability, adequate transparency, robustness to laser damage threshold and grow in large single crystals. These limitations have been on the basis for the continuing search of suitable materials more efficient than the well-known organic and inorganic compounds, e.g., urea or lithium niobate, which crystals are easy to grow and are commercially available to be used as frequency doublers. In principle, compounds with high quadratic hyperpolarizabilities certainly are good candidates for the solid state applications; however the achievement of a high macroscopic nonlinearity (second-order susceptibility, $\chi^{(2)}$), which is proportional to the tensorial sum of the molecular hyperpolarizabilities, requires a favorable orientation of the NLO chromophores, in a macroscopic non-centrosymmetric structure. Unfortunately, high molecular hyperpolarizabilities and well aligned crystal packing tend to exclude each other because of the large dipole moments, typically associated with push–pull systems which tend to favor anti-parallel alignment of neighboring molecules, thus cancelling their bulk second-order NLO responses. For this reason, about 75 % percent of the organic and organometallic compounds presenting this structural requisite crystallize in centrosymmetric space groups and albeit their high quadratic hyperpolarizability values, the SHG property at macroscopic level is zero.

Table 5. Kurtz powder measurements for "RuCp" complexes

Compound	SHG[a]	Fund.(nm)	Ref.
$[RuCp(PPh_3)_2(C{\equiv}C\text{-}2\text{-}C_5H_3N)]$ (79)	<<1	1064	[82]
$[RuCp(PPh_3)_2(C{\equiv}C\text{-}2\text{-}C_5H_3N\text{-}5\text{-}NO_2)]$ (40)	<<1	1064	[82]
$[RuCp(PPh_3)_2(C{=}CPhN{=}NPh)]BF_4$ (48)	0.48	1064	[92]
$[RuCp(PPh_3)_2(C{=}CPhN{=}NPh)](4\text{-}MeC_6H_4SO_3)$ (80)	0.50	1064	[92]
$[RuCp(PPh_3)_2(C{=}CPhN{=}NPh)]NO_3$ (81)	0.57	1064	[92]
$[RuCp(PPh_3)_2(C{=}CPhN{=}NPh)]Cl$ (82)	0.50	1064	[92]
$[RuCp(PPh_3)_2(C{=}CPhN{=}NPh)]I$ (83)	0.53	1064	[92]
$[RuCp(PPh_3)_2(C{=}CPhN{=}NC_6H_4\text{-}4\text{-}OMe)]BF_4$ (84)	1.05	1064	[92]
$[RuCp(PPh_3)_2(C{=}CPhN{=}NC_6H_4\text{-}4\text{-}OMe)](4\text{-}MeC_6H_4SO_3)$ (85)	<0.05	1064	[92]
$[RuCp(PPh_3)_2(C{=}CPhN{=}NC_6H_4\text{-}4\text{-}OMe)]NO_3$ (86)	<0.05	1064	[92]
$[RuCp(PPh_3)_2(C{=}CPhN{=}NC_6H_4\text{-}4\text{-}OMe)]Cl$ (51)	<0.05	1064	[92]
$[RuCp(PPh_3)_2(C{=}CPhN{=}NC_6H_4\text{-}4\text{-}OMe)]I$ (87)	<0.05	1064	[92]
$[RuCp(PPh_3)_2(C{=}CPhN{=}NC_6H_4\text{-}2\text{-}OMe)]BF_4$ (88)	0.63	1064	[92]
$[RuCp(PPh_3)_2(C{=}CPhN{=}NC_6H_4\text{-}2\text{-}OMe)](4\text{-}MeC_6H_4SO_3)$ (89)	<0.05	1064	[92]
$[RuCp(PPh_3)_2(C{=}CPhN{=}NC_6H_4\text{-}2\text{-}OMe)]NO_3$ (90)	<0.05	1064	[92]
$[RuCp(PPh_3)_2(C{=}CPhN{=}N)C_6H_4\text{-}2\text{-}OMe)]Cl$ (91)	<0.05	1064	[92]
$[RuCp(PPh_3)_2(C{=}CPhN{=}NC_6H_4\text{-}2\text{-}OMe)]I$ (92)	<0.05	1064	[92]
$[RuCp(PPh_3)_2(C{=}CPhN{=}NC_6H_4\text{-}4\text{-}NO_2)]BF_4$ (52)	<0.05	1064	[92]
$[RuCp(PPh_3)_2(C{=}CPhN{=}NC_6H_4\text{-}4\text{-}NO_2)](4\text{-}MeC_6H_4SO_3)$ (56)	<0.05	1064	[92]
$[RuCp(PPh_3)_2(C{=}CPhN{=}NC_6H_4\text{-}4\text{-}NO_2)]NO_3$ (57)	<0.05	1064	[92]
$[RuCp(PPh_3)_2(C{=}CPhN{=}NC_6H_4\text{-}4\text{-}NO_2)]Cl$ (53)	<0.05	1064	[92]
$[RuCp(PPh_3)_2(C{=}CPhN{=}NC_6H_4\text{-}4\text{-}NO_2)]I$ (55)	<0.05	1064	[92]
$[RuCp(PPh_3)_2(C{=}CPhN{=}NC_6H_3\text{-}3,5\text{-}(NO_2)_2)]BF_4$ (93)	<0.05	1064	[92]
$[RuCp(PPh_3)_2(C{=}CPhN{=}NC_6H_3\text{-}3,5\text{-}(NO_2)_2)](4\text{-}MeC_6H_4SO_3)$ (94)	<0.05	1064	[92]
$[RuCp(PPh_3)_2(C{=}CPhN{=}NC_6H_3\text{-}3,5\text{-}(NO_2)_2)]NO_3$ (95)	<0.05	1064	[92]
$[RuCp(PPh_3)_2(C{=}CPhN{=}NC_6H_3\text{-}3,5\text{-}(NO_2)_2)]Cl$ (96)	<0.05	1064	[92]
$[RuCp(PPh_3)_2(C{=}CPhN{=}NC_6H_3\text{-}3,5\text{-}(NO_2)_2)]I$ (97)	<0.05	1064	[92]
$[RuCp(PPh_3)_2(N{\equiv}CC_6H_4\text{-}4\text{-}NH(C{=}O)H)]PF_6$ (98)	1.2	1064	[59]
$[RuCp((+)\text{-}diop)(N{\equiv}CC_6H_4\text{-}4\text{-}NO_2)]PF_6$ (99)	2.7	1064	[93]
$[RuCp((+)\text{-}diop)(N{\equiv}CC_6H_4\text{-}4\text{-}NO_2)]CF_3SO_3$ (100)	10.0	1064	[93]
$[RuCp((+)\text{-}diop)(N{\equiv}CC_6H_4\text{-}4\text{-}NO_2)]Cl$ (101)	0.5	1064	[93]
$[RuCp((+)\text{-}diop)(N{\equiv}CC_6H_4\text{-}4\text{-}NO_2)]Br$ (102)	0.00	1064	[94]
$[RuCp((+)\text{-}diop)(N{\equiv}CC_6H_4\text{-}4\text{-}NO_2)]NO_3$ (103)	1.2	1064	[93]
$[RuCp((+)\text{-}diop)(N{\equiv}CC_6H_4\text{-}4\text{-}NO_2)]BF_4$ (104)	1.9	1064	[93]
$[RuCp((+)\text{-}diop)(N{\equiv}CC_6H_4\text{-}4\text{-}NO_2)]ClO_4$ (105)	2.9	1064	[93]
$[RuCp((+)\text{-}diop)(N{\equiv}CC_6H_4\text{-}4\text{-}NO_2)]p\text{-}CH_3C_6H_4SO_3$ (106)	0.4	1064	[93]
$[RuCp((+)\text{-}diop)(N{\equiv}CC_6H_4\text{-}4\text{-}CH_3)]PF_6$ (107)	0.00	1064	[95]
$[RuCp((+)\text{-}diop)(N{\equiv}CC_6H_4\text{-}4\text{-}OCH_3)]PF_6$ (108)	0.03	1064	[95]
$[RuCp((+)\text{-}diop)(N{\equiv}CC_6H_4\text{-}4\text{-}NH_2)]PF_6$ (109)	0.00	1064	[95]
$[RuCp((+)\text{-}diop))(N{\equiv}CC_6H_4\text{-}4\text{-}C_6H_4\text{-}4\text{-}NO_2)]PF_6$ (110)	0.82	1064	[95]

Compound	SHG[a]	Fund.(nm)	Ref.
$[RuCp((+)\text{-diop})(N{\equiv}C\text{-}(E)\text{-}CH{=}CHC_6H_4\text{-}4\text{-}N(CH_3)_2))]PF_6$ (111)	0.40	1064	[95]
$[RuCp((+)\text{-diop}))(N{\equiv}C\text{-}(E)\text{-}CH{=}CHC_6H_4\text{-}4\text{-}NO_2)]PF_6$ (112)	1.96	1064	[95]
$[RuCp((+)\text{-diop})(N{\equiv}CC_6H_4\text{-}4\text{-}F)]CF_3SO_3$ (113)	0.00	1064	[95]
$[RuCp((+)\text{-diop}))(N{\equiv}C\text{-}(E)\text{-}CH{=}CHC_6H_4\text{-}4\text{-}NO_2)]CF_3SO_3$ (114)	1.20	1064	[95]
$[RuCp((+)\text{-diop}))(N{\equiv}CC_6H_4\text{-}4\text{-}C_6H_4\text{-}4\text{-}NO_2)]CF_3SO_3$ (115)	0.80	1064	[95]
$[RuCp((+)\text{-diop})(N{\equiv}CC_5H_4N)]CF_3SO_3$ (116)	0.00	1064	[94]
$[RuCp((S)\text{-prolophos})(N{\equiv}CC_5H_4N)]PF_6$ (117)	0.49	1064	[94]
$[RuCp(k^2\text{-dppe})(N{\equiv}CC_6H_4\text{-}4\text{-}NO_2)]PF_6$ (1)	0.00	1064	[94]
$[RuCp(k^2\text{-dppe})(N{\equiv}CC_6H_4\text{-}C_6H_5)]PF_6$ (118)	0.00	1064	[94]
$[RuCp(k^2\text{-dppe})(N{\equiv}C\text{-(E)-}CH{=}CHC_6H_4\text{-}4\text{-}NO_2)]PF_6$ (119)	0.00	1064	[94]
$[RuCp(k^2\text{-dppe})(N{\equiv}CC_6H_4\text{-}4\text{-}NO_2)]C_4H_4O_7Sb$ (120)	0.00	1064	[95]
$[RuCp((+)\text{-diop})(N{\equiv}C\text{-}2\text{-Th-}5\text{-}NO_2)]PF_6$ (121)	< 0.01	1064	[60]
$[RuCp((+)\text{-diop})(N{\equiv}C\text{-}2\text{-}\{Th\}_2\text{-}5\text{-}NO_2)]PF_6$ (122)	negligible	1064	[60]
$[RuCp((+)\text{-diop})(N{\equiv}C\text{-}2\text{-}\{Th\}_3\text{-}5\text{-}NO_2)]PF_6$ (123)	negligible	1064	[60]
$[RuCp(PPh_3)_2(\mu\text{-}CN)RuCp(PPh_3)_2]PF_6$ (124)	0.02	1064	[96]
$[RuCp(PPh_3)(CN)]$ (125)	0.001	1064	[96]

[a]Reference: urea (SHG= 1); Th- thiophene backbone (C_4H_2S).

The several classes of "RuCp" complexes studied at molecular level for second-order NLO properties were also evaluated for second-order properties in solid state using the Kurtz-Perry powder method. The SHG efficiencies of several nitrile, vinylidene and alkynyl complexes are listed in Table 5 and the structural formulas of representative compounds being shown in Figure 16.

One of the strategies suggested to overcome the problem of accentric crystallization was the use of ionic salts of push–pull chromophores as second-order NLO crystals. [91] These salts are more likely to form noncentrosymmetric crystals because the Coulombic interactions with the counter-ions can override the detrimental dipole-dipole interactions. The separation and shielding provided by the counter-ions also reduces the dipole-dipole interactions between the chromophores. Thus, not surprisingly, ionic nitrile and vinylidene complexes have been the most studied "RuCp" compounds.

A series of (aryldiazovinylidene)ruthenium salts of general formula $[RuCp(PPh_3)_2(C{=}CPhN{=}NAr)]X$ has been studied by Kurtz method to investigate their effectiveness in second harmonic generation (SHG). [93] However they revealed low efficiencies, compared to urea reference. Compound $[RuCp(PPh_3)_2(C{=}CPhN{=}NAr)]BF_4$ (84) crystallize in centric space group, but surprisingly give nonzero SO NLO response. A result of this type is not unprecedented since some examples of metal complexes have shown the same behavior. [10, 97] A variety of reasons were proposed to explain these results, including the SHG signal arising from particle surfaces, crystal defects, decomposition in the laser beam or fluorescence.

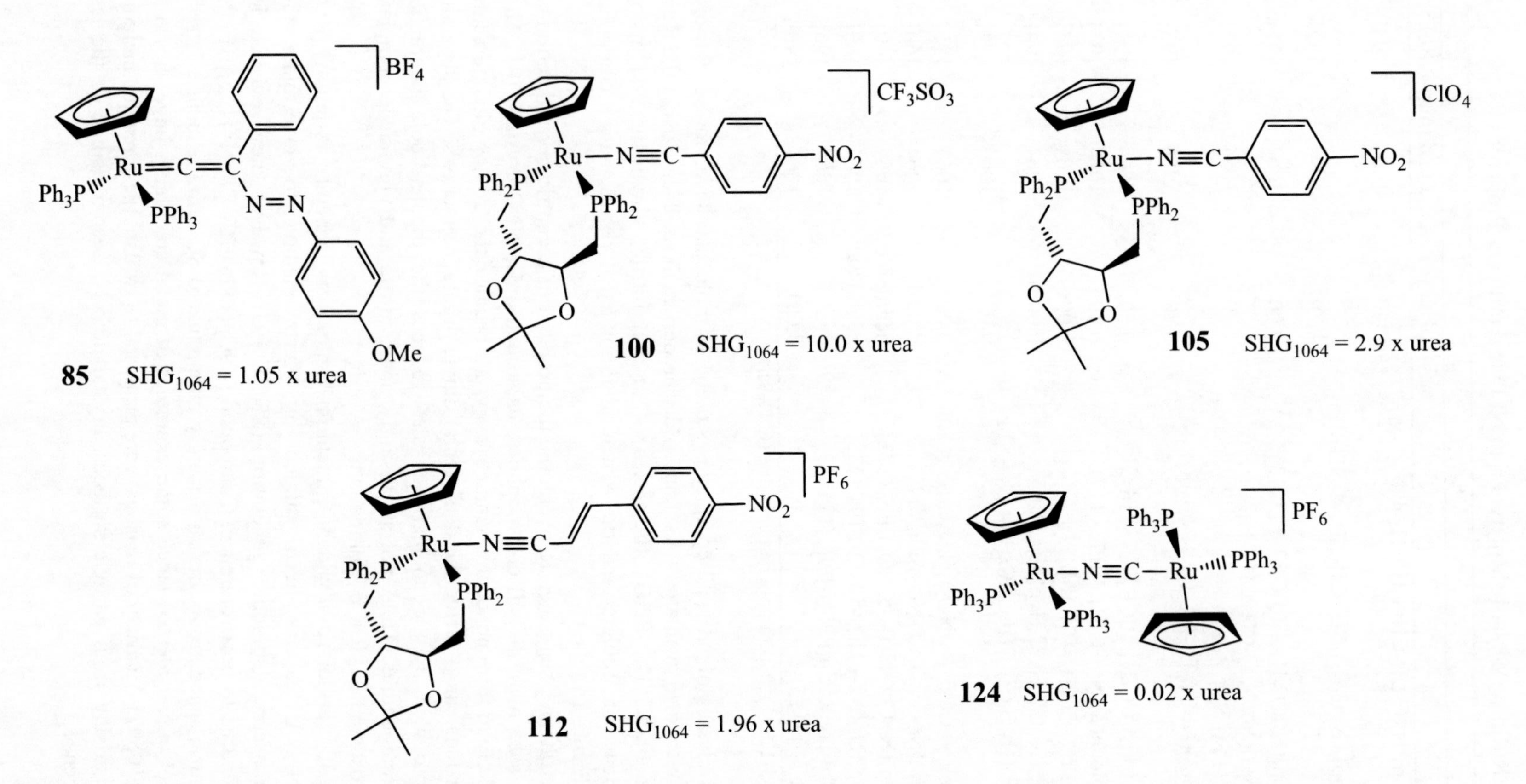

Figure 16. Selected "RuCp" complexes showing the most representative structures for SO NLO properties studied by Kurtz powder technique.

Alternative procedures for organizing favorable lattice alignment have been developed, namely the formation of guest–host inclusion complexes and the incorporation of chiral ligands. Although the former idea has not been applied for "RuCp" complexes, the later approach has been exploited by using chiral co-ligands in a series of nitrile [RuCp(LL)(N≡CR)]Y (LL= (+)-diop, (*S*)-prolophos) complexes. [61, 93-95] The (*S*)-prolophos was only used in the cianopyridine derivative [RuCp((*S*)-prolophos)(N≡CC_5H_4N)]PF_6 (117) giving a low SHG efficiency (0.49 x urea). The observed SHG efficiencies in the chiral (+)-diop series for the most complexes were found to be low to moderate, but some quite high efficiencies were found for [RuCp((+)-diop)(N≡CC_6H_4-4-NO_2)]CF_3SO_3 (100) (10.0 x urea), [RuCp((+)-diop)(N≡CC_6H_4-4-NO_2)]ClO_4 (105) (2.9 x urea) and [RuCp((+)-diop)(N≡CC_6H_4-4-NO_2)]PF_6 (99) (2.7 x urea). [93] Variation of the counter-ion in the series of [RuCp((+)-diop)(N≡CC_6H_4-4-NO_2)]X have showed that SHG powder efficiency can be improved by a factor of 25. This series revealed the importance of the counter-ion role, associated with the non-centrosymmetric crystallization. The importance of the use of chiral ligands on the SHG properties can be viewed in a series of complexes where no chiral ligand is present, [RuCp(k^2-dppe)(N≡CR)]PF_6, for which no SHG signal was detected. A chiral counter-ion was also used to guarantee acentric crystallization in compound [RuCp(k^2-dppe)(N≡CC_6H_4-4-NO_2)][$C_4H_4O_7Sb$] (120), however no SHG signal was produced.

Evaluation of the intermolecular contacts for compounds [RuCp((+)-diop)(N≡CC_6H_4-4-NO_2)]Y (Y= PF_6^- (99), $CF_3SO_3^-$ (100)) [95], revealed the importance of C-H···O hydrogen bonding and also of C-H···F and/or C-H···O between cationic complexes and anions, for the verified supramolecular chromophore alignments. Comparison of the packing features of these compounds also highlights the important role of the counter-ion in crystal packing, this allowing some modeling of the macroscopic NLO properties of these ionic complexes (Figure 17). Nevertheless, the perfect alignment of all the dipoles is not the most important feature for second-harmonic generation purposes. In fact, more important than the perfect alignment of all the dipoles, is the angle between the molecular charge transfer axis (typically along the donor–acceptor axis) and the polar crystal axis. The optimum value for this angle was found to depend on the crystal space group, in order to allow quadratic phase-matched interactions. [98-100] This angle was determined for compounds [RuCp((+)-diop)(N≡CC_6H_4-4-NO_2)]PF_6 (99) (83.5°) and [RuCp((+)-diop)(N≡CC_6H_4-4-NO_2)]CF_3SO_3 (100) (70.3°), both far from the optimum values of 35.26° (for space group $P1$) and 54.74° (for space group $P2_1$). [101] The significant deviation from the optimal phase matching direction (44.74° and 28.76°, respectively), explains the relatively small SHG values found for these compounds and also the poorer value of [RuCp((+)-diop)(N≡CC_6H_4-4-NO_2)]PF_6 (99) when compared with the trifluoromethanesulphonate analogous compound, despite the perfect alignment of the chromophores in the first compound.

Besides the nitrile and vinylidene derivatives only few examples of other type of "RuCp" complexes were evaluated by Kurtz method. Neutral (pyridylalkynyl) complexes were studied but SHG were found to be significantly lower than the urea standard. [82] Also, low SHG efficiencies were observed for neutral cyano complex [RuCp(PPh_3)$_2$(CN)] (125) and cyano-bridged bimetallic [RuCp(PPh_3)$_2$(μ-CN)RuCp(PPh_3)$_2$]PF_6 (124). [96]

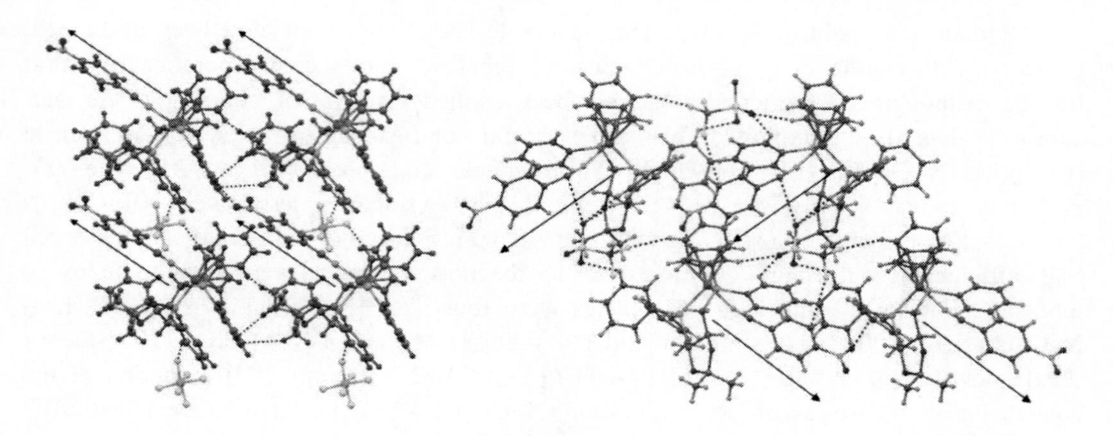

Figure 17. Crystal packing along *a* of compounds [RuCp((+)-diop)(N≡CC$_6$H$_4$-4-NO$_2$)]Y (Y= PF$_6^-$ (left), CF$_3$SO$_3^-$ (right)), showing different dipole alignments. [95]

As emphasized before, the results obtained by Kurtz method do not allow the understand of the structure-NLO relationships due to the involvement of several parameters mainly related with crystallization, phase-matching properties, optical absorption and grain size distribution. X-ray determined crystal structures have been of great importance to understand the NLO solid state properties, allowing not only the determination of the crystallization space group, but also the evaluation of the precise orientation of the molecules in the crystal and the accountable intermolecular interactions. Optimizing molecular alignment is thus important for enhancing SHG efficiencies in non-centrosymmetric space groups. As discussed previously, the introduction of chiral ligands theoretically ensures non-centrosymmetry (although it does not preclude pseudo-centrosymmetric arrangements), but it does not ensure the most favorable molecular arrangement in the lattice. Thus crystal engineering to convert large molecular nonlinearities into significant bulk nonlinearities remains a major challenge.

Although most bulk material second-order measurements have been made on powders, other material forms have also been examined. The molecular alignment achieved in Langmuir-Blodgett monolayer of [RuCp(PPh$_3$)$_2$(N≡CC$_6$H$_4$-4-C$_6$H$_4$-4-C$_6$H$_4$-4-C$_6$H$_5$)]PF$_6$ leads to a quadratic hyperpolarizability of 40 x $^{-50}$ C^{3}m^{3}J^{-2}. [102]

2.6. Third-Order NLO Measurements

In parallel to the studies of second-order NLO properties, the same classes of "RuCp" complexes were also assessed for third-order NLO properties. Nevertheless, the collected data from several sources showed large error margins, thus leading to difficult comparisons. Therefore, attempts to find any structure-property relationships can be particularly challenging. Alkynyl and vinylidene "RuCp" complexes are the most extensively studied (Table 6) and Figure 18 depicts representative examples. Almost all of the studies have been carried out at 800 nm using the Z-scan technique.

Table 6. Cubic NLO measurements for "RuCp" alkynyl and vinylidene complexes

Compound	λ max (nm)	γ_{real} (10^{-36} esu)	γ_{imag} (10^{-36} esu)	γ (10^{-36} esu)	Technique	Solvent	Fund. (nm)	Ref.
[RuCp(PPh$_3$)$_2$(C≡CPh)] (19)	311	≤150	0	≤150	Z-scan	THF	800	[103]
[RuCp(PPh$_3$)$_2$(C≡CC$_6$H$_4$-4-NO$_2$)] (20)	461	-210±50	≤10	-210±50	Z-scan	THF	800	[103]
	461	-		-260±60	DFWM	THF	800	[103]
[RuCp PMe$_3$)$_2$(C≡CC$_6$H$_4$-4-NO$_2$)] (21)	480	-230±70	74±30	240±76	Z-scan	THF	800	[103]
[RuCp(PPh$_3$)$_2$(C≡CC$_6$H$_4$-4-C$_6$H$_4$-4-NO$_2$)] (22)	448	-380±200	320±160	500±260	Z-scan	THF	800	[103]
[RuCp(PPh$_3$)$_2$(C≡CC$_6$H$_4$-4-(*E*)-CH=CHC$_6$H$_4$-4-NO$_2$)] (24)	476	-450±100	210±100	500±140	Z-scan	THF	800	[103]
[RuCp(PPh$_3$)$_2$(C≡CC$_6$H$_4$-4-C≡CC$_6$H$_4$-4-NO$_2$)] (23)	447	-450±100	≤20	-450±100	Z-scan	THF	800	[103]
[RuCp(PPh$_3$)$_2$(C≡CC$_6$H$_4$-4-N=CHC$_6$H$_4$-4-NO$_2$)] (25)	496	-850±300	360±200	920±360	Z-scan	THF	800	[75]
[RuCp(PPh$_3$)$_2$(C≡CC$_6$H$_4$-4-CH{OC(O)Me}$_2$] (36)	326	100±100	0	100±100	Z-scan	THF	800	[80]
[RuCp(PPh$_3$)$_2$(C≡CC$_6$H$_4$-4-Br)] (126)	325	≤150	0	≤150	Z-scan	THF	800	[103]
[RuCp(Pme$_3$)$_2$(C≡CC$_6$H$_4$-4-CHO)] (127)	400	-75±50	210±50	220±60	Z-scan	THF	800	[80]
[RuCp(dppf)(C≡Cpy-4)][Re(CO)$_3$(bpy)]PF$_6$ (128)	409	-590±250	230±40	65±10[a]	Z-scan	CH$_2$Cl$_2$	750	[105]
[RuCp(dppf)(C≡Cpy-4)][Re(CO)$_3$(Me$_2$bpy)]PF$_6$ (129)	407	-230±60	280±20	80±6[a]	Z-scan	CH$_2$Cl$_2$	750	[105]
[RuCp(dppf)(C≡Cpy-4)][Re(CO)$_3$(^{t}Bu$_2$bpy)]PF$_6$ (130)	407	-480±200	200±40	55±10[a]	Z-scan	CH$_2$Cl$_2$	750	[105]
[RuCp(dppf)(C≡Cpy-4)][Re(CO)$_3$(phen)]PF$_6$ (131)	408	-460±150	280±50	80±15[a]	Z-scan	CH$_2$Cl$_2$	750	[105]
[RuCp(dppf)(C≡Cpy-4)][Re(CO)$_3$(tpy)]PF$_6$ (132)	407	-570±250	180±30	50±6[a]	Z-scan	CH$_2$Cl$_2$	750	[105]
[RuCp(PPh$_3$)$_2$(C≡Cpy-4)][Re(CO)$_3$(bpy)]PF$_6$ (133)	410	-560±150	280±40	80±10[a]	Z-scan	CH$_2$Cl$_2$	750	[105]
[RuCp(dppf)(C≡Cpy-4)] (134)	339	40±100	10±4	3±1[a]	Z-scan	CH$_2$Cl$_2$	750	[104]
[RuCp(dppf)(C≡Cpy-4)]$_2$[PtCl$_2$] (135)	393	1800±3000	600±200	170±50[a]	Z-scan	CH$_2$Cl$_2$	750	[104]
[RuCp(PPh$_3$)$_2$(C=CphN=NPh)(PPh$_3$)$_2$]BF$_4$ (48)	363	-160±60	75±25	180±65	Z-scan	CH$_2$Cl$_2$	800	[86]
[RuCp(PPh$_3$)$_2$(C=CphN=NC$_6$H$_4$-2-OMe)]Cl (49)	377	-220±150	70±30	230±150	Z-scan	CH$_2$Cl$_2$	800	[86]
[RuCp(PPh$_3$)$_2$(C=CphN=NC$_6$H$_4$-3-OMe)]BF$_4$ (50)	389	-310±60	90±30	320±65	Z-scan	CH$_2$Cl$_2$	800	[86]
[RuCp(PPh$_3$)$_2$(C=CphN=NC$_6$H$_4$-4-OMe)]Cl (51)	374	-20±40	80±40	80±50	Z-scan	CH$_2$Cl$_2$	800	[86]
[RuCp(PPh$_3$)$_2$(C=CphN=NC$_6$H$_4$-4-NO$_2$)]BF$_4$ (52)	413	-320±100	160±40	360±110	Z-scan	CH$_2$Cl$_2$	800	[86]
[RuCp(PPh$_3$)$_2$(C=CphN=NC$_6$H$_4$-4-NO$_2$)]Cl (53)	413	-630±200	160±50	650±210	Z-scan	CH$_2$Cl$_2$	800	[86]
[RuCp(PPh$_3$)$_2$(C=CphN=NC$_6$H$_4$-4-NO$_2$)]Br (54)	413	-570±150	150±40	590±160	Z-scan	CH$_2$Cl$_2$	800	[86]
[RuCp(PPh$_3$)$_2$(C=CphN=NC$_6$H$_4$-4-NO$_2$)]I (55)	413	-460±50	140±50	480±60	Z-scan	CH$_2$Cl$_2$	800	[86]
[RuCp(PPh$_3$)$_2$(C=CphN=NC$_6$H$_4$-4-NO$_2$)](4-MeC$_6$H$_4$SO$_3$) (56)	413	-580±200	210±50	620±210	Z-scan	CH$_2$Cl$_2$	800	[86]
[RuCp(PPh$_3$)$_2$(C=CphN=NC$_6$H$_4$-4-NO$_2$)]NO$_3$ (57)	413	-460±150	200±50	500±160	Z-scan	CH$_2$Cl$_2$	800	[86]

[a] σ_2(GM).

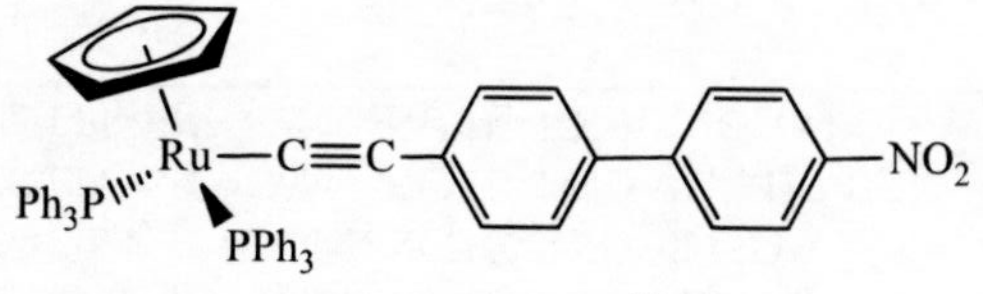

22 $\gamma_{800} = (500 \pm 260) \times 10^{-36}$ esu

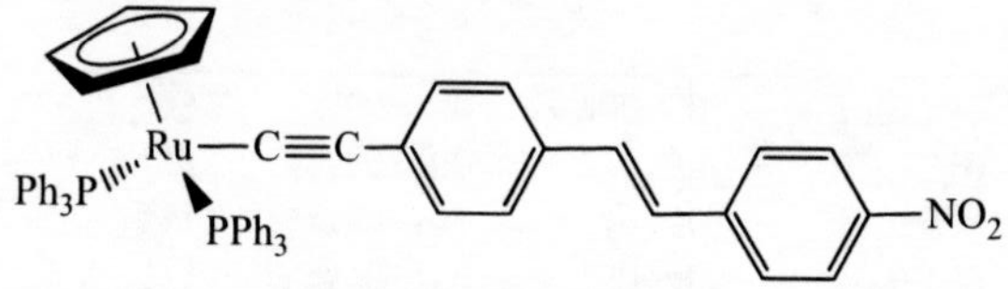

24 $\gamma_{800} = (500 \pm 140) \times 10^{-36}$ esu

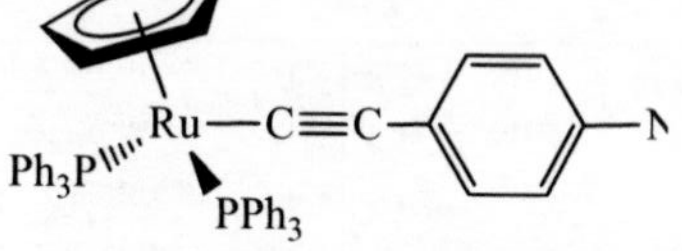

25 $\gamma_{800} = (920 \pm 360) \times 10$

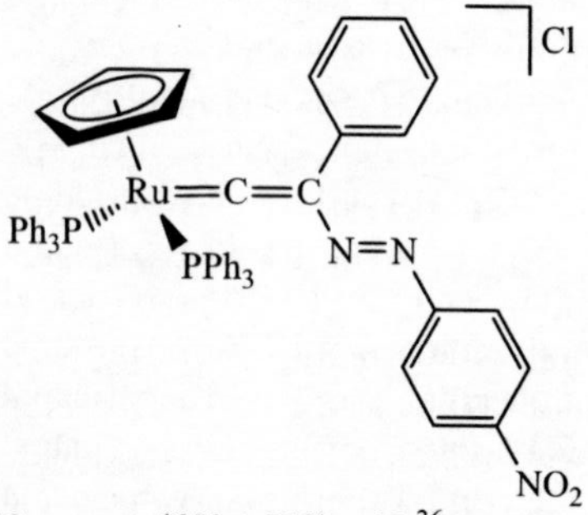

53 $\gamma_{800} = (650 \pm 210) \times 10^{-36}$ esu

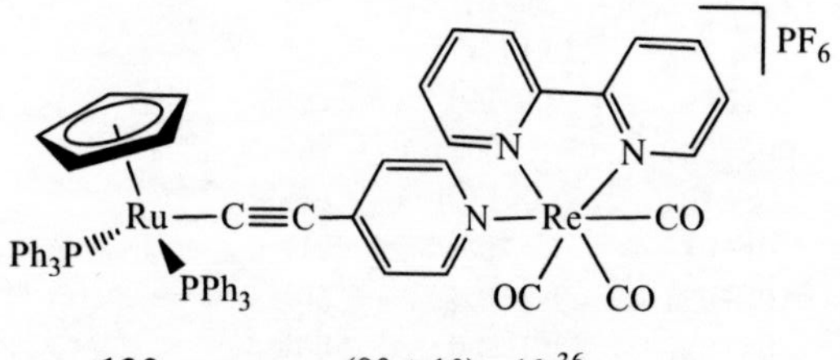

133 $\sigma_{2\,(750)} = (80 \pm 10) \times 10^{-36}$ esu

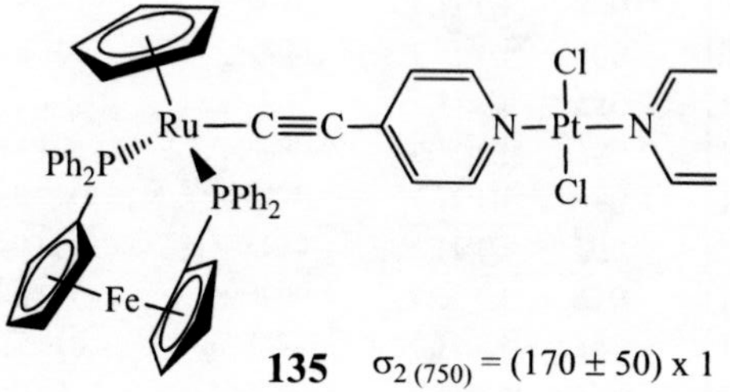

135 $\sigma_{2\,(750)} = (170 \pm 50) \times 1$

Figure 18. Selected "RuCp" alkynyl and vinylidene complexes showing the most representative structures studied for cubic NLO properties.

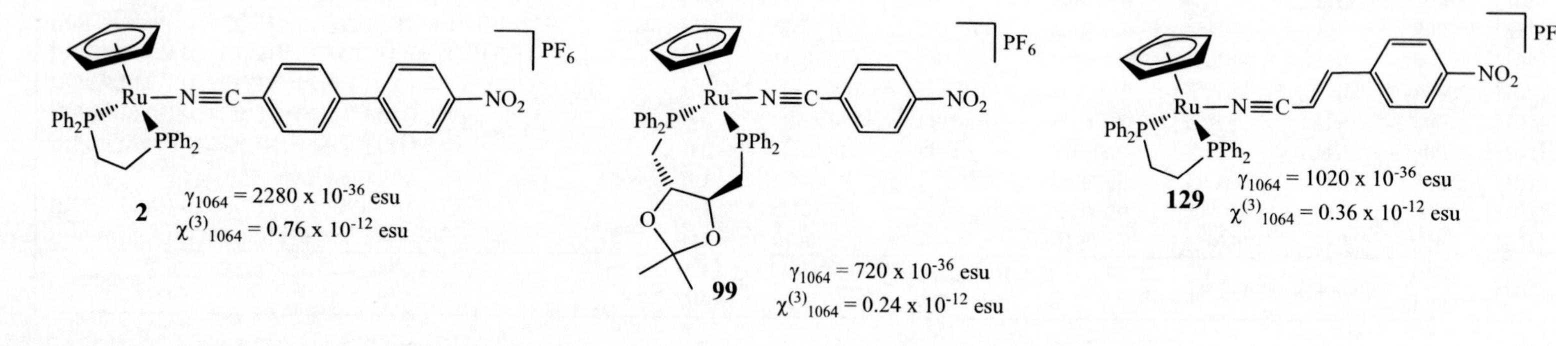

Figure 19. Selected "RuCp" nitrile complexes showing the most representative structures for cubic NLO properties.

Table 7. Cubic NLO measurements for "RuCp" nitrile complexes

Compound	γ (10^{-36} esu)	$\lvert\chi^{(3)}\rvert$ (10^{-12} esu)	Technique	Solvent	Fund. (nm)	Ref.
$[RuCp(k^2\text{-dppe})(N{\equiv}CC_6H_4\text{-}4\text{-}NO_2)]PF_6$ (1)	470	0.17	THG Maker Fringe	PMMA film	1064	[57]
$[RuCp(k^2\text{-dppe})(N{\equiv}CC_6H_4\text{-}4\text{-}NO_2)]BPh_4$ (136)	230	0.07	THG Maker Fringe	PMMA film	1064	[57]
$[RuCp(k^2\text{-dppe})(N{\equiv}CC_6H_4\text{-}4\text{-}NO_2)]CF_3SO_3$ (137)	510	0.23	THG Maker Fringe	PMMA film	1064	[57]
$[RuCp(k^2\text{-dppe})(N{\equiv}CC_6H_4\text{-}4\text{-}NO_2)]p\text{-}CH_3C_6H_4SO_3$ (138)	630	0.23	THG Maker Fringe	PMMA film	1064	[57]
$[RuCp(k^2\text{-dppe})(N{\equiv}CC_6H_4\text{-}4\text{-}NO_2)]BF_4$ (139)	690	0.27	THG Maker Fringe	PMMA film	1064	[57]
$[RuCp((+)\text{-diop})(N{\equiv}CC_6H_4\text{-}4\text{-}NO_2)]PF_6$ (99)	720	0.24	THG Maker Fringe	PMMA film	1064	[57]
$[RuCp((+)\text{-diop})(N{\equiv}CC_6H_4\text{-}4\text{-}NO_2)]CF_3SO_3$ (100)	650	0.21	THG Maker Fringe	PMMA film	1064	[57]
$[RuCp((+)\text{-diop})(N{\equiv}CC_6H_4\text{-}4\text{-}NO_2)]p\text{-}CH_3C_6H_4SO_3$ (106)	320	0.10	THG Maker Fringe	PMMA film	1064	[57]
$[RuCp(k^2\text{-dppe})(N{\equiv}CC_6H_4\text{-}4\text{-}NMe_2)]PF_6$ (140)	590	0.21	THG Maker Fringe	PMMA film	1064	[57]
$[RuCp(k^2\text{-dppe})(CPP)]PF_6$ (141)	660	0.24	THG Maker Fringe	PMMA film	1064	[106]
$[RuCp(k^2\text{-dppe})(N{\equiv}CC_6H_4\text{-}4\text{-}C_6H_5)]PF_6$ (142)	660	0.24	THG Maker Fringe	PMMA film	1064	[57]
$[RuCp(k^2\text{-dppe})(N{\equiv}C\text{-}(E)\text{-}CH{=}CHC_6H_4\text{-}4\text{-}NO_2)]PF_6$ (119)	1020	0.36	THG Maker Fringe	PMMA film	1064	[57]
$[RuCp(k^2\text{-dppe})(N{\equiv}CC_6H_4\text{-}4\text{-}C_6H_4\text{-}4\text{-}NO_2)]PF_6$ (2)	2280	0.76	THG Maker Fringe	PMMA film	1064	[57]

While the molecular structure-NLO properties relationships for third-order processes are less explored when compared with second-order processes, it has been established for organic compounds that enhanced cubic nonlinearities can be obtained, namely, from large π conjugation length (e.g., progressing from small molecules to π-conjugated polymers), electronic asymmetry (by the presence of strong donor and acceptor functional groups) and increasing dimensionality (e.g., from dipolar to quadrupolar or octupolar structures). The studies of dipolar monometallic phenylacetylide complexes, in spite of the relatively lower NLO responses, showed similar trends although the large error margins. [75, 80, 103] In fact, these studies established the importance of a number of molecular modifications for cubic nonlinearity: variation in the 4-phenylalkynyl substituent (introduction of the strong acceptor NO_2 resulted in a significant increase in the NLO response), chain lengthening (increasing nonlinearity in the sequence C_6H_4 < C_6H_4-C_6H_4 < $C_6H_4C{\equiv}CC_6H_4$ < *(E)*-$C_6H_4CH{=}CHC_6H_4$ < *(E)*-$C_6H_4N{=}CHC_6H_4$). However phosphane ligand substitution (replacing triphenylphosphane by trimethylphosphane) resulted in minimal change. One complex, [RuCp(PPh_3)$_2$(C≡CC_6H_4-4-NO_2)] (20) has been studied by both Z-scan and DFWM method. The latter study revealed an equivalent γ value (within the error margins) to the Z-scan-derived response, this confirming the electronic origin of the cubic NLO response for this compound. [103] Negative real components of the cubic nonlinearities (γ_{real}) are observed in many cases and significant imaginary components (γ_{imag}) are seen for almost complexes, consistent with two-photon absorption (TPA) contribution to the observed molecular nonlinearities.

Z-scan studies at 750 nm of the centrosymmetric complex [RuCp(dppf)(C≡Cpy-4)]$_2$[PtCl_2] (135), considered to have a D-π-A-π-D structure, together with its ruthenium monomer [RuCp(dppf)(C≡Cpy-4)] (134) revealed a fifty-fold increment in γ_{imag} on proceeding from the building blocks to the hetero-trimetallic complex. [104] Also a significant increase in nonlinearity of the refractive (γ_{real}) and imaginary (γ_{imag}) components was observed in 4-ethynylpyridyl complexes proceeding from the monomeric [RuCp(dppf)(C≡Cpy-4)] (134) to a series of Ru(II)-Re(I) hetero-bimetallic complexes with general formula [RuCp(dppf)(C≡Cpy-4)][Re(CO)$_3$(L)]PF_6 (L = bpy (128), Me_2bpy (129), ^{t}Bu_2bpy (130), phen (131)) indicating electronic communication between the Ru(II) 4-ethynylpyridine moieties and the Re(I) cationic fragments and thus manifesting that the cubic responses are not simply the sums of nonlinearities of their respective components. [105]

The cubic optical nonlinearities of a series of aryldiazovinylidene complexes have been assessed using Z-scan technique at 800 nm. [86] Real components of the nonlinearities are negative, and the imaginary components are significant, consistent with two-photon absorption contributing to the observed responses. A deep study of the structural variation on the magnitude of the hyperpolarizability could not be assessed due to the large error margins but, as expected, the incorporation of the nitro substituent results in large γ_{real} and $|\gamma|$.

A family of "RuCp" derivatives possessing coordinated *p*-substituted benzonitriles were studied by optical third-harmonic generation (THG) at the fundamental wavelength of 1064 nm. [57] Thin films of the compounds in a polymer matrix of poly(methylmethacrylate) (PMMA) were studied using the Maker fringe approach. The results are collected in Table 7 and representative examples are depicted in Figure 19. Analysis of the results showed an increase of the cubic nonlinearities with π conjugation length of the chromophore, as can be seen in the sequence [RuCp(k^2-dppe)(N≡CC_6H_4-4-NO_2)]PF_6 (1) (γ = 470 x 10^{-36} esu, $|\chi^{(3)}|$ = 0.17 x 10^{-12} esu) < [RuCp(k^2-dppe)(N≡C-(*E*)-CH=CHC_6H_4-4-NO_2)]PF_6 (119) (γ = 1020 x 10^{-36} esu, $|\chi^{(3)}|$ = 0.36 x 10^{-12} esu) < [RuCp(k^2-dppe)(N≡CC_6H_4-4-C_6H_4-4-NO_2)]PF_6 (2) (γ = 2280 x 10^{-36} esu, $|\chi^{(3)}| = 0.76 \times 10^{-12}$ esu) and introduction of a nitro group, as can be seen for the pair $[RuCp(k^2\text{-dppe})(N{\equiv}CC_6H_4\text{-}4\text{-}C_6H_5)]PF_6$ (142) ($\gamma = 660 \times 10^{-36}$ esu, $|\chi^{(3)}| = 0.24 \times 10^{-12}$ esu) / $[RuCp(k^2\text{-dppe})(N{\equiv}CC_6H_4\text{-}4\text{-}C_6H_4\text{-}4\text{-}NO_2)]PF_6$ (2) ($\gamma = 2280 \times 10^{-36}$ esu, $|\chi^{(3)}| = 0.76 \times 10^{-12}$ esu). Changes in the counter-ion as well as the phosphane ligand give rise to small changes in cubic NLO responses taking into account that the data were not corrected for contributions from the PMMA host. The high cubic NLO response for $[RuCp(k^2\text{-dppe})(N{\equiv}CC_6H_4\text{-}4\text{-}C_6H_4\text{-}4\text{-}NO_2)]PF_6$ (2) was rationalized in terms of π-backdonation resulting in an extension of the electronic π-system.

3. Antitumor Properties

The synthetic chemistry of the transition metal ruthenium is well developed and started also to be explored with success in medicinal chemistry, to find alternatives to cisplatin drugs. In fact, the promising results obtained for the inorganic octahedral complexes [ImH][trans-$RuCl_4(DMSO)Im$], NAMI-A, [ImH][trans-$RuCl_4Im_2$] (Im = imidazole) and (Hind)[trans-$RuCl_4(ind)_2$], KP1019, (ind=indazole) that progressed through clinical trials [107-109] paved the way for the continuing exploitation of ruthenium chemistry, having in view anticancer metallodrugs. Thus, organometallic compounds were looked as possible alternatives to overcome the problems originated by the instability and the complicated ligand exchange chemistry of coordination compounds.

In this frame, new "RuCp" containing compounds have been systematically emerging during the last years in the area of potential metallodrugs for cancer therapy. Although the exploitation of "RuCp" fragment for the building of new potential metallodrugs is still in a very early stage, different approaches have been already developed quite successfully. These different approaches are presented below.

3.1. "RuCp" As Scaffold in Protein Kinase Inhibitors

Protein kinases regulate many aspects of cellular physiology and pathophysiology. The mutation and deregulation of these proteins play a role in many human diseases like cancer, making them an important therapeutic target. To the date eight kinase inhibitors are already clinically approved. [110]

The important role of protein kinases in cell biology prompted the search of new organometallic complexes as inert scaffolds to develop protein kinase inhibitors; these compounds will potentially present a strong similarity with staurosporine, which is a nonselective kinase inhibitor. [111] The main idea was focused on the flexibility presented by the special organization of the substituents around the metal center, in a complex, which substantially increases the capacity to build complicated enzyme inhibitor structures. [112] In this approach, the metal is not playing any direct role in the enzyme inhibition, being its sole function to provide the right spatial organization of the substituents around the metal center. Meggers et al. replaced the sugar moiety in the staurosporine molecule (Figure 20) by an organometallic ruthenium fragment carrying a number of substituents; a numerous family of products was prepared and found capable of substantially increase the affinity and selectivity for these proteins, in special for GSK3 (glycogen synthase kinase 3), Pim-1 (proto-oncogene serine/threonine-protein kinase) and PI3K (Phosphatidylinositol-4,5-bisphosphate 3-kinase) [107-113]. As expected, the metal centre played just a structural role; however, as shown on Table 8, the organic ligands can be optimized to occupy the available space in the active site, as well as to provide some additional hydrogen bonding interactions, making the individual inhibitors highly specific. [109] Figure 20 shows some complexes of this family bearing different substituents to illustrate the structural diversity of these complexes; DW12 can be considered the most biologically studied.

Although these complexes have not even demonstrated a direct anticancer activity, using a human melanoma cells *in vitro*, DW12 showed capability to inhibit both GSK3β and PI3K leading cell death by apoptosis mediated by p53 protein and the mitochondrial pathway; moreover a strong inhibition of cell invasion was found, suggesting the high potential of this strategy to get new drugs. [110]

Table 8. IC_{50} values for five ruthenium complexes against two enzymes PI3Kγ and GSK3β, showing the affinity and selectivity of these compounds to specific kinases [109]

Enzymes	IC_{50} values (μM)				
	HB12	DW12	DW12Me	EAd125	E5
PI3Kγ	>>1	0.75	0.5	0.18	0.04
GSK3β	0.05	0.0014	>1	0.7	4

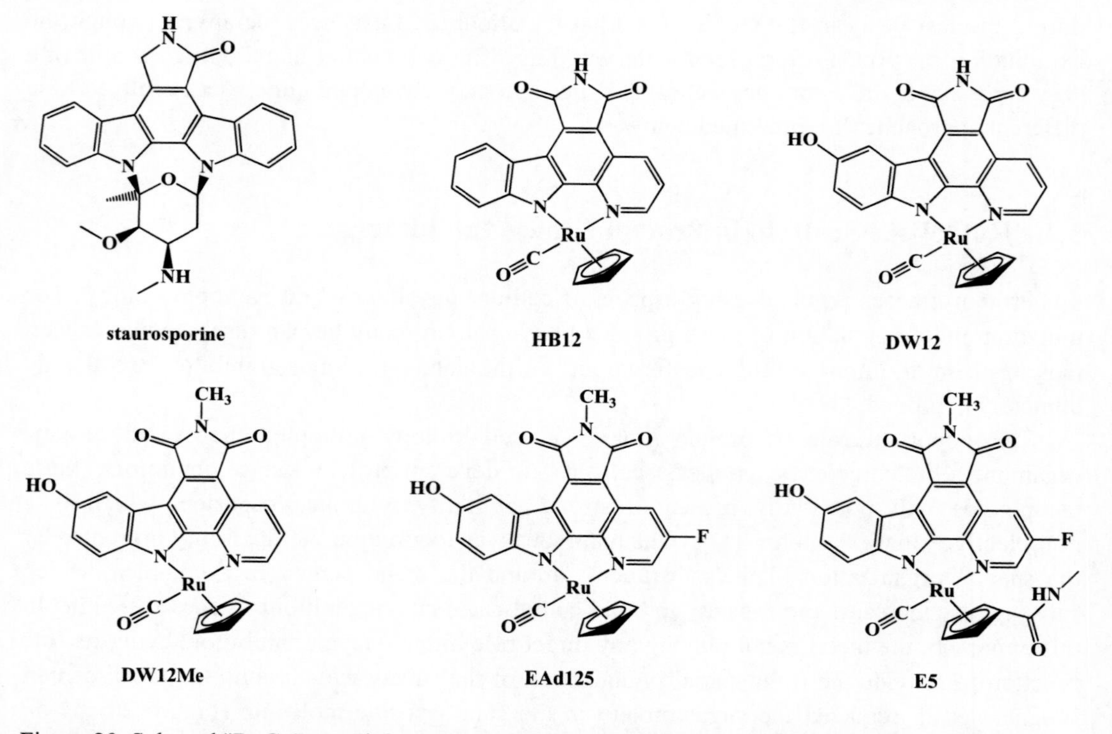

Figure 20. Selected "RuCp" containing enzyme inhibitors developed by E. Meggers, illustrating the structural diversity of these complexes.

Table 9. IC_{50} values for ruthenium compounds against T2 (T-cell leukemia) and SKOV3 (ovarian) human cancer cell lines [115]

Compound	IC_{50} (Tumor cell line) (μM)	Compound	IC_{50} (Tumor cell line) (μM)
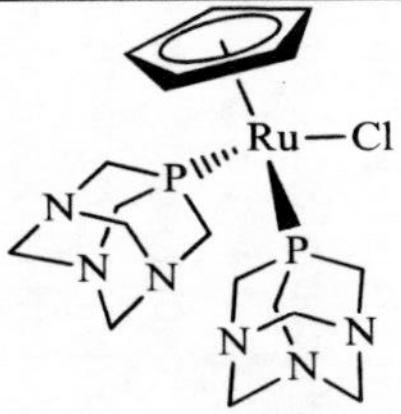	>50 (T2) >50 (SKOV3)	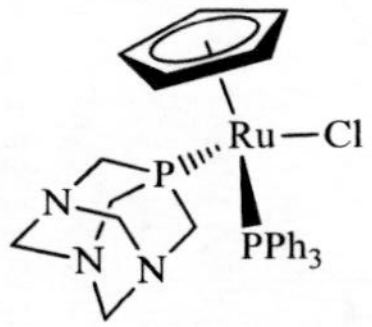	10 - 50 (T2) >50 (SKOV3)
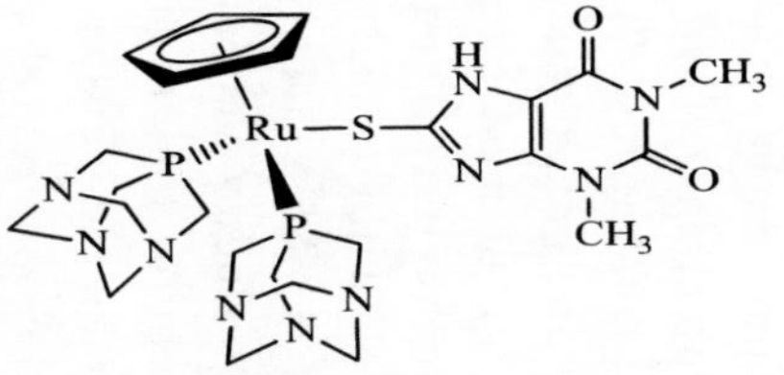	>50 (T2) >50 (SKOV3)	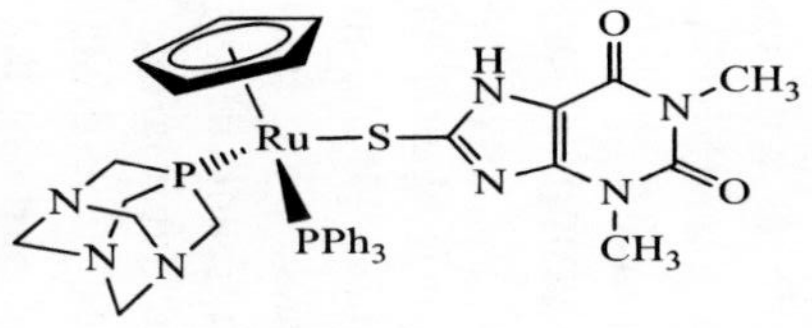	50 (T2) >50 (SKOV3)
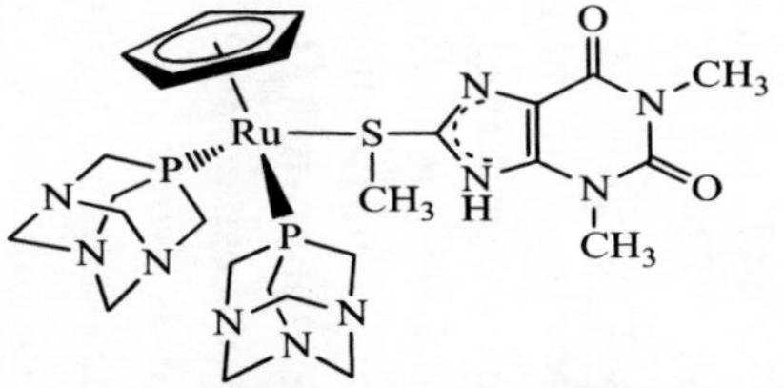	>50 (T2) >50 (SKOV3)	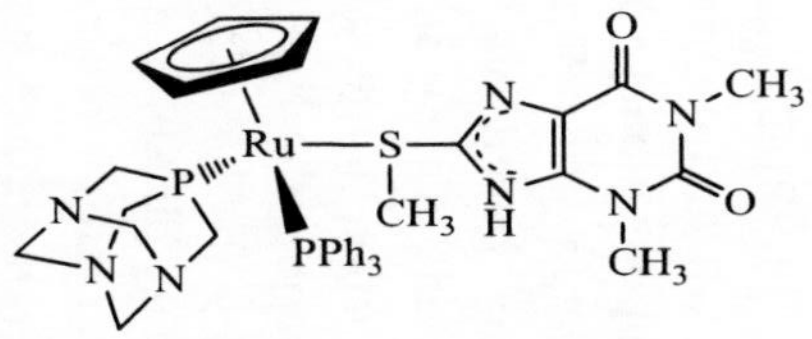	50 (T2) >50 (SKOV3)
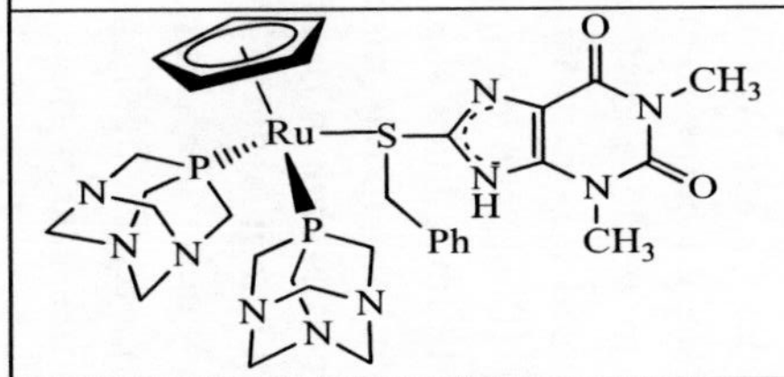	>50 (T2) >50 (SKOV3)	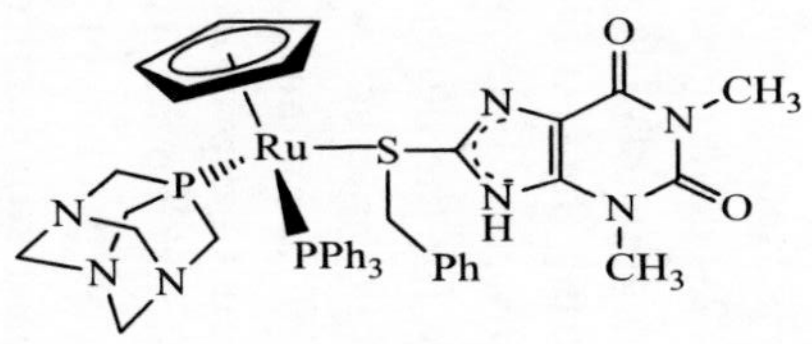	2 - 10 (T2) >50 (SKOV3)

3.2. "RuCp" Complexes with Anticancer Properties

In the last years, some new families of ruthenium(II) complexes based on the piano-stool geometry started to be develop, but in contrast with the complexes presented above, the organometallic fragment, plays a direct role in the anticancer activity.

In 2007, a family of "RuCp" piano-stool complexes with several phosphane ligands, with the general formula [RuCp(Phosphane)$_3$], was developed by Romerosa and coworkers that found their capability to bind *in vitro* to DNA. Further studies on their DNA binding activity revealed dependency on the phosphane ligand bonded to the metal. [114] Recently, Romerosa et al. reported the activity of "RuCp" complexes with two phosphane and thiopurine ligands against T-cell leukemia (T2) and ovarian cancer (SKOV3) cell lines (Table 9); nevertheless these compounds showed poor bioactivity. [115]

During the last five years, our research group has been focused on a new family of piano stool structured complexes based on "RuCp" fragment with heteroaromatic ligands. Our strategy for the development of new antitumor agents had in view the design of compounds that might interact with other targets besides DNA, in order to achieve new alternatives modes of action and overcome the limitations of the existing drugs in the market. The piano-stool structure provided by the "RuCp" fragment allows to play with various groups in the "piano legs" positions; thus, phosphane and heretoaromatic ligands coordinated by N, O, S, etc. atoms (mono- or bidentate) were chosen. The design of these compounds can lead to a significant structural diversity, since several parts of the molecule can be changed and their electronic properties fine-tuned; moreover, one also can play with Cp ring functionalization, coordination numbers, nature of the coligands and the counter-ion itself. Some of these features can be extremely important to control the solubility of the compounds and to optimize the biological activity and stability. For example, the substitution of the phosphane PPh_3 by a sulphonated phosphane leads to a severe change on the water solubility of the complexes.

The cytotoxic activity of all of our studied complexes was evaluated *in vitro* on a variety of human tumor cell lines, including LoVo (colon adenocarcinoma), MiaPaca (pancreatic carcinoma), HL60 (promyelocytic leukemia cells), A2780 (ovarian carcinoma), A2780CisR (ovarian carcinoma resistant to cisplatin), MCF7 (breast adenocarcinoma, estrogen dependent) MDAMB231 (adenocarcinoma breast cancer, estrogen-independent), PC3 (prostate carcinoma) and HT29 (colon carcinoma). [116-122] These lines were chosen in order to enclose different sensitivities to treatment with metallodrugs including the most diagnosed types, prostate cancer (in men) and breast cancer (in women). As can be seen on Table 10 all the compounds presented high or moderately cytotoxic *in vitro* for the nine human tumor lines studied, with IC_{50} values on micro- and nanomolar order. [116-123] Most of them are much more cytotoxic than cisplatin (metallodrug in clinical use). Of all the compounds shown on the Table 10, TM34, TM85 and TM90 complexes are the most studied at the biological level. For these complexes studies were also carried out in the presence of a healthy cell line, and it is worth of mention that these compounds revealed quite low cytotoxicity for the healthy cell line V79 (Chinese hamster ovary cells) with IC_{50} values 60 to 130 times higher than those for cancer cells, thus revealing a significant intrinsic selectivity (Figure 21). [119, 122]

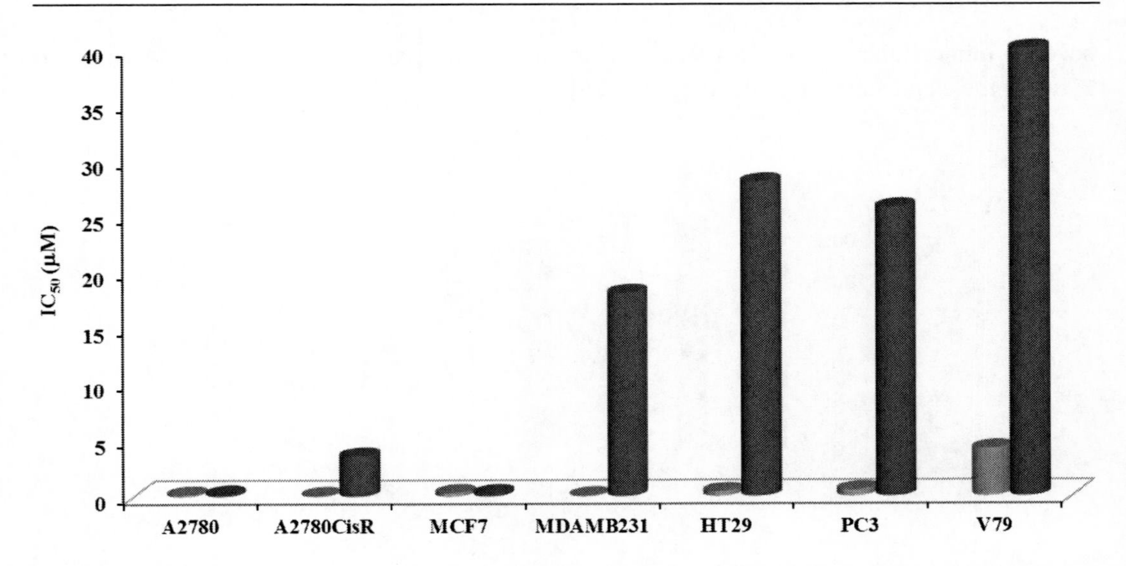

Figure 21. *In vitro* cytotoxic activity for compounds TM34 (), and TM85 (); IC_{50} values (μM) obtained after 72 h of incubation of compounds, with different tumor human cell lines and a non-tumorigenic cell line (V79). [119, 122]

In a first approach to understand the pharmacokinetic profile of these compounds, its interaction with human serum proteins (albumin and transferrin) was evaluated by fluorescence spectroscopy and cyclic voltammetry, since the drug-protein binding influences the distribution and pharmacokinetic properties of a drug. The main function of albumin, which is the principal and most abundant drug transport carrier protein of the circulatory system, is to transport fatty acids as well as a broad range of drug molecules to their targets. By other hand, binding to transferrin, which is an iron-binding blood plasma glycoprotein, can constitute a major advantage for a drug selective delivery to cancer cells, due to the huge amount of transferrin receptors in these cells.

Our studies revealed the formation of stable adducts with these transport proteins, essential condition to be transported to their targets. However, considering the possibility that the binding to these proteins could affect the drug biological activity and toxicity, the cytotoxicity in the presence of albumin and transferrin was also checked. Our cell viability assays in the presence of these proteins (albumin and transferrin) showed that the formation of these adducts did not affect the cytotoxic properties of the complexes (Figure 22); interestingly, it was found in some cases, that binding to transferrin did facilitate the entry into cells. [119, 121, 122, 124, 125]

Although the mechanism of action for these complexes is still not fully understood, it is already recognized in our ICP-MS studies, of metal distribution within the several cellular components, that these ruthenium complexes are preferentially retained in the cell membrane; even so, a small percentage reaches the cytosol, nucleus and cytoskeleton (Figure 25). Moreover, it was found that entry in the cells occurs by an energy dependent process (active mechanism) identified as endocytosis, with the preferred protein clathrin-mediated process. [121, 122, 125] Some intracellular targets have been already identified by means of transmission electron microscopy (TEM) that revealed changes in the Golgi apparatus and mitochondria originated by these compounds (Figure 23); these alterations may be related to the mechanism of cell death. [121, 122, 125] Our mass spectrometric studies also identified several intracellular targets for these compounds, in particular ubiquitin protein and cytochrome c and superoxide dismutase. [125]

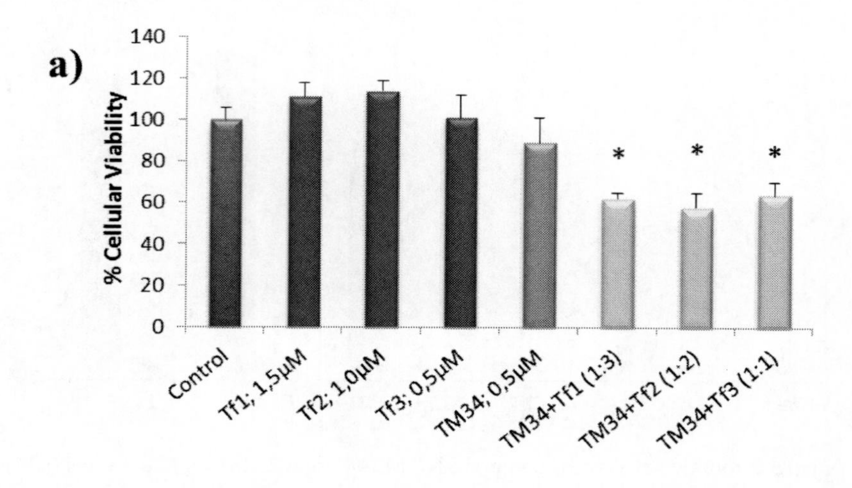

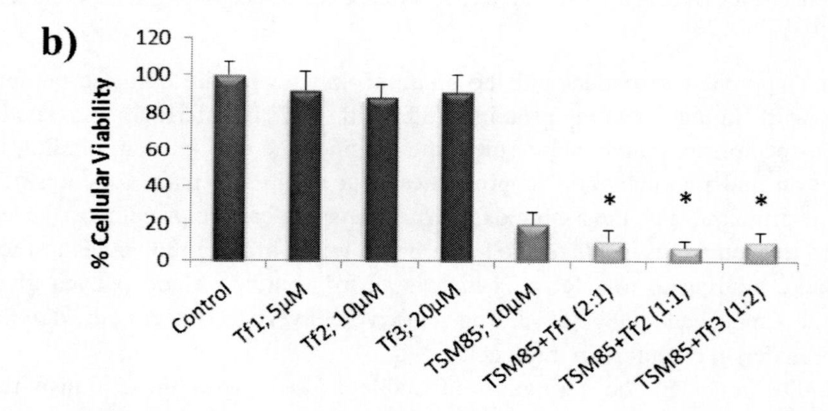

Figure 22. Effect of transferrin (Tf) on the cytotoxicity of complexes a) TM34, b) TM85 against A2780 cells, after a 24 h challenge, with different complex:protein molar ratios. Data represent: cells with no treatment (control); cells treated with Tf alone at different concentrations, Tf1, Tf2, Tf3; cells treated with complex-transferrin conjugates. Adapted from reference [126].

Recently, the development of a new family based on the same general formula, with fructose and galactose derived ligands was initiated by Fernandes et al.. [127] The main idea is the use of these carbohydrates as a vehicle to entry in the cells (due to the high requirement that tumor cells have to receive sugars and nutrients) and targeting DNA. The few results obtained for this family of compounds showed that these compounds are highly to moderately cytotoxic for human cervical carcinoma cells (HeLa), with IC_{50} values for most of them much lower than those found for cisplatin [127] (Table 11).

Table 10. *In vitro* **cytotoxic activity, IC_{50} values found for LoVo (colon adenocarcinoma), MiaPaca (pancreatic carcinoma), HL60 (promyelocytic leukemia cells), A2780 (ovarian carcinoma), A2780CisR (ovarian carcinoma resistant to cisplatin), MCF7 (breast adenocarcinoma, estrogen dependent) MDAMB231 (adenocarcinoma breast cancer, estrogen-independent), PC3 (prostate carcinoma) and HT29 (colon carcinoma) human cancer cells**

Compound	IC_{50} (Tumor cell line) (μM)	Ref.	Compound	IC_{50} (Tumor cell line) (μM)	Ref.
	0.30 (LoVo)	[116]		0.60 (LoVo)	[116]
	0.25 (MiaPaca)			0.44 (MiaPaca)	
	0.69 (HL60)	[117]		0.94 (HL60)	[117]
	0.53 (HL60)	[117]		2.26 (HL60)	[117]
	0.38 (HL60)	[118]		1.06 (HL60)	[118]
				0.42 (HL60)	
				0.14 (A2780)	
	0.92 (HL60)	[118]	**TM34**	0.07 (A2780CisR)	[118, 119]
				0.29 (MCF7)	
				0.54 (PC3)	
	0.10 (A2780)			0.19 (A2780)	
	0.09(A2780CisR)			0.21(A2780CisR)	
	0.29 (MCF7)			0.05 (MCF7)	
	0.10 (MDAMB231)	[121]	**TM90**	0.03 (MDAMB231)	[120]
	0.09 (HT29)			0.08 (HT29)	
	0.44 (PC3)			0.41 (PC3)	
	0.18 (A2780)			0.46 (A2780)	
	0.32(A2780CisR)			0.47(A2780CisR)	
	0.03 (MCF7)	[120]		0.41 (MCF7)	[120]
	0.06 (MDAMB231)			0.23 (MDAMB231)	
	0.32 (HT29)			0.53 (HT29)	
	0.30 (PC3)			1.90 (PC3)	
	4.70 (A2780)			0.21 (A2780)	
	5.20 (A2780CisR)			3.6 (A2780CisR)	
	0.49 (MCF7)	[120]	**TM85**	0.28 (MCF7)	[122]
	0.26 (MDAMB231)			18.1 (MDAMB231)	
	4.80 (HT29)			28.1 (HT29)	
	5.50 (PC3)			25.8 (PC3)	

Table 11. IC_{50} values for ruthenium carbohydrate compounds against HeLa cells (human cervical carcinoma cells) [127]

Compound	IC_{50} (Tumor cell line) (μM)	Compound	IC_{50} (Tumor cell line) (μM)
	2.63 (HeLa)		9.26 (HeLa)
	3.58 (HeLa)		6.07 (HeLa)
	6.39 (HeLa)		4.49 (HeLa)
	3.92 (HeLa)		10.61 (HeLa)
	6.81 (HeLa)		4.64 (HeLa)

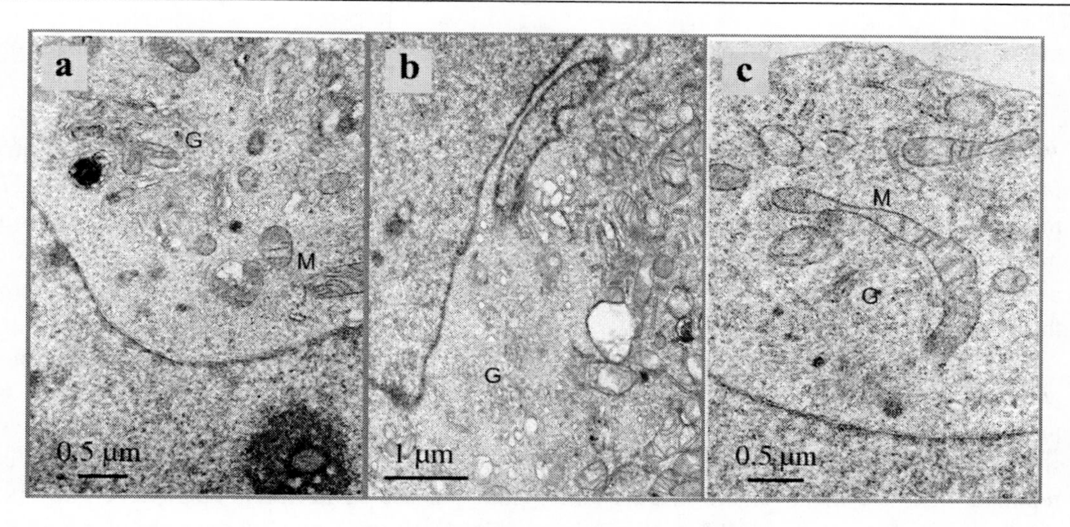

Figure 23. Representative TEM images showing the ultrastructure of MDAMB231cells. (a) control, cells without treatment; (b) cells after treatment with TM85 (100 µM, 3h), (c) cells after treatment with TM85 (100µM, 24h). Controls showing well developed Golgi apparatus; treated cells showing vesiculation of the Golgi apparatus (100 µM, 3 h), small Golgi apparatus and elongated mitochondria (100 µM, 24 h). G — Golgi apparatus; M — mitochondria. Adapted from reference [122].

3.3. "RuCp" As Scaffolds of Macromolecules for Targeting Therapy

As described above, "RuCp" low molecular weight drugs [116-125] are currently assuredly chemotherapeutic candidates. Importantly, several studies already proved the good stability in an aqueous environment of the $[RuCp(P)(bpy)]^+$ family (P = phosphane coligand, bpy = bipyridine). [121, 122, 125] This feature stimulated the synthesis of a second generation of compounds using polymers into their backbone, while maintaining the same organometallic core which presents anticancer properties. [128] The approach for to the design of this new family of compounds was based on one common property to all macromolecular drugs, *i.e.*, the EPR (enhanced permeation and retention) effect. This phenomenon was first identified in 1986 by Maeda et al. [129] and describes that macromolecules selectively accumulate in malignant tissues comparatively to healthy tissues. This is due to the defective vascular system and diminished lymphatic drainage of tumors, resulting in passive targeting of macromolecules in these tissues. This discovery was a landmark in the anticancer nanomedicine field since the drug concentration in the tumor can considerably increase (comparing to the drug in the blood) [130, 131], also aiding to decrease the severe side effects of chemotherapy. [132] In this frame, polymer conjugates share several features with other macromolecular approaches, however they have the advantage of chemical versatility. [133, 134] Thus, our research group started to develop a second generation of "RuCp" drugs in view to targeting therapy, with the synthesis and preliminary *in vitro* results concerning the first polymer-"ruthenium-cyclopentadienyl" conjugate, published in 2013 by Valente et al. [128] $[RuCp(PPh_3)(bpyPLA)]^+$ (RuPMC; bpyPLA = 2,2'-bipyridine-4,4'-*D*-glucose end-capped polylactide, Figure 24) has been synthesized by halide abstraction from the parental $[RuCp(PPh_3)_2Cl]$ with $AgCF_3SO_3$, in CH_2Cl_2 in the presence of the bpyPLA macroligand. Importantly, either the molecular weight of the bpyPLA macroligand and the chain-end groups can be easily modified, allowing the development of several compounds sharing the same cytotoxic fragment.

Interestingly, the new RuPMC presents a pH-dependent hydrolysis at acidic pH (*vs.* physiologic pH – 7.4; results obtained by UV-visible spectroscopy). This is an important feature when developing anticancer drugs, since the pH of most solid tumors ranges from 5.7 to 7.2, while the blood remains well buffered at 7.4. [135] Therefore, the fact that there is a pH-dependent hydrolysis discards the need for a cleavable linker and offers the possibility of a targeted drug delivery within, for example, the endosomal/lysosomal compartments, where the pH drops to 4.5–6.0. [136]

In terms of cytotoxic performance, RuPMC is cytotoxic against human MCF7 and MDAMB231 breast and A2780 ovarian adenocarcinoma, with IC_{50} values of 3.9, 3.8 and 1.6 μM, respectively. Finally, ICP-MS (inductively coupled plasma mass spectrometry) studies showed that the RuPMC is able to enter MCF7 estrogen receptor positive cancer cells and is retained *ca.* 50% in the nucleus, thus anticipating its use in hormone-responsive cancers. Curiously, its Ru-precursor TM34, $[RuCp(bipy)(PPh_3)]^+$), (see Table 10) was mainly found in the membrane (*ca.* 80%). These results forecast different mechanisms of cellular uptake and of cell death for these two compounds. Figure 25 compares the percentages of TM34 and RuPMC complexes in several cell compartments.

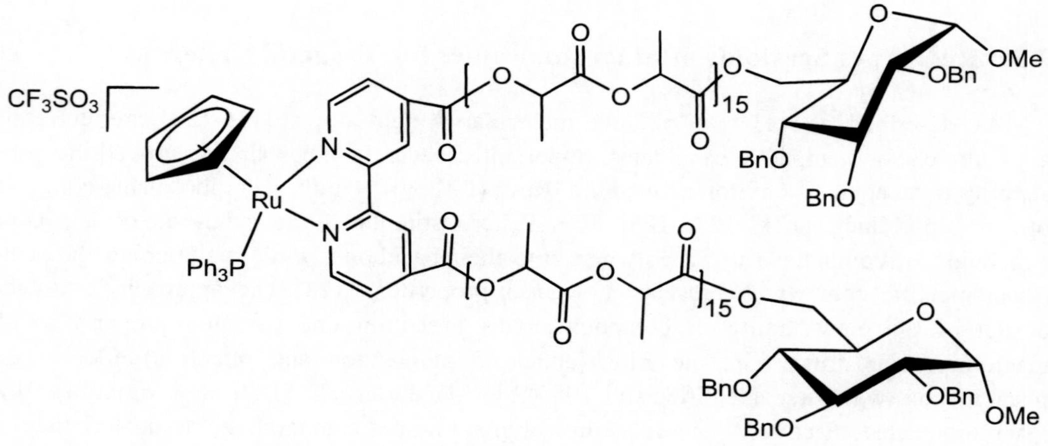

RuPMC

Figure 24. D-Glucose end-capped polylactide ruthenium-cyclopentadienyl (RuPMC) [128].

It also worth some mention a new class of air-stable cationic zero generation metallodendrimers bearing "RuCp" appended fragments, which started to be exploited by Rodrigues et al. [137]. The synthesis of these compounds is based on nitrile-functionalized poly(alkylidenamine). Tetrakis-ruthenium dendrimers (Figure 26) were prepared in reasonably good yields (57%–74%) by functionalization of the corresponding dendrimer. Spectroscopic and mass spectrometry techniques confirmed that all the dendritic arms were functionalized with the metal moiety. Preliminary stability studies by NMR spectroscopy in DMSO-d_6 at 37 °C showed that they are quite unstable. However, the use of metallodendrimers might be an interesting alternative on the design of metallodrugs once improved their problems of solubility and stability in aqueous media.

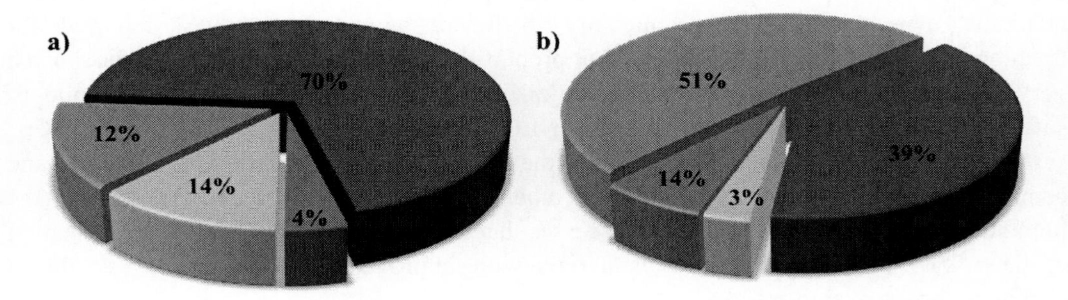

Figure 25. Comparison of the complexes percentage of TM34 (a) and RuPMC (b) in several cell compartments. Legend: membrane (■), nucleus (■), cytosol (■) cytoskeletal (■) [125, 128].

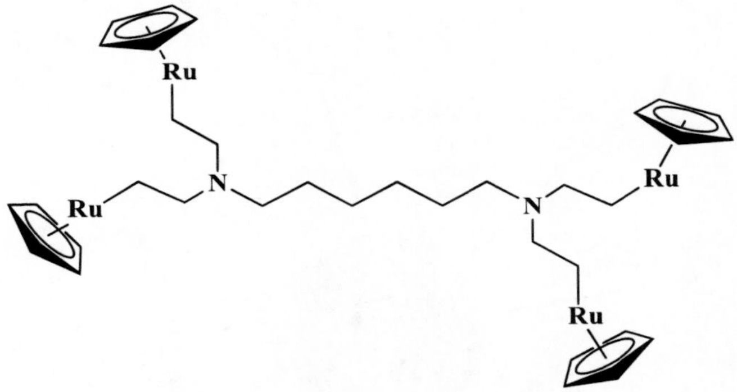

Figure 26. "RuCp" Dendrimers [137].

CONCLUSION

This overview illustrates the versatility of the very stable "RuCp" unit for the building of organometallic complexes with remarkable properties either as NLO chromophores or as promising anticancer drugs (Figure 27). One of the main features of this class of compounds is due to the versatility of the piano stool structure that allows playing with a variety of co-ligands and "active ligands" that can impart specific properties to the whole molecule. For example, chiral phosphane coligands can be introduced to ensure acentric crystallization for solid state second-order nonlinear optical (SO NLO) properties or a sulphonated phosphane can be used to increase the complex solubility in aqueous media as required for medicinal drugs. Besides, these coligands can also be used to tune the electronic properties at the ruthenium centre, and consequently control the electronic density towards the "active ligand" (a NLO-chromophore or a ligand that-potentiates the anticancer properties of the complex). As a consequence, important ruthenium-ligand π-backdonation effects involving nitrile, alkynyl or heteroaromatic derivatives were found to play an important role either on the SO NLO properties or biological stability of compounds with anticancer potentiality.

The relatively high number and variety of studied chromophores allowed a significant development on structure-NLO property relationships in families of neutral alkynyl and cationic nitrile and vinylidene complexes. These studies led to compounds with high quadratic hyperpolarizabilities, some of which are among the highest reported for organometallic compounds. For cubic NLO properties, however, data collected so far showed very often large error margins that make difficult any reliable comparison. In spite of sufficiently large molecular second-order NLO responses already achieved for "RuCp" systems, most of compounds fail to fulfill the requirements for practical applications and commercialization, as also was found for other metallo-organic systems published in the literature. Thus, the understanding of processes that might control and favor the organization of these systems to produce bulk materials with improved NLO properties, remains a challenge for the next years.

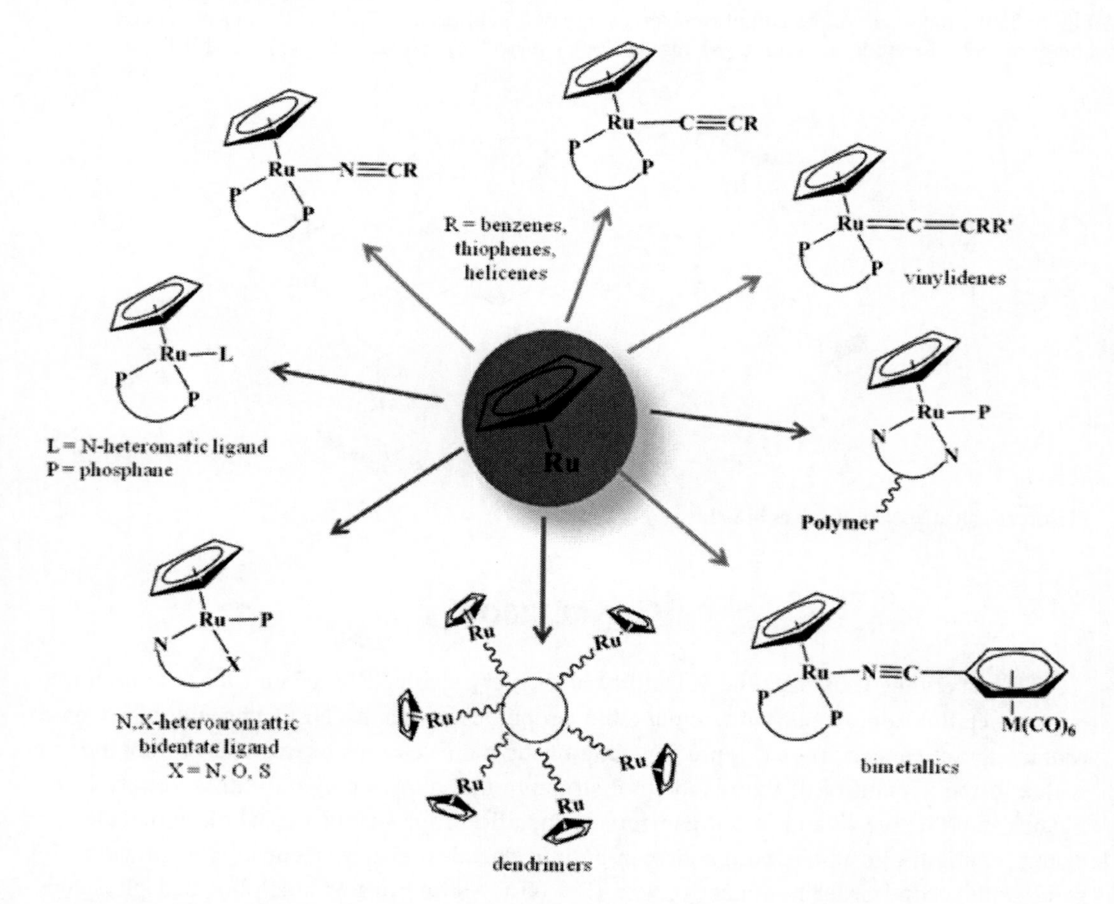

Figure 27. Overview of the structural diversity presented on this chapter.

This challenge is certainly extended to the emerging area of "RuCp" anticancer drugs. Although the limited number of studied compounds avoids the finding of consistent structure-activity relationships, it was possible to outline significant cytotoxicities for cationic "RuCp" complexes bearing heteroaromatic bidentate ligands together with one phosphane coligand. Moreover, while this family of compounds interacts mainly with the cell membrane, their RuPMC derivatives can be internalized in the cell by the EPR (enhanced permeation and retention) effect, targeting mainly the cell nucleus. To conclude, the results already obtained for this class of complexes might foresee a promising and significant contribution of "RuCp" based drugs for the field of medicinal chemistry.

REFERENCES

[1] Prasad P. N. W. D. J., Introduction to nonlinear optical effects in molecules and polymers, Wiley, New York, 1991.
[2] Butcher P. N. C. D., The elements of nonlinear optics, Cambridge University Press, Cambridge; New York, 1990.
[3] Zyss J., Molecular nonlinear optics : materials, physics, and devices, Academic Press, Boston, 1994.
[4] Khoo I.-C. S. F. U. C., Novel optical materials and applications, Wiley, New York, 1997.
[5] Roundhill D. M. F. J. P., Optoelectronic properties of inorganic compounds, Plenum Press, New York, 1999.
[6] Chemla D. S., Nonlinear Optical Properties of Organic Molecules and Crystals, Elsevier Science, 2012.
[7] Green M. L. H., Marder S. R., Thompson M. E., Bandy J. A., Bloor D., Kolinsky P. V., Jones R. J., *Nature*.330 (1987) 360-362.
[8] Nalwa H. S., *Appl. Organomet. Chem*.5 (1991) 349-377.
[9] Long N. J., *Angew. Chem.-Int. Edit. Engl.* 34 (1995) 826-826.
[10] Whittall I. R., McDonagh A.M., Humphrey M.G., Samoc M., in: F.G.A. Stone, W. Robert (Eds.), Advances in Organometallic Chemistry, vol. Volume 42, Academic Press, 1998, pp. 291-362.
[11] Di Bella S., *Chem. Soc. Rev.* 30 (2001) 355-366.
[12] Goovaerts E., Wenseleers W. E., Garcia M. H., Cross G. H., in: H. S. Nalwa (Ed.), Handbook of Advanced Electronic and Photonic Materials and Devices, Academic Press, Burlington, 2001, pp. 127-191.
[13] Powell C. E., Humphrey M. G., *Coord. Chem. Rev.* 248 (2004) 725-756.
[14] Cariati E., Pizzotti M., Roberto D., Tessore F., Ugo R., *Coord. Chem. Rev.* 250 (2006) 1210-1233.
[15] Morrall J. P., Dalton G. T., Humphrey M. G., Samoc M., in: A. F. H. Robert West, J. F. Mark (Eds.), Advances in Organometallic Chemistry, vol. Volume 55, Academic Press, 2007, pp. 61-136.
[16] Di Bella S., Dragonetti C., Pizzotti M., Roberto D., Tessore F., Ugo R., in: H. Bozec, V. Guerchais (Eds.), Molecular Organometallic Materials for Optics, vol. 28, Topics in Organometallic Chemistry, Springer Berlin Heidelberg, 2010, pp. 1-55.
[17] Humphrey M., Cifuentes M., Samoc M., in: H. Bozec, V. Guerchais (Eds.), Molecular Organometallic Materials for Optics, vol. 28, Topics in Organometallic Chemistry, Springer Berlin Heidelberg, 2010, pp. 57-73.
[18] Garcia M. H., Florindo P., in: H. F. Chin (Ed.), Organometallic compounds : preparation, structure and properties, Nova Science Publishers, New York 2010.

[19] Green K. A., Cifuentes M. P., Samoc M., Humphrey M. G., *Coord. Chem. Rev.* 255 (2011) 2025-2038.

[20] Green K. A., Cifuentes M. P., Samoc M., Humphrey M. G., *Coord. Chem. Rev.* 255 (2011) 2530-2541.

[21] Humphrey M. G., Schwich T., West P. J., Cifuentes M. P., Samoc M., in: J. Reedijk, K. Poeppelmeier (Eds.), Comprehensive Inorganic Chemistry II (Second Edition), Elsevier, Amsterdam, 2013, pp. 781-835.

[22] Coe B. J., *Coord. Chem. Rev.* 257 (2013) 1438-1458.

[23] Grelaud G., Cifuentes M. P., Paul F., Humphrey M. G., *J. Organomet. Chem.* 751 (2014) 181-200.

[24] Madeira P. J. A., Morais T. S., Silva T. J. L., Florindo P., Garcia M. H., Rapid Communications in Mass Spectrometry. 26 (2012) 1675-1686.

[25] Pigeon P., Top S., Vessières A., Huché M., Hillard E. A., Salomon E., Jaouen G., *Journal of Medicinal Chemistry*.48 (2005) 2814-2821.

[26] Hillard E.A., Vessières A., Top S., Pigeon P., Kowalski K., Huché M., Jaouen G., *J. Organomet. Chem.* 692 (2007) 1315-1326.

[27] Kemp K. C., Nell M. J., Van Rensburg C. E. J., Swarts J. C., *Anticancer Research.* 32 (2012) 2915-2918.

[28] Garcia M. H., Valente A., Florindo P., Morais T. S., Piedade M. F. M., Duarte M. T., Moreno V., Aviles F. X., Loreno J., *Inorg. Chim. Acta.* 363 (2010) 3765-3775.

[29] Non-linear optical properties of matter from molecules to condensed phases, http://public.eblib.com/EBLPublic/PublicView.do?ptiID=302026,

[30] Ostroverkhova O., Handbook of organic materials for optical and (opto)electronic devices: properties and applications, 2013.

[31] Thierry Verbiest, Koen Clays, Rodriguez V., Second-order Nonlinear Optical Characterization Techniques: An Introduction, CRC Press, 2009.

[32] Sutherland R. L., Handbook of nonlinear optics, Marcel Dekker, New York, 1996.

[33] Kleinman D. A., *Physical Review*.126 (1962) 1977-&

[34] Oudar J. L., Chemla D. S., *The Journal of Chemical Physics*. 66 (1977) 2664-2668.

[35] Levine B. F., Bethea C. G., *Appl. Phys. Lett.* 24 (1974) 445-447.

[36] Levine B. F., Bethea C. G., *The Journal of Chemical Physics*. 63 (1975) 2666-2682.

[37] Clays K., Persoons A., *Phys. Rev. Lett.* 66 (1991) 2980-2983.

[38] Clays K., Persoons A., *Rev. Sci. Instrum.* 63 (1992) 3285-3289.

[39] Zyss J., Ledoux I., *Chem. Rev.* 94 (1994) 77-105.

[40] Cyvin S. J., Rauch J. E., Decius J. C., *The Journal of Chemical Physics*. 43 (1965) 4083-4095.

[41] Kurtz S. K., Perry T. T., *J. Appl. Phys.* 39 (1968) 3798-&

[42] Levenson M. D., Quantum Electronics, *IEEE Journal* of.10 (1974) 110-115.

[43] Sheik-Bahae M., Said A. A., Wei T.H., Hagan D.J., Van Stryland E.W., Quantum Electronics, *IEEE Journal* of. 26 (1990) 760-769.

[44] Kajzar F., Messier J., *Phys. Rev. A.* 32 (1985) 2352-2363.

[45] Hohenberg P., Kohn W., *Physical Review*. 136 (1964) B864-B871.

[46] Kohn W., Sham L. J., *Physical Review*.140 (1965) 1133-&

[47] Isborn C. M., Leclercq A., Vila F. D., Dalton L. R., Bredas J. L., Eichinger B. E., Robinson B. H., *J. Phys. Chem. A.* 111 (2007) 1319-1327.

[48] Kanis D. R., Ratner M. A., Marks T. J., *Chem. Rev.* 94 (1994) 195-242.

[49] Casida M. E., Huix-Rotllant M., *Annu. Rev. Phys. Chem.*63 (2012) 287-323.
[50] Marques M. A. L., Gross E. K. U., *Annual Review of Physical Chemistry*. 55 (2004) 427-455
[51] Oudar J. L., *The Journal of Chemical Physics*. 67 (1977) 446-457.
[52] Oudar J. L., Hierle R., *J. Appl. Phys.* 48 (1977) 2699-2704.
[53] Calabrese J. C., Cheng L. T., Green J. C., Marder S. R., Tam W., *J. Am. Chem. Soc.* 113 (1991) 7227-7232.
[54] Garcia M. H., Mendes P. J., Robalo M. P., Dias A. R., Campo J., Wenseleers W., Goovaerts E., *J. Organomet. Chem.* 692 (2007) 3027-3041.
[55] Garcia M. H., Florindo P., Piedade M. F. M., Duarte M. T., Robalo M. P., Goovaerts E., Wenseleers W., *J. Organomet. Chem.* 694 (2009) 433-445.
[56] Di Bella S., *New J. Chem.* 26 (2002) 495-497.
[57] Dias A. R., Garcia M. H., Rodrigues J. C., Petersen J. C., Bjornholm T., Geisler T., *J. Mater. Chem.* 5 (1995) 1861-1865.
[58] Wenseleers W., Gerbrandij A. W., Goovaerts E., Garcia M. H., Robalo M. P., Mendes P. J., Rodrigues J. C., Dias A. R., *J. Mater. Chem.* 8 (1998) 925-930.
[59] Valente A., Royer S., Narendra M., Silva T. J. L., Mendes P. J. G., Robalo M. P., Abreu M., Heck J., Garcia M. H., *J. Organomet. Chem.* 736 (2013) 42-49.
[60] Garcia M. H., Mendes P. J., Robalo M. P., Duarte M. T., Lopes N., *J. Organomet. Chem.* 694 (2009) 2888-2897.
[61] Garcia M. H., Mendes P. J., Florindo P., Robalo M. P., Piedade M. F. M., Duarte M. T., Campo J., Wenseleers W., Goovaerts E.
[62] Silva T. J. L., Mendes P. J., Garcia M. H., Robalo M. P., Ramalho J. P. P., Carvalho A. J. P., Buchert M., Wittenburg C., Heck J., *Eur. J. Inorg. Chem.* 2013 (2013) 3506-3517.
[63] Garcia M. H., Florindo P., Piedade M. F. M., Duarte M. T., Robalo M. P., Heck J., Wittenburg C., Holtmann J., Licandro E., *J. Organomet. Chem.* 693 (2008) 2987-2999.
[64] Garcia M. H., Royer S., Robalo M. P., Dias A. R., Tranchier J. P., Chavignon R., Prim D., Auffrant A., Rose-Munch F., Rose E., Vaissermann J., Persoons A., Asselberghs I., *Eur. J. Inorg. Chem.* (2003) 3895-3904.
[65] Mata J. A., Peris E., Uriel S., Llusar R., Asselberghs I., Persoons A., *Polyhedron*. 20 (2001) 2083-2088.
[66] Laidlaw W. M., Denning R. G., Verbiest T., Chauchard E., Persoons A., *Nature*. 363 (1993) 58-60.
[67] Laidlaw W. M., Denning R. G., Verbiest T., Chauchard E., Persoons A. P., Second-order nonlinearity in mixed-valence metal chromophores 19942143 14-19.
[68] Qin Y., Kim J. Y., Frisbie C. D., Hillmyer M. A., *Macromolecules*. 41 (2008) 5563-5570.
[69] Morrison I. D., Denning R. G., Laidlaw W. M., Stammers M. A., *Rev. Sci. Instrum.* 67 (1996) 1445-1453.
[70] Houbrechts S., Clays K. J., Persoons A. P., Cadierno V., Gamasa M. P., Gimeno J., Whittall I. R., Humphrey M. G., New organometallic materials for nonlinear optics: metal σ-arylacetylides 19962852 98-108.
[71] Whittall I. R., Humphrey M. G., Persoons A., Houbrechts S., *Organometallics*. 15 (1996) 1935-1941.
[72] Wu I. Y., Lin J. T., Luo J., Li C. S., Tsai C., Wen Y. S., Hsu C. C., Yeh F. F., Liou S., *Organometallics*. 17 (1998) 2188-2198.

[73] McDonagh A. M., Whittall I. R., Humphrey M. G., Skelton B. W., White A. H., *J. Organomet. Chem.* 519 (1996) 229-235.
[74] Silva T. J. L., Mendes P. J., Santos A. M., Garcia M. H., Robalo M. P., Ramalho J. P. P., Carvalho A. J. P., Büchert M., Wittenburg C., Heck J., *Organometallics*.(2014).
[75] Whittall I. R., Cifuentes M. P., Humphrey M. G., Luther-Davies B., Samoc M., Houbrechts S., Persoons A., Heath G. A., Hockless D. C. R., *J. Organomet. Chem.* 549 (1997) 127-137.
[76] Garcia M. H., Robalo M. P., Dias A. R., Duarte M. T., Wenseleers W., Aerts G., Goovaerts E., Cifuentes M. P., Hurst S., Humphrey M. G., Samoc M., Luther-Davies B., *Organometallics*.21 (2002) 2107-2118.
[77] McDonagh A. M., Lucas N. T., Cifuentes M. P., Humphrey M. G., Houbrechts S., Persoons A., *J. Organomet. Chem.* 605 (2000) 193-201.
[78] McDonagh A. M., Cifuentes M. P., Lucas N. T., Humphrey M. G., Houbrechts S., Persoons A., *J. Organomet. Chem.* 605 (2000) 184-192.
[79] Powell C. E., Cifuentes M. P., McDonagh A. M., Hurst S. K., Lucas N. T., Delfs C. D., Stranger R., Humphrey M. G., Houbrechts S., Asselberghs I., Persoons A., Hockless D. C. R., *Inorg. Chim. Acta.* 352 (2003) 9-18.
[80] Hurst S. K., Lucas N. T., Cifuentes M. P., Humphrey M. G., Samoc M., Luther-Davies B., Asselberghs I., Van Boxel R., Persoons A., *J. Organomet. Chem.* 633 (2001) 114-124.
[81] Babgi B. A., Al-Hindawi A., Moxey G. J., Razak F. I. A., Cifuentes M. P., Kulasekera E., Stranger R., Teshome A., Asselberghs I., Clays K., Humphrey M. G., *J. Organomet. Chem.* 730 (2013) 108-115.
[82] Naulty R. H., Cifuentes M. P., Humphrey M. G., Houbrechts S., Boutton C., Persoons A., Heath G. A., Hockless D. C. R., LutherDavies B., Samoc M., *J. Chem. Soc.-Dalton Trans.* (1997) 4167-4174.
[83] Wu I. Y., Lin J. T., Luo J., Sun S. S., Li C. S., Lin K. J., Tsai C. T., Hsu C. C., Lin J. L., *Organometallics*. 16 (1997) 2038-2048.
[84] Marder S. R., Cheng L. T., Tiemann B. G., *J. Chem. Soc.-Chem. Commun.* (1992) 672-674.
[85] Marder S. R., Beratan D. N., Cheng L. T., *Science*. 252 (1991) 103-106.
[86] Cifuentes M. P., Driver J., Humphrey M. G., Asselberghs I., Persoons A., Samoc M., Luther-Davies B., *J. Organomet. Chem.* 607 (2000) 72-77.
[87] Whittall I. R., Humphrey M. G., Hockless D. C. R., Skelton B. W., White A. H., *Organometallics*. 14 (1995) 3970-3979.
[88] Mendes P. J., Silva T. J. L., Carvalho A. J. P., Ramalho J. P. P., *Theochem-J. Mol. Struct.* 946 (2010) 33-42.
[89] Mendes P. J., Silva T. J. L., Garcia M. H., Ramalho J. P. P., Carvalho A. J. P., *J. Chem. Inf. Model.* 52 (2012) 1970-1983.
[90] Kanis D. R., Ratner M. A., Marks T. J., *J. Am. Chem. Soc.* 114 (1992) 10338-10357.
[91] Marder S. R., Perry J. W., Schaefer W. P., *Science*. 245 (1989) 626-628.
[92] Whittall I. R., Cifuentes M. P., Costigan M. J., Humphrey M. G., Goh S. C., Skelton B. W., White A. H., *J. Organomet. Chem.* 471 (1994) 193-199.
[93] Dias A. R., Garcia M. H., Rodrigues J. C., Green M. L. H., Kuebler S. M., *J. Organomet. Chem.* 475 (1994) 241-245.

[94] Garcia M. H., Rodrigues J., Dias A. R., Piedade M. F. M., Duarte M. T., Robalo M. P., Lopes N.

[95] Garcia M. H., Rodrigues J. C., Dias A. R., Piedade M. F. M., Duarte M. T., Robalo M. P., Lopes N., *J. Organomet. Chem.* 632 (2001) 133-144.

[96] Ornelas C., Gandum C., Mesquita J., Rodrigues J., Garcia M. H., Lopes N., Robalo M. P., Nattinen K., Rissanen K., *Inorg. Chim. Acta.* 358 (2005) 2482-2488.

[97] Bandy J. A., Bunting H. E., Garcia M. H., Green M. L. H., Marder S. R., Thompson M. E., Bloor D., Kolinsky P. V., Jones R. J., Perry J. W., *Polyhedron.*1 1 (1992) 1429-1435.

[98] Oudar J. L., Zyss J., *Phys. Rev. A.* 26 (1982) 2016-2027.

[99] Zyss J., Oudar J. L., *Phys. Rev. A.* 26 (1982) 2028-2048.

[100] Zyss J., Nicoud J. F., Coquillay M., *The Journal of Chemical Physics.* 81 (1984) 4160-4167.

[101] Zyss J., Chemla D. S., in: D. S. Chemla, J. Zyss (Eds.), Nonlinear Optical Properties of Organic Molecules and Crystals, Academic Press, 1987, pp. 23-191.

[102] Richardson T., Roberts G. G., Polywka M. E. C., Davies S. G., *Thin Solid Films.* 160 (1988) 231-239.

[103] Whittall I. R., Humphrey M. G., *Organometallics.* 14 (1995) 5493-5495.

[104] Ge Q. C., Dalton G. T., Humphrey M. G., Samoc M., Hor T. S. A., *Chem.-Asian J.* 4 (2009) 998-1005.

[105] Ge Q., Corkery T. C., Humphrey M. G., Samoc M., Hor T. S. A., *Dalton Trans.* (2009) 6192-6200.

[106] Dias A. R., Garcia M. H., Rodrigues J., Petersen J. C., Bjornholm T., Geisler T.

[107] Maksimoska J., Feng L., Harms K., Yi C. L., Kissil J., Marmorstein R., Meggers E., *J. Am. Chem. Soc.* 130 (2008) 15764-+

[108] Bregman H., Meggers E., *Org. Lett.* 8 (2006) 5465-5468.

[109] Xie P., Williams D. S., Atilta-Gokcumen G. E., Milk L., Xiao M., Smalley K. S. M., Herlyn M., Meggers E., Marmorstein R., *ACS Chem. Biol.* 3 (2008) 305-316.

[110] Bergamo A., Gaiddon C., Schellens J. H. M., Beijnen J. H., Sava G., *J. Inorg. Biochem.* 106 (2012) 90-99.

[111] Zhang L., Carroll P., Meggers E., *Org. Lett.* 6 (2004) 521-523.

[112] Bregman H., Williams D. S., Atilla G. E., Carroll P. J., Meggers E., *J. Am. Chem. Soc.* 126 (2004) 13594-13595.

[113] Debreczeni J. E., Bullock A. N., Atilla G. E., Williams D. S., Bregman H., Knapp S., Meggers E., *Angew. Chem.-Int. Edit.* 45 (2006) 1580-1585.

[114] Romerosa A., Saoud M., Campos-Malpartida T., Lidrissi C., Serrano-Ruiz M., Peruzzini M., Garrido J. A., Garcia-Maroto F., *Eur. J. Inorg. Chem.* (2007) 2803-2812.

[115] Hajji L., Saraiba-Bello C., Romerosa A., Segovia-Torrente G., Serrano-Ruiz M., Bergamini P., Cannella A., *Inorg. Chem.* 50 (2011) 873-882.

[116] Garcia M. H., Morais T. S., Florindo P., Piedade M. F. M., Moreno V., Ciudad C., Noe V., *J. Inorg. Biochem.* 103 (2009) 354-361.

[117] Moreno V., Lorenzo J., Aviles F. X., Garcia M. H., Ribeiro J. P., Morais T. S., Florindo P., Robalo M. P., *Bioinorg. Chem. Appl.* (2010).

[118] Moreno V., Font-Bardia M., Calvet T., Lorenzo J., Aviles F. X., Garcia M. H., Morais T. S., Valente A., Robalo M. P., *J. Inorg. Biochem.* 105 (2011) 241-249.

[119] Tomaz A. I., Jakusch T., Morais T. S., Marques F., de Almeida R. F. M., Mendes F., Enyedy E. A., Santos I., Pessoa J. C., Kiss T., Garcia M. H., *J. Inorg. Biochem.* 117 (2012) 261-269.

[120] Morais T. S., Silva T. J. L., Marques F., Robalo M. P., Avecilla F., Madeira P. J. A., Mendes P. J. G., Santos I., Garcia M. H., *J. Inorg. Biochem.* 114 (2012) 65-74.

[121] Morais T. S., Santos F., Corte-Real L., Marques F., Robalo M. P., Madeira P. J. A., Garcia M. H., *J. Inorg. Biochem.*122 (2013) 8-17.

[122] Morais T. S., Santos F. C., Jorge T. F., Corte-Real L., Madeira P. J. A., Marques F., Robalo M. P., Matos A., Santos I., Garcia M. H., *J. Inorg. Biochem.* 130 (2014) 1-14.

[123] Morais T. S., Garcia M. H., Advances in Organometallic Chemistry and Catalysis, John Wiley & Sons, Inc., 2013, pp. 581-587.

[124] Morais T. S., Santos F. C., Corte-Real L., Garcia M. H., *J. Inorg. Biochem.* 129 (2013) 94-101.

[125] Corte-Real L., Matos A. P., Alho I., Morais T. S., Tomaz A. I., Garcia M. H., Santos I., Bicho M. P., Marques F., *Microsc. microanal.* 19 (2013) 1122-1130.

[126] Côrte-Real L., Mendes F., Coimbra J., Morais T., Tomaz A., Valente A., Garcia M. H., Santos I., Bicho M., Marques F., *J. Biol. Inorg. Chem.* (2014) 1-15.

[127] Florindo P., Marques I. J., Nunes C. D., Fernandes A. C., *J. Organomet. Chem.* 760 (2014) 240-247.

[128] Valente A., Garcia M. H., Marques F., Miao Y., Rousseau C., Zinck P., *J. Inorg. Biochem.* 127 (2013) 79-81.

[129] Matsumura Y., Maeda H., *Cancer Res.* 46 (1986) 6387-6392.

[130] Maeda H., Bharate G. Y., Daruwalla J., *Eur. J. Pharm. Biopharm.* 71 (2009) 409-419.

[131] Duncan R., Dimitrijevic S., Evagorou E. G., *STP Pharma Sci.* 6 (1996) 237-263.

[132] Kopecek J., Kopeckova P., Minko T., Lu Z. R., *Eur. J. Pharm. Biopharm.* 50 (2000) 61-81.

[133] Duncan R., *Biochem. Soc. Trans.* 35 (2007) 56-60.

[134] Andreia V., Garcia M. H., Inorganics.2 (2014).

[135] Tannock I. F., Rotin D., *Cancer Res.* 49 (1989) 4373-4384.

[136] Duncan R., *Nat. Rev. Drug Discov.* 2 (2003) 347-360.

[137] Rodrigues J., Jardim M. G., Figueira J., Gouveia M., Tomas H., Rissanen K., *New J. Chem.* 35 (2011) 1938-1943.

In: Ruthenium
Editor: Gary P. Keeler
ISBN: 978-1-63321-657-0

Chapter 5

RUTHENIUM-CATALYZED ISOMERIZATION OF ALLYLIC AND PROPARGYLIC ALCOHOLS IN NON-CONVENTIONAL SOLVENTS

Noel Nebra[1,*] and Joaquín García-Álvarez[2,†,*]
[1]ICIQ (Institut Català d'Investigació Química), Tarragona, Spain
[2]Laboratorio de Compuestos Organometálicos y Catálisis (Unidad Asociada al CSIC), Red ORFEO–CINQA - Centro de Innovación en Química Avanzada, Departamento de Química Orgánica e Inorgánica, Instituto Universitario de Química Organometálica "Enrique Moles", Facultad de Química, Universidad de Oviedo, Oviedo, Spain

1.1. ABSTRACT

In this contribution, the catalytic activity of a plethora of ruthenium complexes in the isomerization of allylic and propargylic alcohols in non-conventional solvents [water, ionic liquids (*ILs*), glycerol and Deep Eutectic Solvents (*DESs*)] is reviewed. On the one hand, the search for organic reactions proceeding with efficiency, selectivity and atom economy has emerged as a prime goal in synthetic chemistry. Among the organic reactions that proceed with atom economy, isomerization reactions are typical examples because no by-products are generated. To this regard, the ruthenium-catalyzed isomerizations of readily accessible allylic and propargylic alcohols, mainly giving carbonyl compounds, provide a simple synthetic route to these very valuable raw materials in organic chemistry. On the other hand, combination of ruthenium-catalyzed isomerization reactions and non-conventional solvents has led in recent years to the development of a huge number of new and *greener* synthetic methodologies. In this chapter, an overview of the progress achieved on the ruthenium-catalyzed isomerization of allylic and propargylic alcohols in environmentally-friendly solvents will be presented, with special emphasis on synthetic applications.

---

* Noel Nebra: ICIQ (Institut Català d'Investigació Química), Avgda. Països Catalans 16, 43007, Tarragona, Spain. E-mail address: nnebra@iciq.es.
† Joaquín García-Álvarez: Laboratorio de Compuestos Organometálicos y Catálisis (Unidad Asociada al CSIC), Red ORFEO–CINQA - Centro de Innovación en Química Avanzada, Departamento de Química Orgánica e Inorgánica, Instituto Universitario de Química Organometálica "Enrique Moles", Facultad de Química, Universidad de Oviedo, Julián Clavería 8, E-33006 Oviedo, Spain. E-mail address: garciajoaquin@uniovi.es.

1.2. INTRODUCTION

The application of organometallic ruthenium complexes as catalyst in organic synthesis has experimented a spectacular growth during the last decades (Figure 1). Until the 80s, few examples of organic transformations promoted by ruthenium complexes were reported (limited to oxidation [1], hydrogenation [2, 3], and transfer hydrogenation reactions [3]). However, and as a result of: *i*) the maturity gained by the coordination chemistry of ruthenium (with a robust first coordination sphere and able to adopt a huge number of geometries [4]); *ii*) the wide range of oxidation states offered by ruthenium (i.e., from oxidation state -2 in $[Ru(CO)_4]^{2-}$ to +8 in RuO_4 [4a]); *iii*) its facility to transfer electrons and its properties as Lewis acid; *iv*) the high tolerance to a variety of functional groups; and *v*) its low price when compared with other transition metals (i.e., Rh, Ir, Pt, Pd and Au); *Ruthenium* holds nowadays a prominent role within the toolbox of both academic and industrial organic synthetic chemists [5]. Also, it is important to note that although the studies of the catalytic activity of ruthenium complexes in organic synthesis are relatively recent, this field has been already recognized with the award of two Nobel Prizes in Chemistry to R. Noyori (2001) and R. H. Grubbs (2005).

Due to both environmental and economic issues, *Chemistry* is driven to reduce waste and re-use materials in order to meet the standards of the *12 Principles of Green Chemistry* [6].

In this sense, one of the crucial points in realizing a catalytic *Green Chemical* process involves the choice of a safe, non-toxic and cheap solvent [7], as one of the largest areas of consumption of petroleum-based chemicals, in a conventional metal-catalyzed organic reaction, is the solvent used as reaction media (i.e., solvents account for 80-90% of mass utilization in a typical pharmaceutical/fine chemical operational process) [8].

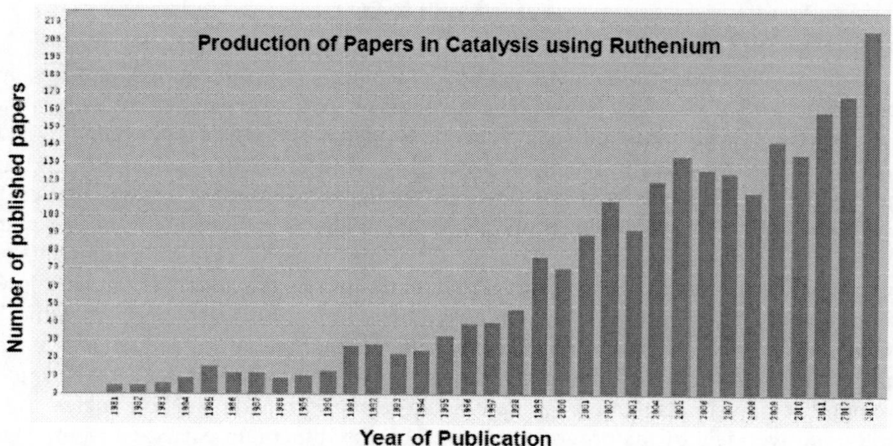

Data extracted from Web of Science using "ruthenium-catalyzed" as keyword.

Figure 1. Evolution of the number of papers where ruthenium complexes are used as catalysts during the last 30 years.

Therefore, there has been a global demand for the development of environmentally-friendly solvents that are not based on crude petroleum. In top of that, conventional volatile organic solvents (*VOCs*), commonly used as reaction media, can cause well-established environmental problems due to their: *i*) high toxicity; *ii*) non-biodegradability; *iii*) accumulation in the atmosphere (low boiling points); and *iv*) flammability [9]. Despite these intrinsic drawbacks of *VOCs*, most of the chemical transformations are performed in solution (using these hazardous solvents) to: *i*) achieve homogeneity of reagents and products; *ii*) efficiently control the heat flow; *iii*) ensure rapid and safe conversion; and *iv*) avoid undesired side products by dilution, thus enhancing the reaction rate. To overcome the aforementioned drawbacks of traditional *VOCs* and still benefit from the solvent effects [10], remarkable research efforts have been focused on the replacement of traditional organic solvents by *Green Solvents* [7]. In theory, an ideal *green* solvent should be safe for both human beings and the environment, with its use and manufacture being also sustainable [11]. Therefore, to be qualified as *green* media, these solvents have to meet different criteria such as availability, non-toxicity, biodegradability, recyclability, non-flammability and low price. Up to now, these *green* solvents (the number of available *green* solvents is still nowadays rather limited) include: *i*) supercritical fluids (i.e., *sc*CO_2); *ii*) Ionic Liquids (*ILs*) and Deep Eutectic Solvents (*DESs*); *iii*) water; *iv*) perflourinated solvents; and *v*) biomass derived solvents (i.e., 2-methyl-THF, lactic acid, γ-valerolactone and glycerol). These new solvents are emerging as very promising alternatives to traditional *VOCs* and occupy a strategic place within the framework of *Green Chemistry* [6, 7].

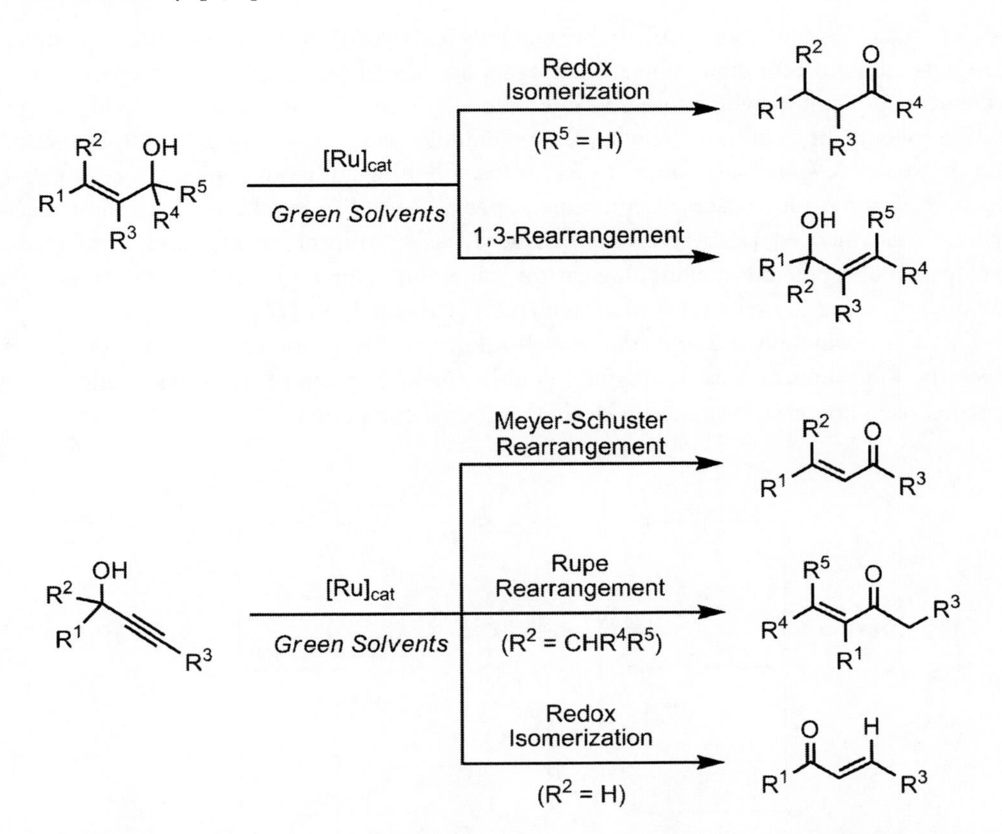

Scheme 1. Ruthenium-catalyzed isomerizations of allylic and propargylic alcohols performed in environmentally-friendly solvents.

Together with the choice of a safe, non-toxic, biorenewable and cheap solvent; the search for organic reactions proceeding with high levels of efficiency, selectivity and atom economy [12] (i.e., all atoms of the reactants end up in the final product) has emerged as one of the crucial points to perform a *Catalytic Green Chemical* process. Among all the reactions that proceed with high atom economy, isomerization processes are typical examples as no by-products are generated. In this sense, the isomerization of readily accessible allylic and propargylic alcohols catalyzed by transition-metal complexes is a useful and straightforward synthetic route to both saturated and unsaturated carbonyl derivatives (Scheme 1), which are very important raw materials in organic synthesis.

Thus, the aim of this chapter is to provide a detail overview on the developments achieved in the ruthenium-catalyzed isomerization of allylic and propargylic alcohols using non-conventional solvents [water, Ionic Liquids (*ILs*), Deep Eutectic Solvents (*DESs*) and glycerol], covering the literature published in this field up to May 2014.

1.3. Ruthenium-Catalyzed Isomerization of Allylic Alcohols

The redox isomerization of allylic alcohols catalyzed by transition metal complexes represents an atom economic, powerful, elegant and *green* methodology to prepare saturated carbonyl compounds, where otherwise a two-step sequence of oxidation and reduction reactions would be required (Scheme 2); potentially using toxic and/or harsh reagents. In addition, sensitive substrates may not survive the conditions of oxidation and/or reduction and therefore catalytic redox isomerization are especially used in synthesis when mild reaction conditions are needed [13]. Over the last decades, significant efforts have been made to develop metal-mediated methodologies for obtaining carbonyl compounds from allylic alcohols [14], after the seminal works from Blum [15] and Trost [16].

This transformation is based on the well-known ability of transition-metal complexes to induce the migration of a carbon-carbon double bound to produce an enolate followed by a spontaneous tautomerization into the desired carbonyl compound.

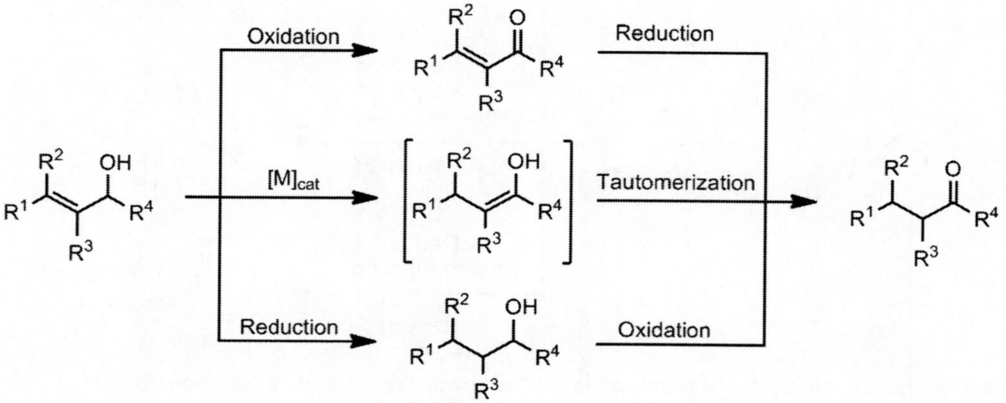

Oxidation
Reduction
$[M]_{cat}$
Tautomerization
Reduction
Oxidation

Scheme 2. Redox isomerization of allylic alcohols.

Thus, a large variety of group 6, 8, 9 and 10 metal complexes have shown to catalyze this isomerization [14]; however, most of them show restricted scope with regard to the nature of the reaction media (non-conventional solvents are usually the most challenging). In this sense, a variety of ruthenium complexes have been employed as catalysts in this transformation using environmentally-friendly solvents.

Thus, this section of the chapter provides an overview of the ruthenium-catalyzed redox isomerization of allylic alcohols in the non-conventional solvents: *i*) *water*; *ii*) *Ionic Liquids (ILs)*; and *iii*) *Deep Eutectic Solvents (DESs)*.

1.3.1. Ru-Catalyzed Redox Isomerization of Allylic Alcohols in Water

As previously mentioned in the introduction, water is attracting attention as a replacement for traditionally used organic solvents as an inexpensive, available and renewable feedstock [17]. Indeed, their unique properties have attracted a great deal of consideration in its potential applications in catalysis including, in particular, the Ru-catalyzed redox isomerization of allylic alcohols.

Thus, this section is intended to cover the progress made within the three broad families of ruthenium catalysts active in this transformation in water, which are *ruthenium(II)*, *ruthenium(III)* and *ruthenium(IV)* precursors.

1.3.1.a. Ruthenium(II) Catalysts

- Octahedral ruthenium(II) complexes

Various octahedral ruthenium(II) complexes have been reported to date in the literature for this transformation in aqueous media. In fact, the first ruthenium(II) catalyst used in water was a hexaaqua-octahedral complex, namely $[Ru(H_2O)_6][OTs]_2$ (**1**, OTs = *p*-toluene-sulfonate, Scheme 3), reported by Grubbs and co-workers [18]. This complex proved to be an effective catalyst for the isomerization of both aliphatic allylic alcohols and related allylic ethers [19], in pure aqueous medium under mild reaction conditions (45 °C) [20]. However, this complex presents two important catalytic drawbacks: *i*) high catalytic loadings are required to achieve quantitative conversions (10 mol%); and *ii*) oxidation by-products were also observed in some cases. To overpass all these limitations, the related dicationic ruthenium complex *cis*-$[Ru(6,6'\text{-}Cl_2bipy)_2(H_2O)_2][OTf]_2$ (6,6'-Cl_2bipy = 6,6′-dichloro-2,2′-bipyridine; OTf = $CF_3SO_2^-$) [21], was employed as selective catalyst for the isomerization reaction of 3-butene-2-ol in water, with a substrate/catalyst ratio of 1000 (0.1 mol% in ruthenium). However, it required higher reaction temperatures (90 °C) and the presence of an external base (KOH) [22].

$[Ru(H_2O)_6][OTs]_2$ (**1**)
(10 mol%)
H_2O / 45 °C
R^1 = H; R^2 = H, Me, Et
R^1 = Me; R^2 = H

Scheme 3. Isomerization of aliphatic allylic alcohols in water promoted by the octahedral Ru(II) complex $[Ru(H_2O)_6][OTs]_2$ (**1**).

Introduction of hydrophilic ligands in the coordination sphere of octahedral ruthenium(II) complexes is one the most popular methodologies for the preparation of new water-soluble catalysts [23]. In this sense, several octahedral and pentacoordinated ruthenium(II) complexes containing different types of water-soluble phosphines have been synthesized and used in the catalytic redox isomerization of allylic alcohols in aqueous media (complexes **2-7**, Figure 2).

Firstly, the water-soluble sulfonated phosphine TPPMS [(3-sulfonatophenyl) diphenylphosphine sodium salt] was employed by Joó et al. in 2008 for the preparation of the dinuclear ruthenium(II) complexes $[Na]_4[\{RuCl(\mu\text{-}Cl)(TPPMS)_2\}_2]$ (**2**, Figure 2) and $[Na]_4[\{RuCl(\mu\text{-}Cl)(C{=}C{=}CPh_2)(TPPMS)_2\}_2]$ (**3**, Figure 2) [24].

Similar catalytic properties were observed for both complexes in the isomerization of several C=C mono-substituted allylic alcohols (alk-1-en-3-ols) in aqueous media or biphasic systems, showing turnover frequencies (TOFs) in the range of 70-100 h^{-1} for the isomerization of this particular class of allylic alcohols. More recently, Kathó and co-workers prepared a series of air-stable octahedral ruthenium(II) derivatives **4-7** (Figure 2), containing the hydrophilic phosphine ligand PTA [1,3,5-triaza-7-phosphaadamantane] and its *N*-alkylated derivatives (PTA-Me and PTA-CH_2Ph) [25].

However, these new octahedral ruthenium(II) complexes (**4-7**) showed only moderate activity and selectivity under mild reaction conditions (80 °C, in the presence of sodium formate as base), when compared with their metallic precursor *cis*-$[RuCl_2(dmso)_4]$ (dmso = dimethyl sulfoxide) in the isomerization of mono-substituted aliphatic allylic alcohols.

- Half-sandwich ruthenium(II) complexes

Since the aforementioned work reported by Grubbs and co-workers [18], several half-sandwich ruthenium(II) catalysts active in water have been developed for this transformation, most of them being cyclopentadienyl- or arene-Ru(II) complexes. In this sense, Kulaweic and Trost were the pioneers in the study of the catalytic activity of a cyclopentadienyl-Ru(II)-like complex (namely $[RuCl(\eta^5\text{-}Cp)(PPh_3)_2]$ in combination with $[Et_3NH][PF_6]$) in the redox isomerization of allylic alcohols, although a conventional organic solvent and high reaction temperatures (dioxane at 100 °C) were used [16].

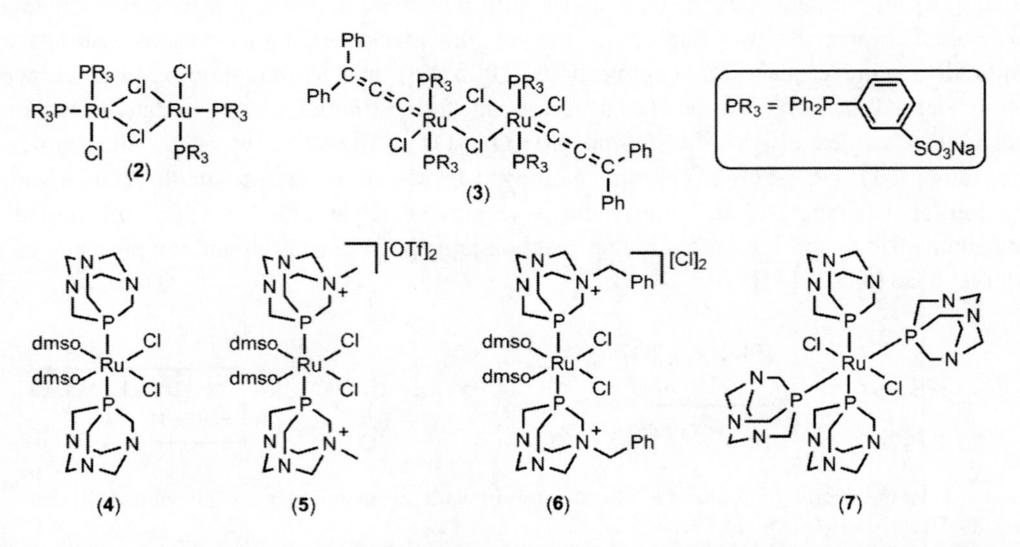

Figure 2. Structure of the pentacoordinated (**2**) and octahedral (**3-7**) ruthenium(II) complexes containing water soluble phosphine ligands.

After this seminal study, a variety of new cyclopentadienyl-Ru(II) catalysts have been prepared containing the aforementioned water-soluble phosphines TPPMS or PTA. Firstly, Joó and co-workers reported the water-soluble bis-phosphine complex $[Na]_2[RuCl(\eta^5\text{-}Cp)(TPPMS)_2]$ (**8**, Figure 3) as the best cyclopentadienyl-Ru(II) catalyst (with excellent TOF values, up to 2226 h^{-1}) for the isomerization of both mono-substituted allylic alcohols (into ketones) and primary allylic alcohols (into aldehydes) in water, working under acidic conditions (buffered solution at pH 2) and employing mild reaction temperatures (from room temperature to 60 ºC) [24]. At this point, it is important to note that the authors observed a remarkably lower activity for the related derivative $[Na][Ru(\eta^5\text{-}Cp)(CO)(TPPMS)_2]$ (**9**, Figure 3), in which the chloride ligand was replaced by carbon monoxide (C≡O). Latter, Romerosa et al., employed the water soluble phosphine PTA [and its protonated (PTA-H) and methylated (PTA-Me) derivatives], for the synthesis of a variety of cyclopentadienyl-Ru(II) derivatives (**10-15**, Figure 3) [26].

As previously mentioned for their TPPMS counterparts, a strong dependence between the pH of the reaction medium and the reaction rate was observed; best results were obtained again under acidic conditions and using phosphate buffers [26]. These results showed unambiguously that the phosphate buffer is not innocent, interacting with the catalytically active metal center and therefore strongly modulates its catalytic activity.

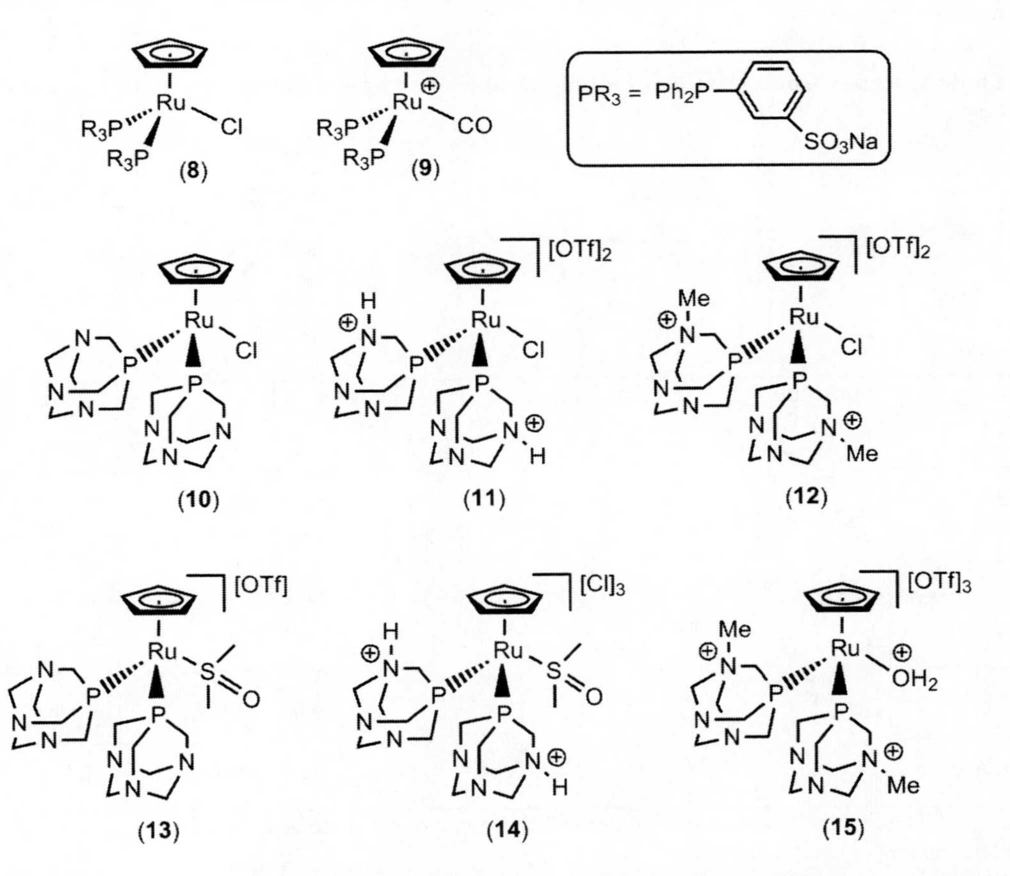

Figure 3. Structure of the cyclopentadienyl-ruthenium(II) complexes **8-15** containing water soluble phosphine ligands.

Half-sandwich tethered ruthenium(II) complexes, containing cyclopentadienyl ligands functionalized with *N*-heterocyclic carbenes (Cp^x,**16-17**, Table 1), have been reported by Rollo, Peris and co-workers as suitable catalysts for the redox isomerization of allylic alcohols in pure water [27].

Interestingly, the authors found that complex **16** was far more active than **17** (entries 4 and 5, Table 1). To explain this experimental fact, they attributed the remarkable differences in activity to the highly sterically hindered environment present in complex **17** (with bulky benzyl groups).

Thus, complex **16** showed to be an efficient catalyst for the isomerization of C=C mono-substituted substrates (entries 1-4, Table 1, TOF values from 124 to 248 h^{-1}), although low conversions were observed for di-substituted olefins (entry 6, Table 1).

Addition of three equivalents of AgOTf was mandatory in order to activate the pre-catalyst **16** and to facilitate the solubilization of the complex in water, probably *via* formation of the corresponding aqua-derivative [Ru(η^5-Cp^x)(CO)(H_2O)][OTf].

Remarkably, the catalytic reactions proceeded in the absence of an external base and with low catalyst loading (0.2 mol%) at 75 ºC.

As previously mentioned, the second main family of half-sandwich ruthenium(II) catalysts employed in the redox isomerization of allylic alcohols in water is constituted by η^6-arene derivatives.

Table 1. Redox isomerization of allylic alcohols in water catalyzed by complexes 16-17[a]

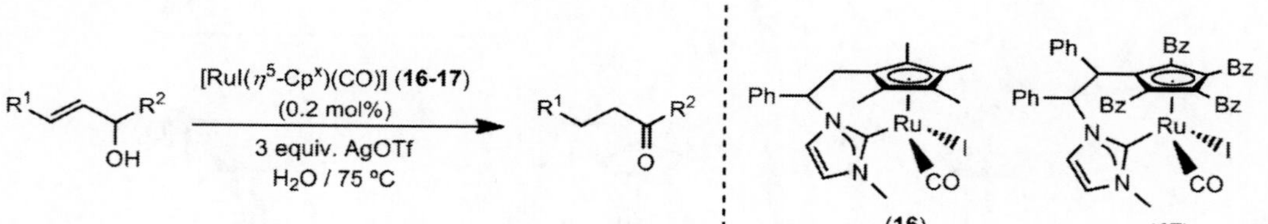

R1 (allylic alcohol, OH, R2) → [RuI(η^5-Cp^x)(CO)] (**16-17**) (0.2 mol%), 3 equiv. AgOTf, H_2O / 75 ºC → R1 (ketone, O, R2)

(16) (17)

entry	Substrate	Product	Catalyst	Time	Yield (%)[b]
1	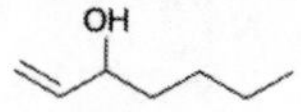	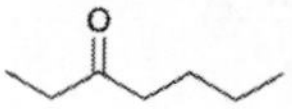	**16**	4 h	99
2	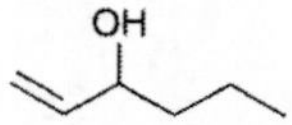	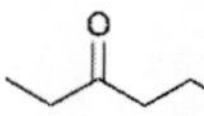	**16**	4 h	99
3	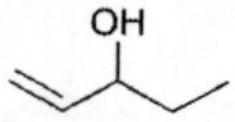	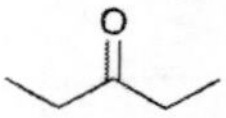	**16**	4 h	99
4	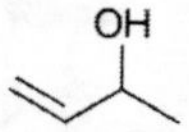	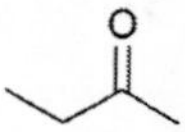	**16**	2 h	99
5[c]	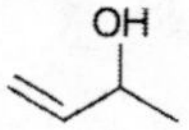	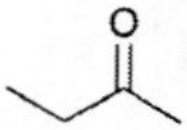	**17**	24 h	20
6	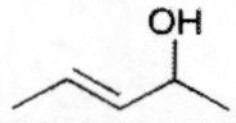	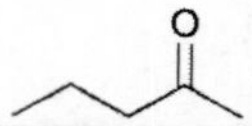	**16**	24 h	20

[a]General Conditions: Reactions carried out with 0.4 mmol of substrate in 4 mL of water.
[b]Yield determined by ^{1}H NMR.
[c]1 mol% of catalyst **17** was employed.

At the beginning of 2004, Cadierno, Gimeno et al. illuminated the way to follow by studying the catalytic activity of a family of water-soluble arene-Ru(II) derivatives containing hydrophilic phosphine ligands, including the tris(hydroxymethyl)phosphine complexes $[RuCl_2(\eta^6\text{-arene})\{P(CH_2OH)_3\}]$ (arene = C_6H_6, *p*-cymene, C_6Me_6; **18a-c**, Figure 4) and $[RuCl(\eta^6\text{-arene})\{P(CH_2OH)_3\}_2][Cl]$ (arene = C_6H_6, *p*-cymene, C_6Me_6; **19a-c**, Figure 4) [28a].

These complexes were found to be efficient catalysts for the isomerization of allylic alcohols [TOF values up to 600 h^{-1}, Turnover number (TON) values up to 782] in the biphasic water/*n*-heptane medium (under N_2 atmosphere, 75 °C), although the presence of an external base (Cs_2CO_3) was mandatory to achieve quantitative conversions.

Latter, in 2006, the same research group reported the phosphino-ammonium derivatives $[RuCl_2(\eta^6\text{-}p\text{-cymene})\{PPh_{(3-n)}(OCH_2CH_2NMe_3)_n\}][SbF_6]_n$ (**20a-c**, Figure 4) as selective and recyclable catalysts for the quantitative conversion of 1-octen-3-ol into 3-octanone [28b]. At this point, it is important to note that complex **20c** is one of the most active catalysts for the isomerization of allylic alcohols (1 mol% of complex is able to catalyze in water the conversion of 1-octen-3-ol into 3-octanone at 75 °C, in the presence of KO^tBu as external base, TON = 990). In the same year and in collaboration with Majoral and co-workers, the aforementioned research group presented the cage-like phosphine precursors $[RuCl_2(\eta^6\text{-arene})(THPA)]$ (THPA = 2,4,10-trimethyl-1,2,4,5,7,10-hexaaza-3-phosphatricyclo[3.3.1.1(3,7)] decane, **21a-d**, Figure 4) and $[RuCl_2(\eta^6\text{-arene})(THPA\text{-}Me)][OTf]$ (**22a-b**, Figure 4) [28c]. Good catalytic activities (TOF up to 200 h^{-1}) were obtained with these complexes in the redox isomerization of mono-substituted allylic alcohols using pure water both in the presence and in the absence of an external base.

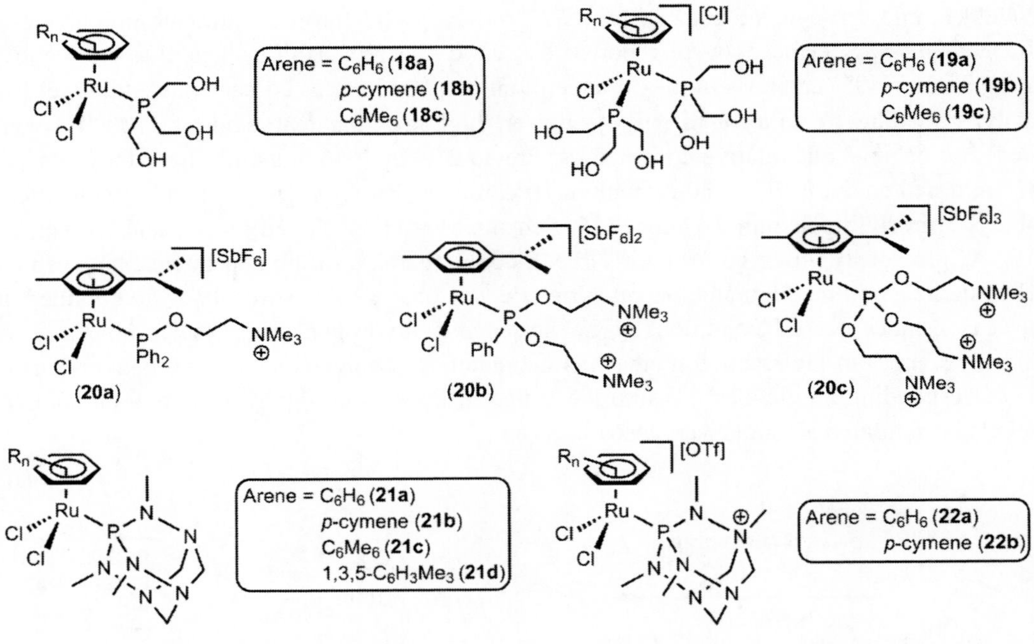

Figure 4. Structure of the arene-ruthenium(II) complexes **18-22** containing water soluble phosphine ligands.

The catalyst recycling was investigated using the isomerization of the 1-octen-3-ol into 3-octanone as a model reaction. Thus, after a simple extraction process with *n*-hexane and diethyl ether, the catalysts **21-22** could be re-used in a maximum number of four consecutive times. Finally, in 2013, Cadierno et al. reported the catalytic activity of the arene-ruthenium(II) complex [RuCl$_2$(η^6-C$_6$H$_6$)(PTA-Me)][Cl] in the conversion of 1-octen-3-ol into 3-octanone in pure water. However, longer reaction times (24 h, 75 ºC) and the presence of an external base (K_2CO_3) were needed to achieve quantitative conversions [28d].

Extremely active functionalized-arene-ruthenium(II) catalysts (**23a-c**, Scheme 4) for the isomerization of allylic alcohols in water (without containing hydrophilic phosphines) were developed by Crochet and co-workers [29]. In this sense, complex **23a** is one of the most active catalysts for the conversion of di-substituted olefins into their corresponding saturated carbonyl compounds (1 mol% of this complex is able to isomerize 3-penten-2-ol at 75 ºC, in the presence of KO^{t}Bu as external base, in only 30 min). The trend observed for the catalytic activity of complexes **23a-c** in this isomerization (TOF values from 200 to 20 h^{-1}, respectively) was explained by the authors taking into account the increasing steric hindrance when moving from **23a** to **23c**, that makes the coordination of the C=C bound of the allylic alcohol to the metallic center more difficult. For comparison, the same research group showed that the parent complex [RuCl$_2$(η^6-*p*-cymene){P(OEt)$_3$}] quantitatively converted 1-octen-3-ol into 3-octanone in water, although a longer reaction time was required (130 min, TOF = 46 h^{-1}).

A different approach for the synthesis of water soluble arene-ruthenium(II) complexes was made by Peris´ group in 2010, employing sulfonate-functionalized *NHC*-carbenes [30]. Thus, the new half-sandwich-ruthenium(II) *NHC*-complexes [Cs][Ru(κ^2-*O*,*O*-CO$_3$)(η^6-arene)(*NHC*)] [arene = *p*-cymene and C$_6$Me$_6$; *NHC* = 1-methyl-3-(propanesulfonate)imidazolin-2-ylidene; **24a-b**, Scheme 5] were reported as active and recyclable (up to five consecutive times, TON = 495) catalysts in the absence of an external base as co-catalysts and under low catalytic loading (0.5 mol% in Ru). However, high reaction temperatures (100 ºC) were needed to achieve quantitative conversions. Previously, in 2006, a similar base free catalytic system based on the *NHC*-arene-ruthenium(II) complex [RuCl$_2$(η^6-*p*-cymene)(*NHC*)] (*NHC* = 1-butyl-3-methylimidazolin-2-ylidene; **25**, Scheme 5) was developed by Joó and co-workers [31]. As previously observed for their TPPMS counterparts, a strong dependence between the pH of the reaction medium and the catalytic rate was observed (best results were obtained, in this case, under neutral conditions). The presence of hydrogen (H_2, 1 bar) and NaCl (as chloride source) in the reaction media was mandatory to achieve quantitative conversions of the corresponding allylic alcohols into the expected ketones or aldehydes (small amounts of the related saturated alcohols were also observed).

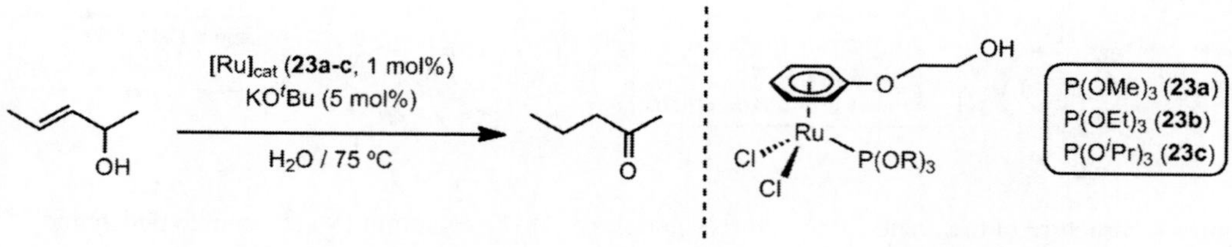

Scheme 4. Isomerization of 3-penten-2-ol in water promoted by the arene-ruthenium(II) complexes **23a-c**.

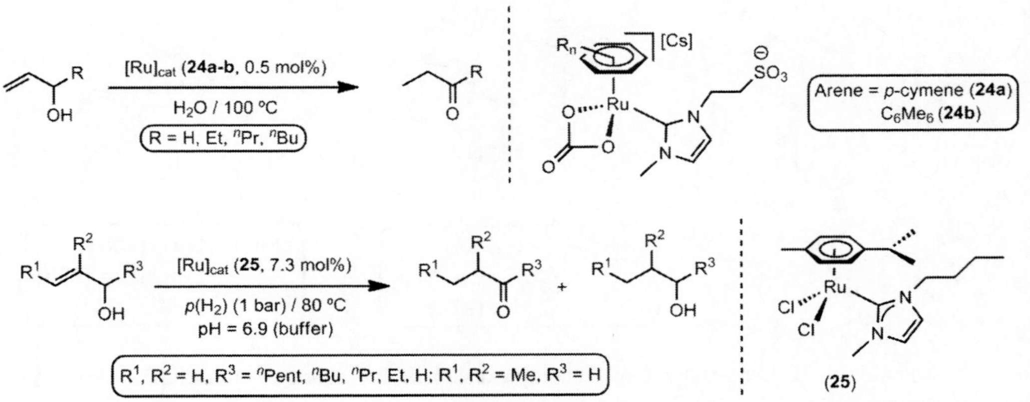

Scheme 5. Isomerization of allylic alcohols in water catalyzed by the arene-ruthenium(II) complexes containing *NHC* ligands.

Both NaCl and hydrogen gas could be avoided when the less sterically hindered *NHC*-derivative [$RuCl_2$(η^6-*p*-cymene)(*NHC*)] (*NHC* = 1,3-dimethylimidazolin-2-ylidene) and higher reaction temperature (100 °C *vs* 80 °C) were employed.

Finally, several *N*-donor ligands have been used for the synthesis of a variety of arene-ruthenium(II) catalysts active in the redox isomerization of 1-octen-3-ol in pure water as solvent. In this sense, Cadierno and co-workers studied the catalytic activity of the ruthenium (II)-arene complex [RuCl{κ^2-*N,N'*-C(N-4-C_6H_4Br)(N^{i}Pr)NH^{i}Pr}(η^6-*p*-cymene)] (**26**, Figure 5), containing an asymmetrical guanidinate ligand [32]. Unfortunately, this complex presented only a moderate activity in the isomerization of 1-octen-3-ol in pure water as solvent in the absence of base (1 mol% in Ru, 80 °C, 3 h, 15% yield of 3-octanone). More efficient arene-ruthenium(II) catalysts, containing different azole ligands (five-membered nitrogenated heterocyclic rings), were synthesized in Gimeno´s research group. In this regard, the benzimidazole based ruthenium(II) complexes [$RuCl_2$(η^6-arene)(κ^1-*N*-benzimidazole)] (**27a-c**, Figure 5) showed to be active catalysts in the quantitative conversion of the aforementioned substrate (1-octen-ol) into the corresponding saturated 3-octanone in pure water and in the absence of base (0.2 mol% in Ru, 75 °C, 0.5-2 h) [33a]. The same authors also demonstrated that other *N*-containing heterocycles (3,5-dimethylpyrazole) can be employed for the synthesis of new arene-ruthenium(II) catalysts (**28a-c**, Figure 5).

These pyrazole-derived complexes (**28a-c**) are active catalysts for this transformation in pure water (0.2 mol% in Ru, 75 °C, base free), although longer reaction times are required to achieve quantitative conversion (2-5 h) [33b].

- Supramolecular and supported ruthenium(II) catalysts

As previously mentioned in the introduction, and trying to meet the sustainability criteria consistent with the *12 Principles of Green Chemistry* [6], the search for efficient methodologies devoted to enable the separation and recycle of the catalysts is considered a main objective within this area [34]. To overcome the intrinsic separation problems associated with homogeneous catalysis, tremendous efforts have been made to immobilize catalysts on a diverse range of supports, such as inorganic solids, polymers, dendrimers or nanoparticles [35]. In this context, several half-sandwich ruthenium(II) complexes have been immobilized on different supports and tested as suitable catalysts for the redox isomerization of allylic alcohols in water.

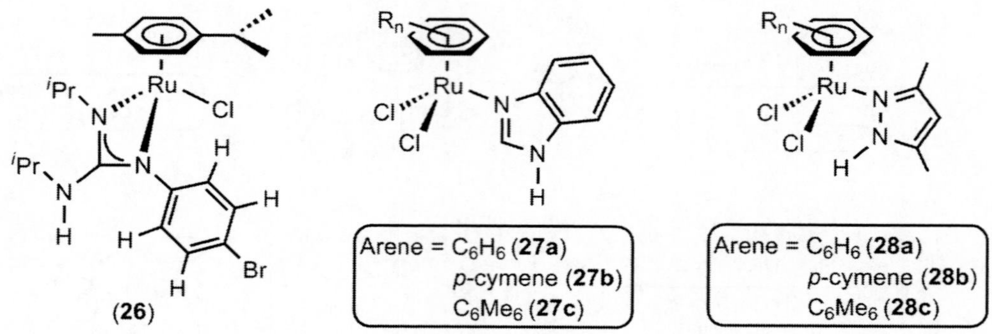

(26)

Arene = C_6H_6 (**27a**)
p-cymene (**27b**)
C_6Me_6 (**27c**)

Arene = C_6H_6 (**28a**)
p-cymene (**28b**)
C_6Me_6 (**28c**)

Figure 5. Structure of the arene-ruthenium(II) complexes **26-28** containing *N*-donor ligands active in the redox isomerization of 1-octen-3-ol in water.

Firstly, Caminade and co-workers decided to take a step ahead in the aforementioned use of water soluble phosphines for the synthesis of ruthenium(II) catalysts (active in the redox isomerization of allylic alcohols in water) by designing a new family of PTA-containing dendrimers [36]. Thus, the dendrimers containing the (*p*-cymene)-Ru(II)-PTA complex as ending group (**29**, Figure 6) were tested in the isomerization of 1-octen-3-ol into 3-octanone in a biphasic mixture water/*n*-heptane at 75 °C, in the presence of an external base as co-catalyst (Cs_2CO_3, 2 mol%). The presence of water is mandatory, as in its absence, no conversion was observed. At the end of the isomerization, the easy phase separation allowed an efficient recycling of the catalyst up to 4 runs. At this point, it is important to note that a positive dendritic effect was observed as the conversion increased from the monomer (38%) to the third generation dendrimer (98%) under the same catalytic conditions. Latter, Cadierno and co-workers supported, in a similar way, the (*p*-cymene)-Ru(II)-PTA complex on the surface of silica-coated ferrite nanoparticles. The resulting heterogeneous catalyst **30** (Figure 6) fully converted mono-, di- and tri-substituted allylic alcohols into the corresponding aldehydes or ketones in pure water as solvent, in the absence of base, using MW-irradiation (150 °C) and with low catalyst loadings (1.58 mol% in Ru) [37a]. Moreover, this magnetic material was easily separated with the aid of an external magnet and reused in three further catalytic runs without notable decrease in its activity and selectivity.

Finally, Bergman, Raymond and co-workers employed a different approach using the supramolecular catalyst **31** (Scheme 6), generated by encapsulation of the half-sandwich cyclopentadienyl-Ru(II) cation $[Ru(\eta^5\text{-}Cp)(PMe_3)(NCMe)_2]^+$ in the host assembly $[M_4L_6]^{-12}$ [M = Al^{3+}, Fe^{3+}, Ga^{3+}; LH_4 = 1,5-bis(2,3-dihydroxybenzoylamino)-naphthalene, Scheme 6] [38]. Both the isolated complex $[Ru(\eta^5\text{-}Cp)(PMe_3)(NCMe)_2]^+$ and its encapsulated version **31** showed to be active catalyst for the isomerization of allylic alcohols in water at low temperatures (42 °C). However, through encapsulation, the stability of the organometallic complex in aqueous solutions considerably increased from few hours to several days.

Furthermore, its water-solubility was also greatly improved, by at least one order of magnitude. Finally, the inclusion of the active species in the supramolecular guest allowed the modulation of its reactivity. As a matter of fact, both aliphatic and aromatic allylic alcohols (i.e., prop-2-en-1-ol, but-3-en-2-ol, 1-phenylprop-2-en-1-ol) could be converted by the free cyclopentadienyl-ruthenium(II) cation, while only aliphatic ones reacted with the supramolecular catalyst **31**; that is, the most hindered substrates could not insert into the internal cavity and remained unaltered.

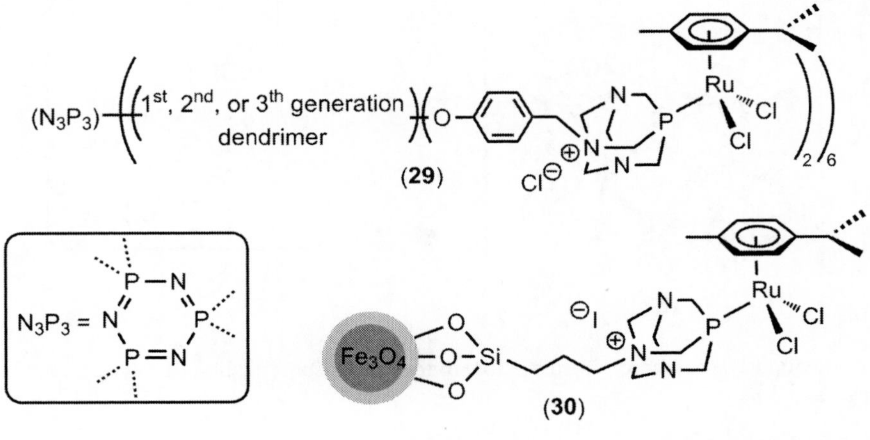

Figure 6. Structure of the arene-ruthenium(II) complex [$RuCl_2(\eta^6$-*p*-cymene)(PTA)] supported in a dendrimer (**29**) or in silica-coated ferrite nanoparticles (**30**).

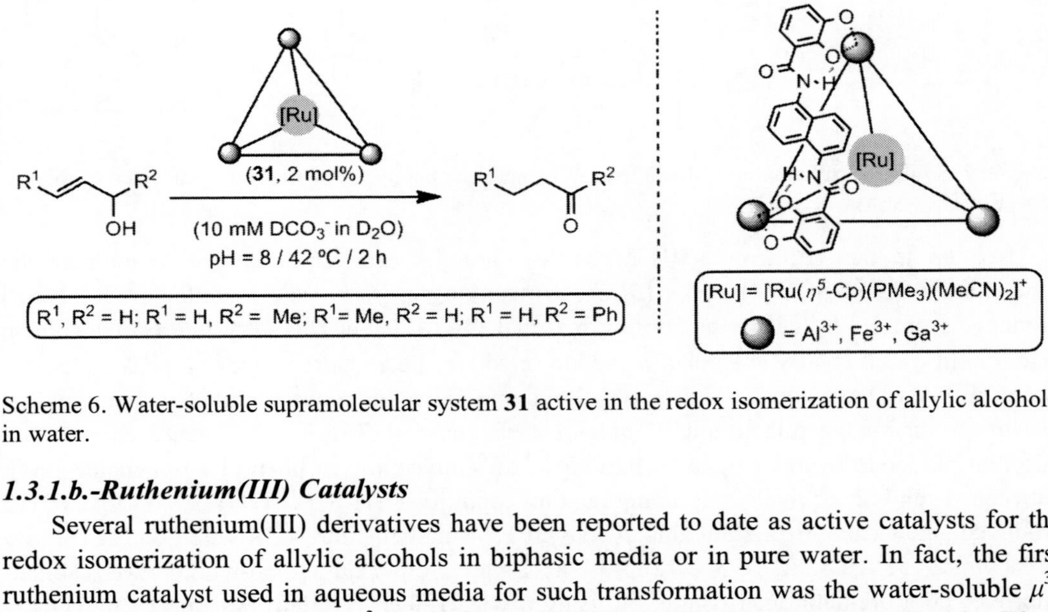

Scheme 6. Water-soluble supramolecular system **31** active in the redox isomerization of allylic alcohols in water.

1.3.1.b.-Ruthenium(III) Catalysts

Several ruthenium(III) derivatives have been reported to date as active catalysts for the redox isomerization of allylic alcohols in biphasic media or in pure water. In fact, the first ruthenium catalyst used in aqueous media for such transformation was the water-soluble μ^3-oxo-triruthenium cluster [$Ru_3(\mu^3$-O)$(OAc)_6(H_2O)_3$][OAc] (**32**, Figure 7), described by Blum and co-workers back in 1979 [39a]. By performing the catalytic reactions at 120 °C, they were able to isomerize a variety of secondary allylic alcohols (with general formula RCH(OH) $CH=CH_2$; R = alkyl group) into the corresponding saturated ketones, albeit with only modest conversions.

Unfortunately, allylic alcohols with long *n*-alkyl chains (e.g., dec-1-en-3-ol), which are poorly miscible with water, barely reacted even at high temperatures (120 °C). This limitation could be overcome, to some extent, by adding a surfactant to the medium. Low conversions were also obtained using the hydrated salt $RuCl_3{\cdot}(H_2O)_x$ combined with the hydrophilic ligand TPPMS [39b].

Moreover, the corresponding saturated alcohols, generated by a competitive hydrogen transfer process, were also observed as by-products.

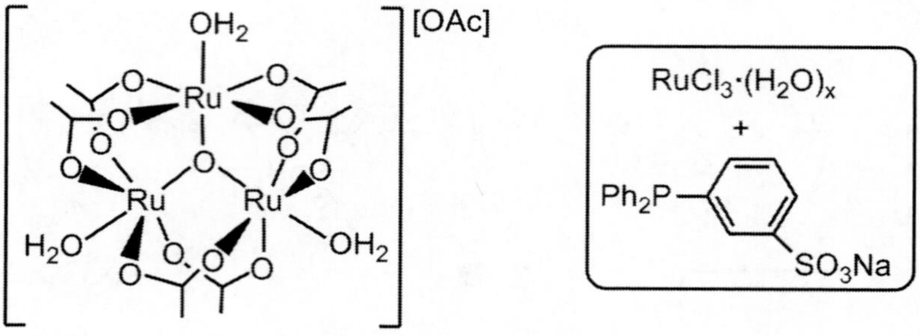

Figure 7. Ruthenium(III) catalytic systems active in the redox isomerization of allylic alcohols in aqueous media.

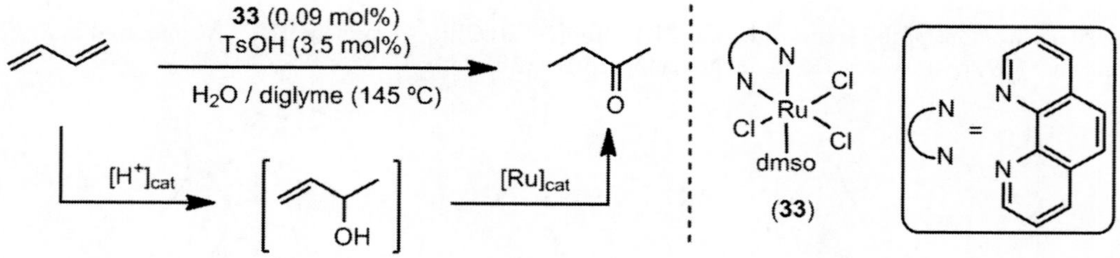

Scheme 7. Synthesis of butanone (MEK) from 1,3-butadiene catalyzed by the ruthenium(III) complex *mer*-[$RuCl_3$(dmso)(phen)] (**33**).

Related to that, ruthenium(III) derivatives are the catalyst of choice to mediate the production of methyl(ethyl)ketone (*MEK*, a megaton-per year scale manufactured solvent) produced from 1,3-butadiene as starting material [40, 41]. For this very interesting *tandem* reaction, in which an allylic alcohol is the intermediate specie, pure water or biphasic medium (water/diglyme) have been used as solvent (Scheme 7). In this sense, Drent et al. reported that *in situ* mixing of the ruthenium(III) precursor [$Ru(acac)_3$] (Hacac = 2,4-pentanedione) and different bidentate *N*-donor ligands [like bipy (2,2′-bipyridine) or phen (1,10-phenantroline); between 1 and 2 equivalents], under acidic conditions (H_2SO_4, TsOH, H_3PO_4, TfOH); produced a new catalytic system able to convert 1,3-butadiene into *MEK* with good selectivity (95% yield, 155 ºC, 32 h, TON = 1200) [42a]. Latter, Bouwman and co-workers were able to improve the aforementioned results by using a $RuCl_3$-phen catalytic system (10 h, TON = 2750, TOF = 960 h^{-1}) [42b]. Finally, the same research group reported that the octahedral ruthenium(III) complex *mer*-[$RuCl_3$(dmso)(phen)] (**33**), in the presence of TsOH, is also an efficient catalyst for the direct transformation of 1,3-butadiene into butanone (*MEK*, 7 h, TON = 2050) [20].

1.3.1.c. Ruthenium(IV) Catalysts

Even though both coordination and organometallic chemistry of ruthenium(IV) complexes are well-known [4], their catalytic applications are relatively much less studied as compared with ruthenium(0), (II) and (III) compounds [5]. Among other organoruthenium (IV) derivatives, bis(allyl)ruthenium(IV) are particularly appealing since they are: *i*) readily accessible through well-established synthetic routes starting from $RuCl_3·(H_2O)_x$ and several dienes (**34-35**, Scheme 8) [43, 44]; *ii*) air-stable compounds with a high thermal stability; and *iii*) water-stable and able to form aquo complexes [14c]. Thus, this section of the chapter deals with a comprehensive account of the catalytic activity of bis(allyl)-ruthenium(IV) complexes in the redox isomerization of allylic alcohols in water.

The use of Ru(IV)-complexes for the isomerization of allyllic alcohols was not addressed until very recently [45]. In their seminal work, Cadierno, Gimeno et al. found, for the first time, that bis(allyl)-ruthenium(IV) complexes $[Ru(\eta^3:\eta^2:\eta^3\text{-}C_{12}H_{18})Cl_2]$ (**34**) and $[\{Ru(\eta^3:\eta^3\text{-}C_{10}H_{16})(\mu\text{-}Cl)Cl\}_2]$ (**35**) were able to promote the isomerization of a broad family of allylic alcohols into their corresponding carbonyl compounds in pure aqueous media. In this sense, these ruthenium(IV)-catalysts **34** and **35** showed to be very efficient for the selective isomerization of mono-substituted allylic alcohols, the reaction proceeding under mild conditions (0.2 mol% Ru, base free conditions, 70 ºC) [45a]. The addition of catalytic amounts of Cs_2CO_3 to the reaction media induces an enhancement on the reaction rate. Interestingly, this effect was more pronounced when the reaction was performed in organic solvents, as a consequence of the higher polarity of water *vs* THF. This fact promotes the easy chloride dissociation and the alkoxide coordination to ruthenium leading to the active Ru(IV) species. The exceptional catalytic activity of complex **35** was confirmed at very low catalyst loadings (10^{-4} mol% Ru). Under optimized conditions, 3-buten-2-ol was quantitatively converted into butanone (24 h, TON = 10^6, TOF = 41667 h^{-1}). These TON and TOF values are ranked among the highest reported to date for the isomerization of allylic alcohols. At this point, it is important to note that catalysts **34** and **35** were found to be less prone to promote the isomerization of highly substituted allylic alcohols, as previously observed for other catalytic systems [14]. In fact, higher metallic charges (5-10 mol% Ru) were used for the isomerization of di-substituted allylic alcohols, and heating to 90 ºC was required to achieve 89% of conversion when 3-methylbutyraldehyde was targeted. Due to the poor solubility of these bis(allyl)-ruthenium(IV) complexes in water, the catalyst recycling was efficiently achieved by fractioned distillation of the carbonyl compounds after complete conversion. This technique was restricted to the isomerization of volatile allylic alcohols such as 3-buten-2-ol, 1-penten-3-ol and 1-hexen-3-ol during 3-4 consecutive cycles.

In addition, and taking advantage from the great ability of complex **35** to promote olefin migrations (Scheme 9), the aforementioned research group explored the isomerization reaction of other allylic substrates such as *N*-allylamines [46a], *N*-allylamides [46b], *O*-allylethers [46c], and allylaromatics [46d].

The high catalytic activity showed by complex **35** has attracted much attention of both academic and industrial organic synthetic chemists. This great interest has already crystallized in the first potential application for the synthesis of hydromorphone and hydrocodone *via* isomerization reaction of morphine and codeine precursors [47].

Scheme 8. Synthesis and structure of the bis(allyl)-ruthenium(IV) complexes **34-35**.

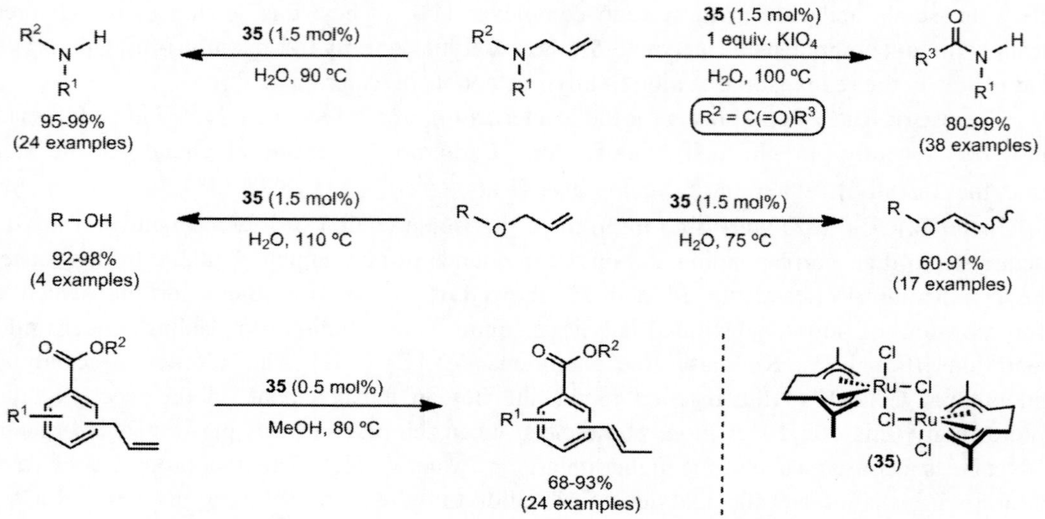

Scheme 9. Other allylic group isomerizations promoted by catalyst **35**.

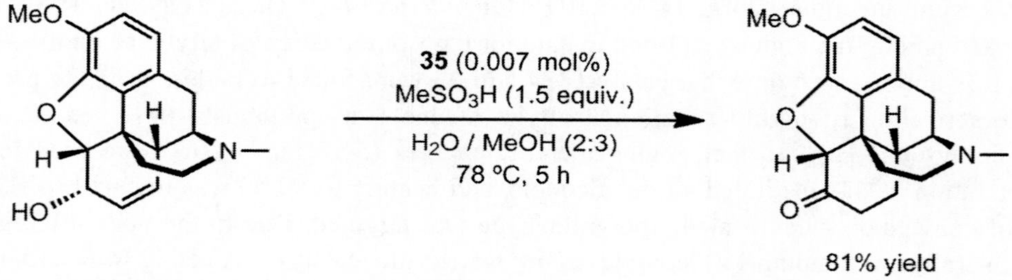

Scheme 10. Synthesis of hydrocodone from codeine in aqueous media catalyzed by complex **35**.

Thus, the use of 0.007 mol% of catalyst **35** combined with methanesulphonic acid (150 mol%) in a mixture water/methanol conducted to the isomerization of codeine into the desired hydrocodone in very good isolated yield (81%, 5 h; Scheme 10).

Alternatively, hydromorphone can be isolated starting from morphine sulphate in 87% of yield under very similar conditions.

More recently, Gimeno et al. focused their efforts toward the developing of a second generation of ruthenium(IV)-catalysts derived from complex **35**. The selective introduction of basic organic ligands increases the solubility of the new ruthenium(IV)-complexes in water, thereby producing better catalytic activity and favouring the catalyst recycling. Thus, in a first approach, they studied the use of the previously reported [48] acetate complex [Ru(η^3:η^3-$C_{10}H_{16}$)(κ^2-*O,O*-CH_3CO_2)Cl] (**36**) for the isomerization of a broad variety of allylic alcohols in water [49]. Catalyst **36** was very efficient when mono-substituted allylic substrates were used. The isomerization of 1-octen-3-ol in pure water catalyzed by 0.2 mol% of **36** and assisted by the presence of the acetate ligand proceeded in only 5 min leading to octan-3-one in quantitative yield (TOF = 6000 h^{-1}). The excellent TOF achieved by this catalyst was found to be the best reported value for this base- and phosphine-free transformation in aqueous media (Scheme 11). This acetate ruthenium(IV)-complex also presented good activity for the isomerization of di- and tri-substituted allylic alcohols, then requiring longer reaction times and catalyst loadings (5-10 mol%). The high solubility in water of complex **36** allowed performing the easy recycling of the active species after complete isomerization reaction of 1-octen-3-ol by simple extraction to organic phase of octan-3-one with *n*-hexane. Remarkably, the authors were able to make the catalyst recycling during at least 6 consecutive times.

As we have previously mentioned for arene-Ru(II) complexes [33], Gimeno et al. introduced the use of two-electron donor *N*-heterocyclic ligands (pyrazoles, indazole, imidazoles and/or benzimidazole) as intramolecular bases in bis(allyl)-ruthenium(IV) complexes [50]. Encouraged by the previously reported beneficial effect of intra- and intermolecular hydrogen bonding interactions in the catalytic bifunctional substrate activation [51], the authors deeply studied and evidenced the crucial role of the N-H and C=O polarized groups for promoting such kind of interactions. Initially, the ruthenium(IV)-complex **37a** was synthesized by reacting complex **35** in methylene chloride with the corresponding 6-azauracil ligand **L1a** (Scheme 12). The new ruthenium(IV)-complex **37a** was isolated as an orange powder in good yield (76%) and the X-ray diffraction analysis revealed that: *i*) the ruthenium (IV) centre presents a distorted trigonal bipyramid geometry considering both allyl groups as monodentate ligands [both chlorine atoms are occupying both apical positions, with the two allyl groups and the *N*-heterocyclic ligand placed at equatorial positions (bonded through the iminic *N*-atom)]; *ii*) the distance between the N-H and the chloride ligand (2.30 Å), the N-H···Cl angle (137 °) and the observed dihedral angle formed by the planes containing the Ru-N-N-H skeleton and the Cl-Ru-Cl moiety are consistent with the presence of intramolecular H-bonding of the N-H unit from the ligand and one of the chlorine atoms; and *iii*) the unit cell also evidenced two additional intermolecular N-H···O=C interactions (the distance and the angle for the H···O contact were 2.00 Å and 162 °, respectively); thereby **37a** crystallizes as a dimeric structure.

The presence of hydrogen bonds in solution was confirmed by ^{1}H NMR, VT NMR and DOSY experiments. Firstly, the N-H protons involved in the hydrogen bonds were located at 11.74 and 9.10 ppm as broad signals. The analysis of different samples of complex **37a** in CD_2Cl_2 at different concentrations (5-24 mM) showed a shift of the signal at 9.10 ppm to lower fields, while the signal at 11.74 remained unaffected.

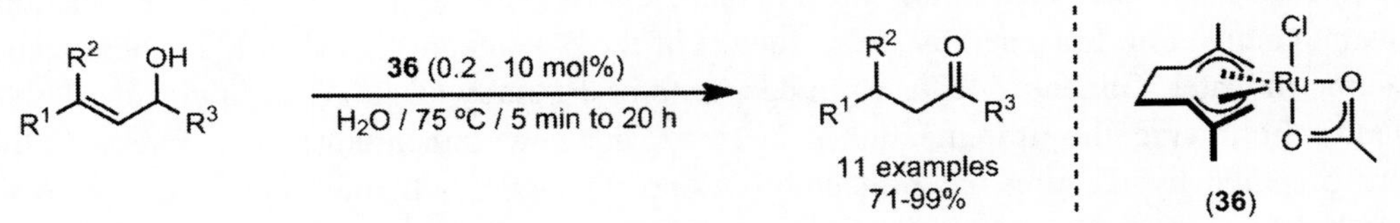

Scheme 11. Isomerization of allylic alcohols catalyzed by complex **36**.

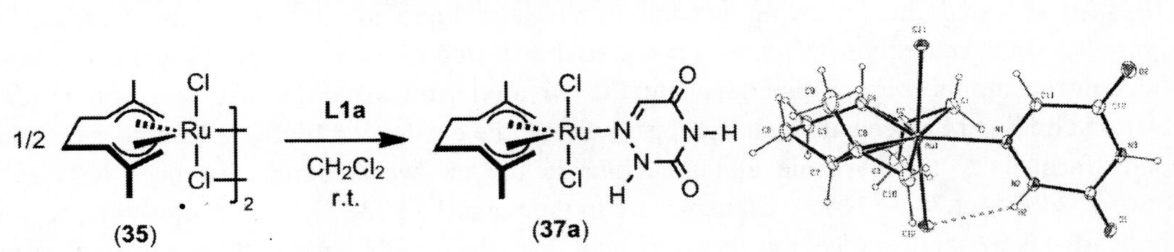

Scheme 12. Synthesis and *ORTEP* representation of the ruthenium(IV)-complex **37a** starting from complex **35** by coordination of **L1a**.

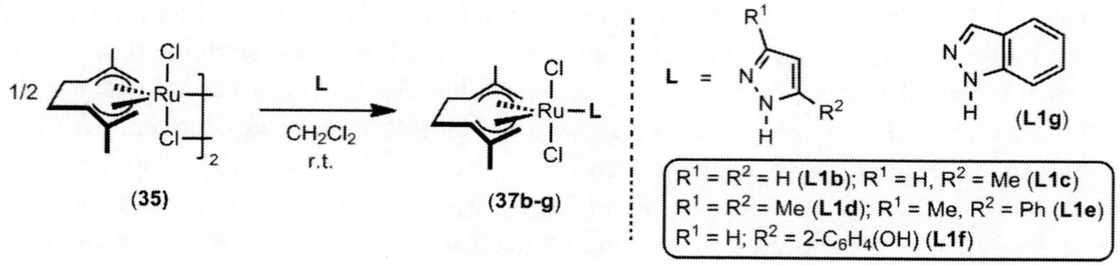

$R^1 = R^2 = H$ (**L1b**); $R^1 = H$, $R^2 = Me$ (**L1c**)
$R^1 = R^2 = Me$ (**L1d**); $R^1 = Me$, $R^2 = Ph$ (**L1e**)
$R^1 = H$; $R^2 = 2\text{-}C_6H_4(OH)$ (**L1f**)

Scheme 13. Synthesis of the ruthenium(IV)-complexes **37b-g**.

The chemical shift modification in function of the concentration clearly illustrates the involvement of the N-H unit on intermolecular hydrogen bonds. Secondly, the participation of the additional N-H signal on intramolecular hydrogen bond interactions was evidenced by VT NMR experiments. The free rotation of the Ru-N=C bond in the complex **37a** was restricted at low temperature (183 K), thus observing the splitting of the allylic protons as well as the methylene protons from the ligand. This restricted rotation can be attributable to the existence of intramolecular hydrogen bonding between the N-H unit and the chlorine atom bonded to Ru. Finally, the crucial role of the intermolecular interactions in solution was clearly demonstrated by DOSY experiences. The diffusion coefficient for complex **37a** (D_{37a} = 1.17 x 10^{-9} m^2s^{-1}) was considerably smaller than the obtained for the reference complex [Ru(η^3:η^3-$C_{10}H_{16}$)Cl_2(pyridine)] (D_{RuPy} = 1.44 x 10^{-9} m^2s^{-1}) confirming the higher hydrodynamic volume of **37a** *vs* [Ru(η^3:η^3-$C_{10}H_{16}$)Cl_2(pyridine)]. The ratio D_{RuPy} /D_{37a} = 1.23 was very similar to the theoretically expected for two spherical molecules, one having twice the volume of the other (1.26). The catalytic activity of complex **37a** for the isomerization of allylic alcohols in water was then addressed. This complex was highly active for the quantitative transformation of 1-octen-3-ol under standard conditions (i.e., 0.2 mol% Ru, 75 ºC, base free) into octan-3-one (10 min; TOF = 2970 h^{-1}). The efficiency of complex **37a** in water was much better than performing the reaction in organic solvents (24 h were required in THF), and its catalytic activity is still suited among the most efficient promoters reported to date. The great catalytic activity of catalyst **37a** is associated to the high ability of the 6-azauracil ligand for promoting hydrogen bonds, thus facilitating the interaction with the allylic alcohol *via* bifunctional substrate activation. Intrigued by the influence of the 6-azauracil ligand in this isomerization reaction in water, Gimeno, Lledós et al. deepened in the study of the role of pyrazole-derived ligands. Following the aforementioned strategy, the new ruthenium(IV)-complexes **37b-g** were prepared by reacting the ruthenium(IV) precursor **35** with the appropriate pyrazolyl ligands **L1b-g** [50]. The targeted complexes **37b-g** were purely isolated as orange powders from moderate to good yields (57-86%; Scheme 13). X-ray diffraction analysis for complexes **37b-d,f-g** revealed the following general trends (structures for **37b-d,f-g** are depicted in Figure 8): *i*) the ruthenium(IV) atom presented a distorted trigonal bipyramid geometry with both chlorine atoms at apical positions, and the two allyl groups and the N=C unit from the *N*-heterocyclic ligand placed at equatorial positions; *ii*) the existence of intramolecular hydrogen bonds formed by the pyrazole and the chloride ligands were found [distances N-H···Cl between 2.27(5)-2.78 Å; N-H···Cl angles are in the range 102-138 º]; and *iii*) close inspection of the distances and angles for the N-H unit and the neighbouring chlorine atoms also confirmed the presence of intermolecular hydrogen bonds (the distance and the angle for the N-H···Cl interaction were included in the range 2.45-2.77 Å and 132-198.7 º, respectively).

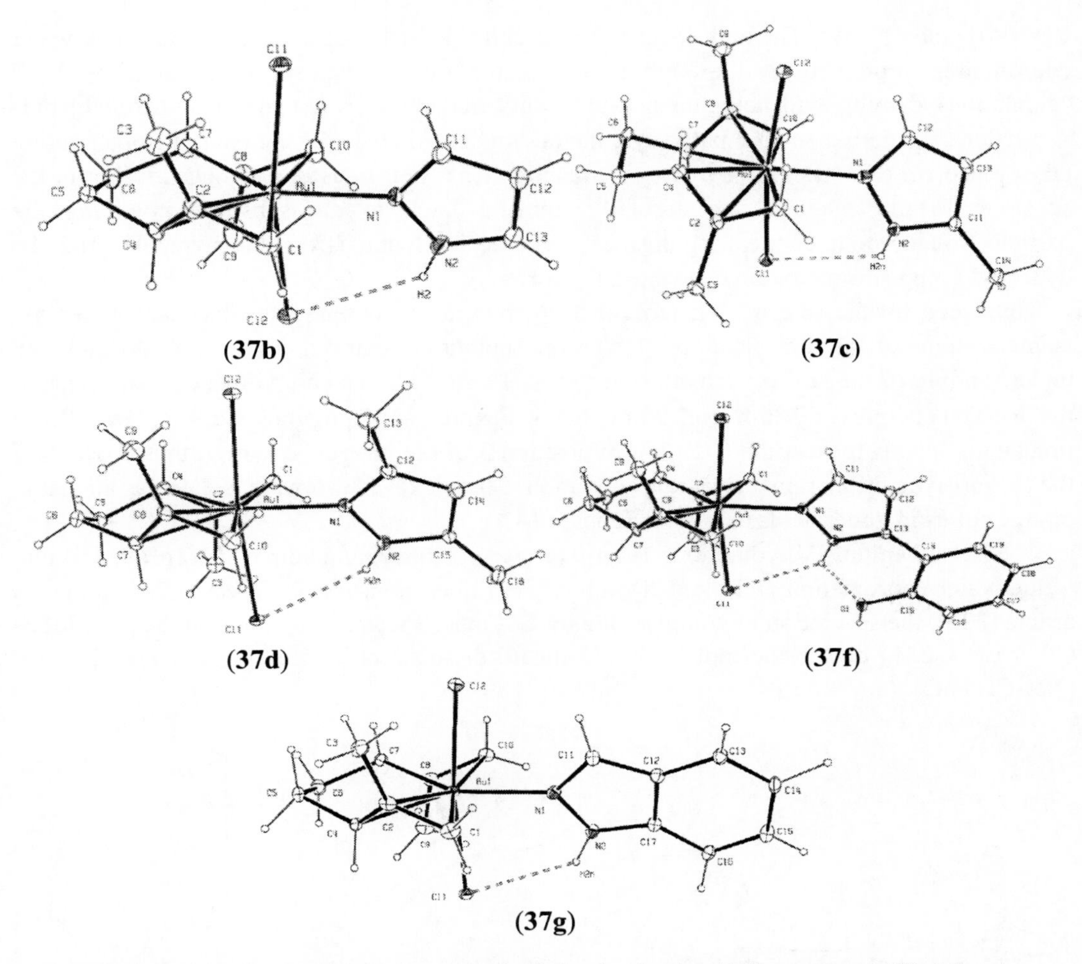

Figure 8. *ORTEP* representations for the pyrazole-derived ruthenium(IV)-complexes **37b-d,f-g**.

The authors selected complex **37b** as catalyst for the optimization of the reaction conditions in the isomerization of the model substrate (1-octen-3-ol) [33b]. Catalyst **37b** promoted the full conversion of 1-octen-3-ol into octan-3-one under classical conditions in water (i.e., 0.2 mol% Ru, 75 ºC) in only 10-15 min (TOF = 2000 and 3000 h^{-1}, in presence or absence of KO^{t}Bu, respectively). Despite the reaction rate decreased, the reaction could be performed at lower temperatures (55 ºC and 35 ºC; 60 min and 6 h were required). Complex **37b** was found to be the most efficient catalyst, probably due to its higher solubility in water in comparison with its parent complexes **37c-g**. Catalyst **37b** was highly efficient in the isomerization of a large variety of allylic alcohols (13 examples were efficiently converted into the corresponding ketone under heating at 75 ºC).

As commented above, the rate of reaction is strongly dependent from the substitution grade on the olefin, and higher ruthenium charges and/or reaction time were needed for promoting the migration of secondary and tertiary olefins.

In order to understand the behaviour of complexes **37b-g** in water solutions, the reaction of complex **37b** with water was analyzed by ESI mass spectroscopy. Carefully interpretation revealed the fast formation of cations [**37b**-Cl]$^+$ (*m/z* = 341) and its aqueous derivative [**37b**-

Cl+H_2O]$^+$ (m/z = 359). The high facility for the chloride ligand dissociation induced by water coordination prompted to the authors to engage the mechanism elucidation by DFT calculations, thereby evidencing the non-innocent behaviour of water and the pyrazole ligand.

After considering several pathways, the authors concluded that the overall isomerization takes place *via* two successive hydrogen-transfer steps: first transfer hydrogenation from the substrate to the catalyst, and secondly, transfer back to the substrate involving the participation of both cooperating ligands, i.e., the N-H unit (from the pyrazole) and the hydroxyl group (from coordinated water, Figure 9).

Intrigued by the role of *N*-heterocyclic ligands in the outer-sphere mechanism for the isomerization of allylic alcohols, the same authors enhanced more efforts into the understanding of the real participation of the N-H units. To this end, Gimeno et al. prepared the Ru(IV)-complexes **38a-b** containing the 1,3-azole β-N-H ligands **L2a-b** [33a]. These imidazole ligands present the N-H unit in position 3 of the heterocyclic ring, thus preventing the Noyori-type bifunctional substrate activation. Complexes **38a-b** were isolated as air stable orange solids in good yields (63-73%; Scheme 14).

These ruthenium(IV)-complexes react with water producing acidic media (pH = 5.5) due to the water coordination and the concomitant HCl liberation. As observed in their previous article [33b], the speciation of complex **38a** by ESI mass spectroscopy showed the peak [**38a**-Cl]$^+$ (m/z = 341) due to the rapid chloride ligand dissociation and easy water coordination [**38a**-Cl+H_2O]$^+$ (m/z = 359).

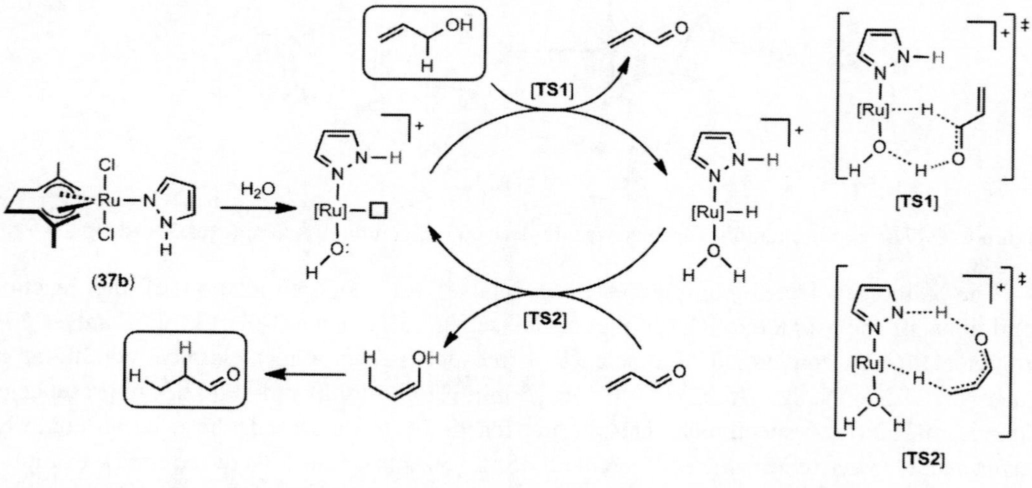

Figure 9. Simplified outer-sphere mechanism theoretically found for the isomerization of allylic alcohols catalyzed by complex **37b**.

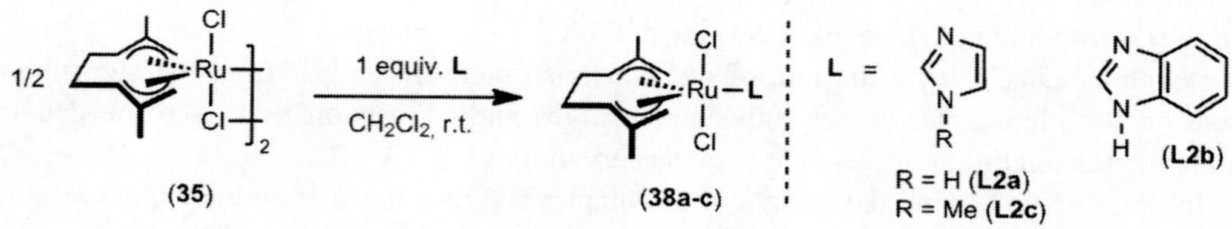

Scheme 14. Synthesis of the imidazole-derived Ru(IV)-complexes **38a-c**.

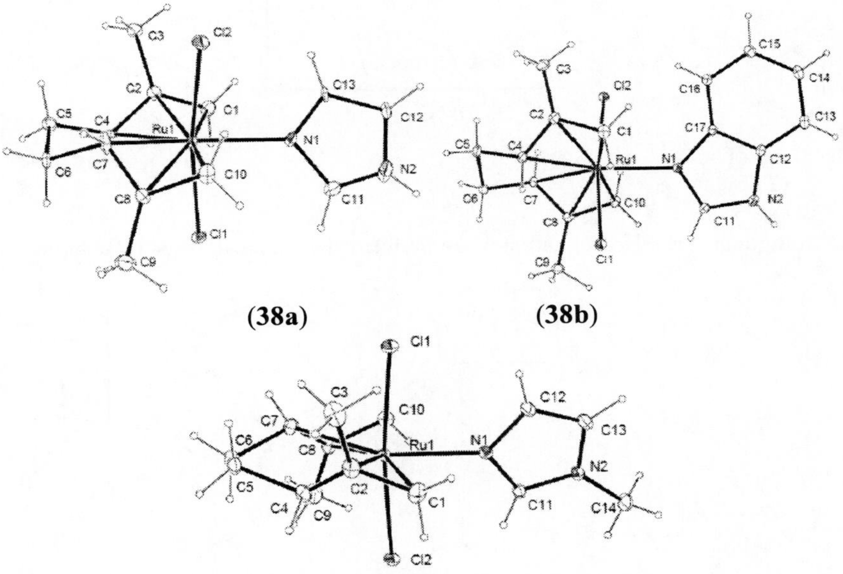

(38a) (38b)

(38c)

Figure 10. *ORTEP* representations for the imidazole-derived Ru(IV)-complexes **38a-c**.

Finally, X-ray diffraction analysis for complexes **38a-c** confirmed the proposed structures depicted in Scheme 14. The most remarkable points are as follow: *i*) they crystallized in distorted trigonal bipyramid geometry with both chloride ligands at apical positions and both allyl groups and the N=C unit from the imidazole placed at equatorial positions; *ii*) the orientation of the N-H bond in **38a-b** prevented the formation of any intramolecular hydrogen bonding; *iii*) complexes **38a-b** display intermolecular hydrogen bonds in their packing structure between the N-H unit and the neighbouring chloride ligand (Figure 10).

The catalytic activity of **38a-c** in water was evaluated for the isomerization of 1-octen-3-ol into octan-3-one under optimized conditions (i.e., 0.2 M of 1-octen-3-ol, 0.2 mol% Ru, base free, heating at 75 ºC in water). The imidazole-derived Ru(IV)-complexes provided full conversion in only 5-20 min.

Complex **38b** was the most efficient catalyst for such a transformation requiring only 5 min to achieve quantitative conversion. A variety of allylic alcohols was efficiently transformed into their corresponding carbonyl compounds catalyzed by **38b**, however longer reaction times and/or elevated catalyst loadings were needed for highly substituted substrates. Interestingly, complex **38b** was still active at room temperature.

Thus, the model substrate (1-octen-3-ol) was quantitatively transformed into the desired product in 5 min using lower catalyst loadings (0.02 mol%; TOF = 60000 h^{-1}). This TOF value in water is the best reported to date so far.

In addition, catalyst **38b** was used for the isomerization of α-vinylbenzylalcohol at multigrame scale (20 mmol) providing 1-phenylpropan-1-one in 89% isolated yield (Scheme 15). Remarkably, catalyst **38b** was efficiently recycled remaining active up to seven cycles.

Mechanistically more important, the ruthenium(IV)-catalyst **38c** containing the *N*-methyl substituted imidazole ligand (**L2c**) was also highly efficient for the isomerization of the model substrate (1-octen-3-ol). This high activity is even more intriguing when compared to the catalytic activity of **38a** containing the analogous deprotected ligand (**L2a**).

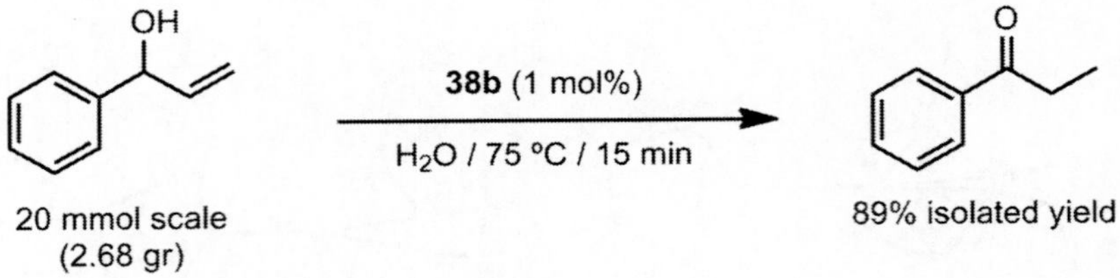

Scheme 15. Multigrame-scale isomerization of α-vinylbenzylalcohol catalyzed by complex **38b**.

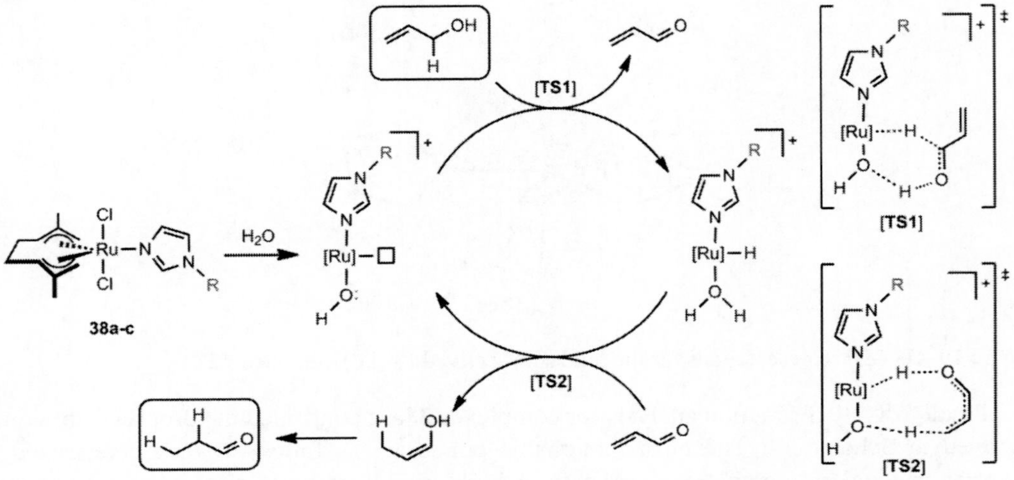

Figure 11. Simplified outer-sphere mechanism for the isomerization of the simplest allylic alcohol catalyzed by complexes **38a-c**.

Both catalysts conducted to the quantitative transformation of the model substrate driving to octan-3-one after only 20 min, thereby providing same TOF values (1500 h^{-1}). These results ruled out the key participation of the N-H bond in a Noyori-type outer-sphere mechanism and other pathways are thus involved. The authors carried out DFT analysis illustrating the decisive role of the hydroxo ligands generated from water coordination, while the *N*-heterocyclic ligand remains as mere spectator in the reaction media. The calculations demonstrated the key role of water as cooperating ligand and the viability of a catalytic process involving two successive hydrogen transfer steps (Figure 11). In this new outer-sphere mechanism, first the hydrogenation transfer from the allylic alcohol to the catalytically active hydroxo-ruthenium(IV) specie occurs *via* [TS1], and secondly, the hydrogen transfer back to the olefin takes place *via* [TS2] with participation of the coordinated water and the preformed Ru-H bond.

1.3.2. Ru-Catalyzed Redox Isomerization of Allylic Alcohols in Other Non-Conventional Reaction Media: Ionic Liquids (*ILs*) and Deep Eutectic Solvents (*DESs*)

Green technology seeks for the developing of new synthetic strategies involving the use of non-conventional solvents to replace the volatile organic solvents (*VOCs*), commonly used in both academic and industrial processes. Over the past two decades, Ionic liquids (*ILs*) received much attention as a new class of non-conventional solvents [52]. *ILs* are ionic salts with low melting point (ideally near to room temperature) presenting at least one organic moiety. *ILs* are commonly accepted as *Green Solvents* because of their unique properties: *i*) wide range of temperatures for liquid state (over 300 °C); *ii*) low viscosities; *iii*) low vapor pressure; *iv*) high thermal and/or chemical stability; *v*) high ionic conductivity [suitable for microwave (MW)-assisted organic synthesis)]; *vi*) excellent solubilizing agents; *vii*) possibility of recycling; *viii*) non flammable nature; and *ix*) modulable properties by selective tuning of the ion pair (i.e., modification of anion) [53]. During the last years, *ILs* are becoming very important solvents for both industrial and academic proposes, but only few examples related to the Ru-catalyzed isomerization reactions of allylic alcohols have recently appeared in the literature.

To the best of our knowledge, Gimeno et al. reported for the first time the allylic alcohol isomerization reaction promoted by Ru-catalysts in ionic liquids. The aforementioned acetate complex [Ru(η^3:η^3-$C_{10}H_{16}$)(κ^2-*O,O*-CH_3CO_2)Cl] (**36**) was found to be an excellent catalyst for the isomerization of 1-octen-3-ol in [BMIM][BF_4] (BMIM = 1-butyl-3-methylimidazolium) [49]. The model substrate was quantitatively transformed into 3-octanone using 1 mol% of complex **36** at 75 °C in the ionic liquid after only 5 min (TOF = 1200 h^{-1}). This acetate Ru(IV)-catalyst was also able to promote the isomerization of an array of allylic alcohols (mono- and di-substituted olefins; Scheme 16).

Catalyst **36** was found to be highly efficient for the isomerization of the parent mono-substituted allylic alcohols using low catalyst loading. In contrast, higher ruthenium charges (5-10 mol% Ru) and reaction time (1-22 h) were required when di-substituted allylic alcohols were targeted. Unfortunately, complex **36** was unsuccessful for the isomerization reaction of the challenging tri-substituted allylic alcohols.

In addition, the high solubility of complex **36** in the ionic liquid [BMIM][BF_4] (4.8 mg/mL), along with the immiscibility of *ILs* and non-polar organic solvents allowed for the recyclability of this catalyst during 5 consecutive cycles in the isomerization of 1-octen-3-ol by simple extraction of the isomerized product (octan-3-one) with *n*-hexane.

More recently, García-Álvarez et al. reported the redox isomerization of allylic alcohols in *ILs* catalyzed by the aforementioned bis(allyl)-ruthenium(IV) complexes [Ru(η^3:η^3-$C_{10}H_{16}$)Cl_2(κ^1-*N*-L)] (**37b** [50], **38b** [33a]) containing the *N*-heterocyclic ligands pyrazole (**L1b**) and benzimidazole (**L2b**), respectively [54]. Complexes **37b** and **38b** were found to be competent for the base-free isomerization of 1-octen-3-ol using low catalyst loadings (1 mol% Ru) under heating at 110 °C in [BMIM][BF_4]. Complex **38b** was the most efficient catalyst requiring only 10 min to achieve the full transformation into the desired ketone (TOF = 594 h^{-1}).

Scheme 16. Isomerization of allylic alcohols in *ILs* catalyzed by complex **36**.

Scheme 17. Isomerization of allylic alcohols in *ILs* catalyzed by the Ru(IV)-complex **38b**.

The nature of the counter anion in the ionic liquid plays a key role on the catalyst activity, therefore the strongest coordinative ability of the counter anion the lower reaction rate for the isomerization reaction. Interestingly, the isomerization of the model substrate in [BMIM][BF_4] proceeds faster than in conventional organic solvents. Complex **38b** was also active for the isomerization of a variety of mono- and di-substituted allylic alcohols (Scheme 17). For the related mono-substituted allylic alcohols the corresponding ketones were quantitatively formed under optimized conditions in less than 1 h, but higher ruthenium amounts (5-10 mol% Ru) were employed for the di-substituted olefins. As introduced above, the use of *ILs* facilitates the recovery of the catalytic system. Thus, the extraction of the carbonyl compound with organic solvents after full conversion allowed to the recycling of **38b** and the ionic liquid [BMIM][BF_4] up to 7 consecutive runs.

Despite water and *ILs* are commonly accepted *Green Solvents*, they still are far from the ideal. The costly purification of water after the reaction along with the possible side-reactions (hydrolysis) remains problematic for water to be industrially applied. Also, the use of *ILs* as *green* reaction media has to be evaluated as many reports pointed the hazardous toxicity and the very poor biodegradability of most ionic liquids [55]. Additionally, the majority of ionic liquids are non-biorenewable and their synthesis is far to be environmentally-friendly since it generally requires a large amount of salts and solvents in order to completely exchange anions [56]. To overcome all these limitations a new family of *green* and biorenewable solvents is strongly needed. In this sense, recent pioneering work from several synthetic laboratories around the worlds has recognized the potential of *Deep Eutectic Solvents* [*DESs*, also known in the literature as *Deep Eutectic Ionic Liquids* (*DEILs*), *Low Melting Mixtures* (*LMM*) or *Low-Transition Temperature Mixtures* (*LTTM*)] as superior *green* and biorenewable solvents with applications as environmentally-friendly reaction media in a variety of chemical applications (i.e., electrochemistry, biocatalysis, metal extraction, material chemistry, and purification of biodiesel) [57, 58]. In contrast, the use of these deep eutectic solvents as *green* solvents in metal-mediated organic reactions is still rare [59]. In most of the cases, *DESs* are obtained by mixing a quaternary ammonium salt with a hydrogen-bond donor that has the ability to form a complex with the halide anion of the ammonium salt. One of the widespread ammonium salt used for the synthesis of these *DESs* is choline chloride (*ChCl*, Scheme 18) [60]. In combination with a safe, biorenewable and non-toxic hydrogen-bond donor [i.e., glycerol (*Gly*), lactic acid, urea or water] *ChCl* is able to form an eutectic mixture.

In this sense, García-Álvarez et al. described the unique example reported to date for the redox isomerization of allylic alcohols in *DESs* catalyzed by the Ru(IV)-complex [Ru(η^3:η^3-$C_{10}H_{16}$)Cl_2(κ^1-*N*-benzimidazole)] (**38b**) [61].

After solvent and reaction conditions screening the authors found that catalyst **38b** was highly efficient for the transformation of 1-octen-3-ol into octan-3-one in a mixture 1:2 of choline chloride (*ChCl*) and glycerol (*Gly*).

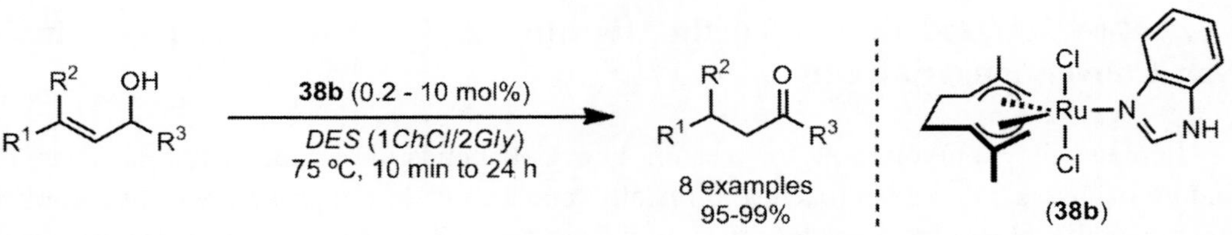

Scheme 18. Isomerization of allylic alcohols in *DES* (1*ChCl*/2*Gly*) catalyzed by complex **38b**.

The heating at 75 ºC using 0.2 mol% of **38b** in absence of base conducted to the isolation of octan-3-one in 98% after only 10 min (TOF = 2970 h^{-1}). The modification of the *ChCl*/*Gly* ratio and/or the substitution of one of those two components dramatically decreased the reaction rate. Remarkably, the catalytic activity of **38b** in the mixture 1:2 of *ChCl*/*Gly* is much higher than the reported for ionic liquids [54], thus suggesting a relevant role of the hydrogen interactions with the solvent.

This observation was confirmed by comparison with the catalytic activity displayed by the catalysts **35** and **38c** (unable to perform hydrogen bonds) under the optimized conditions (TOF = 1485 h^{-1} for **35**; 495 h^{-1} for **38c**). Catalyst **38b** was also efficient for the isomerization of a family of allylic alcohols mono- and di-substituted (Scheme 18).

The analogous mono-substituted substrates were quantitatively converted into the carbonyl compound using low catalyst loadings (0.2-1 mol% Ru) in less than 20 min (except for allylic alcohol which requires 12 h to achieve propanal in 99%).

As observed before by others [14], a strong dependence upon the substitution grade on the olefin was observed, thereby higher ruthenium charges (5-10 mol% Ru) and reaction time (8-24 h) were required to promote the isomerization of di-substituted allylic alcohols. Finally, the mentioned conditions allowed for the recycling of the catalytic system during 4 consecutive cycles, with no significant observation of loss of activity during the two first runs.

1.4. Ruthenium-Catalyzed *Tandem* Processes Involving a Redox Isomerization Step of Allylic Alcohols in Non-Conventional Solvents

As we have quoted in the *Introduction* of this chapter, one of the biggest challenges in the current chemistry is the developing of *green* synthetic methodologies for promoting organic transformations under environmentally benign and safe conditions [6].

In this sense, the design of *one-pot* reactions is an important area of research in *Green Chemistry*.

These *tandem* processes are not time consuming and they contribute to the decreasing of chemical waste generation, energy consumption and global cost for the synthetic process.

The development of new strategies to achieve multistep organic transformations is possible due to the ability of organometallic complexes to promote successive transformations under same conditions [62].

Hereafter, some recent examples of Ru-catalyzed *tandem* processes in *Green Solvents* involving a redox isomerization step of allylic alcohols will be summarized.

1.4.1. Ru-Catalyzed *Tandem* Olefin Migration/Aldol Reaction Sequence in Non-Conventional Solvents

Enolates play a pivotal role for creating new C–C bonds in organic synthesis. Thus, the finding of new synthetic approaches to metallic enolates is an important area of research in organometallic chemistry nowadays [63]. In this context, allylic alcohols are latent precursors of enols and/or enolates by simple olefin migration.

Taking in mind the mechanism for the Ru-catalyzed isomerization of allylic alcohols (*General Introduction*, Scheme 2), the formation of the Ru-enolate intermediate offers great opportunities to design new *tandem* processes (see Figure 12).

- Ru-catalyzed *tandem* olefin migration/aldol reaction sequence in water

Built on the aforementioned premises, the group headed by Prof. Li reported for the first time the use of catalytic amounts of $[RuCl_2(PPh_3)_3]$ (**39**) to promote the coupling of 3-buten-2-ol and aldehydes in aqueous media [64a]. This *tandem* process involves a first olefin migration step to generate the corresponding Ru-enolate, which may be captured by aldehydes in the subsequent aldol reaction.

The aldol formation reaction was carried out heating both coupling partners at 110 °C in a biphasic H_2O/Toluene mixture catalyzed by complex **39** (3 mol% Ru). After 5 h, the corresponding aldol-type products were obtained in most of cases in good isolated yield (27-76%) and with moderate *syn*-selectivity (*syn:anti* ratio from 51:49 to 79:21; Scheme 19). The methodology developed by Li and co-workers was found to be compatible with the introduction of functional groups in the aromatic ring such as halides (F, Cl, Br) or anisole group, but failed for the coupling with aliphatic aldehydes.

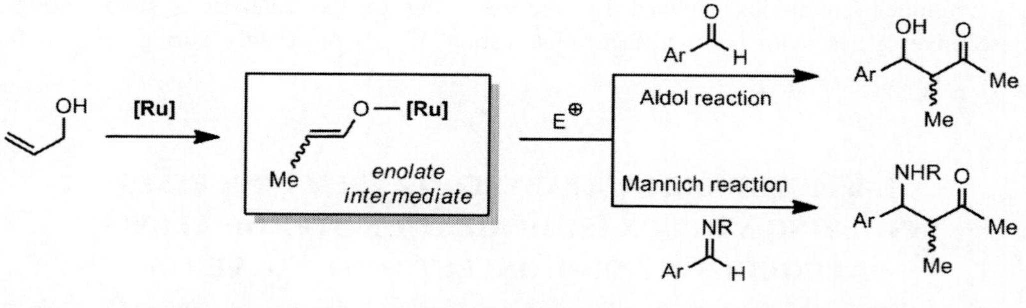

Figure 12. Schematic approach for the Ru-promoted C-C bond formation reaction using allylic alcohols as latent enolates.

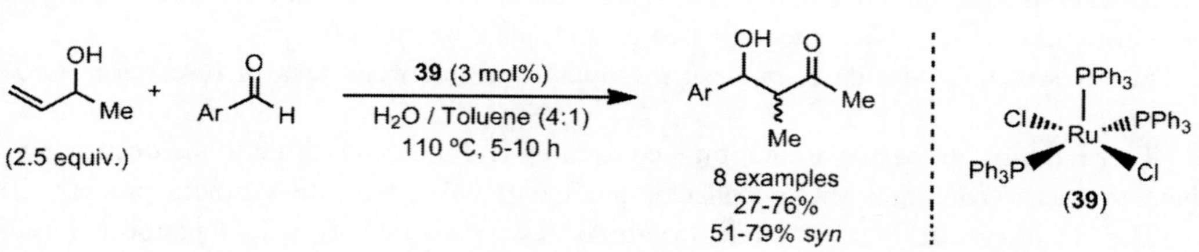

Scheme 19. Isomerization of 3-buten-2-ol/aldol reaction sequence in water catalyzed by the complex $[RuCl_2(PPh_3)_3]$ (**39**).

Later, Li et al. discovered the beneficial effect of Lewis acids for the coupling of α-vinylbenzyl alcohol with aldehydes [64b]. For the model reaction, i.e., the coupling of α-vinylbenzyl alcohol and benzaldehyde, the aldol was only formed in very low yield (10%) under classical conditions (3 mol% Ru, 110 °C, mixture 4:1 H_2O/Toluene). The addition of $[In(OAc)_3]$ as co-catalyst dramatically increased the reaction yield till 80% with a *syn/anti* ratio of 68:32 [65]. This great improvement on the efficiency of the coupling process can be attributed to the cooperative action of complex **39** promoting the enolate formation while the synergetic activation of the aldehyde occurs induced by the $[In(OAc)_3]$ co-catalyst, then favoring the aldol formation. Thus, the aldol-type products were successfully isolated in good yield (51-82%) displaying moderate *syn*-selectivity (Scheme 20).

The authors were also successful to make the coupling of the model substrate 3-buten-2-ol and imines leading to the Mannich-type products in moderate yield (35-47%) with predominant *syn*-formation (Scheme 21). In this particular case, the presence of $[In(OAc)_3]$ as co-catalyst resulted unfruitful probably due to the catalytic ability of Lewis acids for promoting the imine hydrolysis. In fact, important amounts of aldol product (23-35%) derived from the imine were liberated as side-product in the reaction media.

Based on the previous findings of Li and co-workers [64], Uozumi et al. developed an original approach to achieve the catalytic *tandem* olefin migration/aldol sequence under heterogeneous conditions [66]. Prof. Uozumi used the amphiphilic polystyrene-poly(ethylene glycol) resin triarylphosphine ligand {(PS-PEG)-Ar_3P} to anchor the Ru(III)-fragment $[RuCl_2(\eta^5\text{-}Cp^*)]$. The corresponding complex $[RuCl_2(\eta^5\text{-}Cp^*)$\{(PS-PEG)-$Ar_3P$\}] (**40**) was thereby synthesized, and its catalytic activity was evaluated for the cross-coupling of a variety of allylic carbinols and aromatic aldehydes (Scheme 22). Catalyst **40** was found to be highly active for the olefin migration/aldol reaction process using low catalyst loadings (0.5 mol% Ru) under slight heating (45 °C) in pure water. The aldol-type products were isolated after 2 h in good yield (45-74%) and good *syn*-selectivity (*syn:anti* ratio from 74:26 to 82:18).

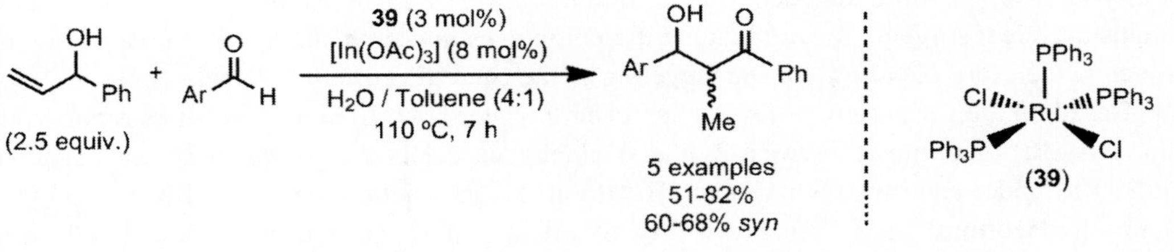

OH, Ph (2.5 equiv.) + Ar–CHO → **39** (3 mol%), $[In(OAc)_3]$ (8 mol%), H_2O / Toluene (4:1), 110 °C, 7 h → Ar–CH(OH)–CH(Me)–CO–Ph; 5 examples, 51-82%, 60-68% *syn*. (**39**): PPh_3, Cl, Ru, PPh_3, Ph_3P, Cl

Scheme 20. *Tandem* isomerization of α-vinylbenzyl alcohol/aldol reaction process in water catalyzed by complex $[RuCl_2(PPh_3)_3]$ (**39**).

OH, Me (2.5 equiv.) + Ar–CH=NR → **39** (3 mol%), H_2O / Toluene (1:4), 110 °C, 5 h → Ar–CH(NHR)–CH(Me)–CO–Me + Ar–CH(OH)–CH(Me)–CO–Me; 5 examples, 35-47%, 55-76% *syn*. (**39**): PPh_3, Cl, Ru, PPh_3, Ph_3P, Cl

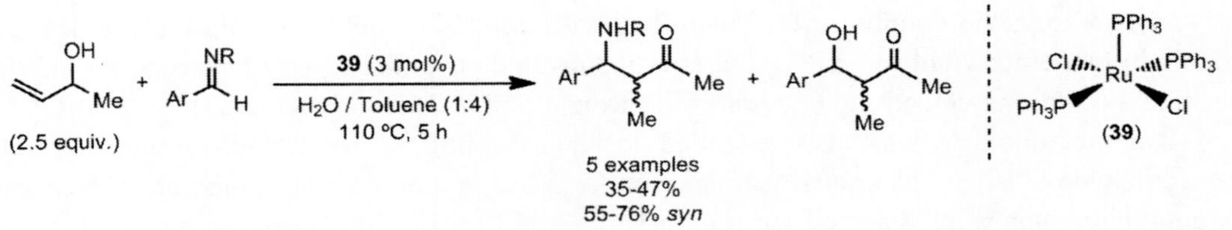

Scheme 21. Ru-catalyzed olefin migration/Mannich reaction sequence under biphasic conditions (H_2O/ Toluene) catalyzed by complex $[RuCl_2(PPh_3)_3]$ (**39**).

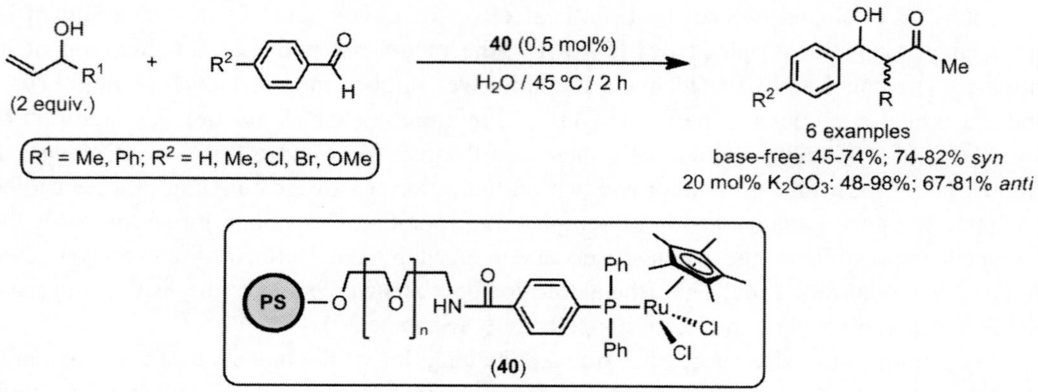

Scheme 22. *Tandem* olefin migration/aldol reaction sequence in pure water catalyzed by $[RuCl_2(\eta^5\text{-}Cp^*)\{(PS\text{-}PEG)\text{-}Ar_3P\}]$ (**40**).

The improvement reached by Uozumi's catalyst in comparison with Li's system was attributed to the high hydrophobicity of allylic alcohols along with the fast substrate diffusion into the PS-PEG matrix, thus allowing to self-concentrated conditions and inducing the aldol condensation. In sharp contrast to the observations of Li et al. [64], Prof. Uozumi evidenced the strong influence of bases in such a transformation. The addition of 20 mol% of K_2CO_3 drove to the isolation of the aldol-type products in good yield (48-98%), this time displaying the opposed *anti*-selectivity (*syn:anti* ratio from 19:81 to 33:67). In addition, catalyst **40** was reused in two consecutive runs with only a small erosion of the activity or selectivity (1st run: 78% isolated yield and 67% *anti*-selectivity; 2nd run: 81% isolated yield with 63% *anti*-selectivity).

- Ru-catalyzed *tandem* olefin migration/aldol reaction sequence in ionic liquids (*ILs*)

Interested on the development of *greener* synthetic methods, Li et al. studied the coupling of allylic alcohols and aldehydes in ionic liquids (*ILs*) [67]. Due to their high polarity, ionic liquids are ideal solvents for organometallic complexes and immiscible with most of organic solvents, therefore *ILs* allow for the recycling of the catalytic system [52, 53].

Based on their preliminary results achieved in water [64], Li and co-workers reported the first *one-pot* coupling of 3-buten-2-ol and aldehydes catalyzed by the Ru-complex **39** (5 mol% Ru) under heating at 90 °C using $[BMIM][PF_6]$ as reaction media (BMIM = 1-butyl-3-methylimidazolium) [67a]. As previously found in water, when aromatic aldehydes were employed the aldol-type products were isolated in good yield (68-94%) with moderate *syn*-selectivity. The use of ionic liquids increased the efficiency of **39** in terms of yield and reaction time (1-2 h).

Remarkably, the coupling of 3-buten-2-ol with aliphatic aldehydes afforded the desired aldols in moderate yield (46-67%), but strong substrate dependence was observed providing the unexpected *anti*-selectivity (*syn:anti* ratio from 42:58 to 16:84; Scheme 23).

The methodology was also extended to the coupling of α-vinylbenzyl alcohol and benzaldehydes. When substrates were submitted to the optimized conditions, only traces of coupling product were detected. In contrast, the addition of $[In(OAc)_3]$ as co-catalyst (10 mol%) allowed to the isolation of the aldol-type products (45-83% yield).

Surprisingly, the *anti*-diastereomer was preferred formed (*syn*:*anti* ratio from 47:53 to 38-62%), independently from the benzaldehyde nature.

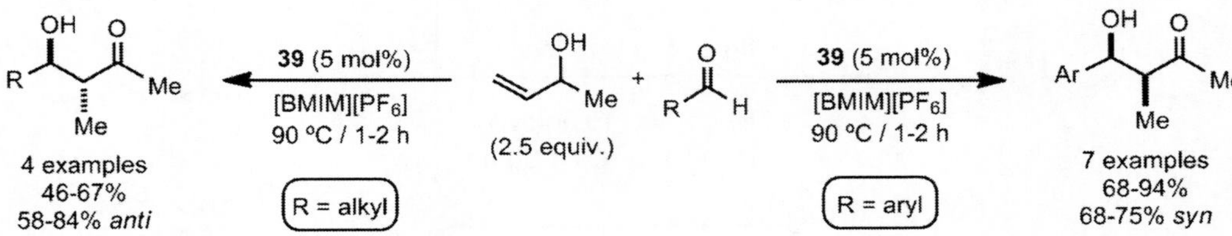

Scheme 23. *Tandem* olefin migration/aldol reaction sequence catalyzed by complex $[RuCl_2(PPh_3)_3]$ (**39**) in $[BMIM][PF_6]$.

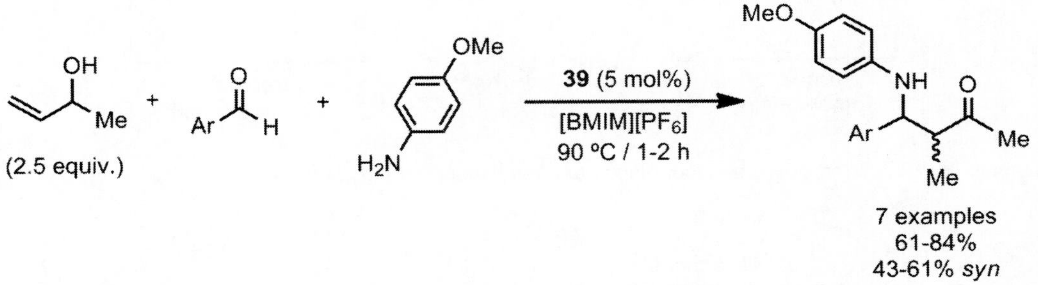

Scheme 24. *Tandem* olefin migration/Mannich reaction sequence catalyzed by complex $[RuCl_2(PPh_3)_3]$ (**39**) in $[BMIM][PF_6]$.

Ionic liquids played a relevant role for the improvement reached in this olefin migration/aldol condensation catalyzed by **39**. Encouraged by this finding, the authors focused efforts to make possible the challenging C-C bond formation between allylic alcohols and imines *via* olefin migration/Mannich reaction in ionic liquids [67b]. The use of *ILs* as reaction media prevents the hydrolysis of the imine reagent, therefore favouring the formation of the Mannich-type product instead of the aldol side-products.

Thus, Li et al. carried out the three-component coupling of 3-buten-2-ol, benzaldehydes and *p*-anisidine catalyzed by **39** (5 mol% Ru; Scheme 24). After heating at 90 °C in $[BMIM][PF_6]$, the Mannich-type products were purely isolated in good yield (61-84%), but low *syn*-selectivity was reached (*syn:anti* ratio from 43:57 to 61:49).

To the best of our knowledge, this was the first cross-coupling of allylic alcohols and imines reported to synthesize the β-aminoketones in high yield. Finally, the authors successfully recycled the solvent/catalyst system during 5 runs for the coupling of 3-buten-2-ol and 2-naphthaldehyde without loss of catalytic activity or *syn*-selectivity.

1.4.2. Ru-Catalyzed *Tandem* Redox Isomerization of Allylic Alcohols/ Transfer Hydrogenation Process (*TH*) in Non-Conventional Solvents

During their studies on ruthenium catalysis and transformations of allylic substrates, Cadierno et al. developed an unprecedented *tandem* process involving a first redox isomerization step of allylic alcohols to form the corresponding carbonyl compound, followed by a transfer hydrogenation (*TH*) step in both organic and/or aqueous media [68]. The overall transformation allows to the reduction of the allylic C=C bond, thus avoiding the use of hazardous and highly flammable $H_{2(g)}$.

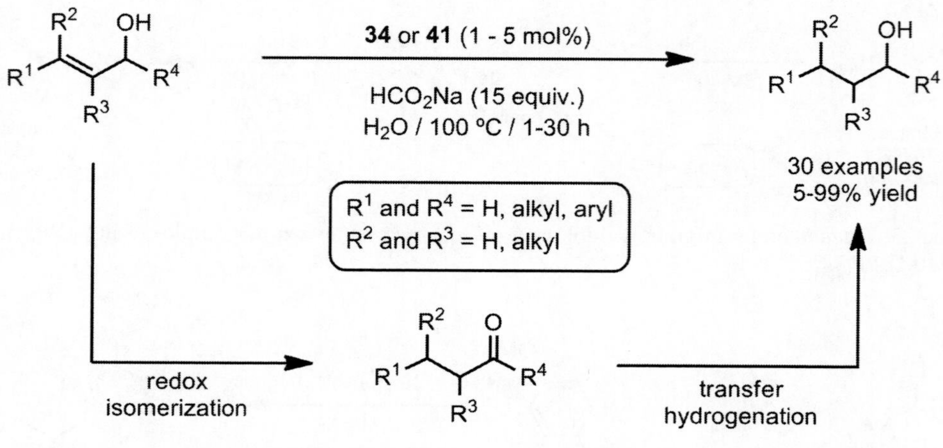

34 or **41** (1 - 5 mol%)
HCO_2Na (15 equiv.)
H_2O / 100 °C / 1-30 h
R^1 and R^4 = H, alkyl, aryl
R^2 and R^3 = H, alkyl
30 examples
5-99% yield
redox isomerization
transfer hydrogenation

Scheme 25. Reduction of allylic alcohols *via tandem* isomerization/TH in pure water as solvent.

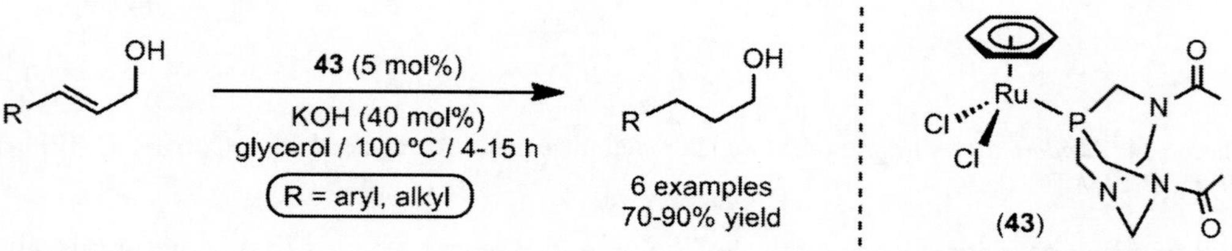

43 (5 mol%)
KOH (40 mol%)
glycerol / 100 °C / 4-15 h
R = aryl, alkyl
6 examples
70-90% yield
(**43**)

Scheme 26. Reduction of terminal allylic alcohols in technical grade glycerol catalyzed by $[RuCl_2(\eta^6\text{-}C_6H_6)(DAPTA)]$ (**43**).

This allylic alcohol isomerization/transfer hydrogenation sequence was catalyzed by the mononuclear bis(allyl)-Ru(IV) complex $[Ru(\eta^3{:}\eta^2{:}\eta^3\text{-}C_{12}H_{18})Cl_2]$ (**34**) or the binuclear arene-ruthenium(II) complex $[\{RuCl(\mu\text{-}Cl)(\eta^6\text{-}C_6Me_6)\}_2]$ (**41**) (1-5 mol% Ru) using 10-15 equiv. of NaO_2CH at refluxing temperature in pure water (see Scheme 25).

Thus, a variety of allylic alcohols were reduced into the corresponding saturated alcohols in moderate to excellent yields. Despite several C=C bonds are present in the structure, the challenging terpenoid derivatives nerol and geraniol were exclusively hydrogenated in α-position to the alcohol group. Cadierno and co-workers later on developed an analogous reduction process of allylic alcohols in glycerol catalyzed by Ru-catalysts [69]. This time, glycerol plays two roles, i.e., solvent and reducing agent. First, the reaction conditions were optimized for the reduction of (*E*)-3-phenyl-2-propen-1-ol into 3-phenylpropan-1-ol catalyzed by the binuclear *p*-cymene Ru(II)-complex $[\{RuCl(\mu\text{-}Cl)(\eta^6\text{-}p\text{-cymene})\}_2]$ (**42**). Different bases, temperatures and catalyst loadings were tested, and the best conditions found were as follow: 2.5 mol% of **42** (i.e., 5 mol% Ru), 80 mol% KOH in inexpensive technical grade glycerol under heating at 100 °C, thus providing 97% yield after 6 h. To increase the catalyst activity, different Ru(II)-complexes possessing hydrophilic phosphines were made and checked for the model reaction. The complex $[RuCl_2(\eta^6\text{-}C_6H_6)(DAPTA)]$ (**43**) was found to be the most efficient catalyst displaying quantitative formation of 3-phenylpropan-1-ol after only 4 h, and only 40 mol% of base was required in this case.

Catalyst **43** was also highly efficient for the reduction of a variety of terminal allylic alcohols with very good isolated yields (70-90% in 4-15 h; Scheme 26).

The excellent solubility and stability of catalyst **43** in technical glycerol allowed to the catalyst recycling, and 4 consecutive runs were performed. This achievement represents a great improvement in comparison with the methodologies previously reported in water by the same research group, where catalyst recycling was unsuccessful.

1.5. Ruthenium-Catalyzed 1,3-Rearrangement of Allylic Alcohols

The direct 1,3-allylic rearrangement of allylic alcohols, in which both the olefin and the alcohol group exchange positions (Scheme 27), is a useful reaction because one regioisomer is often more difficult to prepare than the other.

This skeletal reshuffle has been typically mediated by superstoichiometric amounts of strong acids under severe conditions (i.e., mixture of acetic acid/acetic anhydride containing a catalytic amount of TsOH [70a]; glacial acetic acid containing a catalytic amount of I_2 [70b]; H_2SO_4 [70c]; methanesulfonic acid [70d] or benzoic acid [70e]).

Such conditions often result in poor yields, particularly with sensitive substrates, due to a plethora of competing reactions, including undesired rearrangements, eliminations, and formation of oligomeric by-products.

High-oxidation-state transition metal-oxo complexes have been also employed in this rearrangement [71], however these metallic species are moisture-sensitive and highly expensive.

To overcome all these problems, ruthenium derivatives have been employed in this 1,3-rearrangement using water as environmentally-friendly reaction media. In this sense, Li and co-workers described the selective 1,3-transposition of several α-arylallylic alcohols using the aforementioned commercially available ruthenium(II) complex $[RuCl_2(PPh_3)_3]$ (**39**, Scheme 28) in water and in the presence of air [72a].

At this point, it is important to note the following catalytic features: *i*) these reactions only operate in aqueous media (thus suggesting that water is directly involved in the catalytic cycle); *ii*) the reactions are highly stereoselective (thermodynamically more stable *E*-isomers are predominantly formed); and *iii*) pure aliphatic allylic alcohols (i.e., oct-2-en-4-ol) are only partially isomerized (an equilibrium mixture of the starting material and the rearranged product is observed). The authors proposed the formation of a Ru(II)-hydride intermediate as the catalytically active specie.

Latter, the same research group reported the isomerization of α-aryl homoallylic alcohols into the corresponding conjugated allylic alcohols in water using again catalyst **39** (Scheme 29) [72b].

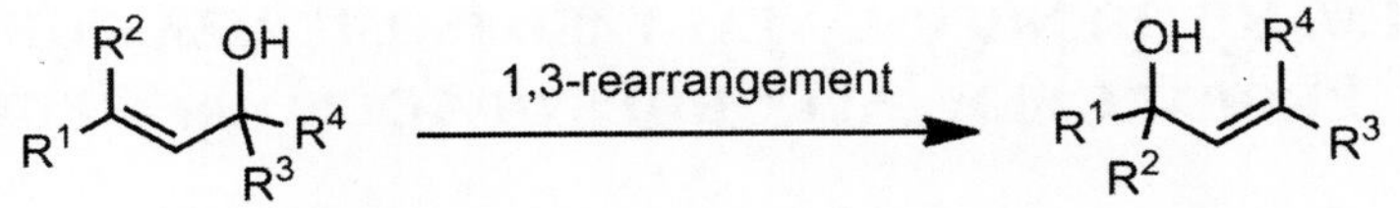

R² OH R¹ R⁴ R³ —1,3-rearrangement→ OH R⁴ R¹ R³ R²

Scheme 27. 1,3-rearrangement of allylic alcohols.

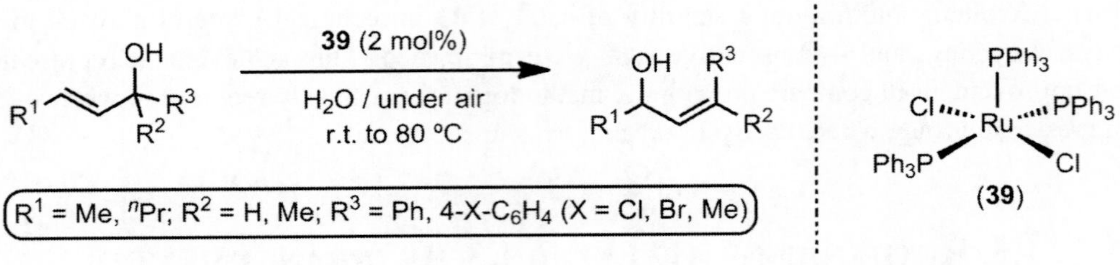

Scheme 28. 1,3-rearrangement of allylic alcohols in water catalyzed by $[RuCl_2(PPh_3)_3]$ (**39**).

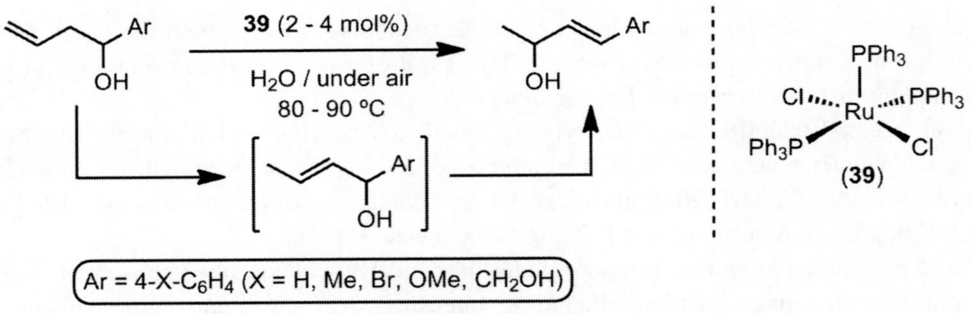

Scheme 29. Isomerization of α-aryl homoallylic alcohols in water catalyzed by complex $[RuCl_2(PPh_3)_3]$ (**39**).

As a matter of fact, this ruthenium(II)-mediated transformation involves a *tandem* process based on an initial C=C bond migration, followed by a concomitant 1,3-rearrangement of the new allylic alcohol. In this case, the reaction required more severe conditions (higher metal loading and temperature) to achieve quantitative conversions. This experimental fact seems to indicate that the initial olefin migration is the rate limiting step. Due to the employment of harsher reaction conditions, formation of mixtures containing the desired conjugated allylic alcohol and the corresponding ketone (derived from the redox isomerization of the allylic alcohol; alcohol/ketone ratio from 1.2:1 to >20:1) was observed. To overcome the intrinsic separation problems associated with homogeneous catalysis, complex $[RuCl_2(PPh_3)_3]$ (**39**) was immobilized on: *i*) various mesoporous structured materials with a PPh_2-ligand incorporated (i.e., SBA-15, FDU-12 and silica) [73a-c,e-f]; and *ii*) surfactant-assembly silanes [73d]. These supported catalytic systems exhibited comparable activity and selectivity than their homogeneous counterpart and could be recycled up. Finally, we should mention that Qu and co-workers have recently reported that simple hot water (40-100 ºC) is able to promote the 1,n-rearrangement (n = 3, 5, 7, 9) of allylic alcohols, acting as mildly acidic catalyst [74].

1.6. Ruthenium-Catalyzed Isomerization of Propargylic Alcohols in Aqueous Media

Carbonyl compounds are an important class of raw material in total synthesis since they are involved in many organic transformations. Inside this group of chemicals, α,β-unsaturated carbonyl compounds are particularly interesting because of their several reactive positions to provide high value products [75].

In this sense, the isomerization of propargylic alcohols into α,β-unsaturated carbonyl compounds is a *green* approach for accessing to these building blocks without the concomitant generation of by-product waste.

Thus, this isomerization reaction takes place involving three alternative pathways: *i*) the Meyer-Schuster rearrangement [76]; *ii*) the Rupe rearrangement [77]; and *iii*) the redox isomerization process to simultaneously oxidize and reduce the alcohol and the alkyne moiety [78], respectively (see Figure 13).

Classically, these isomerization processes were organocatalyzed by Brønsted acids (Meyer-Schuster and Rupe reactions) [79] or Lewis bases (redox isomerization) [80], providing low selectivity and substrate scope. The use of metallic catalysts allowed to more selective and efficient procedures requiring milder conditions.

In sharp contrast with the finding of several applications for the metal-promoted isomerization of propargylic alcohols in the total synthesis of natural products using *VOC* solvents [81], the developing of isomerization processes which take place in *Green Solvents* is still rare. Hereafter, we will introduce the main advances dealing with the Ru-catalyzed isomerization of propargylic alcohols in water.

The very first approach to this field was achieved by Wakatsuki et al. in 2002 [82a]. In this seminal work, they reported the use of the half sandwich cyclopentadienyl derivative $[RuCl(\eta^5\text{-}Cp)(PMe_3)_2]$ (**44**) [82b] as an efficient catalyst to promote the Meyer-Schuster reaction of an array of propargylic alcohols in a 2-propanol/water (3:1) reaction mixture (Scheme 30).

Unfortunately, the conjugated enals were isolated as a mixture of *E/Z* isomers (*E/Z* ratio from 94/6 to 80/20), and the isomerization of tertiary propargylic alcohols resulted unsuccessful. The authors proposed the *anti*-Markovnikov hydration of the alkyne moiety and concomitant dehydration of the hydroxyl group, thus liberating the corresponding Meyer-Schuster type product. However, despite the efforts performed to elucidate the reaction mechanism (experiments were carried out with ^{18}O-labelled water), they were not able to rule out the possible formation of the allenylidene (**A**) and/or hydroxylvinylidene (**B**) species as relevant intermediates (Scheme 30).

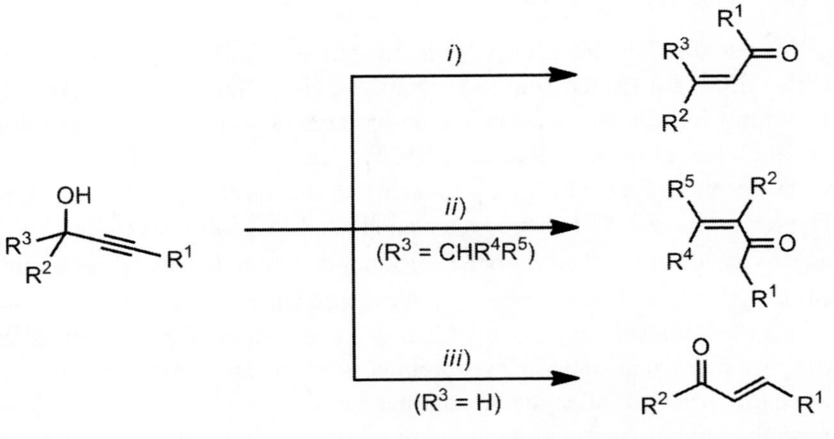

OH
R^3 R^2 R^1
i)
ii)
(R^3 = CHR^4R^5)
iii)
(R^3 = H)
R^1 R^3 O R^2
R^5 R^2 R^4 O R^1
O R^2 R^1

Figure 13. Possible pathways for the isomerization of propargylic alcohols into α,β-unsaturated carbonyl compounds.

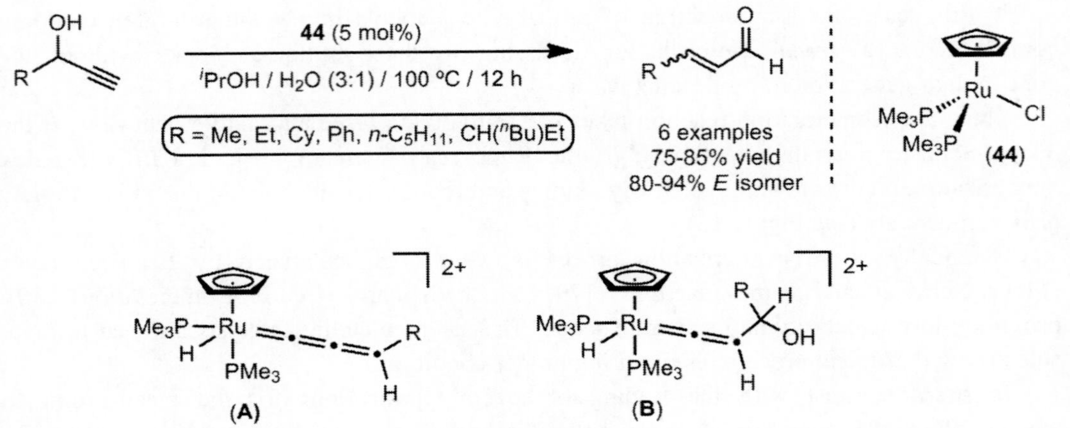

Scheme 30. Meyer-Schuster rearrangement of propargylic alcohols promoted by complex [RuCl(η^5-Cp)(PMe_3)$_2$] (**44**).

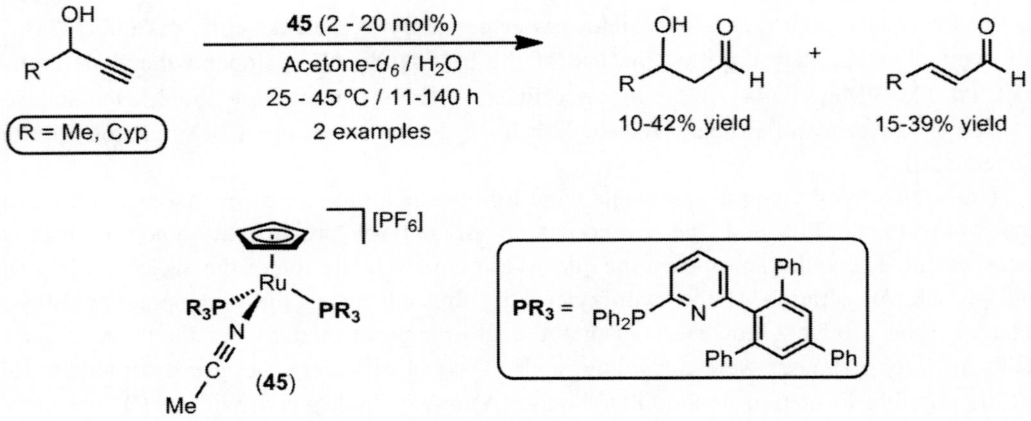

Scheme 31. Catalytic hydration *vs* Meyer-Schuster reaction of propargylic alcohols promoted by the cationic complex [Ru(η^5-Cp)(MeCN)(PR_3)$_2$]$^+$ (**45**).

During their studies on the Ru-catalyzed hydration of propargylic alchols in aqueous media, Bressan [83a] and Hintermann [84] found the formation of the Meyer-Schuster type by-products in low yields. First, Bressan and co-workers [83a] used the water soluble Ru(II)-complex sulfophthalocyanine (**RuPcS**) [83b] and the heterogeneous ruthenium hydroxyapatite species (**RuHAP**) [83c] to achieve the hydration of several propargylic alcohols. The heating at 80 °C in pure water conducted to good conversions (65-95%), but very low selectivity toward α,β-unsaturated carbonyl compounds was reached (only 0-5% of Meyer-Schuster type product was formed). However, considerable amount of α,β-unsaturated carboxylic acids (0-22%) were presumably formed *via* oxidation of the preformed enal.

Interestingly, deuterium labelling experiments with D_2O were performed, thereby excluding the participation of allenylidene intermediates.

More recently, Hintermann et al. reported the activity of the cationic Ru(II)-complex [Ru(η^5-Cp)(MeCN)(PR_3)$_2$]$^+$ [**45**; PR_3 = (2,4,6-triphenyl)-pyridyl-2-diphenylphosphine)] for the catalytic hydration of propargylic alcohols in acetone by adding 5-10 equiv. of water [84].

In contrast, the competitive Meyer-Schuster rearrangement was observed and the corresponding enals were achieved in moderate yields (15-39%; Scheme 31).

In addition, Hintermann and co-workers also demonstrated the ability of catalyst **45** (5-10 mol% Ru) for promoting the Meyer-Schuster rearrangement of *O*-protected propargylic alcohols when targeting the hydration of 1-octyn-3-ol derivatives (5 examples were employed to provide 3-39% yield of the corresponding enals).

CONCLUSION

This chapter clearly exemplifies the maturity gained by the ruthenium-catalyzed isomerizations of readily accessible allylic and propargylic alcohols in *Green Solvents* within organic modern chemistry. As the reader will have noticed, a plethora of ruthenium complexes (with a wide range of oxidation states and geometries) can be used under environmentally-friendly conditions mainly giving carbonyl compounds, providing simple and *green* synthetic routes to these very valuable raw materials in organic chemistry.

Also, it is important to note that, enhanced or completely new reactivities have been in some cases observed by using different *Green Solvents* (water, *ILs*, *DESs* or glycerol).

In many cases, catalyst recovery and reuse was also possible thus giving to the synthetic protocols a sustainable character.

Certainly, the study of new chemical pathways to create novel ruthenium complexes and their application in a variety of catalytic transformations in *Green Solvents* will continue to be a fast-moving topic for the next several years, with the discovery of new applications being expected in the near future.

In this sense, the easy fine-tuning of the properties of ruthenium complexes through the adequate election of their components opens a gate for the preparation of *a la carte* catalytic procedures mediated by ruthenium complexes and under environmentally-friendly conditions.

ACKNOWLEDGMENTS

Financial support by the MICINN (project CTQ2010-14796/BQU) of Spain and COST action Smart Inorganic Polymers (SIPs-CM1302) is gratefully acknowledged. JG-A thanks MICINN and the European Social Fund for the award of a “Ramón y Cajal” contract. NN is grateful to ICIQ and Marie Curie Actions for the award of a co-funded “ICIQ-IPMP” postdoctoral grant (reference agreement: 291787).

REFERENCES

[1] (a) Lee, D. G., van den Engh, M. In: *Oxidation in Organic Chemistry*; Trahanovsky, W. S. Ed.; Academic Press: New York, 1973, part B, chapter 4. (b) Courtney, J. L. In: *Organic Synthesis by Oxidation with Metal Compounds*; Mijs, W. J., de Jonge, C. R. H. I. Eds.; Plenum Press: New York, 1986, chapter 8, p. 445. (c) Martín, V. S., Palazón, J.

M., Rodríguez, C. M. In: *Encyclopedia of Reagents for Organic Synthesis;* Paquette, L. A. Ed.; John Wiley and Sons: Chichester, 1996, vol. 6, p. 4415.

[2] Siegel, V. S. In: *Encyclopedia of Reagents for Organic Synthesis;* Paquette, L. A. Ed.; John Wiley and Sons: Chichester, 1996, vol. 6, p. 4410.

[3] (a) Freifelder, M. In: *Practical Catalytic Hydrogenation*; Wiley: New York, 1971. (b) James, B. R. In: *Homogeneous Hydrogenation*; Wiley: New York, 1973. (c) Bennett, M. A., Matheson, T. W. In: *Comprehensive Organometallic Chemistry I*; Wilkinson, G., Stone, F. G. A., Abel, E. W. Eds.; Pergamon: Oxford, 1982, vol. 4, p. 931.

[4] See for example: (a) Seddon, E. A., Seddon, K. R. In: *The Chemistry of Ruthenium*; Elsevier: Amsterdam, 1984. (b) *Comprehensive Organometallic Chemistry II*; Abel, E. W., Stone, F. G. A., Wilkinson, G. Eds.; Pergamon: Oxford, 1995, vol. 7, chapter 5.16. (c) *Comprehensive Organometallic Chemistry III*; Crabtree, R. H., Mingos, D. M. P. Eds.; Elsevier: Oxford, 2007, vol. 6, chapter 6.11-6.25.

[5] For books covering this topic, see: (a) *Ruthenium in Organic Synthesis*; Murahashi, S.-I. Ed.; Wiley-VCH: Weinheim, 2004. (b) *Ruthenium Catalysts and Fine Chemistry*; Bruneau, C., Dixneuf, P. H. Eds.; Springer: Berlin, 2004. (c) *Ruthenium: Properties, Production and Applications*; Watson, D. B. Ed.; Nova Science Publishers: New York, 2011. (d) *Ruthenium Oxidation Complexes: Their Uses as Homogeneous Organic Catalysts*; Griffith, W. P. Ed.; Springer: Dordrecht, 2011.

[6] (a) Anastas, P. T., Warner, J. C. In: *Green Chemistry Theory and Practice*; Oxford University Press: Oxford, 1998. (b) Matlack, A. S. In: *Introduction to Green Chemistry*; Marcel Dekker: New York, 2001. (c) Poliakoff, M., Fitzpatrick, J. M., Farren, T. R., Anastas, P. T. *Science,* 2002, 297, 807-810. (d) Lancaster, M. In: *Green Chemistry: An Introductory Text*; RSC Publishing: Cambridge, 2002. (e) Sheldon, R. A., Arends, I. W. C. E., Hanefeld, U. In: *Green Chemistry and Catalysis*; Wiley-VCH, Weinheim, 2007.

[7] Anastas, P. T. In: *Handbook of Green Chemistry, Vol. 4, 5 and 6, Green Solvents: Volume 4: Supercritical Solvents*; Leitner, W., Jessop, P. G. Eds. *Volume 5: Reactions in Water*; Li, C.-J. Ed. *Volume 6: Ionic Liquids*; Wasserschied, P., Stark, A. Eds.; Wiley-VCH: Weinheim, 2010.

[8] Solvents are responsible of most of the waste generated in the chemical industries and laboratories. Constable, D. J. C., Jiménez-González, C., Henderson, R. K. *Org. Process Res. Dev.,* 2007, 11, 133-137.

[9] (a) Clark, J. H., Tavener, S. J. *Org. Process Res. Dev.,* 2007, 11, 149-155. (b) Jessop, P. G. *Green Chem.,* 2011, 13, 1391-1398. (c) A recent editorial in *Organic Process Research and Development* discourage chemists to use solvents that are either known to be toxic, dangerous for large scale preparations or expensive to dispose as waste. Laird, T. *Org. Process Res. Dev.,* 2012, 16, 1-2.

[10] Reichardt, C. In: *Solvents and Solvents Effects in Organic Chemistry*; Wiley-VCH: Weinheim, 3rd Edition, 2003.

[11] Moity, L., Durand, M., Benazzouz, A., Pierlot, C., Molinier, V., Aubry, J.-M. *Green Chem.,* 2012, 14, 1132-1145.

[12] (a) Trost, B. M. *Science*, 1991, 254, 1471-1477. (b) Trost, B. M. *Angew. Chem. Int. Ed. Eng.*, 1995, 34, 259-281. (c) Sheldon, R. A. *Pure Appl. Chem.*, 2000, 72, 1233-1246. (d) Trost, B. M. *Acc. Chem. Res.*, 2002, 35, 695-705. (e) Trost, B. M., Fredericksen, M. U., Rudd, M. T. *Angew. Chem. Int. Ed.*, 2005, 44, 6630-6666. (f) Sheldon, R. A. *Green Chem.*, 2007, 9, 1273-1283. (g) Sheldon, R. A. *Chem. Commun.*, 2008, 3352-3365.

[13] Metal-catalyzed redox isomerization of allylic alcohols is now used in the multi-step elaboration of high value added compounds, like pheromones, alkaloids fragrances or antitumor agents: (a) Ito, M., Kitahara, S., Ikariya, T. *J. Am. Chem. Soc.,* 2005, 127, 6172-6173. (b) Bartoszewicz, A., Martín-Matute, B. *Org. Lett.,* 2008, 11, 1749-1752. (c) Bovo, S., Scrivanti, A., Bertoldini, M., Beghetto, V., Metteoli, U. *Synthesis*, 2008, 2547-2550. (d) Tanaka, N., Suzuki, T., Matsumura, T., Hosoya, Y., Nakada, M. *Angew. Chem. Int. Ed.,* 2009, 48, 2580-2583. (e) Bouziane, A., Régnier, T., Carreaux, F., Carboni, B., Bruneau, C., Renaud, J. L. *Synlett*, 2010, 207-210. (f) Fehr, C., Magpantay, I., Saudan, L., Sommer, H. *Eur. J. Org. Chem.,* 2010, 6153-6156. (g) Sabitha, G., Nayak, S., Bhikshapathi, M., Yadav, J. S. *Org. Lett.,* 2011, 13, 382-385. (h) Quintard, A., Alexakis, A., Mazet, C. *Angew. Chem. Int. Ed.,* 2011, 50, 2354-2358.

[14] (a) van der Drift, R. C., Bouwman, E., Drent, E. *J. Organomet. Chem.,* 2002, 650, 1-24. (b) Uma, R., Crésvisy, C., Greé, R. *Chem. Rev.*, 2003, 103, 27-52. (c) Cadierno, V., Crochet, P., García-Garrido, S. E., Gimeno, J. *Curr. Org. Chem.,* 2006, 10, 165-183. (d) Cadierno, V., Crochet, P., Gimeno, J. *Synlett*, 2008, 1105-1124. (e) Mantilli, L., Mazet, C. *Chem. Lett.*, 2011, 40, 341-344. (f) Lorenzo-Luis, P., Romerosa, A., Serrano-Ruiz, M. *ACS Catal.*, 2012, 2, 1079-1086. (g) Alhsten, N., Bartoszewicz, A., Martín-Matute, B. *Daltons Trans.*, 2012, 41, 1660-1670. (h) García-Álvarez, J., García-Garrido, S. E., Crochet, P., Cadierno, V. *Curr. Top. Catal.*, 2012, 10, 35-56.

[15] Zoran, A., Sasson, Y., Blum, J. *J. Org. Chem.,* 1981, 46, 255-260.

[16] Trost, B. M., Kulawiec, R. J. *J. Am. Chem. Soc.,* 1993, 115, 2027-2036.

[17] (a) *Aqueous-Phase Organometallic Catalysis: Concepts and Applications*; Cornils, B., Herrmann, W. A. Eds.; Wiley-VCH: Weinheim, 1998. (b) Joó, F. In: *Aqueous Organometallic Catalysis*; Kluver: Dordrecht, 2001. (c) Li, C.-J., Chan, T. H. In: *Comprehensive Organic Reactions in Aqueous Media*; John Wiley and Sons: Hoboken, 2007. (d) *Organic Reactions in Water: Principles, Strategies and Applications*; Lindstrom, U. M. Ed.; Blackwell Publishing Ltd: Oxford, 2007. (e) *Water in Organic Synthesis*; Kobayashi, S. Ed.; Thieme-Verlag: Stuttgart, 2012. (f) *Metal-Catalyzed Reactions in Water*; Dixneuf, P. H., Cadierno, V. Eds.; Wiley-VCH: Weinheim, 2013.

[18] (a) McGrath, D. V., Grubbs, R. H. *J. Am. Chem. Soc.*, 1991, 113, 3611-3613. (b) McGrath, D. V., Grubbs, R. H. *Organometallics*, 1994, 13, 224-235.

[19] Karlen, T., Ludi, A. *Helv. Chim. Acta*, 1992, 75, 1604-1606.

[20] In contrast, the octahedral ruthenium(II) complex *cis*-[$RuCl_2$(dmso)$_4$] (dmso = dimethyl sulfoxide) was applied as catalyst for the isomerization of 3-buten-2-ol to butan-2-one in homogeneous water-diglyme solvent mixtures, requiring as high temperatures as 130 ºC to achieve meaningful reaction rates. van der Drift, R. C., Sprengers, J. W., Bouwman, E., Mul, W. P., Kooijman, H., Spek, A. L., Drent, E. *Eur. J. Inorg. Chem.,* 2002, 2147-2155.

[21] Complex *cis*-[Ru(6,6'-Cl_2bipy)$_2$(H_2O)$_2$][OTf]$_2$ has been known for decades, but its applications as catalyst for organic reactions are still quite limited: (a) Lau, T. C., Che, C. M., Lee, W. O., Poon, C. K. *J. Chem. Soc., Chem. Commun.,* 1988, 1406-1407. (b) Lau, C. P., Cheng, L. *Inorg. Chim. Acta,* 1992, 195, 133-134. (c) Lau, C. P., Cheng, L. *J. Mol. Catal.,* 1993, 84, 39-50. (d) Che, C.-M., Cheng, K.-W., Chan, M. C. W., Lau, T.-C., Mak, C.-K. *J. Org. Chem.,* 2000, 65, 7996-8000. (e) Xie, Z., Schlaf, M. *J. Mol. Catal. A: Chem.*, 2005, 229, 151-158.

[22] Liu, P. N., Ju, K. D., Lau, C. P. *Adv. Synth. Catal.*, 2011, 353, 275-280.

[23] (a) Pinault, N., Bruce, D. W. *Coord. Chem. Rev.,* 2003, 241, 1-25. (b) Phillips, A. D., Gonsalvi, L., Romerosa, A., Vizza, F., Peruzzini, M. *Coord. Chem. Rev.,* 2004, 248, 955-993. (c) Shaughnessy, K. H. *Chem. Rev.,* 2009, 109, 643-710. (d) Herrerias, C. I., Yao, X., Li, Z., Li, C.-J. *Chem. Rev.,* 2007, 106, 2546-2562. (e) Cadierno, V., Crochet, P. *Advances in Organometallic Chemistry Research;* Yamamoto, K. Ed.; Nova Science Publishers: New York, 2007, pp. 37–65.

[24] Campos-Malpartida, T., Fekete, M., Joó, F., Kathó, A., Romerosa, A., Saoud, M., Wojtków, W. *J. Organomet. Chem.*, 2008, 693, 468-474.

[25] Udvardy, A., Bényei, A. C., Kathó, A. *J. Organomet. Chem.*, 2012, 717, 116-122.

[26] (a) González, B., Lorenzo-Luis, P., Serrano-Ruiz, M., Papp, E., Fekete, M., Csépkec, K., Ősz, K., Kathó, A., Joó, F., Romerosa, A. *J. Mol. Catal. A: Chem.,* 2010, 326, 15-20. (b) Serrano-Ruiz, M., Lorenzo-Luis, P., Romerosa, A., Mena-Cruz, A. *Dalton Trans.,* 2013, 42, 7622-7630.

[27] Pontes da Costa, A., Mata, J. A., Royo, B., Peris, E. *Organometallics*, 2010, 29, 1832-1838.

[28] (a) Cadierno, V., Crochet, P., García-Garrido, S. E., Gimeno, J. *Dalton Trans.,* 2004, 3635-3641. (b) Crochet, P., Díez, J., Fernández-Zúmel, M. A., Gimeno, J. *Adv. Synth. Catal.,* 2006, 348, 93-100. (c) Díaz-Álvarez, A. E., Crochet, P., Zablocka, M., Duhayon, C., Cadierno, V., Gimeno, J., Majoral, J. P. *Adv. Synth. Catal.,* 2006, 348, 1671-1679. (d) Menéndez-Rodríguez, L., Crochet, P., Cadierno, V. *J. Mol. Catal. A: Chem.*, 2013, 366, 390-399.

[29] Lastra-Barreira, B., Díez, J., Crochet, P. *Green Chem.,* 2009, 11, 1681-1686.

[30] Azua, A., Sanz, S., Peris, E. *Organometallics*, 2010, 29, 3661-3664.

[31] Fekete, M., Joó, F. *Catal. Commun.,* 2006, 7, 783-786.

[32] García-Álvarez, R., Suárez, F. J., Díez, J., Crochet, P., Cadierno, V., Antiñolo, A., Fernández-Galán, R., Carrillo-Hermosilla, F. *Organometallics*, 2012, 31, 8301-8311.

[33] (a) Díez, J., Gimeno, J., Lledós, A., Suárez, F. J., Vicent, C. *ACS Catal.,* 2012, 2, 2087-2099. (b) Bellarosa, L., Díez, J., Gimeno, J., Lledós, A., Suárez, F. J., Ujaque, G., Vicent, C. *Chem. Eur. J.,* 2012, 18, 7749-7765.

[34] (a) Cole-Hamilton, D., Tooze, R. In: *Catalyst Separation, Recovery and Recycling. Chemistry and Process Design*; Springer: Dordrecht, The Netherlands, 2006. (b) *Recoverable and Recyclable Catalyst;* Benaglia, M. Ed.; John Wiley and Sons: Chichester, UK, 2009.

[35] (a) Corma, A., García, H. *Top. Catal.*, 2008, 48, 8-31. (b) Weckhuysen, B. M. *Nat. Chem.,* 2009, 1, 690-691. (c) Hutchings, G. J. *J. Mater. Chem.,* 2009, 19, 1222-1235. (d) Wittmann, S., Shätz, A., Grass, R. N., Stark, W. J., Reiser, O. *Angew. Chem.,* 2010, 122, 1911-1914; *Angew. Chem. Int. Ed.,* 2010, 49, 1867-1870 and references cited therein. (e) *Nanocatalysis: Synthesis and Applications*; Polshettiwar, V., Asefa, T. Ed.; John Wiley and Sons: Hoboken, 2013.

[36] Servin, P., Laurent, R., Gonsalvi, L., Tristany, M., Peruzzini, M., Majoral, J.-P., Caminade, A.-M. *Dalton Trans.*, 2009, 4432-4434.

[37] (a) García-Garrido, S. E., Francos, J., Cadierno, V., Basset, J.-M., Polshettiwar, V. *ChemSusChem*, 2011, 4, 104-111. Similarly, the Ru(II) complex $[RuCl_2(PPh_3)_3]$ (**39**) supported on different mesoporous materials has been used as catalysts for the 1,3-rearrangement of allylic alcohols in water. For details see section "*1.5-Ruthenium-Catalyzed 1,3-Rearrangement of Allylic Alcohols*" and ref. 73.

[38] Brown, C. J., Miller, G. M., Johnson, M. W., Bergman, R. G., Raymond, K. N. *J. Am. Chem. Soc.*, 2011, 133, 11964-11966.

[39] (a) Sasson, Y., Zoran, A., Blum, J. *J. Mol. Catal.,* 1979, 6, 289-292. (b) Hernández, M., Kalck, P. *J. Mol. Catal. A: Chem.,* 1997, 116, 131-146.

[40] *Ullmann's Encyclopedia of Industrial Chemistry*, 6th Electronic Release Ed.; Wiley-VCH: Weinheim, 2000.

[41] Within this context, it is important to stress that the presence of dienes such as 1,3-butadiene completely inhibits the catalytic activity of organometallic complexes, and therefore these catalytic achievements are particularly relevant.

[42] (a) Stunnenberg, F., Niele, F. G. H., Drent, E. *Inorg. Chim. Acta*, 1994, 222, 225-233. (b) van der Drift, R. C., Mul, W. P., Bouwman, E., Drent, E. *Chem. Commun.*, 2001, 2746-2747.

[43] (a) Porri, L., Gallazi, M. C., Colombo, A., Allegra, G. *Tetrahedron Lett.*, 1965, 6, 4187-4189. (b) Salzer, A., Bauer, A., Geyser, S., Podewils, F. *Inorg. Synth.,* 2004, 34, 59-65.

[44] (a) Lydon, J. E., Nicholson, J. K., Shaw, B. L., Truter, M. R. *Proc. Chem. Soc.,* 1964, 421-422. (b) Nicholson, J. K., Shaw, B. L. *J. Chem. Soc.,* 1966, 807-808.

[45] (a) Cadierno, V., García-Garrido, S. E., Gimeno, J. *Chem. Commun.,* 2004, 232-233. (b) Cadierno, V., García-Garrido, S. E., Gimeno, J., Varela-Álvarez, A., Sordo, J. A. *J. Am. Chem. Soc.,* 2006, 128, 1360-1370.

[46] (a) Cadierno, V., García-Garrido, S. E., Gimeno, J., Nebra, N. *Chem. Commun.,* 2005, 4086-4088. (b) Cadierno, V., Gimeno, J., Nebra, N. *Chem. Eur. J.,* 2007, 13, 6590-6594. (c) Varela-Álvarez, A., Sordo, J. A., Piedra, E., Nebra, N., Cadierno, V., Gimeno, J. *Chem. Eur. J.,* 2011, 17, 10583-10599. (d) Díaz-Álvarez, A. E., Crochet, P., Cadierno, V. *Tetrahedron*, 2012, 68, 2611-2620.

[47] Díaz-Álvarez, A. E., Cadierno, V. *Recent Patents Catal.,* 2012, 1, 43-50.

[48] For the synthesis of complex **36** see: Kavanagh, B., Steed, J. W., Tocher, D. A. *J. Chem. Soc., Dalton Trans.,* 1993, 327-335.

[49] García-Álvarez, J., Gimeno, J., Suárez, F. J. *Organometallics,* 2011, 30, 2893-2896.

[50] Díez, J., Gimeno, J., Merino, I., Rubio, E., Suárez, F. J. *Inorg. Chem.,* 2011, 50, 4868-4881.

[51] For recent reviews and articles covering bifunctional substrate activation and catalysis see: (a) Grotjahn, D. B. *Chem. Eur. J.*, 2005, 11, 7146-7153. (b) Saburi, H., Tanaka, S., Kitamura, M. *Angew. Chem. Int. Ed.*, 2005, 44, 1730-1732. (c) Ikariya, T., Muratta, K., Noyori, R. *Org. Biomol. Chem.*, 2006, 4, 393-406. (d) Ikariya, T., Blacker, J. *Acc. Chem. Res.*, 2007, 40, 1300-1380. (e) Grotjahn, D. B. *Chem. Lett.*, 2010, 39, 908-914. (f) Grotjahn, D. B. *Dalton Trans.*, 2008, 6497-6508. (g) Ikariya, T., Gridnev, I. D. *Top. Catal.*, 2010, 53, 894-902.

[52] (a) Welton, T. *Chem. Rev.*, 1999, 99, 2071-2083. (b) Wasserscheid, P., Keim, W. *Angew. Chem. Int. Ed.*, 2000, 39, 3772-3789. (c) Sheldon, R. *Chem. Commun.,* 2001, 2399-2407. (d) Dupont, J., de Souza, R F., Suárez, P. A. Z. *Chem. Rev.*, 2002, 102, 3667-3691. (e) Parvulescu, V. I., Hardacre, C. *Chem. Rev.*, 2007, 107, 2615-2665. (f) Hallet, J. P., Welton, T. *Chem. Rev.*, 2011, 111, 3508-3576.

[53] For some recent reviews about ionic liquids and their applications, see: (a) Das, R. N., Roy, K. *Mol. Divers*, 2013, 17, 151-196. (b) Cecchini, M. M., Charnay, C., De Angelis, F., Lamaty, F., Martinez, J., Colacino, E. *ChemSusChem*, 2014, 7, 45-65. (c) Pollet, P.,

Davey, E. A., Ureña-Benavides, E. E., Eckerta, C. A., Liotta, C. L. *Green Chem.*, 2014, 16, 1034-1055.

[54] Suárez, F. J., Vidal, C., García-Álvarez, J. *Curr. Green Chem.*, 2014, 1, 121-127.

[55] (a) Grabinska-Sota, E., Kalka, J. *Environ. Int.*, 2003, 28, 687-690. (b) Jastorff, B., Störmann, R., Ranke, J., Mölter, K., Stock, F., Oberheitmann, B., Hoffmann, W., Hoffmann, J., Nüchter, M., Ondruschka, B., Filser, J. *Green Chem.*, 2003, 5, 136-142. (c) Gathergood, N., García, M. T., Scammells, P. J. *Green Chem.*, 2004, 6, 166-175. (d) Zhang, C., Malhotra, S. V., Francis, A. J. *Chemosphere*, 2011, 82, 1690-1695.

[56] Welton, T. *Green Chem.*, 2011, 13, 225-225.

[57] Several reviews and accounts have been published about this field in recent years: (a) Abbott, A. P., Harris, R. C., Ryder, K., d'Agostino, C., Gladden, L., Mantle, M. D. *Green Chem.*, 2011, 13, 82-90. (b) Ruβ, C., König, B. *Green Chem.*, 2012, 14, 2969-2982. (c) Carriazo, D., Serrano, M. C., Gutiérrez, M. C., Ferrer, M. L., Monte, F. *Chem. Soc. Rev.*, 2012, 41, 4996-5014. (d) Zhang, Q., De Oliveira Vigier, K., Royer, S., Jérôme, F. *Chem. Soc. Rev.*, 2012, 41, 7108-7146. (e) Francisco, M., van den Bruinhorst, A., Kroon, M. C. *Angew. Chem. Int. Ed.*, 2013, 52, 3074-3085. (f) Tang, B., Row, K. H. *Monatsh. Chem.*, 2013, 144, 1427-1454. (g) Gu, Y., Jérôme, F. *Chem. Soc. Rev.*, 2013, 42, 9550-9570. (h) Paiva, A., Craveiro, R., Aroso, I., Martins, M., Reis, R. L., Duarte, A. R. C. *ACS Sustainable Chem. Eng.*, 2014, 2, 1063-1071.

[58] García-Álvarez, J. In: *Deep Eutectic Solvents and their Applications as New Green and Biorenewable Reaction Media*; *Handbook of Solvents, Volume 2, Second Edition: Use, Health, and Environment*; Wypych, G. Ed.; ChemTec Publishing: Toronto, 2014.

[59] (a) Imperato, G., Höger, S., Lenoir, D., König, B. *Green Chem.*, 2006, 8, 1051-1055. (b) Imperato, G., Vasold, R., König, B. *Adv. Synth. Catal.*, 2006, 348, 2243-2247. (c) Ilgen, F., König, B. *Green Chem.*, 2009, 11, 848-854. (d) Vidal, C., García-Álvarez, J., Hernán-Gómez, A., Kennedy, A. R., Hevia, E. *Angew. Chem. Int. Ed.*, 2014, 53, 5969-5973.

[60] *ChCl* (2-hydroxy-*N,N,N*-trimethylethanaminium chloride; so-called vitamin B_4, an essential micro- and human nutrient) is produced on the scale of million metric tons per year as an additive for chicken feed and many other applications. This ammonium salt is not only cheap and easy to obtain (can be extracted from biomass) but also non-toxic and biodegradable. (a) Blusztajn, J. K. *Science*, 1998, 281, 794-795. (b) Petkovic, M., Ferguson, J. L., Gunaratne, H. Q. N., Ferreira, R. M., Leitão, C., Seddon, K. R., Rebelo, L. P. N., Pereira, C. S. *Green. Chem.*, 2010, 12, 643-649.

[61] Vidal, C., Suárez, F. J., García-Álvarez, J. *Catal. Commun.*, 2014, 44, 76-79.

[62] For recent reviews on the field, see for example: (a) Fogg, D. E., dos Santos, E. *Coord. Chem. Rev.*, 2004, 248, 2365-2379. (b) Chapman, C. J., Frost, C. *Synthesis*, 2007, 1-21. (c) Patil, N. T., Shinde, V. S., Gajula, B. *Org. Biomol. Chem.*, 2012, 10, 211-224.

[63] For a recent review concerning the use of allylic alcohols as latent enolates in organic synthesis see ref. 14g.

[64] (a) Wang, M., Li, C.-J. *Tetrahedron Lett.*, 2002, 43, 3589-3591. (b) Wang, M., Yang, X.-F., Li, C.-J. *Eur. J. Org. Chem.*, 2003, 998-1003.

[65] Note that the coupling of α-vinylbenzylalcohol and benzaldehyde in presence of [In $(OAc)_3$] (8 mol%) allowed the improvement in the yield from 10 to 80% under same reaction conditions (i.e., 3 mol% Ru, 110 ºC, mixture 4:1 H_2O/Toluene).

[66] Oe, Y., Uozumi, Y. *Synlett,* 2011, 6, 787-790.

[67] (a) Yang, X.-F., Wang, M., Varma, R. S., Li, C.-J. *Org. Lett.*, 2003, 5, 657-660. (b) Yang, X.-F., Wang, M., Varma, R. S., Li, C.-J. *J. Mol. Cat. A.: Chem.*, 2004, 214, 147-154.

[68] (a) Cadierno, V., Francos, J., Gimeno, J., Nebra, N. *Chem. Commun.*, 2007, 2536-2538. (b) Cadierno, V., Crochet, P., Francos, J., García-Garrido, S. E., Gimeno, J., Nebra, N. *Green Chem.*, 2009, 11, 1992-2000.

[69] Díaz-Álvarez, A. E., Crochet, P., Cadierno, V. *Catal. Commun.*, 2011, 13, 91-96.

[70] (a) Babler, J. H. *Tetrahedron Lett.*, 1975, 16, 2045-2048. (b) Letourneux, Y., Lee Lo, M. M., Choudhari, N., Gut, M. *J. Org. Chem.*, 1975, 40, 516-518. (c) Yoshihito, A., Akio, O., Hiroshi, I. *Chem. Pharm. Bull.*, 1982, 30, 881-886. (d) Leleti, R. R., Hu, B., Prashad, M., Repic, O. *Tetrahedron Lett.*, 2007, 48, 8505-8507. (e) McCubbin, J. A., Voth, S., Krokhin, O. V. *J. Org. Chem.*, 2011, 76, 8537-8542.

[71] (a) Bellemin-Laponnaz, S., Gisie, H., Le Ny, J.-P., Osborn, J. A. *Angew. Chem. Int. Ed.*, 1997, 36, 976-978. (b) Morrill, C., Grubbs, R. H. *J. Am. Chem. Soc.*, 2005, 127, 2842-2843. (c) Akai, S., Tanimoto, K., Kanao, Y., Egi, M., Yamamoto, T., Kita, Y. *Angew. Chem. Int. Ed.*, 2006, 45, 2592-2595. (d) Morrill, C., Beutner, G. L., Grubbs, R. H. *J. Org. Chem.*, 2006, 71, 7813-7825. (e) Herrmann, A. T., Saito, T., Stivala, C. E., Tom, J., Zakarian, A. *J. Am. Chem. Soc.*, 2010, 132, 5962-5963.

[72] (a) Li, C.-J., Wang, D., Chen, D.-L. *J. Am. Chem. Soc.*, 1995, 117, 12867-12868. (b) Wang, D., Chen, D., Haberman, J. X., Li, C.-J. *Tetrahedron*, 1998, 54, 5129-5142.

[73] (a) Li, H., Zhang, F., Wan, Y., Lu, Y. *J. Phys. Chem. B*, 2006, 110, 22942-22946. (b) Li, H., Zhang, F., Yin, H., Wan, Y., Lu, Y. *Green Chem.*, 2007, 9, 500-505. (c) Wan, Y., Zhang, F., Lu, Y., Li, H. *J. Mol. Catal. A: Chem.*, 2007, 267, 165-172. (d) Li, H., Yin, H., Zhang, F., Li, H., Huo, Y., Lu, Y. *Environ. Sci. Technol.*, 2009, 43, 188-194. (e) Liu, G., Sun, Y., Wang, J., Sun, C., Zhang, F., Li, H. *Green Chem.*, 2009, 11, 1477-1481. (f) Huang, J., Zhu, F., He, W., Zhang, F., Wang, W., Li, H. *J. Am. Chem. Soc.*, 2010, 132, 1492-1493.

[74] Li, P.-F., Wang, H.-L., Qu, J. *J. Org. Chem.*, 2014, 79, 3955-3962.

[75] To get some information about the reactivity of α,β-unsaturated carbonyl compounds, see: (a) Tietze, L. F., Eicher, T., Diederichsen, U., Speicher, A. In: *Reactions and Synthesis in the Organic Chemistry Laboratory;* Wiley-VCH: Weinheim, 2007. (b) Starkey, L. S. In: *Introduction to Strategies for Organic Synthesis*; John Wiley and Sons Inc: New Jersey, 2012. (c) Totani, K., Tadano, K.-I. In: *Carbohydrates - Tools for Stereoselective Synthesis*; 1st Edition, pp. 27-45; Boysen, M. M. K. Ed.; Wiley-VCH: Weinheim, 2013.

[76] Meyer, K. H., Schuster, K. *Ber. Dtsch. Chem. Gess.*, 1922, 55, 819-823.

[77] Rupe, H., Kambli, E. *Helv. Chim. Acta*, 1926, 9, 672-672.

[78] (a) Ma, D., Lu, X. *J. Chem. Soc., Chem. Commun.*, 1989, 890-891. (b) Trost, B. M., Livingston, R. C. *J. Am. Chem. Soc.*, 1995, 117, 9586-9587.

[79] Swaminathan, S., Narayanan, K. V. *Chem. Rev.*, 1971, 71, 429-438.

[80] (a) Lu, X., Zhang, C., Xu, Z. *Acc. Chem. Res.*, 2001, 34, 535-544. (b) Erenler, R., Biellmann, J. F. *Tetrahedron Lett.*, 2005, 46, 5683-5685. (c) Sonye, J. P., Koide, K. *J. Org. Chem.*, 2006, 71, 6254-6257. (d) Sonye, J. P., Koide, K. *J. Org. Chem.*, 2007, 72, 1846-1848.

[81] (a) Yamano, Y., Tode, C., Ito, M. *J. Chem. Soc., Perkins Trans.*, 1995, 1, 1895-1904. (b) Trost, B. M., Lee, C. *J. Am. Chem. Soc.*, 2001, 123, 12191-12201. (c) Trost, B. M.,

Livingston, R. C. *J. Am. Chem. Soc.,* 2008, 130, 11970-11978. (d) Hodgson, D. M., Talbot, E. P. A., Clark, B. P. *Org. Lett.,* 2011, 13, 5751-5753.

[82] (a) Suzuki, T., Tokunaga, M., Wakatsuki, Y. *Tetrahedron Lett.,* 2002, 43, 7531-7533. (b) For the synthesis of complex $[RuCl(\eta^5\text{-}Cp)(PMe_3)_2]$ (**44**), see: Bruce, M. I., Wong, F. S., Skelton, B. W., White, A. H. *J. Chem. Soc., Dalton Trans.,* 1981, 1398-1405.

[83] (a) d'Alessandro, N., Di Deo, M., Bonetti, M., Tonucci, L., Morvillo, A., Bressan, M. *Eur. J. Inorg. Chem.,* 2004, 810-817. (b) For the synthesis of the **RuPcS**, see: Bressan, M., Celli, N., d'Alessandro, N., Liberatore, L., Morvillo, A., Tonucci, L. *J. Organomet. Chem.,* 2000, 593-594, 416-420. (c) For the synthesis of the **RuHAP**, see: Yamaguchi, K., Mori, K., Mizugaki, T., Ebitani, K., Kaneda, K. *J. Am. Chem. Soc.,* 2000, 122, 7144-7145.

[84] Hintermann, L., Kribber, T., Labonne, A., Paciok, E. *Synlett,* 2009, 15, 2412-2416.

In: Ruthenium
Editor: Gary P. Keeler

ISBN: 978-1-63321-657-0

Chapter 6

Voltammetric and Spectroscopic Methods for the Ruthenium Determination in the Environment at Ultra-Trace Concentration Level: Critical Comparison and Application to Airborne Particulate Matter, Vegetables, Superficial Waters, Mussels, Clams and Soils

Clinio Locatelli[*] and Dora Melucci
Department of Chemistry «G. Ciamician», University of Bologna, Bologna, Italy
CIRSA (Centro Inter-dipartimentale di Ricerca per le Scienze Ambientali), Laboratory of Environmental Analytical Chemistry, University of Bologna, Ravenna, Italy

Abstract

The problem related to the presence of Platinum Group Metals (PGMs) in the environment has raised much attention and great interest in the scientific community. This is due to the fact that the PGMs are widely used in various fields, such as anticancer drugs, jewels production, photographic operations, industrial catalysts, and especially autocatalytic converters. In the last case, their continuous use and deterioration implies a considerable release of these metals in the environment.

It should be noted that the metals initially used in autocatalytic converters were platinum, palladium and rhodium, but in recent years such PGMs were gradually and partially replaced, or alloyed with osmium and especially ruthenium. Their addition in the manufacture of autocatalytic converters helps them withstand high temperatures and wear, thus increasing the product life.

Thus, the increasing use of autocatalytic converters shows two decidedly conflictual effects on the environment: an evident and drastic reduction of the concentration levels of

[*] Corresponding Author: Fax: +39-051-209-94-56. E-mail: clinio.locatelli@unibo.it.

lead, and, at the same time, an equally evident and widespread increase of the PGMs concentration, and in particular of ruthenium, due to its increasing use in recent years.

This work proposes a voltammetric method for the determination of ultra-trace ruthenium in environmental samples: airborne particulate matter, vegetables, superficial waters, mussels, clams and soils/sediments.

To better validate the proposed analytical procedure, a critical comparison with spectroscopic measurements — electrothermal atomic absorption spectroscopy (ET–AAS) because of its well established and tested robustness — has been also carried out and discussed here. All the parameters of interest for the set-up of an analytical method, such as trueness and precision (accuracy), limit of detection and quantification, selectivity and, especially, sensitivity were taken into account.

Keywords: Ruthenium, airborne particulate matter, vegetables, superficial waters, mussels, clams, soils/sediments, voltammetry, spectroscopy

1. Introduction

In the last decade, a topical subject of great interest has been the problem relevant to the presence in the environment of platinum group metals (PGMs). This is due to the fact that the PGMs concentration is significantly increasing with the more and more considerable use of them in industrial catalysts production, autocatalytic converters, anticancer drugs, jewel production and photographic operations [1]. In this contest, it is important to highlight that great attention has been addressed to platinum(II), palladium (II) and rhodium (III), whereas osmium (VIII), ruthenium (III) and iridium (III) have been rarely investigated [2 and therein references].

Ruthenium, rarely used in its pure state, is nonetheless considered an important alloying agent, especially in high-wear applications, owing to strong corrosion and heat resistance. In fact, in recent years, and more and more frequently, this element has been employed as alloying with platinum, palladium and rhodium in the manufacture of autocatalytic converters, in order to withstand high temperatures and high wear, so increasing the life time of the same autocatalytic converters. Considering the compelling use of autocatalytic converters, this fact has evidently been the most important and perhaps the only cause of an increasing concentration of such metals in all the environmental matrices.

All PGMs can be dangerous for human health by direct contact with the dust, by inhalation of fine particulate matter (aerodynamic diameter < 10 μm) and also through food and water. Ruthenium in particular does not show to have any biological role, but it is absolutely toxic and carcinogenic, and it is also subject to bioaccumulation in the bones.

In our laboratories it is underway for some years an important line of research on the development of analytical methods for the voltammetric determination of PGMs, starting with those most investigated (platinum, palladium, rhodium) [3-8] to finish those generally considered, at least until a few years ago, less important from the environmental pollution point of view (ruthenium, osmium and iridium) [9-15].

Thus, restricting the field of investigation only to ruthenium, the present work intends to be a critical discussion about its determination in environmental matrices, currently of the highest interest, by voltammetric and spectroscopic techniques. Advantages as well as disadvantages are highlighted.

The discussion will be based on the sample typology. In this context, the matrices considered are: 1) Airborne Particulate Matter, 2) Vegetables, 3) Superficial Waters (Fresh- and Sea- Waters), 4) Mussels and Clams and 5) Soils/Sediments.

2. EXPERIMENTAL

Voltammetry

All voltammetric curves were recorded by an Amel Model 433 multipolarograph, employing a conventional three-electrode cell: a hanging mercury drop electrode (HMDE) as working electrode, an Ag | AgCl | $Cl^{-}_{satd.}$ electrode and platinum wire as reference and auxiliary electrode, respectively. The Teflon voltammetric cell was rinsed every day with supra-pure concentrated nitric acid in order to prevent any contamination. Standard additions were made with disposable plastic tips. Keeping the temperature at 20.0 ± 0.5 °C, the solutions were deaerated by water-saturated pure nitrogen for 5 min prior to measurements, while a nitrogen blanket was maintained above the solution during the analysis. The solutions were deaerated after each standard addition for 1 min. In the electrolysis step the solutions were stirred using a magnetic stirrer.

Spectroscopy

Atomic absorption spectrometric measurements were performed using a Perkin-Elmer Mod. A-Analyst 100 Atomic Absorption Spectrometer, equipped with a deuterium background corrector, Autosampler AS-72 and with HGA 800 graphite furnace. Single-element Lumina (Perkin-Elmer) hollow-cathode lamps were used. All measurements were carried out after studying the relevant ashing and atomization curves for each considered element [16].

3. REAGENTS AND REFERENCE SOLUTIONS

All acids and chemicals were suprapure grade (Merck, Germany). Acidic stock solutions of ruthenium(III) (1000 mg L^{-1}, Sigma-Aldrich, Germany) were respectively employed in the preparation of reference solutions at varying concentrations for each element, using water - demineralized through a Milli-Q system - to dilute samples.

4. SAMPLING SITES

For all the considered matrices, with the exception of mussels and clams, the sampling sites were chosen considering the different influence by vehicle traffic (A>B>C). The first (site A) was a densely peopled urban at very high anthropic impact, in the proximity of a heavily trafficked superhighway (Ferrara area, Italy); the second (site B) was near a heavy traffic route (Portomaggiore area, Italy) and the third (site C) was in a bay (Goro Bay) directly connected with the Adriatic Sea, a remote zone considered non-polluted or, in any case, at very low pollution load from vehicle traffic.

As regards mussels and clams, they were sampled only in two sites, the former within the mouth of the Po river (Goro Bay, Italy) and the latter at open Adriatic Sea.

5. Airborne Particulate Matter

The airborne particulate matter is mainly responsible for the spread in the environment of the Ru(III) resulting from abrasion and wear and tear of catalytic converters. For this reason, great attention has been addressed to the determination of all the platinum group metals (PGMs) in this matrix, even if the mainly used technique is spectroscopy [17, 18].

In this context, very interesting are the works that employ the inductively coupled plasma in optical emission spectroscopy (ICP-OES) [19, 20], atomic emission spectroscopy (ICP-AES) [21, 22], mass spectroscopy (ICP-MS) [23, 24], or in combined with a chromatographic separation [25]. As regards the determination of ruthenium by voltammetry, the literature reports an interesting work [12], which proposes a procedure for the simultaneous determination of ruthenium, osmium and lead in airborne particulate matter using the peak area as instrumental signal that allows to achieve extremely high sensitivity and consequently very low detection limits.

5.1. Determination of Ru(III) in Airborne Particulate Matter

The procedure here proposed is a substantial modification of previous procedures, already partially present in literature and published by the same authors [12].

5.1.1. Standard Reference Materials

Mintek-Sarm-7 was employed as standard reference material for optimizing and setting up the analytical procedure.

5.1.2. Sampling and Sample Preparation

Atmosphere particulate matter (PM < 10 μm) was collected during 30 days (October 1-30, 2013) in three sites differently influenced by vehicle traffic (A > B > C) (see section 4 "Sampling Sites") by using multi-stage and multi-orifice Andersen 1 ACFM Non-viable Ambient Particle Sizing Sampler cascade impactor (ThermoAndersen, Smyrna, GA, USA) with 10.0-0.4 μm particle diameter fractionation range.

Sampling was carried out employing cellulose nitrate filters and a 28.3 L/min constant flow rate. Each filter relevant to < 10 μm aerodynamic particle size, previously conditioned and weighed, was accurately weighed, placed in a pyrex digestion tube inserted into a cold home-made block digester and dissolved in 7 mL $69\%_{w/w}$ HNO_3 + 5 mL 37 $_{w/w}$ HCl at 130-150 °C.

The mixture was evaporated to dryness and, after cooling, soluble salts were dissolved in 25 mL 0.5 mol L^{-1} acetate buffer pH 4.3 + 0.1 mol L^{-1} $NaBrO_3$ + 2.7 10^{-4} mol L^{-1} EDTA-Na_2.

Model experiments exactly simulating the filter mineralisation procedure were performed to verify that the filter would not be contaminated. In all cases the blank concentrations for each element were lower than the respective limits of detection.

5.1.3. Analytical Procedure for the Voltammetric Determination of Ruthenium(III) in Airborne Particulate Matter

10 mL sample aliquots of 0.5 mol L^{-1} acetate buffer pH 4.3 + 0.1 mol L^{-1} $NaBrO_3$ + 2.7 10^{-4} mol L^{-1} EDTA-Na_2 aqueous reference solution or of solutions obtained in the mineralisation step of the standard reference material and of the filters, were pipetted into the voltammetric cell and deaerated for 5 min by bubbling water-saturated pure nitrogen. The Ru(III) determination was carried out by Square Wave Catalytic Voltammetry (SWCV) using HMDE electrode.

The voltammetric experimental conditions were:

- Deposition potential E_d (V/ Ag|AgCl|$Cl^-_{satd.}$): -0.150; initial potential E_i (V/ Ag|AgCl|$Cl^-_{satd.}$): -0.150; final potential E_f (V/ Ag|AgCl|$Cl^-_{satd.}$): -0.550; electrodeposition time t_d (s): 360; delay time before the potential sweep t_r (s): 10; potential scan rate dE/dt (mV/s): 100; step amplitude ΔE (mV): 50; sampling time τ (s): 0.010; wave period ν (s): 0.100; wave increment η (mV): 10; stirring rate r (r.p.m.): 600.

Under these experimental conditions, Ru(III) shows the following peak potentials E_p (V/ Ag|AgCl|$Cl^-_{satd.}$):

0.5 mol L^{-1} acetate buffer pH 4.3 + 0.1 mol L^{-1} $NaBrO_3$ + 2.7 10^{-4} mol L^{-1} EDTA-Na_2 Aqueous Reference Solutions	-0.349±0.010
Solution obtained by digestion of Standard Reference Material Mintek-Sarm-7	-0.361±0.015
Solutions obtained by digestion of the filters Site A	-0.379±0.015
Site B	-0.367±0.010
Site C	No Signal

The determined values were the mean of 5 independent determinations ± confidence interval at 95 % confidence level.

As regards the composition of the supporting electrolyte, it should be emphasized that the presence of EDTA-Na_2 is necessary to obtain better resolution for the Ru(III) peak.

Indeed, in the atmospheric particulate it is always and inevitably present Pb(II), which unfortunately shows to have a peak potential very close to that of Ru(III). In the supporting electrolyte without the presence of EDTA-Na_2 the peak potentials E_p (V/ Ag|AgCl|$Cl^-_{satd.}$) are: $E_{p\ Ru(III)}$ = -0.255±0.010 and $E_{p\ Pb(II)}$ = -0.305±0.010.

The problem is decidedly important, considering that the same problem is also present in the standard reference material and in the real samples collected in the three sampling sites. Our methodological procedure, already reported in a previous work [9], proposes the possibility to shift the Pb(II) interferent peaks towards more cathodic potential values by adding EDTA-Na_2. The presence of 2.7 10^{-4} mol L^{-1} EDTA-Na_2 shifts towards more cathodic potential values either of Ru(III) or of Pb(II) [Ru(III): -0.349±0.015; Pb(II): -0.677±0.010 V *vs.* Ag|AgCl|$Cl^-_{satd.}$]. Evidently the new peak position of the elements allows their resolution and then also their quantitative determination.

To better validate the voltammetric analytical procedure, the proposed voltammetric analytical method was compared with electrothermal atomic absorption spectroscopy (ET-AAS): such a technique was chosen because of its well-established and tested robustness.

The experimental conditions for the spectroscopic measurements were:

Wavelength (nm)	349.9
Slit (nm)	0.3
Drying Temperature (°C)	100
Charring Temperature (°C)	1375
Atomisation Temperature (°C)	2500

Sample volume injected: 20 μL.

Argon flow was 300 mL min^{-1} at all steps except during atomization (60 mL min^{-1}).

5.2. Results and Discussion

In this section, in a synthetic way, the fundamental parameters that characterize a correct analytical procedure — limits of detection, linearity range, trueness and precision — are reported.

5.2.1. Limits of Detection and Linearity Range

In the aqueous reference solution, in the solutions obtained by digestion of the standard reference material and of the filters containing the particulate matter, the limits of detection (LOD) for both techniques, voltammetry and spectroscopy (Table 1) were obtained by the equation LOD=$K\ s_{y/x}/b$ [26], where $s_{y/x}$ and b are the estimated standard deviation and the slope of the analytical calibration function of each element, respectively, with a 95 % (K=3) confidence level [27].

Table 1. Limits of detection (LOD) [a] for Ru(III) determined in the aqueous reference solutions (μg L^{-1}), in the solutions obtained by digestion of the standard reference material Mintek-Sarm-7 and by digestion of the filters (calculated in μg L^{-1} and expressed in μg kg^{-1})

0.5 mol L^{-1} acetate buffer pH 4.3 + 0.1 mol L^{-1} $NaBrO_3$ + 2.7 10^{-4} mol L^{-1} EDTA-Na_2 Aqueous Reference Solutions	0.047
Solution obtained by digestion of Standard Reference Material Mintek-Sarm-7	2.5
Solutions obtained by digestion of the filters Site A	2.1
Site B	2.3
Site C	No signal

[a]In the case of spectroscopic measurements, the limit of detection (μg L^{-1}) in the aqueous reference solution was 0.096. Considering a sample weight exactly equal to 0.5 g (see section 5.1.2. "Sampling and Sample Preparation"), the same limit of detection, calculated in μg kg^{-1} was 4.8.

In the case of voltammetric technique, since the analytical calibration functions were determined by standard addition method, it was possible to obtain the LODs directly also in the real matrix (Table 1).

In the experimental employed conditions, the linearity range for Ru(III) in the aqueous reference solutions is < LOD – 0.35 μg L^{-1}.

5.2.2. Quality Control and Quality Assessment

The method set up in aqueous reference solutions was applied to standard reference material Mintek-Sarm-7 (from Council for Mineral Technology (MINTEK), Republic of South Africa) in order to confirm and verify the applicability of the analytical procedure, determining its trueness and precision (Table 2).

About 0.5 g of the standard reference material, accurately weighed, was mineralized using the same acidic attack mixture and the same procedure employed as in the case of filters samples (see section 5.1.2. “Sampling and Sample Preparation”).

At the experimental conditions employed, precision as repeatability [26], expressed as relative standard deviation (s_r %) on five independent determinations, was satisfactory, being, in all cases, lower than 5%, while trueness, expressed as relative error (*e* %) was generally lower than 7% (Table 2).

Trueness and precision results for the spectroscopic measurements are also reported in Table 2.

Table 2. Accuracy and precision of the analytical procedure. Standard Reference Material: Mintek-Sarm-7. The determined values are the mean of 5 independent determinations ± confidence interval at 95 % confidence level. Concentrations expressed in μg kg^{-1}. Experimental conditions: see section 5.1.3.

Voltammetric Measurements				Spectroscopic Measurements			
Certified concentration	Determined concentration	e (%)	s_r (%)	Certified concentration	Determined concentration	e (%)	s_r (%)
43±6	45±3	+4.7	5.1	43±6	40±4	-7.0	5.3

5.2.3. Practical Application

Once the procedure for the Ru(III) determination was set up, the method was applied to atmospheric particulate matter sampled in three sites differently influenced by vehicle traffic (see section 4, “Sampling Sites”).

The experimental results are reported in Table 3.

Table 3. Mean values for Ru(III) concentrations (μg kg^{-1}) relevant to atmospheric particulate matter (PM < 10 μm) sampled in three sites differently influenced by vehicle traffic (A > B > C, see section 4, “Sampling Sites”). The determined values are the mean of 5 independent determinations ± confidence interval at 95 % confidence level

Technique	A	B	C
Voltammetry	9.6 ± 0.5	3.6 ± 0.2	< LOD
Spectroscopy (ET-AAS)	9.2 ± 0.6	< LOD	< LOD

6. VEGETABLES

The works reported in the literature concerning the determination of PGMs in vegetable matrices are really very few: two interesting reviews [2, 28] and a work that shows an analytical procedure for the sequential determination of Ir(III) and Pb(II) [13].

As regards specifically the determination of Ru(III) in vegetable matrices, the literature reports only two really interesting works [15, 29], which for the first time show the possibility of using vegetable matrices as bio-monitors to address the problem of atmospheric pollution by Ru(III) due to vehicular traffic.

6.1. Determination of Ru(III) in Vegetable Matrices

Also for this matrix, the procedure here proposed, with some substantial modifications, is already partially present in literature and published by the same authors [15].

6.1.1. Standard Reference Materials

Olive Leaves BCR-CRM 062 (from Institute for Reference Materials and Measurements, European Commission, Joint Research Centre, Geel, Belgium) and Tomato Leaves NIST-SRM 1573a (from National Institute of Standards and Technology, Gaithersburg, MD, USA) were employed as standard reference materials for optimizing and setting up the analytical procedure.

6.1.2. Sampling and Sample Preparation

Laurel leaves were collected in three sites differently influenced by vehicle traffic (A > B > C) (see Section 4 "Sampling Sites").

The sample preparation for Olive Leaves BCR-CRM 062, Tomato Leaves NIST-SRM 1573a and for real samples of laurel leaves was the following: approximately 0.5 g, accurately weighed, were placed in a platinum crucible and dissolved in 4 mL 69 $\%_{w/w}$ HNO_3 + 3 mL 37 $\%_{w/w}$ HCl + 5 mL 98% $_{w/w}$ H_2SO_4 at 130-150 °C. The mixture was evaporated to dryness and, after cooling, soluble salts were dissolved in 25 mL 0.3 mol L^{-1} acetate buffer pH 4.7 + 7.7 10^{-2} mol L^{-1} $NaBrO_3$ + 2.5 10^{-4} EDTA-Na_2. The obtained solutions were then diluted, if necessary, before spectroscopic measurements.

6.1.3. Analytical Procedure for the Voltammetric Determination of Ruthenium(III) in Vegetables

10 mL sample aliquots of 0.3 mol L^{-1} acetate buffer pH 4.7 + 7.7 10^{-2} mol L^{-1} $NaBrO_3$ + 2.5 10^{-4} EDTA-Na_2 aqueous reference solution or of solutions obtained in the mineralization step of the standard reference material and of the real samples, were pipetted into the voltammetric cell and deaerated for 5 min by bubbling water-saturated pure nitrogen. The Ru(III) determination was carried out by Differential Pulse Catalytic Voltammetry (DPCV) using HMDE electrode.

The voltammetric experimental conditions are reported in Table 4.

The spectroscopic experimental conditions are reported in section 5.1.3.

Table 4. Instrumental parameters for the determination of Ru(III) by Differential Pulse Catalytic Voltammetry (DPCV) [a]. Supporting electrolyte: 0.3 mol L^{-1} acetate buffer pH 4.7 + 7.7 10^{-2} mol L^{-1} $NaBrO_3$ + 2.5 10^{-4} mol L^{-1} EDTA-Na_2

E_i	-0.175
E_d	-0.175
E_f	-0.600
t_d	360
t_r	10
dE/dt	20
ΔE	50
τ	0.065
ν	0.250
r	600

[a]E_i: initial potential (V/Ag, AgCl, $Cl^-_{satd.}$); E_d: deposition potential (V/Ag, AgCl, $Cl^-_{satd.}$); E_f: final potential (V/Ag, AgCl, $Cl^-_{satd.}$); t_d: electrodeposition time (s); t_r: delay time before the potential sweep (s); dE/dt: potential scan rate (mV/s); ΔE: superposed potential amplitude (mV); τ: superposed pulse duration (s); υ: superposed pulse repetition (s); r: stirring rate (r.p.m.).

6.1.4. Supporting Electrolyte and Peak Potentials

0.3 mol L^{-1} acetate buffer pH 4.7 + 7.7 10^{-2} mol L^{-1} $NaBrO_3$ + 2.5 10^{-4} mol L^{-1} EDTA-Na_2 was employed as supporting electrolyte. Also in this case the presence of EDTA-Na_2 is required for the previously given reasons (see section 5.1.3)

At these experimental conditions, Ru(III) shows the following peak potentials E_p (V/ Ag | AgCl | $Cl^-_{satd.}$):

0.3 mol L^{-1} acetate buffer pH 4.7 + 7.7 10^{-2} mol L^{-1} $NaBrO_3$ + 2.5 10^{-4} mol L^{-1} EDTA-Na_2 Aqueous Reference Solutions	-0.363±0.010
Solution obtained by digestion of Olive Leaves BCR-CRM 062 Standard Reference Material	-0.377±0.015
Solution obtained by digestion of Tomato Leaves NIST-SRM 1573a Standard Reference Material	-0.355±0.010
Solutions obtained by digestion of the laurel leaves Site A	-0.349±0.015
Site B	-0.358±0.015
Site C	No signal

The determined values are the mean of 5 independent determinations ± confidence interval at 95 % confidence level.

6.2. Results and Discussion

In this section, the fundamental parameters that characterize a correct analytical procedure — limits of detection, linearity range, trueness and precision — are synthetically reported.

6.2.1. Limits of Detection and Linearity Range

In the aqueous reference solution, in the solutions obtained by digestion of Olive Leaves BCR-CRM 062 and Tomato Leaves NIST-SRM 1573a standard reference materials, and in the solutions obtained by digestion of laurel leaves the limits of detection (LOD) (Table 5) for both techniques were calculated as described in section 5.2.1.

Table 5. Limits of detection (LOD) [a] of Ru(III) determined in the aqueous reference solutions (μg L^{-1}), in the solutions obtained by digestion of the standard reference material Olive Leaves BCR-CRM 062 and Tomato Leaves NIST-SRM 1573a and by digestion of laurel leaves (calculated in μg L^{-1} and expressed in μg kg^{-1}). The determined values are the mean of 5 independent determinations ± confidence interval at 95 % confidence level

0.25 mol L^{-1} acetate buffer pH 4.9 + 5.3 10^{-2} mol L^{-1} $NaBrO_3$ + 2.7 10^{-4} mol L^{-1} EDTA-Na_2 Aqueous Reference Solution.	0.069
Solution obtained by digestion of Standard Reference Material Olive Leaves BCR-CRM 062	3.5
Solution obtained by digestion of Standard Reference Material Tomato Leaves NIST-SRM 1573a	3.7
Solutions obtained by digestion of laurel leaves Site A	3.2
Site B	3.1
Site C	No signal

[a] In the case of spectroscopic measurements, the limit of detection in the aqueous reference solution was 0.123 μg L^{-1}. Considering a sample weight exactly equal to 0.5 g (see section 6.1.2. "Sampling and Sample Preparation), the same limit of detection, calculated in μg kg^{-1} was 6.15.

At the experimental employed conditions, the linearity range for Ru(III) in the aqueous reference solutions is < LOD – 0.5 μg L^{-1}.

6.2.2. Quality Control and Quality Assessment

In order to confirm and verify the applicability of the analytical procedure, the method set up in aqueous reference solutions was applied to standard reference materials Olive Leaves BCR-CRM 062 and Tomato Leaves NIST-SRM 1573a. Trueness and precision were determined (Table 6).

Table 6. Trueness and precision of the analytical procedure. The determined values are the mean of 5 independent determinations ± confidence interval at 95 % confidence level. Concentrations expressed in μg g^{-1}

Olive Leaves BCR-CRM 062.						
	Voltammetry			*Spectroscopy*		
Certified Concentration [a]	Determined Concentration	*e* (%)	s_r (%)	Determined Concentration	*e* (%)	s_r (%)
7.5	7.8±0.5	+4.0	5.2	7.1±0.6	-5.3	5.5
Tomato Leaves NIST-SRM 1573a.						
	Voltammetry			*Spectroscopy*		
Certified Concentration	Determined Concentration	*e* (%)	s_r (%)	Determined Concentration	*e* (%)	s_r (%)
7.5	7.1±0.4	-5.3	5.3	8.0±0.7	+6.7	5.2

[a] The concentration listed in the certified value column has been added to the standard reference material at the beginning of the digestion step.

About 0.5 g of the standard reference material, accurately weighed, was mineralized using the procedure reported in section 6.1.2. "Sampling and Sample Preparation".

In the experimental employed conditions, precision as repeatability [26], expressed as relative standard deviation (s_r %) on five independent determinations, was satisfactory, being, in all cases, lower than 5%, while accuracy, expressed as relative error (e %) was generally lower than 7% (Table 6).

Trueness and precision data for the spectroscopic measurements are also reported in Table 6.

6.2.3. Practical Application

Once the procedure for the Ru(III) determination was set up, the method was applied to laurel leaves sampled in three sites differently influenced by vehicle traffic (see section 4, "Sampling Sites").

To prepare real samples for voltammetric and spectroscopic analyses, each vegetable sample was split into two aliquots; one was accurately washed many times using Milli-Q deionised water, the other one kept as such. Then all samples, washed and unwashed, were lyophilised, powdered, homogenised, dried at 80 °C for 24h and solubilised for the analyses as described above (see section 6.1.2 "Sampling and Sample Preparation").

Basing on these results, it is not possible to discriminate between the metal content fractions ascribed to the endogenous portion naturally present in the soil and the metal content due to environmental pollution. In fact, specific aspects relevant to this issue would require further surveys, which are beyond the scope of the present work.

Clearly, the difference between the concentrations between unwashed and washed samples can be reasonably ascribed to air pollution, which in the case of Ru(III) is totally due to the malfunction of the catalytic converters. This could entail an interesting use of vegetable matrices for bio-environmental monitoring, which, although strongly criticized by many researchers, in our opinion shows two important advantages: 1) it allows to monitor the pollution load in large areas and not only in individual points, and 2) it allows to verify the long-term trend of pollution itself.

The experimental results are reported in Table 7.

Table 7. Mean values of Ru(III) concentrations (μg kg^{-1}) relevant to laurel leaves sampled in three sites differently influenced by vehicle traffic (A > B > C, see section 4, "Sampling Sites"). The determined values are the mean of 5 independent determinations ± confidence interval at 95 % confidence level

Technique	A	B	C
Voltammetry	13.6 ± 0.9	5.5 ± 0.4	< LOD
Spectroscopy (ET-AAS)	12.9 ± 0.8	< LOD	< LOD

7. SUPERFICIAL WATERS: FRESH- AND SEA-WATERS

Also for these matrices the literature reports very few articles describing analytical methods for the determination of ruthenium in the surface waters. Among these, in addition to those that exclusively employ spectroscopic techniques [30-33], an important work Ciffroy et al. [34], concerning the probabilistic distribution coefficients of some isotopes in fresh-water including precisely the ruthenium, and two interesting works by Locatelli [9, 11] must be highlighted. The latter ones propose analytical procedures employing voltammetry as instrumental technique for the determination of ruthenium in surface water in the presence of osmium and iridium [9] and in the presence of osmium, copper and lead [11].

7.1. Determination of Ru(III) in Superficial Waters

As for the previous two matrices, the procedure here proposed turns out to be, with some also substantial modifications, the results of methods already partially present in literature and published by the same authors [9, 11].

7.1.1. Standard Reference Materials

Fresh Water NIST-SRM 1643d (from National Institute of Standards and Technology, Gaithersburg, MD, USA) and Sea Water BCR-CRM 403 (from Institute for Reference Materials and Measurements, European Commission, Joint Research Centre, Geel, Belgium) were employed as standard reference materials for optimizing and setting up the analytical procedure.

7.1.2. Sampling and Sample Preparation

Superficial water samples (fresh-, sites A and B, and sea-water, site C, see section 4 "Sampling Sites") were taken with a portable suction pump made of stainless steel and pyrex glass, neither of which would yield contamination with ruthenium to be determined. Model experiments exactly simulating the sampling procedure were performed with simulated fresh and sea water, to verify that the samples would not be contaminated by the sampling device. The ruthenium concentrations in these artificial samples were found to be lower than the relevant limits of detection.

Water samples were immediately filtered on the spot through 0.22 μm cellulose membranes and transferred into polyethylene bottles, previously soaked in 1:1 nitric acid for 48 h and rinsed many times with deionized water (Milli-Q).

The samples were cooled to 4 °C for transport, stored at this temperature and analysed within 72 h. Before voltammetric measurements the samples were kept at room temperature overnight.

7.1.3. Analytical Procedure for the Voltammetric Determination of Ruthenium(III) in Superficial Waters

10 mL sample aliquots of 0.35 mol L^{-1} acetate buffer pH 5.1 + 8.3 10^{-2} mol L^{-1} $NaBrO_3$ + 4.9 10^{-4} EDTA-Na_2 aqueous reference solution or of fresh- and sea-water containing 0.35 mol L^{-1} acetate buffer pH 5.1 + 8.3 10^{-2} mol L^{-1} $NaBrO_3$ + 4.9 10^{-4} EDTA-Na_2 were pipetted into the voltammetric cell and deaerated for 5 min by bubbling water-saturated pure nitrogen. The determination of Ru(III) was carried out by Square Wave Catalytic Voltammetry (SWCV) using HMDE electrode.

The voltammetric experimental conditions are reported in Table 8.

Table 8. Instrumental parameters for the determination of Ru(III) by Square Wave Catalytic Voltammetry (SWCV) [a]. Supporting electrolyte: 0.35 mol L^{-1} acetate buffer pH 5.1 + 8.3 10^{-2} mol L^{-1} $NaBrO_3$ + 4.9 10^{-4} mol L^{-1} EDTA-Na_2

E_i	-0.075
E_d	-0.075
E_f	-0.550
t_d	340
t_r	10
dE/dt	100
ΔE	50
τ	0.010
ν	0.100
η	10
u	600

[a]E_i: initial potential (V/Ag, AgCl, $Cl^-_{satd.}$); E_d: deposition potential (V/Ag, AgCl, $Cl^-_{satd.}$); E_f: final potential (V/Ag, AgCl, $Cl^-_{satd.}$); t_d: electrodeposition time (s); t_r: delay time before the potential sweep (s); dE/dt: potential scan rate (mV/s); ΔE: superposed potential amplitude (mV); τ: sampling time (s); υ: wave period (s); η: wave increment (mV); u: stirring rate (r.p.m.).

The spectroscopic experimental conditions are reported in Section 5.1.3.

7.1.4. Supporting Electrolyte and Peak Potentials

0.35 mol L^{-1} acetate buffer pH 5.1 + 8.3 10^{-2} mol L^{-1} $NaBrO_3$ + 4.9 10^{-4} EDTA-Na_2 was employed as supporting electrolyte.

Also in this case the presence of EDTA-Na_2 is required for the reasons previously given (see Section 5.1.3)

In these experimental conditions, Ru(III) shows the following peak potentials E_p (V/ Ag|AgCl|$Cl^-_{satd.}$):

0.35 mol L^{-1} acetate buffer pH 5.1 + 8.3 10^{-2} mol L^{-1} $NaBrO_3$ + 4.9 10^{-4} mol L^{-1} EDTA-Na_2 Aqueous Reference Solutions	-0.311±0.015
Sea Water BCR-CRM 403 Standard Reference Material	-0.323±0.010
Fresh Water NIST-SRM 1643d Standard Reference Material	-0.296±0.010
Fresh Water Site A	-0.343±0.015
Fresh Water Site B	-0.335±0.010
Sea Water Site C	No signal

The determined values are the mean of 5 independent determinations ± confidence interval at 95 % confidence level.

7.2. Results and Discussion

In this section, in a synthetic way, the fundamental parameters that characterize a correct analytical procedure — limits of detection, linearity range, accuracy and precision — are reported.

7.2.1. Limits of Detection and Linearity Range

In the aqueous reference solution, in Fresh Water NIST-SRM 1643d and in Sea Water BCR-CRM 403 standard reference materials, and in real samples, the limits of detection (LOD) (Table 9) for both techniques were calculated as described in section 5.2.1.

Table 9. Limits of detection (LOD) [a] ($\mu g\ L^{-1}$) of Ru(III) determined in the aqueous reference solutions, in Fresh Water NIST-SRM 1643 d and in Sea Water BCR-CRM 403 standard reference materials, and in real samples. The determined values are the mean of 5 independent determinations ± confidence interval at 95 % confidence level

0.35 mol L^{-1} acetate buffer pH 5.1 + 8.3 10^{-2} mol L^{-1} $NaBrO_3$ + 4.9 10^{-4} mol L^{-1} EDTA-Na_2 Aqueous Reference Solution	0.015
Fresh Water NIST-SRM 1643 d	0.021
Sea Water BCR-CRM 403	0.023
Fresh Water Site A	0.027
Fresh Water Site B	0.025
Sea Water Site C	No signal

[a]In the case of spectroscopic measurements, the limit of detection in the aqueous reference solution was: 0.055 $\mu g\ L^{-1}$.

In the employed experimental conditions, the linearity range for Ru(III) in the aqueous reference solutions is < LOD – 0.35 $\mu g\ L^{-1}$.

7.2.2. Quality Control and Quality Assessment

In order to confirm and verify the applicability of the analytical procedure, the method set up in aqueous reference solutions was applied to standard reference materials Fresh Water NIST-SRM 1643d and Sea Water BCR-CRM 403, and its trueness and precision were determined (Table 10).

Table 10. Trueness and precision of the analytical procedure. The determined values are the mean of 5 independent determinations ± confidence interval at 95 % confodence level. Concentrations expressed in $\mu g\ L^{-1}$. In all cases the spiked-sample concentration was 0.250 $\mu g\ L^{-1}$

Fresh Water NIST-SRM 1643d					
Voltammetry			*Spectroscopy*		
Determined Concentration	*e* (%)	s_r (%)	Determined Concentration	*e* (%)	s_r (%)
0.263±0.017	+5.2	5.1	0.269±0.021	+7.6	5.3
Sea Water BCR-CRM 403					
Voltammetry			*Spectroscopy*		
Determined Concentration	*e* (%)	s_r (%)	Determined Concentration	*e* (%)	s_r (%)
0.234±0.019	-6.4	5.2	0.267±0.023	+6.8	5.5

However it is important to highlight that, to test trueness and precision of the analytical procedure, the metal concentration listed in Table 10 has been spiked in the above Reference

Materials. This may seem an anomalous procedure, but, in our opinion, it resulted to be the only way, considering that Standard Water (fresh and sea water) Reference Materials containing certified concentrations of Ru(III) were not available, even if, under these conditions, the trueness and precision data may be doubtful and prudentially considered and/or discussed.

In the employed experimental conditions, precision as repeatability [26], expressed as relative standard deviation (s_r %) on five independent determinations, was satisfactory, being, in all cases, lower than 6%, while accuracy, expressed as relative error (e %) was generally lower than 8% (Table 10).

Trueness and precision results for the spectroscopic measurements are also reported in Table 10.

7.2.3. Practical Application

Once the procedure for the Ru(III) determination was set up, the method was applied to superficial waters sampled in three sites differently influenced by vehicle traffic (see section 4, "Sampling Sites").

The experimental results are reported in Table 11.

Table 11. Mean values of Ru(III) concentrations (μg L^{-1}) relevant to superficial waters sampled in three sites differently influenced by vehicle traffic (A > B > C, see section 4 "Sampling Sites"). The determined values are the mean of 5 independent determinations ± confidence interval at 95 % probability level

Technique	A	B	C
Voltammetry	0.096 ± 0.007	0.068 ± 0.005	< LOD
Spectroscopy (ET-AAS)	0.101 ± 0.006	0.063 ± 0.006	< LOD

8. Mussels and Clams

To date, the literature does not report works on the determination of ruthenium in these matrices. Considering the fact that mussels and clams are, at least in our opinion, exceptional bio-monitors being filtering organisms — an adult organism is able to filter up to 5 L h^{-1} depending on weight —, in our laboratories a research line is active which addressed to the determination of PGMs in these matrices linked to the vehicular traffic pollution.

The preliminary results relevant to ruthenium (III) are reported in the present work.

8.1. Determination of Ru(III) in Mussels and Clams

8.1.1. Standard Reference Materials

Mussel Tissue BCR-CRM 278 (from Institute for Reference Materials and Measurements, European Commission, Joint Research Centre, Geel, Belgium) and Oyster Tissue NIST-SRM 1566a (from National Institute of Standards and Technology, Gaithersburg, MD, USA) were employed as standard reference materials for optimizing and setting up the analytical procedure.

8.1.2. Sampling and Sample Preparation

About 8 kg of *Mytilus Galloprovincialis* and of *Tapes Philippinarum* were collected in two sites (see section 4 "Sampling Sites"), the former within the mouth of the Po river (Goro Bay, Italy) and the latter at open Adriatic Sea, taken to the laboratory and prepared for analyses. They were opened with a plastic appliance and the organisms were carefully extracted and placed in polyethylene containers, previously treated with suprapure HNO_3 diluted in 1:1 proportion with water and followed by repeated rinsing for 48 h with Milli-Q water in order to avoid any contamination. The samples were frozen for and then lyophilised for 30 h. After that treatment, the samples were homogenized thoroughly in an agate mortar.

The sample preparation for Mussel Tissue BCR-CRM 278, Oyster Tissue NIST-SRM 1566a and for real samples of mussels and clams was the following: approximately 0.5-1.0 g, accurately weighed, was placed in a platinum crucible and dissolved in 5 mL 69 $\%_{w/w}$ HNO_3 + 3 mL 37 $\%_{w/w}$ HCl + 7 mL 98$\%_{w/w}$ H_2SO_4 at 130-150 °C. The mixture was evaporated to dryness and, after cooling, soluble salts were dissolved in 25 mL 0.15 mol L^{-1} dibasic ammonium citrate buffer pH 5.5 + 6.9 10^{-2} mol L^{-1} $NaBrO_3$ + 3.5 10^{-4} mol L^{-1} EDTA-Na_2. The so obtained solutions were then diluted, if necessary, before spectroscopic measurements.

8.1.3. Analytical Procedure for the Voltammetric Determination of Ruthenium(III) in Mussels and Clams

10 mL sample aliquots in 0.15 mol L^{-1} dibasic ammonium citrate buffer pH 5.5 + 6.9 10^{-2} mol L^{-1} $NaBrO_3$ + 3.5 10^{-4} mol L^{-1} EDTA-Na_2 aqueous reference solution or of solutions obtained in the mineralization step of the standard reference material and of real samples, were pipetted into the voltammetric cell and deaerated for 5 min by bubbling water-saturated pure nitrogen. The Ru(III) determination was carried out by Square Wave Catalytic Voltammetry (SWCV) using HMDE electrode.

The voltammetric experimental conditions were reported in Table 12.

Table 12. Instrumental parameters for the determination of Ru(III) by Square Wave Catalytic Voltammetry (SWCV) [a]. Supporting electrolyte: 0.15 mol L^{-1} dibasic ammonium citrate buffer pH 5.5 + 6.9 10^{-2} mol L^{-1} $NaBrO_3$ + 3.5 10^{-4} mol L^{-1} EDTA-Na_2

E_i	-0.075
E_d	-0.075
E_f	-0.550
t_d	570
t_r	10
dE/dt	100
ΔE	50
τ	0.010
ν	0.100
η	10
u	600

[a] E_i: initial potential (V/Ag, AgCl, $Cl^-_{satd.}$); E_d: deposition potential (V/Ag, AgCl, $Cl^-_{satd.}$); E_f: final potential (V/Ag, AgCl, $Cl^-_{satd.}$); t_d: electrodeposition time (s); t_r: delay time before the potential sweep (s); dE/dt: potential scan rate (mV/s); ΔE: superposed potential amplitude (mV); τ: sampling time (s); υ: wave period (s); η: wave increment (mV); u: stirring rate (r.p.m.).

The spectroscopic experimental conditions are reported in Section 5.1.3.

8.1.4. Supporting Electrolyte and Peak Potentials

0.15 mol L^{-1} dibasic ammonium citrate buffer pH 5.5 + 6.9 10^{-2} mol L^{-1} $NaBrO_3$ + 3.5 10^{-4} mol L^{-1} EDTA-Na_2 was employed as supporting electrolyte.

Also in this case the presence of EDTA-Na_2 is required for the previously given reasons (see Section 5.1.3). In these experimental conditions, Ru(III) shows the following peak potentials E_p (V/ Ag | AgCl | $Cl^-_{satd.}$):

The determined values are the mean of 5 independent determinations ± confidence interval at 95 % confidence level.

0.15 mol L^{-1} dibasic ammonium citrate buffer pH 5.5 + 6.9 10^{-2} mol L^{-1} $NaBrO_3$ + 3.5 10^{-4} mol L^{-1} EDTA-Na_2 Aqueous Reference Solutions	-0.396±0.015
Mussel Tissue BCR-CRM 278 Standard Reference Material	-0.415±0.010
Oyster Tissue NIST-SRM 1566a Standard Reference Material	-0.403±0.010
Mussels Site A	-0.423±0.015
Mussels Site B	No signal
Clams Site A	-0.411±0.015
Clams Site B	No signal

8.2. Results and Discussion

In this section the fundamental parameters that characterize a correct analytical procedure — limits of detection, linearity range, trueness and precision — are synthetically reported.

8.2.1. Limits of Detection and Linearity Range

In the aqueous reference solution, in Mussel Tissue BCR-CRM 278 and Oyster Tissue NIST-SRM 1566a standard reference materials, and in real samples, the limits of detection (LOD) (Table 13) for both techniques were calculated as described in section 5.2.1.

Table 13. Limits of detection (LOD) [a] of Ru(III) determined in the aqueous reference solution (ng L^{-1}), in the solutions obtained by digestion of Mussel Tissue BCR-CRM 278 and Oyster Tissue NIST-SRM 1566a standard reference materials, and in the solutions obtained by digestion of real samples (calculated in ng L^{-1} and expressed in μg kg^{-1}). The determined values are the mean of 5 independent determinations ± confidence interval at 95 % confidence level

0.15 mol L^{-1} dibasic ammonium citrate buffer pH 5.5 + 6.9 10^{-2} mol L^{-1} $NaBrO_3$ + 3.5 10^{-4} mol L^{-1} EDTA-Na_2 Aqueous Reference Solution	6.7
Mussel Tissue BCR-CRM 278	0.23
Oyster Tissue NIST-SRM 1566a	0.31
Mussels Site A	0.21
Mussels Site B	No signal
Clams Site A	0.25
Clams Site B	No signal

[a]In the case of spectroscopic measurements, the limit of detection in the aqueous reference solution was: 0.059 μg L^{-1}. Considering a sample weight exactly equal to 0.5 g (see section 8.1.2. "Sampling and Sample Preparation), the same limit of detection, calculated in μg kg^{-1} was 1.94.

At the experimental conditions employed, the linearity range for Ru(III) in the aqueous reference solutions is <LOD – 0.2 μg L^{-1}.

8.2.2. Quality Control and Quality Assessment

The method set up in aqueous reference solutions was applied to Mussel Tissue BCR-CRM 278 and Oyster Tissue NIST-SRM 1566a standard reference materials in order to confirm and verify the applicability of the analytical procedure. Trueness and precision were determined (Table 14).

However it is important to highlight that, to test trueness and precision of the analytical procedure, the metal concentrations listed in Table 14 have been spiked in the above Reference Materials. As previously emphasized, this procedure may appear anomalous, but, in our opinion, it resulted to be the only way, considering that Standard Water (fresh and sea water) Reference Materials containing certified concentrations of Ru(III) were not available. However, under these conditions, the trueness and precision results may be doubtful and prudentially considered and/or discussed.

At the experimental conditions employed, precision as repeatability [26], expressed as relative standard deviation (s_r %) on five independent determinations, was satisfactory, being, in all cases, lower than 6%, while accuracy, expressed as relative error (e %) was generally lower than 8% (Table 14).

Trueness and precision results for the spectroscopic measurements are also reported in Table 14.

Table 14. Trueness and precision of the analytical procedure. The determined values are the mean of 5 independent determinations ± confidence interval at 95 % confidence level. Concentrations expressed in μg kg^{-1}. In all cases the spiked-sample concentration was 77.1 μg kg^{-1}

Mussel Tissue BCR-CRM 278					
Voltammetry			*Spectroscopy*		
Determined Concentration	e (%)	s_r (%)	Determined Concentration	e (%)	s_r (%)
81.5±5.3	+5.7	5.3	82.1±5.9	+6.5	5.5
Oyster Tissue NIST-SRM 1566a					
Voltammetry			*Spectroscopy*		
Determined Concentration	e (%)	s_r (%)	Determined Concentration	e (%)	s_r (%)
72.0±5.8	-6.6	5.6	82.3±6.0	+6.7	5.7

8.2.3. Practical Application

Once the procedure for the Ru(III) determination was set up, the method was applied to mussels and clams sampled in two sites differently influenced by vehicle traffic (see section 4, "Sampling Sites").

The experimental results relevant to both matrices and to both techniques are reported in Table 15.

Table 15. Mean values of Ru(III) concentrations (μg kg^{-1}) relevant to mussels and clams sampled in two sites differently influenced by vehicle traffic (A > B, see section 4 "Sampling Sites"). The determined values are the mean of 5 independent determinations ± confidence interval at 95 % confidence level

Technique	Kind of matrix	A	B
Voltammetry	Mussels	2.77 ± 0.19	< LOD
	Clams	0.49 ± 0.03	< LOD
Spectroscopy (ET-AAS)	Mussels	2.96 ± 0.21	< LOD
	Clams	< LOD	< LOD

9. Soils/Sediments

Soils/Sediments are certainly the most investigated matrices about their PGMs content, which is closely linked to vehicular traffic and to the technological evolution of the catalytic converters, as reported in interesting articles [25, 29, 35-36]. Even for such a matrix, the most used techniques are the spectroscopic ones, with particular reference to the inductively coupled plasma mass spectrometry (ICP-MS) [23,37-41] and to the isotope dilution inductively coupled plasma mass spectrometry (ID-ICP-MS) [25, 35-36, 42-43]. For the Ru(III) determination in soils, the inductively coupled plasma is also used either in atomic emission spectrometry (ICP-AES) [29] and optical emission spectrometry (ICP-OES) [44], while, rarely and in not recent years, also atomic absorption spectroscopy (AAS) [45,46] has been employed. Finally, works using methods which are alternative to spectroscopy to quantify the ruthenium in soils and sediments are also interesting. For instance, instrumental neutron activation analysis (INAA) [47-49] and the ion-exchange resins [50] have been employed. Works using voltammetric techniques for the determination of ruthenium in soils and sediments are absolutely absent in the literature. For this reason, the present section of the work reports and discusses, for the first time, the preliminary data of an analytical procedure for the voltammetric determination of Ru (III) in soils and sediments.

9.1. Determination of Ru(III) in Soils/Sediments

9.1.1. Standard Reference Materials

Montana Soil Moderately Elevated Traces NIST-SRM 2711 (from National Institute of Standards and Technology, Gaithersburg, MD, USA) and Estuarine Sediment BCR-CRM 277 (from Institute for Reference Materials and Measurements, European Commission, Joint Research Centre, Geel, Belgium) were employed as standard reference materials for optimizing and setting up the analytical procedure.

9.1.2. Sampling and Sample Preparation

Soils and sediments samples (sites A and B: soils classified as vertisol according to the United States Department of Agriculture [51]; site C: sedimentary texture shows that clay and silt are the predominant size fraction, *i.e.,* overall higher than 70 % in all cases — the remaining part is made of sand —, see section 4 "Sampling Sites") were collected by a plexiglas device. Single carrots of superficial soils or sediment (height 10 cm) were drawn out and stored in polyethylene bottles previously washed with a diluted 1:1 suprapure HNO_3 solution for 48 h. The samples, dried at 60 °C for 48 h, were sieved through a 40 mesh sieve to eliminate coarse material, then through another 150 mesh sieve, and lastly powdered by means of a corundum ball mill. Soils and sediments were then mineralised following a common procedure: approximately 0.5 g of sample, accurately weighed in a platinum crucible was dissolved by adding 4 mL 69 $\%_{w/w}$ HNO_3 + 5 mL 37 $\%_{w/w}$ HCl at 130-150 °C. The mixture was evaporated to dryness and, after cooling, soluble salts were dissolved in 25 mL 0.23 mol L^{-1} dibasic ammonium citrate buffer pH 5.9 + 9.6 10^{-2} mol L^{-1} $NaBrO_3$ + 5.7 10^{-4} mol L^{-1} EDTA-Na_2. The obtained solutions were then diluted, if necessary, before spectroscopic measurements. For all samples collected in the sites A, B, C, an additional mineralization was also carried out, through an acidic mixture including HF acid to obtain the complete disgregation of the samples (4 mL mL 69 $\%_{w/w}$ HNO_3 + 5 mL 37 $\%_{w/w}$ HCl + 5 mL 48 $\%_{w/w}$ HF at 130-150 °C). This to verify whether the Ru (III) was present as integral part itself of the matrix soil and sediment.

The data relevant to the content of Ru (III) in the various samples, in the presence and in the absence of HF, shows no significant differences at a 95 % confidence level. This indicates that the presence of Ru (III) in soils/sediments is not endogenous of the matrix itself, but it is exclusively due to environmental pollution reasons.

9.1.3. Analytical Procedure for the Voltammetric Determination of Ruthenium(III) in Soils/Sediments

10 mL sample aliquots of 0.23 mol L^{-1} dibasic ammonium citrate buffer pH 5.9 + 9.6 10^{-2} mol L^{-1} $NaBrO_3$ + 5.7 10^{-4} mol L^{-1} EDTA-Na_2 aqueous reference solution or of solutions obtained in the mineralization step of the standard reference material and of real samples, were pipetted into the voltammetric cell and deaerated for 5 min by bubbling water-saturated pure nitrogen.

Table 16. Instrumental parameters for the determination of Ru(III) by Square Wave Catalytic Voltammetry (SWCV) [a]. Supporting electrolyte: 0.23 mol L^{-1} dibasic ammonium citrate buffer pH 5.9 + 9.6 10^{-2} mol L^{-1} $NaBrO_3$ + 5.7 10^{-4} mol L^{-1} EDTA-Na_2

E_i	-0.200
E_d	-0.200
E_f	-0.700
t_d	390
t_r	10
dE/dt	100
ΔE	50
τ	0.010
ν	0.100
η	10
u	600

[a] E_i: initial potential (V/Ag, AgCl, $Cl^-_{satd.}$); E_d: deposition potential (V/Ag, AgCl, $Cl^-_{satd.}$); E_f: final potential (V/Ag, AgCl, $Cl^-_{satd.}$); t_d: electrodeposition time (s); t_r: delay time before the potential sweep (s); dE/dt: potential scan rate (mV/s); ΔE: superposed potential amplitude (mV); τ: sampling time (s); υ: wave period (s); η: wave increment (mV); u: stirring rate (r.p.m.).

The Ru(III) determination was carried out by Square Wave Catalytic Voltammetry (SWCV) using HMDE electrode.

The voltammetric experimental conditions were reported in Table 16.

The spectroscopic experimental conditions are reported in Section 5.1.3.

9.1.4. Supporting Electrolyte and Peak Potentials

0.23 mol L^{-1} dibasic ammonium citrate buffer pH 5.9 + 9.6 10^{-2} mol L^{-1} $NaBrO_3$ + 5.7 10^{-4} mol L^{-1} EDTA-Na_2 was employed as supporting electrolyte.

Also in this case the presence of EDTA-Na_2 is required for the reasons previously given (see Section 5.1.3).

In these experimental conditions, Ru(III) shows the following peak potentials E_p (V/ Ag | AgCl | $Cl^-_{satd.}$):

0.23 mol L^{-1} dibasic ammonium citrate buffer pH 5.9 + 9.6 10^{-2} mol L^{-1} $NaBrO_3$ + 5.7 10^{-4} mol L^{-1} EDTA-Na_2 Aqueous Reference Solutions	-0.469±0.010
Montana Soil Moderately Elevated Traces NIST-SRM 2711 Standard Reference Material	-0.455±0.010
Estuarine Sediment BCR-CRM 277 Standard Reference Material	-0.477±0.015
Soil Site A	-0.485±0.010
Soil Site B	-0.471±0.015
Sediment Site C	No signal

The determined values are the mean of 5 independent determinations ± confidence interval at 95 % confidence level.

9.2. Results and Discussion

In this section, the fundamental parameters characterizing a correct analytical procedure — limits of detection, linearity range, trueness and precision — are synthetically reported.

9.2.1. Limits of Detection and Linearity Range

In the aqueous reference solution, in Montana Soil Moderately Elevated Traces NIST-SRM 2711 and Estuarine Sediment BCR-CRM 277 standard reference materials, and in real samples, the limits of detection (LOD) (Table 17) for both techniques were calculated as described in section 5.2.1.

At the employed experimental conditions, the linearity range for Ru(III) in the aqueous reference solutions is <LOD – 0.3 μg L^{-1}.

9.2.2. Quality Control and Quality Assessment

The method set up in aqueous reference solutions was applied to Montana Soil Moderately Elevated Traces NIST-SRM 2711 and Estuarine Sediment BCR-CRM 277 standard reference materials in order to confirm and verify the applicability of the analytical procedure. Trueness and precision were determined (Table 18).

Table 17. Limits of detection (LOD) [a] of Ru(III) determined in the aqueous reference solution (μg L^{-1}), in the solutions obtained by digestion of Montana Soil Moderately Elevated Traces NIST-SRM 2711 and Estuarine Sediment BCR-CRM 277 standard reference materials and in the solutions obtained by digestion of real samples (calculated in μg L^{-1} and expressed in μg kg^{-1}). The determined values are the mean of 5 independent determinations ± confidence interval at 95 % confidence level

0.23 mol L^{-1} dibasic ammonium citrate buffer pH 5.9 + 9.6 10^{-2} mol L^{-1} $NaBrO_3$ + 5.7 10^{-4} mol L^{-1} EDTA-Na_2 Aqueous Reference Solution	0.027
Montana Soil Moderately Elevated Traces NIST-SRM 2711	3.25
Estuarine Sediment BCR-CRM 277	4.11
Soil Site A	3.73
Soil Site B	3.97
Sediment Site C	No signal

[a]In the case of spectroscopic measurements, the limit of detection in the aqueous reference solution was: 0.063 μg L^{-1}. Considering a sample weight exactly equal to 0.5 g (see section 9.1.2 "Sampling and Sample Preparation"), the same limits of detection, calculated in μg kg^{-1}, was 7.58.

However, it is important to highlight that, to test trueness and precision of the analytical procedure, the metal concentrations listed in Table 18 have been spiked in the above Reference Materials. As previously emphasized, this procedure may appear anomalous; in fact, in our opinion, it resulted to be the only way, considering that, for soils and sediments, standard reference materials containing certified concentrations of Ru(III) were not available. Nonetheless, under these conditions, the trueness and precision resultts may be doubtful and prudentially considered and/or discussed.

At the employed experimental conditions, precision as repeatability [26], expressed as relative standard deviation (s_r %) on five independent determinations, was satisfactory, being, in all cases, lower than 6%, while trueness, expressed as relative error (e %) was generally lower than 8% (Table 18).

Trueness and precision results for the spectroscopic measurements are also reported in Table 18.

Table 18. Trueness and precision of the analytical procedure. The determined values are the mean of 5 independent determinations ± confidence interval at 95 % confidence level. Concentrations expressed in μg kg^{-1}. In all cases the spiked-sample concentration was 69.7 μg kg^{-1}

Montana Soil Moderately Elevated Traces NIST-SRM 2711					
Voltammetry			*Spectroscopy*		
Determined Concentration	e (%)	s_r (%)	Determined Concentration	e (%)	s_r (%)
73.5±4.7	+5.5	5.2	65.1±5.0	-6.6	5.6
Estuarine Sediment BCR-CRM 277					
Voltammetry			*Spectroscopy*		
Determined Concentration	e (%)	s_r (%)	Determined Concentration	e (%)	s_r (%)
65.5±4.9	-6.0	5.3	64.9±5.1	+6.9	5.9

9.2.3. Practical Application

Once the procedure for the Ru(III) determination was set up, the method was applied to soils and sediments sampled in three sites differently influenced by vehicle traffic (see section 4, "Sampling Sites").

The experimental results are reported in Table 19.

Table 19. Mean values of Ru(III) concentrations (μg kg^{-1}) relevant to soils and sediments sampled in three sites differently influenced by vehicle traffic (A > B > C, see section 4, "Sampling Sites"). The determined values are the mean of 5 independent determinations ± confidence interval at 95 % confidence level

Technique	A	B	C
Voltammetry	16.1 ± 0.9	10.3 ± 0.8	< LOD
Spectroscopy (ET-AAS)	15.3 ± 1.0	10.9 ± 0.7	< LOD

CONCLUSION AND FUTURE TRENDS

This paper reports innovative proposals of voltammetric methods, and their comparison with spectroscopic techniques for the determination of Ru (III) in environmental matrices that directly affect the man and his health. While some procedures relevant to particulate matter, vegetables and superficial waters are already present in the literature [9, 11, 12, 15], other procedures, relevant to mussels, clams and soils / sediments, are discussed here for the first time.

A short comment about the critical comparison between the voltammetric and spectroscopic methods was necessary. Voltammetry shows to be certainly a valid analytical technique, simple and suitable for metal determinations in complex matrices. In fact, it shows good precision and trueness (that is, good accuracy) and selectivity; it also presents a satisfactory high sensitivity, allowing to obtain very low limits of detection. Moreover, such a technique may be certainly a good alternative to spectroscopic techniques, which, in the case of the determination of metals at very low concentration in complex matrices, needs too expensive equipment like ICP or better ICP/MS, since ET-AAS sometimes shows to have inadequate limits of detection. This for example the case of site B for airborne particulate matter and vegetables, and site A for clams (see sections 5.2.3, 6.2.3 and 8.2.3 "Practical Application"); in these cases, determination is possible using catalytic voltammetry, impossible, i.e., < LOD, if ET-AAS is employed.

One final comment: It should be taken into responsible consideration that catalytic converters are certainly a source of a high and extremely dangerous environmental pollution. In fact, the catalytic converters are built to have excellent performance and a long operating life if used in long-distance. In the stop-and-go conditions, in which cars are often or almost always employed, the catalytic converters deteriorate within a period of 2-3 thousand km. The so deteriorated catalytic converters inevitably enter the atmosphere, and then the environment large amounts of the catalysts contained in them.

So, regardless of the fact that a catalytic converter contains catalysts of the first generation — platinum, palladium, rhodium [3-8] — or of second generation — ruthenium but also in some cases osmium and iridium [9-15] —, the fundamental experimental data concerns the fact that in the environment, in all its components (particulate matter, vegetables, superficial waters, marine organisms, soils/sediments) a very fast increase of the concentration of these metals is detected. Unfortunately, the problem is not easy to solve.

At least to date, a suggestion/request must be made to the international organizations responsible to establish by law the limits of maximum permissible concentration of metals for the human health. These organizations should definitely consider this issue and operate accordingly, by establishing rigorous legal limits for all PGMs and for all environmental matrices.

References

[1] E. Merian, *Metals and Their Compounds in the Environment – Occurrence, Analysis and Biological Relevance* (VCH, Weinheim, 1991), ch. II.24, pp. 1135-1151.

[2] C. Locatelli, Voltammetric analysis of trace levels of platinum group metals – principles and applications. *Electroanalysis* 19(21) (2007) 2167-2175.

[3] C. Locatelli, Platinum, rhodium, palladium and lead: elements linked to vehicle emissions. Their simultaneous voltammetric determination in superficial water. *Electroanalysis* 17(2) (2005) 140-147.

[4] C. Locatelli, D. Melucci, G. Torsi, Determination of platinum-group metals and lead in vegetable environmental bio-monitors by voltammetric and spectroscopic techniques: critical comparison. *Anal. Bioanal. Chem.* 382 (2005) 1567-1573.

[5] C. Locatelli, Simultaneous square wave stripping voltammetric determination of platinum group metals (PGMs) and lead at trace and ultratrace concentration level. Application to surface water. *Anal. Chim. Acta* 557 (2006) 70-77.

[6] C. Locatelli, Possible interference in the sequential voltammetric determination at trace and ultratrace concentration level of platinum group metals (PGMs) and lead. Application to environmental matrices. *Electrochim. Acta* 52 (2006) 614-622.

[7] C. Locatelli, Voltammetric peak area as instrumental datum. A possibility to improve the determination at ultratrace level concentration of platinum group metals (PGMs) and lead. Application to particulate matter. *Electroanalysis* 19(4) (2007) 445-452.

[8] C. Locatelli, Platinum(II), palladium(II), rhodium (III) and lead(II) voltammetric determination in sites differently influenced by vehicle traffic. *Ann. Chim.* (Rome) 97 (2007) 373-384.

[9] C. Locatelli, Sequential voltammetric determination of ultratrace osmium, ruthenium and iridium Application to superficial water. Electroanalysis 23 (2011) 1329-1336.

[10] C. Locatelli, Catalytic-adsorptive stripping voltammetric determination of ultratrace iridium(III). Application to fresh- and sea-water. *Talanta* 85 (2011) 546-550.

[11] C. Locatelli, Simultaneous determination of osmium, ruthenium, copper and lead by electrocatalytic voltammetry. Application to superficial waters. *Microchem. J.* 102 (2012) 54-60.

[12] C. Locatelli, Ultratrace osmium, ruthenium and lead in airborne particulate matter: peak area as instrumental datum to improve their simultaneous voltammetric determination. *Electroanalysis* 24 (2012) 2273-2282.

[13] C. Locatelli, Iridium and lead as vehicle emission pollutants: their sequential voltammetric determination in vegetable environmental bio-monitors. *Microchem. J.* 106 (2013) 282-288.

[14] C. Locatelli, Use of peak area instrumental datum as possibility to improve the analytical sensitivity in the sequential voltammetric determination of ultra-trace iridium and lead in vehicle emission particulate matter. *Microchem. J.* 110 (2013) 99-106 (2013).

[15] C. Locatelli, Square wave catalytic adsorptive voltammetric determination of osmium, ruthenium and lead in vegetable environmental bio-monitors. *J. Environ. Anal. Chem.* 94(3) (2014) 277-290.

[16] B. Welz, M. Sperling, *Atomic Absorption Spectrometry*, 3rd Edition, Wiley VCH, Weinheim 1999.

[17] C.R.M. Rao, G.S. Reddi, Platinum group metals (PGM); occurrence, use and recent trends in their determination. *Trends Anal. Chem.* 19(9) 2000 565-586.

[18] M. Balcerzak, Methods for the determination of platinum group elements in environmental and biological materials: a review. *Crit. Rev. Anal. Chem.* 41 (2011) 214-235.

[19] N.S. Mokgalaka, R.I. McCrindle, B.M. Botha, L. Marjanovic, Internal standard method for the determination of Au and some platinum group metals using inductively coupled plasma optical emission spectrometry. *S. Afr. J. Chem.* 55 (2002) 72-86.

[20] G. Rampazzo, M. Masiol, F. Visin, E. Rampado, B. Pavoni. Geochemical characterization of PM10 emitted by glass factories in Murano, Venice (Italy). *Chemosfere* 71 (2008) 2068-2075.

[21] A. Arruti, I. Fernandez-Olmo, A. Irabien. Document impact of the global economic crisis on metal levels in particulate matter (PM) at an urban area in the Cantabria Region (Northern Spain). *Environ. Pollut.* 159(5) (2011) 1129-1135.

[22] R. Komendova-Vlasankova, L. Sommer. Separation and preconcentration of platinum group metals and gold on modified silica and XAD sorbents in the presence of cationic surfactants for their determination by ICP-AES. *Collect. Czech. Chem. C.* 67(4) (2002 454-470.

[23] M.T. Jackson, H.M. Prichard, J. Sampson. Platinum-group elements in sewage sludge and incinerator ash in the United Kingdom: assessment of PGE source and mobility in cities. *Sci. Total Environ.* 408(6) (2010) 1276-1285.

[24] J.C. Ely, C.R. Neal, C.F. Kulpa, M.A. Schneegurt, J.A. Seidler, J.C. Jain. Implications of platinum-group element accumulation along U.S. roads from catalytic-converter attrition. *Environ. Sci. Technol.* 35 (2001) 3816-3822.

[25] M. Muller, K.G. Heumann. Isotope dilution inductively coupled plasma quadrupole mass spectrometry in connection with a chromatographic separation for ultra trace determinations of platinum group elements (Pt, Pd, Ru, Ir) in environmental samples. *Fresenius J. Anal. Chem.* 368 (2000) 109-115.

[26] J.C. Miller, J.N. Miller, *Statistics and Chemometrics for Analytical Chemistry*, 6th Edition, Pearson Education Ltd. Publ., Ashford Colour Press Ltd., Gosport, U.K., 2010.

[27] International Union of Pure and Applied Chemistry - Analytical Chemistry Division, Nomenclature, symbols, units and their usage in the spectrochemical analysis-II. Data interpretation, *Spectrochim. Acta B* 33 (1978) 241-245.

[28] B.J. Perry, R.R. Barefoot, J.C. Van Loon. Inductively coupled mass spectrometry for the determination of platinum group elements and gold. *Trends Anal. Chem.* 14(8) (1995) 388-397.

[29] R. Djingova, P. Kovaceva, G. Wagner, B. Markert. Distribution of platinum group elements and other traffic related elements among different plants along some highways in Germany. *Sci. Total Environ.* 308(1-3) (2003) 235-246.

[30] G.I. Bekov, V.S. Letokhov, V.N. Radaev, G.N. Baturin, A.S. Egorov, A.N. Kursky, V.A. Narseyev. Ruthenium in the ocean. *Nature* 312(5996) (1984) 748-750.

[31] H. Minamisawa, H. Kuroki, N. Arai, T. Okutani. Coprecipitation of ruthenium with chitosan and its determination by graphite furnace atomic absorption spectrometry. *Anal. Chim. Acta* 398(2-3) (1999) 289-296.

[32] A.P. Kumar, P.R. Reddy, V.K. Reddy, Y.I. Lee. Document simple and simultaneous method for determination of palladium(II) and ruthenium(III) using second-order-derivative spectrophotometry. *Anal. Lett.* 42(1) (2009) 84-93.

[33] B. Godlewska-Zylkiewicz, E. Zambrzycka, B. Lesniewska, A.Z. Wilczewska. Separation of ruthenium from environmental samples on polymeric sorbent based on imprinted Ru(III)-allyl acetoacetate complex. *Talanta* 89 (2012) 352-359.

[34] P. Ciffroy, G. Durrie, J.-M. Garnier. Probabilistic distribution coefficients (Kds) in freshwater for radioisotopes of Ag, Am, Ba, Be, Ce, Co, Cs, Ir, Mn, Pu, Ra, Ru, Sb, Sr and Th – Implications for uncertainty analysis of models simulating the transport of radionuclides in rivers. *J. Environ. Radioactiv.* 100(9) (2009) 785-794.

[35] S. Rauch, H.F. Hemond, B. Peucker-Ehrenbrink. Recent changes in platinum group element concentrations and osmium isotopic composition in sediments from an urban lake. *Environ. Sci. Technol.* 38(2) (2004) 396-402.

[36] J. Fritsche, T. Meisel. Determination of anthropogenic input of Ru, Rh, Pd, Re, Os, Ir and Pt in soils along Austrian motorways by isotope dilution ICP-MS. *Sci. Total Environ.* 325 (2004) 145-154.

[37] K. Shinotsuka, K. Suzuki. Simultaneous determination of platinum group elements and rhenium in rock samples using isotope dilution inductively coupled plasma mass spectrometry after cation exchange separation followed by solvent extraction. *Anal. Chim. Acta* 603 (2007) 129-139.

[38] W. Pretorius, D. Chipley, K. Kyser, H. Helmstaedt. Direct determination of trace levels of Os, Ir, Ru, Pt and Re in kimberlite and other geological materials using HR-ICP-MS. *J. Anal. Atom. Spectrom.* 18(4) (2003) 302-309.

[39] R. Djingova, H. Heidenreich, P. Kovacheva, B. Markert. On the determination of platinum group elements in environmental materials by inductively coupled plasma mass spectrometry and microwave digestion. *Anal. Chim. Acta* 489 (2003) 245-251.

[40] Y.V. Yi, A. Masuda. Simultaneous determination of ruthenium, palladium, iridium and platinum at ultratrace levels by isotope dilution inductively coupled plasma mass spectrometry in geological samples. *Anal. Chem.* 68(8) (1996) 1444-1450.

[41] D.C. Gregoire. Determination of platinum, ruthenium and iridium geological materials by inductively coupled plasma mass spectrometry with sample introduction by electrothermal vaporisation. *J. Anal. Atom. Spectrom.* 3(2) (1988) 309-314.

[42] C.V. Ly, H. Hidaka. Determination of ruthenium contents in terrestrial minerals by isotope dilution mass spectrometry after preconcentration via distillation. *Geochem. J.* 38(5) (2004) 485-490.

[43] T. Meisel, J. Moser, N. Fellner, W. Wegscheider, R. Schoenberg. Simplified method for the determination of Ru, Pd, Re, Os, Ir and Pt in chromitites and other geological materials by isotope dilution ICP-MS and acidic digestion. *Analyst* 126 (2001) 322-328.

[44] Y. Wu, B. Hu, J. Chen, Z. Jiang. Assessment of YPA4 chelating resin fort he separation and determination of Pt, Pd, Ru, Rh and Au in geological samples by ICP-OES. *Atom. Spectrosc.* 25(6) (2004) 257-262.

[45] E.D. Goldberg. Heavy metal analyses in the marine environment – approaches to quality control. *Mar. Chem.* 22(2-4) (1987) 117-124.

[46] M. Koide, M. Stallard, V. Hodge, E.D. Goldberg. Preliminary studies on the marine chemistry of ruthenium. *Neth. J. Sea Res.* 20(2-3) (1986) 163-166.

[47] M. Wasim, S. Iqbal, M. Arif, M. Ali. Determination of elements in Hunza River sediment by ko instrumental neutron activation analysis. *J. Radioanal. Nucl. Chem.* 298(1) (2013) 563-570.

[48] X. Dai, C. Koeberl, H. Froschl. Determination of platinum group elements in impact breccias using neutron activation analysis and ultrasonic nebulization inductively coupled plasma mass spectrometry after anion exchange preconcentration. *Anal. Chim. Acta* 436 (2001) 79-85.

[49] R.A. Nadkarni, G.H. Morrison. Determination of the noble metals in geological materials by neutron activation analysis. *Anal. Chem.* 46(2) (1974) 232-236.

[50] A. Makishima, M. Nakanishi, E. Nakamura. A group separation method for ruthenium, palladium, rhenium, osmium, iridium and platinum using their bromo complexes and an anion exchange resin. *Anal. Chem.* 73 (2001) 5240-5246.

[51] United States Department of Agriculture, Natural Resources, Conservation Service, Soil Taxonomy — A Basic System of Soil Classification for Making and Interpreting Soil Surveys, *Agriculture Handbook,* Number 436, second edition. USDA, Washington, 1999.

In: Ruthenium
Editor: Gary P. Keeler

ISBN: 978-1-63321-657-0

Chapter 7

DESIGN AND MECHANISTIC INSIGHT INTO MOLECULAR RUTHENIUM-BASED WATER OXIDATION CATALYSTS

Markus D. Kärkäs* and Björn Åkermark*
Department of Organic Chemistry, Arrhenius Laboratory,
Stockholm University, Stockholm, Sweden

ABSTRACT

Sunlight provides the necessary energy for all life through a process called photosynthesis. With today's increasing demand for energy and the diminishing fossil fuel resources, there exists a need to move the society towards a sustainable energy economy. The light-driven splitting of H_2O to H_2 and O_2 thus constitutes an attractive option for solving this energy crisis. However, because of the kinetic and thermodynamic complexity associated with the processes occurring in the natural photosynthetic machinery, reproducing this represents a great scientific challenge. Currently the development of efficient and robust catalysts for oxidizing H_2O to O_2 constitutes the primary bottleneck for advancing towards a carbon-neutral society. This has attracted significant attention to the construction of molecular complexes that are able to carry out the demanding four-electron oxidation of H_2O in the pursuit of viable catalysts that can be used for commercial applications. The design of mono- and dinuclear Ru complexes that can efficiently adapt to accommodate a wide variety of stable redox states is a powerful strategy to overcome the difficulties encountered in H_2O oxidation. This Chapter thus aims at describing and discussing the key aspects and rapid progress of this field, which has certainly contributed to understanding and advancing the art of oxidizing H_2O in artificial photosynthesis.

* Email: bjorn.akermark@organ.su.se; markusk@organ.su.se.

1. INTRODUCTION

The increasing demand for energy due to population and economic growth, coupled with the diminishing resources of fossil fuels, is a growing problem that needs to be addressed for maintaining a high standard of life. Development of green and carbon-neutral energy sources is therefore of utmost importance and calls for novel and groundbreaking technologies. The raw materials for this process need to be abundant, clean and of low cost, which limits the potential alternatives. One of the most attractive options, which meets the above mentioned criteria, is to harness the energy that is provided by the sun. [1, 2, 3]

From a chemical viewpoint, one of the most captivating processes occurs in Nature – photosynthesis. In the photosynthetic machinery, the thermodynamically uphill oxidation of H_2O to molecular oxygen (O_2) takes place, which affords the necessary reducing equivalents for converting CO_2 to valuable building blocks. However, such an artificial system could also use the generated electron from the oxidation of H_2O (Eq. 1) to reduce *e.g.,* protons to molecular hydrogen (H_2) in order to yield a fuel (Eq. 2). Sustainable energy storage schemes would thus split H_2O to produce the solar fuel of choice. This vision has attracted considerable attention in the scientific community and the process of oxidizing H_2O (Eq. 1) has been identified as the critical step for realizing successful solar to fuel conversion technologies. [4]

$$2\ H_2O \rightarrow O_2 + 4\ H^+ + 4\ e^- \quad (1)$$

$$4\ H^+ + 4\ e^- \rightarrow 2\ H_2 \quad (2)$$

$$2\ H_2O \rightarrow O_2 + 2\ H_2 \quad (3)$$

At a first glance the oxidation of H_2O to O_2, i.e., the transformation of two molecules of H_2O to generate one molecule of O_2, looks deceptively simple. However, this transformation requires the collective transfer of four electrons and is associated with a high thermodynamic barrier, thus resulting in a transformation that is relatively complicated to accomplish despite the apparent structural simplicity of the reagents and products. But how has Nature solved the issue of oxidizing H_2O? In the natural photosynthesis, catalytic H_2O oxidation occurs at the oxygen evolving complex (OEC) and is mediated by a Mn_4CaO_5 cluster (Figure 1), [5] which orchestrates the four-electron catalytic reaction close to the thermodynamic potential by maintaining a high degree of redox flexibility at the Mn centers.

As previously mentioned, the H_2O oxidation is often cited as the bottleneck in artificial photosynthetic devices due to its complexity. Design of affordable catalysts which are both robust and efficient is a challenging task, which constitutes a fundamental scientific basis for novel solar fuel technologies. Although Mn is Nature's choice of metal in the catalytic core of the OEC, Ru-based complexes have proven to show superior catalytic activity in the constructed artificial systems. [6, 7, 8] There now exist a wide variety of molecular structures that incorporate either single- or multimetallic catalytic Ru centers that are catalysts for the oxidation of H_2O. This Chapter aims at describing the efforts and breakthroughs that have been made in the development of such Ru-based catalysts and the mechanistic details surrounding these catalysts.

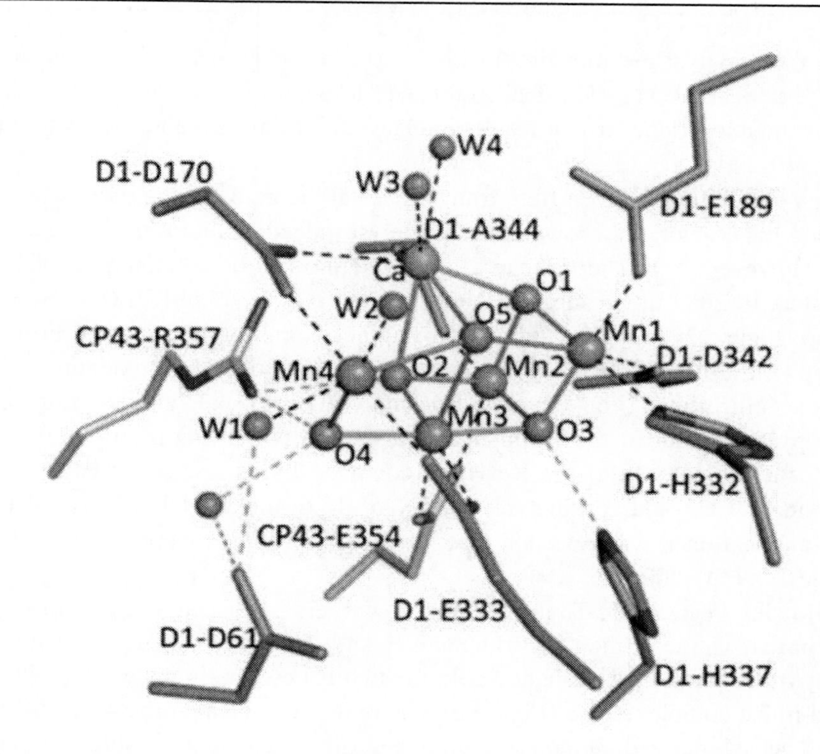

Figure 1. Structural view of the Mn_4CaO_5 cluster with the residues that have been identified as ligands. Adapted by permission from Macmillan Publishers Ltd: Nature, [ref. 5], copyright © 2011.

2. Dinuclear Molecular Ruthenium Complexes as Water Oxidation Catalysts

As highlighted above, H_2O oxidation is a challenging task due to the thermodynamics and the molecular complexity of this transformation. The early reports on water oxidation catalysts (WOCs) consisted of Ru complexes housing two Ru centers in close proximity. This stimulated researchers to focus on designing complexes containing two metal centers. Herein is described the collective efforts made by researchers to develop dinuclear Ru complexes for H_2O oxidation.

2.1. Dinuclear Ruthenium Complexes Based on Neutral Polypyridyl Ligand Scaffolds

More than three decades ago, in 1982, Meyer and co-workers found that the dinuclear Ru complex *cis,cis*-$[(bpy)_2(H_2O)Ru(\mu\text{-}O)Ru(H_2O)(bpy)_2]^{4+}$ (**1**, Figure 2; bpy = 2,2'-bipyridine) was capable of catalyzing the oxidation of H_2O to O_2. [9, 10] This represents the first example of a molecularly well-defined Ru complex reported to mediate this transformation. The complex is generally called the "blue dimer" due to its distinctive color and managed to catalyze H_2O oxidation with a turnover number (TON; defined as moles of produced product per mol catalyst) of 13.2 and a turnover frequency (TOF; defined as moles of produced product per mol catalyst per unit time) of 4.2 · 10^{-3} s^{-1} when using the strong one-electron oxidant Ce^{IV} at pH 1.0. [11, 12] The low catalytic activity was attributed to the inherent instability of the oxo bridge, which results in cleavage of this unit and causes deactivation of the catalyst. [10, 13]

Although the "blue dimer" suffers from low catalytic activity, the early work conducted by Meyer and his co-workers showed that a catalyst indeed could promote the conversion of H_2O to O_2. However, it took more than 20 years before additional examples of Ru catalysts were presented. In 2004 the group of Llobet reported that the *in,in*-$[Ru_2(OH_2)_2(bpp)(tpy)_2]^{3+}$ (**2**, Ru-Hbpp, Figure 2; tpy = 2,2';6',2''-terpyridine) complex, housing the bridging ligand Hbpp (Hbpp = 3,5-bis-(2-pyridyl)pyrazole), could carry out H_2O oxidation. [14, 15] In contrast to the "blue dimer", the dinuclear Ru-Hbpp catalyst lacked an oxo bridge and instead utilized the pyrazole unit in the Hbpp ligand to merge two Ru-O motifs close together in space. The catalytic activity of the Ru-Hbpp complex **2** was also assessed with the strong chemical oxidant Ce^{IV} and resulted in a TON of 18.6 and a TOF of 1.4 · 10^{-2} s^{-1}. In a subsequent publication it was revealed that lowering the catalyst concentration dramatically enhanced the TON to ~500. [16]

The following year, 2005, Thummel and co-workers published a family of dinuclear Ru complexes based on the related bis-tridentate ligand 3,6-bis-[6'-(1'',8''-naphthyrid-2''-yl)-pyrid-2'-yl]pyridazine (L1). This ligand held the two Ru centers in a well-defined orientation and resulted in Ru complexes **3-5** (Figure 2), where the two metal cores were also bridged by a Cl. [17] The synthesized dinuclear complexes displayed high catalytic activity, giving TONs up to ~600 when driven by the chemical oxidant Ce^{IV}, [18] which was a significant step forward compared to the previously reported Ru WOCs **1** and **2**. In a subsequent paper, the same group also reported a library of dinuclear Ru WOCs containing closely related bis-tridentate polypyridine-type systems (**6-15**, Figure 3), which were found to be able to oxidize H_2O. [18]

The thus far reported Ru WOCs contained innocent ligand frameworks, i.e., the ligands were behaving as spectators and were not actively involved in the catalytic oxidation of H_2O. However, an interesting approach was taken by the group of Tanaka, which took advantage of catalytically non-innocent ligand scaffolds. The group of Tanaka synthesized Ru complex **16** (Figure 4), $[Ru_2(OH)_2(3,6\text{-}tBu_2qui)_2(btpyan)]^{2+}$ (tBu_2qui = 3,6-di-*t*-butyl-1,2-benzoquinone; btpyan = 1,8-bis(2,2':6',2''-terpyridyl)anthracene), where the tBu_2qui ligand had an important and active role during catalysis, namely by being redox-active. Incorporation of the quinone ligand resulted in an internal electron reservoir by this ligand's ability of being reversibly oxidized from semiquinone to quinone, thus alleviating the Ru centers from being heavily oxidized. [19] By immobilizing the Tanaka catalyst onto an indium-tin-oxide (ITO) electrode and applying a potential of 1.91 V vs. normal hydrogen electrode (NHE), [20] at pH 4.0, a spectacular TON of 33 500 was obtained. This showed that attachment of Ru complex **16** onto an ITO electrode dramatically increased the stability of the catalyst compared to performing the catalysis under homogeneous conditions. [21]

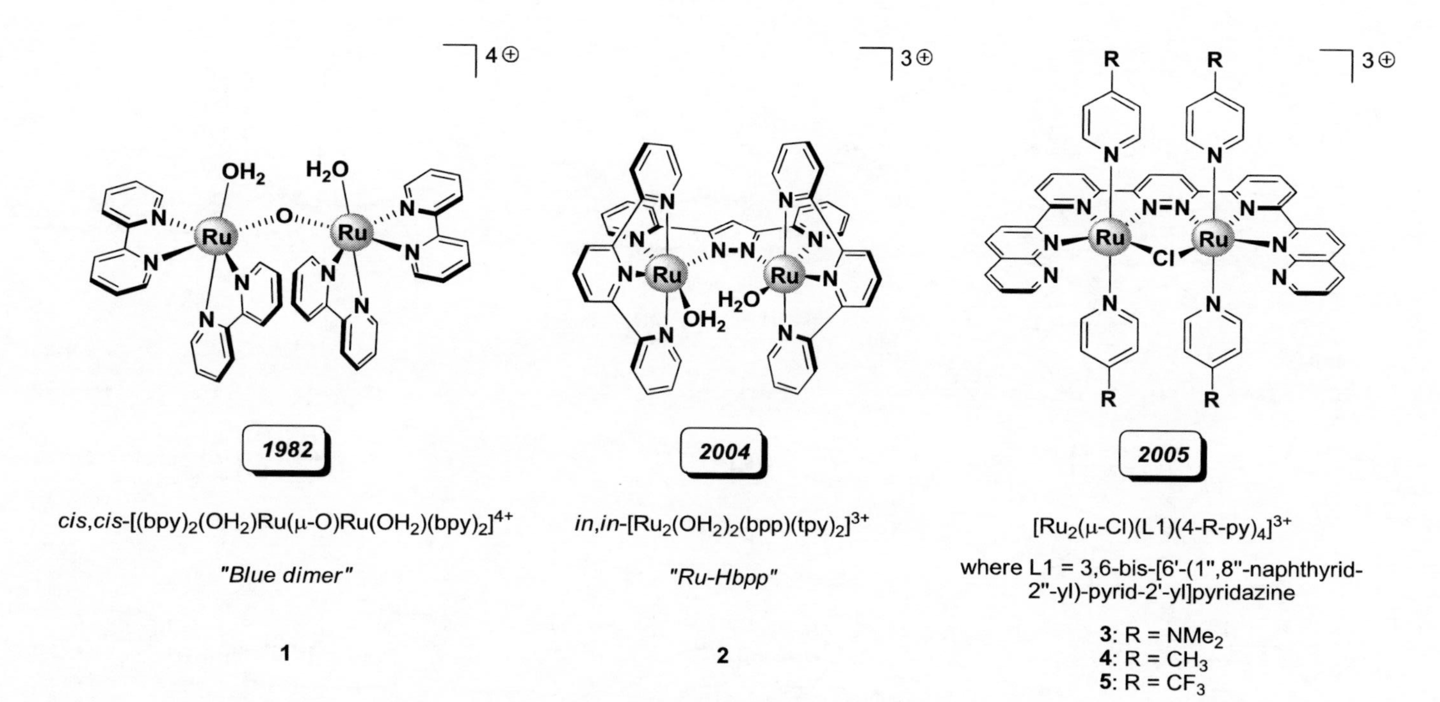

Figure 2. Representation of the early developed dinuclear Ru complexes 1-5.

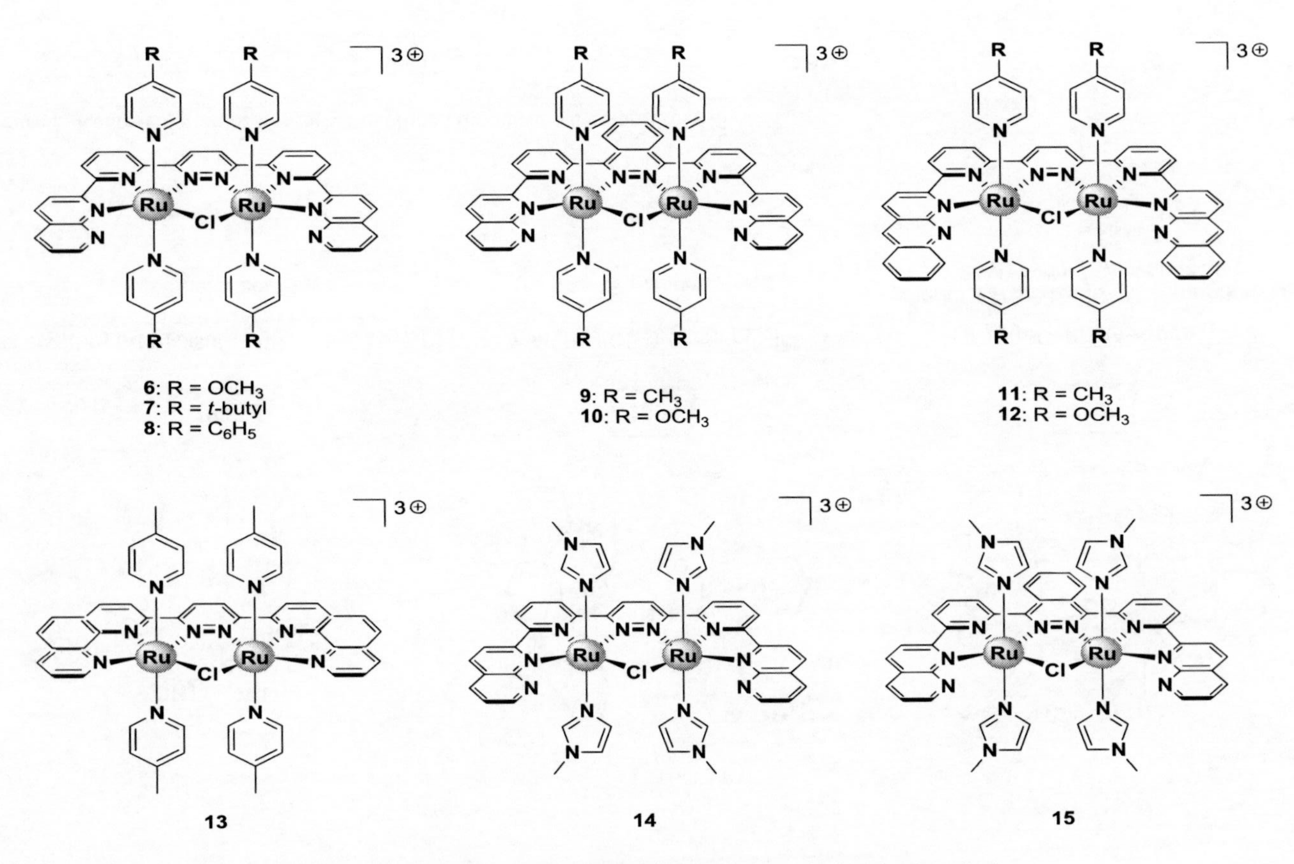

Figure 3. Ru containing bis-tridentate polypyridine ligand WOCs reported by Thummel and co-workers.

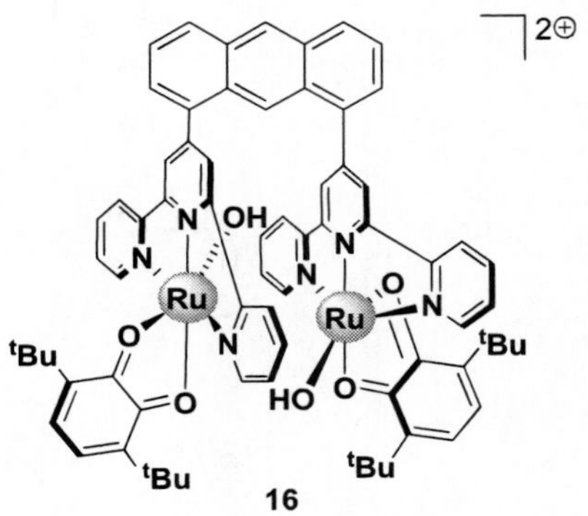

Figure 4. Structure of Tanaka's dinuclear Ru catalyst 16.

2.2. Dinuclear Ruthenium Complexes Housing Negatively Charged Ligand Motifs

In order to drive H_2O oxidation to generate O_2, the chemical driving force for the process needs to be higher than the thermodynamics for the H_2O oxidation reaction (Eq. 1), which is given by Eqs. 4 and 5 (where n = number of electrons mol^{-1} transferred in the reaction, F = Faraday constant).

$$E = E° - 0.059\ V \cdot pH = 1.23\ V - 0.059\ V \cdot pH \quad (4)$$

$$\Delta G = -nFE \quad (5)$$

As noted from the previously described dinuclear Ru catalysts, a strong chemical oxidant, such as Ce^{IV}, is necessary to overcome this thermodynamic limit in order to drive the oxidation of H_2O. The use of Ce^{IV} is required since the developed WOCs containing neutral polypyridyl ligands are associated with high redox potentials to generate the catalytically competent species. Since Ce^{IV} cannot be photochemically regenerated from Ce^{III}, its use in sustainable light-harvesting applications for solar-to-fuel conversion can be questioned. To replace Ce^{IV} with oxidants that can be photochemically produced, such as $[Ru(bpy)_3]^{3+}$ that can be generated from the corresponding well-examined $[Ru(bpy)_3]^{2+}$-type photosensitizers, [22, 23, 24] the redox potentials of the WOCs have to be significantly decreased (see Figure 5 for a schematic depiction).

In the natural system, the presence of imidazole and carboxylate moieties in the environment of the OEC has a dramatic influence on the potential by which H_2O is oxidized. Incorporation of negatively charged functional groups into the ligand frameworks of various transition metal complexes have thus shown to dramatically decrease the redox potentials by stabilizing the metal centers at high-valent states. [25, 26, 27] Inspired by this fact and the OEC the group of Sun and Åkermark decided to focus on crafting WOCs housing ligands with negatively charged units. The group therefore designed the carboxylate containing ligand **17** in the belief that this ligand would accommodate two metal centers in close proximity in a *cis* fashion. However, complexation with Ru instead afforded a dinuclear Ru complex where the two Ru centers were positioned in an *anti*-fashion (**18**, Figure 6). [28]

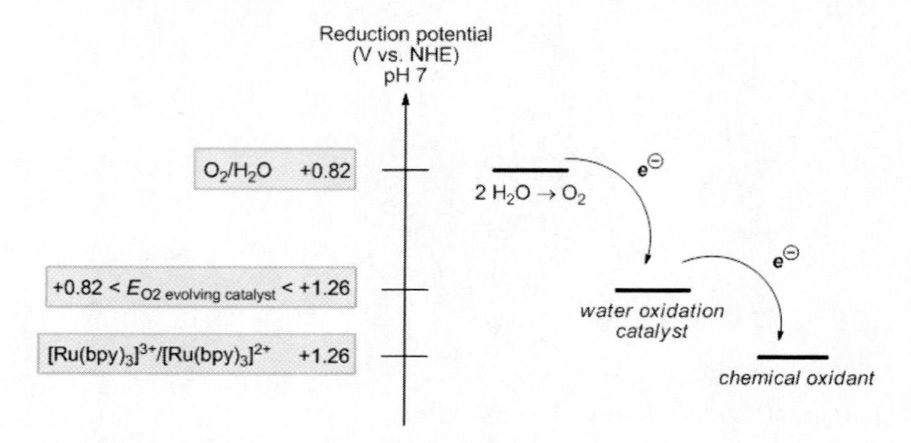

Figure 5. Schematic energy diagram of catalytic H_2O oxidation.

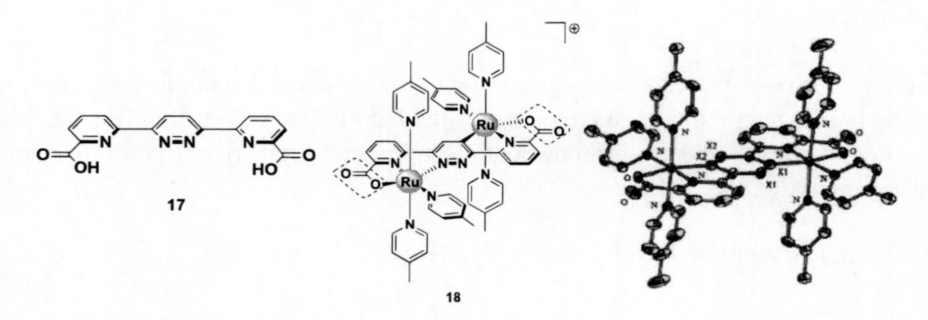

Figure 6. Molecular structures of ligand 17 (left) and the dinuclear Ru complex 18 (middle) and the ORTEP view of Ru complex 18 with thermal ellipsoids at 50% probability level (right; Adapted with permission from ref. 28. Copyright © 2009 American Chemical Society).

Although Ru complex **18** was isolated having an *anti*-structure, the redox potentials were significantly reduced compared to the previously crafted dinuclear Ru complexes containing neutral ligands. The catalytic activity was initially evaluated with Ce^{IV} and resulted in a high TON of ~1700. [28] By decreasing the concentration of the oxidant the TON could be further increased to ~4700. [29] However, more importantly, it could be shown that Ru complex **18** mediated light-driven H_2O oxidation when using $[Ru(bpy)_3]^{2+}$-type photosensitizers **19-21** in a three-component system (Figure 7). [30]

To force the two Ru centers into a *cis* configuration, ligand **22** was synthesized in which the pyridazine unit had been replaced with a phtalazine moiety. This afforded the dinuclear Ru complex **23** with the sought *cis* structure. In addition to being able of catalyzing photo-induced H_2O oxidation, complex **23** proved to outperform the previously synthesized Ru complex **18**, with the *anti*-structure, by providing a TON of ~10400 in the Ce^{IV}-driven H_2O oxidation experiments. [29]

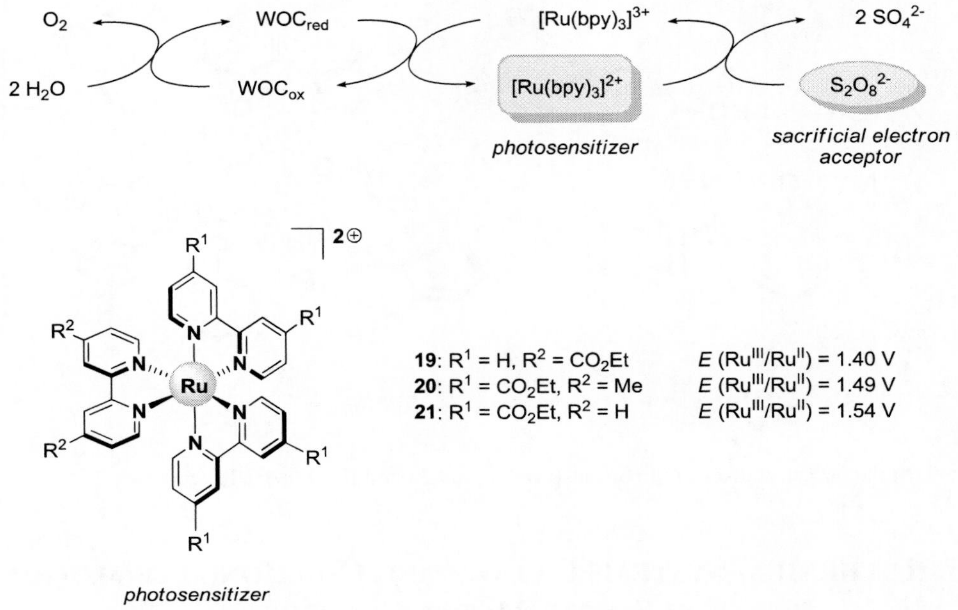

O_2 ⟷ WOC_{red} ⟷ $[Ru(bpy)_3]^{3+}$ ⟷ $2\ SO_4^{2-}$

$2\ H_2O$ ⟷ WOC_{ox} ⟷ $[Ru(bpy)_3]^{2+}$ ⟷ $S_2O_8^{2-}$

photosensitizer *sacrificial electron acceptor*

2⊕

R¹ R² Ru N

19: R¹ = H, R² = CO_2Et — E (Ru^{III}/Ru^{II}) = 1.40 V

20: R¹ = CO_2Et, R² = Me — E (Ru^{III}/Ru^{II}) = 1.49 V

21: R¹ = CO_2Et, R² = H — E (Ru^{III}/Ru^{II}) = 1.54 V

photosensitizer

Figure 7. Light-driven H_2O oxidation mediated by Ru complex 18 in a three-component system consisting of catalyst 18, persulfate as the sacrificial electron acceptor and $[Ru(bpy)_3]^{2+}$ photosensitizers 19-21.

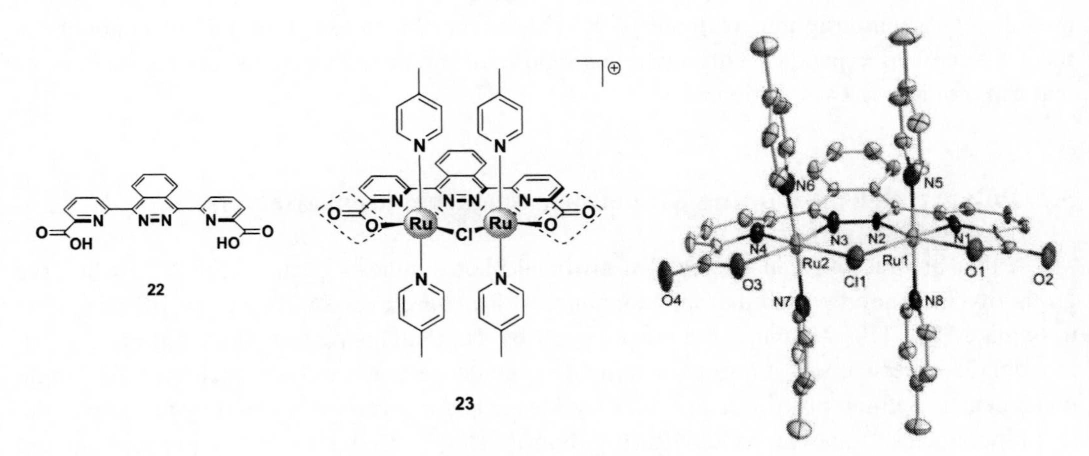

Figure 8. Representation of ligand 22 (left), the dinuclear Ru complex 23 (middle) and the ORTEP view of Ru complex 23 with thermal ellipsoids at 50% probability level (right; Adapted with permission from ref. 29. Copyright © 2010 WILEY-VCH Verlag GmbH & Co. KGaA, Weinheim).

An interesting approach was subsequently undertaken by the group of Åkermark where they incorporated both imidazole and phenol groups into the ligand framework to generate the bio-inspired ligand **24**. Although this did not produce the wanted dinuclear Ru complex, the dimeric Ru complex **25** was isolated, which was able of catalyzing photodriven H_2O oxidation when using $[Ru(bpy)_3]^{2+}$-type photosensitizers. [31] Collectively, this proves that the introduction of negatively charged ligands lowers the redox potentials of the metal complexes and allows H_2O oxidation to be driven photochemically.

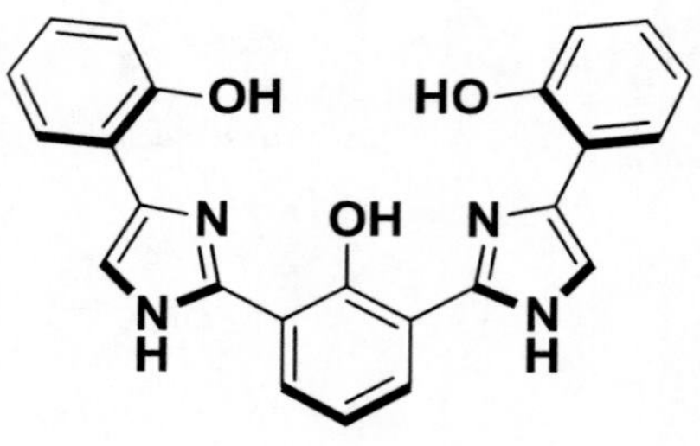

Figure 9. Molecular structures of the bio-inspired ligand 24 and the dimeric Ru complex 25.

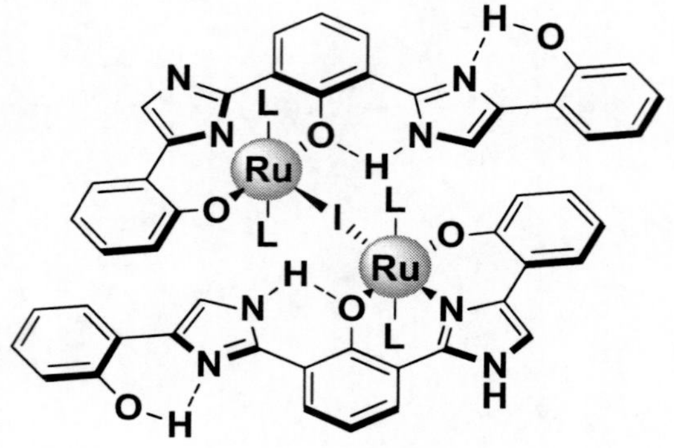

3. Ruthenium Systems Catalyzing O-O Bond Formation at Single Metal Centers

The early success with the dinuclear Ru WOCs, and the fact that the OEC consists of a multimetallic catalytic core, brought about the idea that two or more metal centers was a prerequisite when designing artificial WOCs. However, this initial assumption has now been reconsidered and expanded with numerous reports of molecular mononuclear Ru complexes that can promote H_2O oxidation.

3.1. Polypyridyl Containing Mononuclear Ruthenium Catalysts

A real breakthrough in the field of artificial photosynthesis occurred in 2005 when the group of Thummel reported that the mononuclear Ru complexes **26-28** (Figure 10) were able to oxidize H_2O. [17] Although the initial report by Thummel and co-workers did not contain any detailed mechanistic information providing evidence that catalysis occurred at a single metal center, definite proof was provided by Meyer and co-workers when they developed the two mononuclear aqua Ru WOCs $[Ru(tpy)(bpm)(OH_2)]^{2+}$ (**29**; bpm = 2,2'-bipyrimidine) and $[Ru(tpy)(bpz)(OH_2)]^{2+}$ (**30**; bpz = 2,2'-bipyrazine) (Figure 10) and reported a plausible mechanism for how H_2O could be oxidized at single-site catalysts. [32] In connection with this influential paper by Meyer and co-workers, both Thummel's and Meyer's groups reported extensive series of mononuclear Ru complexes carrying different nitrogen-based derivatives that could catalyze the oxidation of H_2O. [33, 34] Since mononuclear metal complexes have several advantages, such as straightforward design, synthesis and characterization, and also facilitate mechanistic studies, this work has inspired to the preparation of a wide variety of active mononuclear catalysts.

To address the influence that the electronic properties of the ligand frameworks in Ru polypyridyl complexes have on the catalytic activity, several groups have synthesized libraries of the $[Ru(tpy)(bpy)(OH_2)]^{2+}$ scaffold. [35, 36, 37] The group of Yagi synthesized a series of Ru^{II} complexes (**31-35**, Figure 11) where they introduced substituents into the tpy unit. Here, it was noted that the complexes containing stronger electron-donating substituents evolved O_2 more efficiently when using Ce^{IV} as the chemical oxidant. [35] Berlinguette and co-workers have also studied the $[Ru(tpy)(bpy)(OH_2)]^{2+}$ scaffold. In this investigation, both the tpy and bpy moieties were tuned by introduction of different substituents with special focus on catalyst activity and stability. [36,37] Their first study generated a battery of $[Ru(tpy)(bpy)(OH_2)]^{2+}$-type catalysts, which were synthesized according to Scheme 1. Kinetic measurements showed that the O_2 evolution rates exhibited a pseudo-first-order with respect to catalyst concentration for all of the investigated catalysts when excess oxidant (Ce^{IV}) was used. A general trend was that electron-donating substituents, which presumably increase the electron density at the Ru center, resulted in enhanced catalytic rates. This behavior was attributed to the facilitated access to the high-valent Ru^V-oxo level, which should promote O-O bond formation (*vide infra*). Important insight into the catalytic decomposition/deactivation pathways for these Ru catalysts was also given. From mass spectrometry it was found that a significant quantity of the bpy unit had been oxidized to 2,2'-bipyridine *N,N'*-dioxide. The formation of this adduct under the strongly oxidative reaction conditions can probably be considered as a decomposition platform also for related ligands in several other catalytic systems. [36]

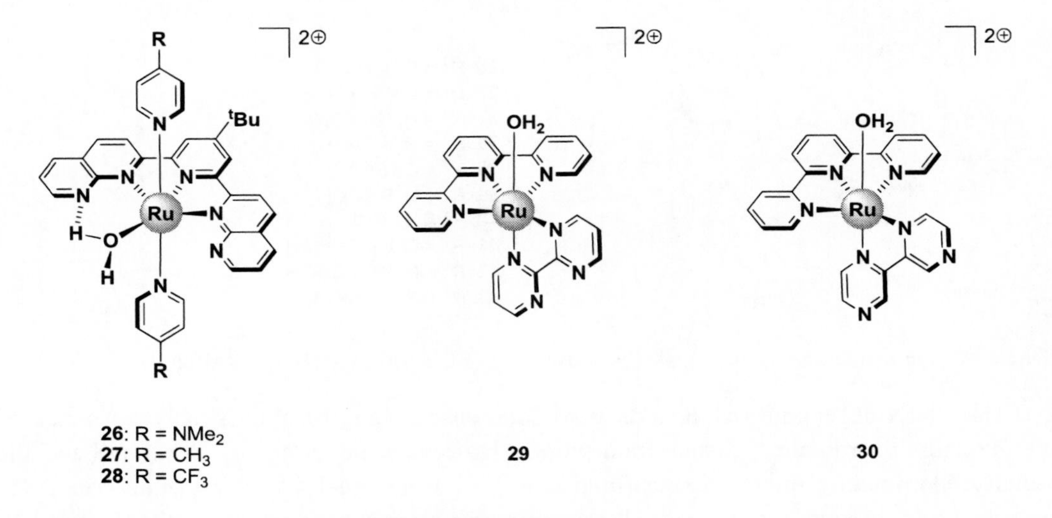

Figure 10. Structures of the mononuclear Ru WOCs 26-30.

In their subsequent work, Berlinguette and co-workers focused on Ru WOCs **36**, **37** and **42** because the previous study concluded that catalytic properties for derivatives with substituents positioned on the bpy scaffold were more sensitive to the alteration. This effect probably originates from the fact that the one of the pyridyl rings of the bpy unit resides *trans* to the vital Ru-O bond. From this study it could be concluded that several different parameters, such as the concentration of the Ce^{IV} oxidant, pH and the presence of different anions, play a key role in the catalytic efficacy and may also alter the reaction pathway for these, and similar, mononuclear Ru catalysts. [37]

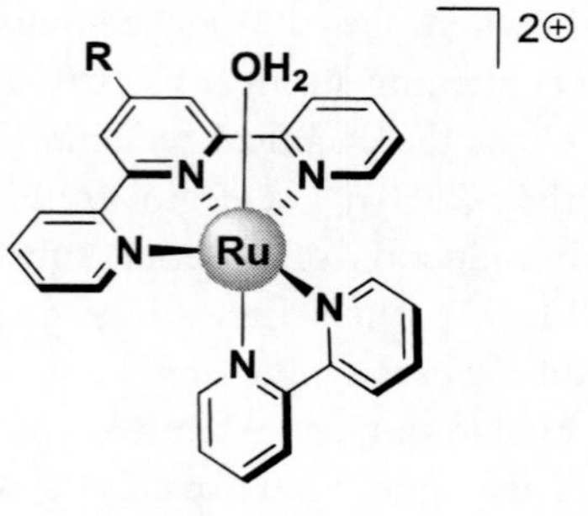

31: R = H
32: R = Me
33: R = OMe
34: R = OEt
35: R = Cl

Figure 11. $[Ru(tpy)(bpy)(OH_2)]^{2+}$-type complexes 31-35 studied by Yagi and co-workers.

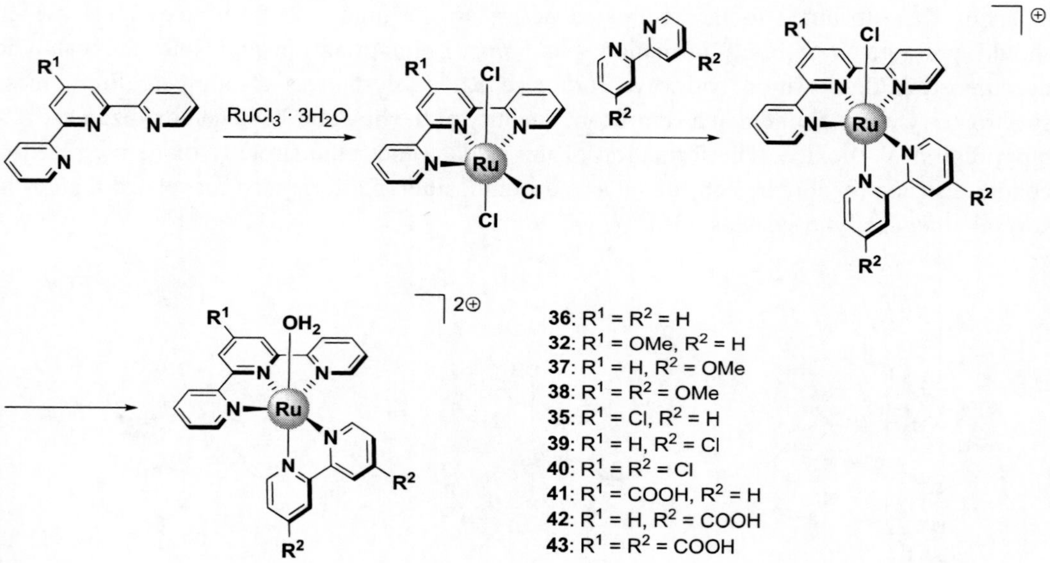

RuCl$_3$ · 3H$_2$O

36: $R^1 = R^2 = H$
32: $R^1 = OMe, R^2 = H$
37: $R^1 = H, R^2 = OMe$
38: $R^1 = R^2 = OMe$
35: $R^1 = Cl, R^2 = H$
39: $R^1 = H, R^2 = Cl$
40: $R^1 = R^2 = Cl$
41: $R^1 = COOH, R^2 = H$
42: $R^1 = H, R^2 = COOH$
43: $R^1 = R^2 = COOH$

Scheme 1. Synthetic route to Ru complexes housing the $[Ru(tpy)(bpy)(OH_2)]^{2+}$ scaffold.

Thus far, the engineered ligands used for constructing Ru WOCs only consisted of meridionally coordinating ligand frameworks. However, the group of Sakai utilized the facially coordinating tmtacn ligand (tmtacn = 1,4,7-trimethyl-1,4,7-triazacyclononane). Ru complexes **44-46** were synthesized, all containing different substituted bpy units (Figure 12). All of the prepared complexes **44-46** did catalyze the oxidation of H_2O when using Ce^{IV} as the chemical oxidant. The authors also monitored the influence of the tmtacn ligand on the electrochemical properties and compared it to the corresponding $[Ru(tpy)(bpy)(OH_2)]^{2+}$ polypyridyl analogue. It was revealed that the Ru^{III}/Ru^{II} and Ru^{IV}/Ru^{III} redox potentials were significantly reduced for complexes **44-46** compared to the $[Ru(tpy)(bpy)(OH_2)]^{2+}$ complex **36**. This difference was assigned to the stronger σ-donating character and lack of π-accepting ability of the facial tmtacn ligand in comparison with tpy. Although the Ru^{III}/Ru^{II} and Ru^{IV}/Ru^{III} redox couples were lowered, the electrochemical overpotential for O_2 evolution was only marginally affected relative to complex **36**, suggesting that the higher redox potential, Ru^{V}/Ru^{IV}, that initiates O_2 production is not dramatically influenced by the tmtacn ligand. [38]

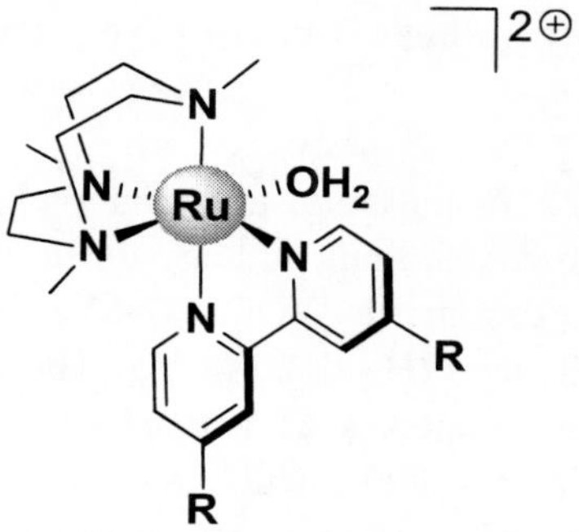

44: R = H
45: R = Me
45: R = OMe

Figure 12. Molecular structures of the tmtacn containing Ru complexes 44-46 (tmtacn = 1,4,7-trimethyl-1,4,7-triazacyclononane).

Carbenes are frequently used ligands for transition metal complexes in homogeneous catalysis and are known to be strong electron-donating ligands. This feature makes carbene ligands attractive for use in H_2O oxidation catalysis. [39, 40, 41] Both normal [42] and abnormal [43] carbenes have therefore been used to construct Ru WOCs (Figure 13). Meyer and co-workers developed the carbene containing Ru complex $[Ru(tpy)(Mebim\text{-}py)(OH_2)]^{2+}$ (**47**; Mebim-py = 3-methyl-1-pyridylbenzimidazol-2-ylidene). Electrochemical measurements revealed that inclusion of the carbene into catalyst **47** led to a lowering of the different redox couples and a remarkable catalytic rate advantage for H_2O oxidation. [42] The group of Albrecht employed another strategy that centered on incorporating abnormal carbenes into the Ru complexes. This resulted in the synthesis of complexes **48-55** (Figure 13), which were all found to be active in the oxidation of H_2O using Ce^{IV} as a chemical oxidant. For the cymene complexes **48-51**, the evolution of O_2 was accompanied by the generation of substantial amounts of CO_2, which was attributed to the oxidative instability of the cymene moiety. In contrast to the cymene-based complexes **48-51**, complexes **52-55** did not produce any CO_2 and were judged as being oxidatively stable, suggesting that the carbene unit in complexes **48-51** is not the weak spot. Comparing the abnormal carbene-based Ru WOCs **52-55** with the homologous Ru complex **56** carrying a normal carbene ligand established the superior catalytic efficiency of Ru WOCs **52-55**, thus highlighting the advantageous role of using the abnormal carbene scaffold. [42]

47

48: R = Me
49: R = Et
50: R = *i*-Pr
51: R = C_6H_5

52: R = Me
53: R = Et
54: R = *i*-Pr
55: R = C_6H_5

56

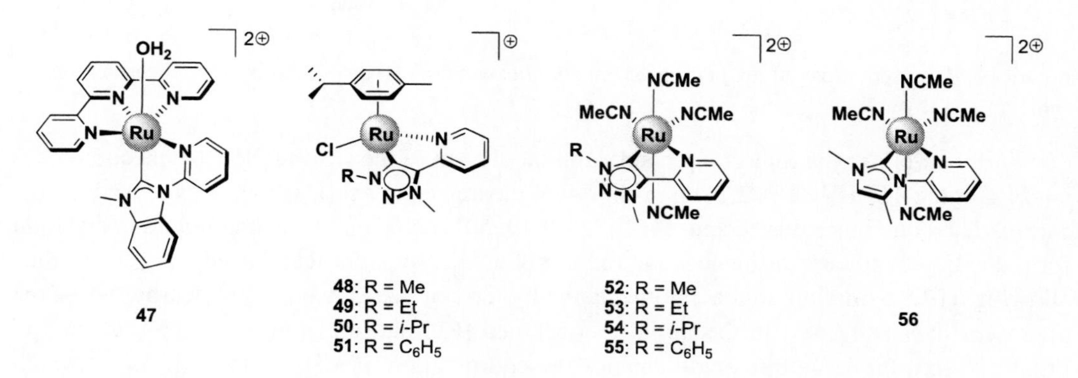

Figure 13. Structures of the carbene-based Ru WOCs 47-56.

3.2. Mononuclear Ruthenium Complexes Carrying Negatively Charged Ligand Scaffolds

The incorporation of functionalized ligands housing negatively charged groups into dinuclear Ru complexes proved to be an encouraging strategy for designing efficient WOCs. This fact inspired the group of Sun to design Ru WOCs **57-63** (Figure 14) based on the tridentate ligand 2,6-pyridinedicarboxylic acid (H_2pdc). [44, 45] The electrochemistry of the dimethyl sulfoxide (DMSO) containing complexes **61** and **62** showed negligible catalytic current and only produced negligible amounts of O_2, which is most likely due to the presence of the DMSO ligand which makes it thermodynamically unfavourable to drive H_2O oxidation. The [Ru(pdc)(L)$_3$] complexes **57-60** were found to catalyze H_2O oxidation when Ce^{IV} was employed as the chemical oxidant. The catalytic activities of these complexes were found to correlate with the electron-donating ability of the axial ligands, i.e., **59** > **58** > **57** > **60**. [45] For the [Ru(pdc)(pic)$_3$] complex **58**, it was observed that the dissociation of the equatorial picoline ligand was necessary in order to generate the active form of the catalyst, namely the [Ru(pdc)(pic)$_2$(OH_2)] aqua complex. This was elegantly shown by introducing the bidentate bpy ligand to produce the [Ru(pdc)(bpy)(pic)] complex **63**, which significantly decreased the efficiency of O_2 evolution compared to the [Ru(pdc)(pic)$_3$] complex **58**. [44] These observations highlight that a small ligand modification can dramatically influence the catalytic activity of the corresponding WOC.

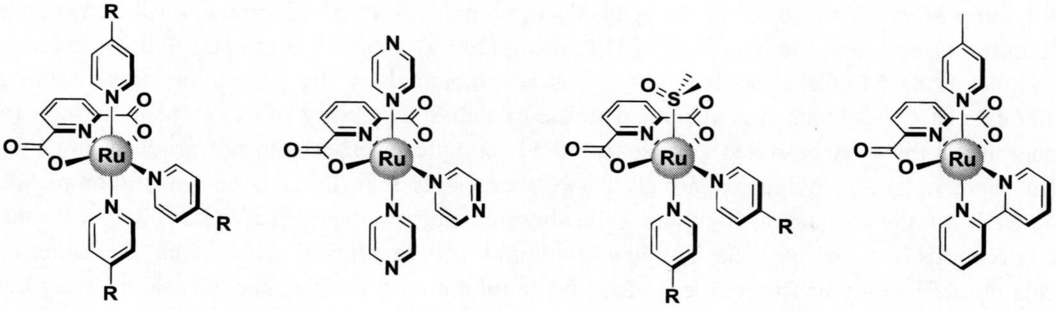

57: R = H
58: R = Me
59: R = OMe

60

61: R = H
62: R = OMe

63

Figure 14. Representations of the pdc-based Ru complexes 57-63 (H_2pdc = 2,6-pyridinedicarboxylic acid).

Further work in the Sun group resulted in the design of the [Ru(bda)(L)$_2$]-type complexes **64-70** (Figure 15; H_2bda = 2,2′-bipyridine-6,6′-dicarboxylic acid), which were based on the carboxylate containing bda ligand. [46, 47, 48, 49, 50] Inclusion of the bda ligand is essential for the catalysis since it influences the redox potentials, by significantly reducing them, thus allowing H_2O oxidation to be photochemically driven when using the [Ru(bpy)$_3$]$^{2+}$-type photosensitizers. [47, 48] In the initially developed [Ru(bda)(pic)$_2$] complex **65**, depicted in Figure 16 left, the large bite angle enables the coordination of a H_2O molecule as a seventh ligand without the need of dissociation of one of the axial picoline ligands to generate the active form of the catalyst. [46]

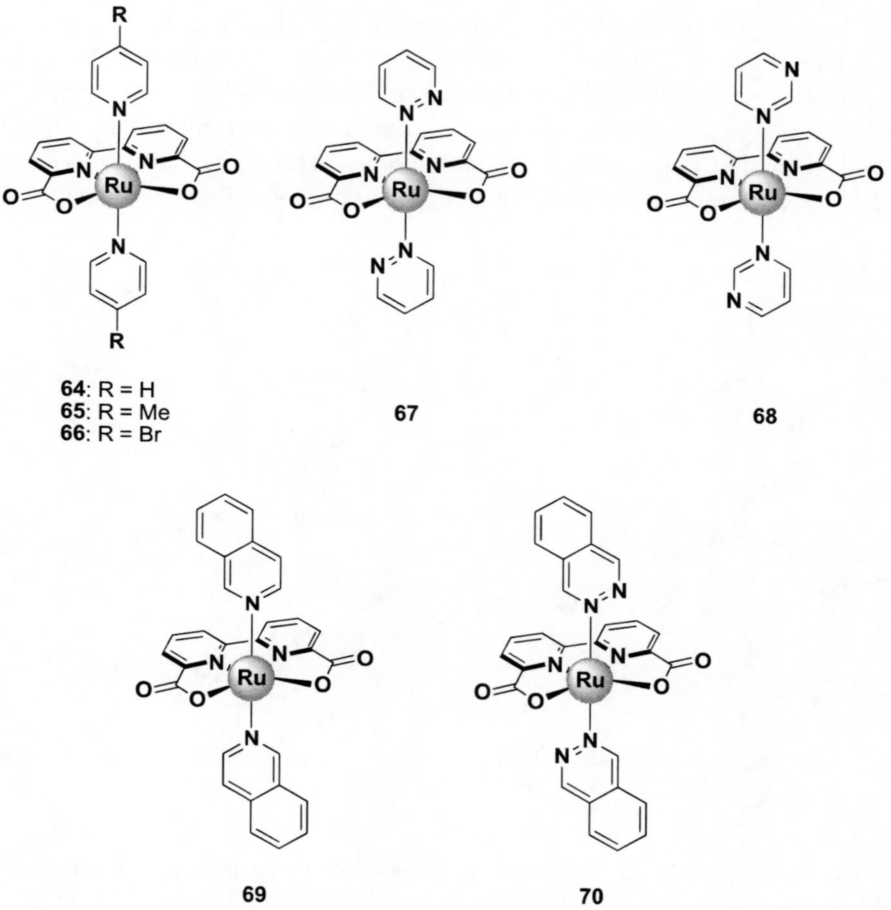

64: R = H
65: R = Me
66: R = Br

67

68

69

70

Figure 15. Molecular structures of the [Ru(bda)(L)$_2$]-type complexes 64-70 developed in the group of Sun.

The stabilization of the high-valent Ru states enabled the isolation of the high-valent seven-coordinated Ru^{IV} intermediate **71** (Figure 16, right). This seven-coordinated intermediate contains two Ru^{IV} cores that are in a pentagonal bipyramidal configuration. Further experiments verified that this high-valent intermediate is involved in the catalytic H_2O oxidation cycle since the Ru^{IV} species **71** was able to catalyze H_2O oxidation in the presence of Ce^{IV} as the chemical oxidant. [46] This work shows that ligand exchange is not required in the octahedral precursor complex **65** to generate the active catalyst. Instead H_2O oxidation occurs through the seven-coordinated Ru^{IV} intermediate **71** without any major structural change of its six-coordinate precursor **65**.

Continuation of the work with the bda ligand led to the development of the [Ru(bda)(isoq)$_2$] complex **69** (Figure 15; isoq = isoquinoline) where the axial picoline ligands were replaced by isoquinoline ligands. Compared to the [Ru(bda)(pic)$_2$] complex **65**, the [Ru(bda)(isoq)$_2$] complex **69** displayed superior catalytic activity towards H_2O oxidation. When using a catalyst concentration of $2.16 \cdot 10^{-4}$ M the isoquinoline complex **69** gave an average TOF of ~300 s^{-1}, in contrast to complex **65** which merely produced a TOF of 32 s^{-1} at the same catalyst concentration. However, this dramatic difference in the catalytic activity could not be ascribed to the electrochemical properties since the two analogous Ru-bda complexes **65** and **69** revealed negligible differences between the different redox couples. The enhanced catalytic efficiency of the [Ru(bda)(isoq)$_2$] complex **69** instead originated from its ability of controlling the O-O bond formation step through non-covalent interactions between two individual catalyst molecules *via* the isoquinoline ligands, thus leading to a significant lowering of the energetic barrier for the coupling step to produce the O-O bond (*vide infra*). [49]

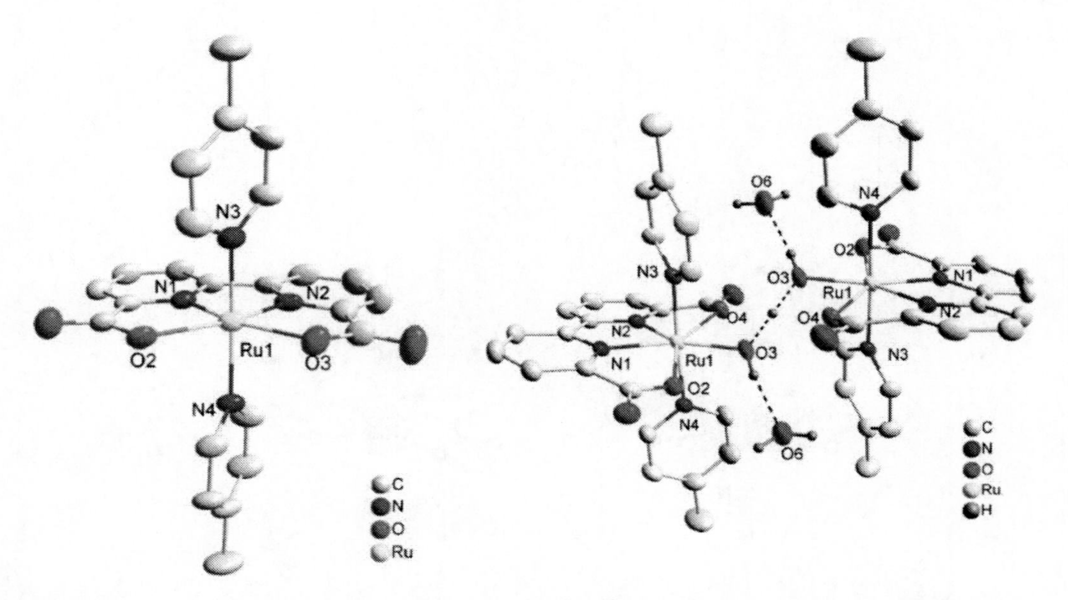

Figure 16. Crystal structures of the [Ru(bda)(pic)$_2$] complex 65 (left) and the Ru^{IV} dimeric complex 71 (right) with thermal ellipsoids at 50% probability level. Adapted with permission from ref. 46. Copyright © 2009 American Chemical Society.

The group of Åkermark synthesized bio-inspired ligand motifs containing carboxylate, imidzole and phenol units, which are all important groups in the natural system. This approach resulted in the crafting of the two mononuclear Ru complexes [Ru(hpbc)(pic)$_3$] **72** (H$_3$hpbc = 2-(2-hydroxyphenyl)-1*H*-benzo[*d*]imida-zole-7-carboxylic acid) and [Ru(hpb)(pic)$_3$] **73** (H$_3$hpb = 2-(2-hydroxyphenyl)-1*H*-benzo[*d*]imidazol-7-ol), showed in Figure 17. The two Ru complexes had significantly reduced redox potentials due to the strong electron-donating influence of the bio-inspired ligand scaffolds. These electronic properties allowed H_2O oxidation to be driven either by pregenerated or photochemically generated [Ru(bpy)$_3$]$^{3+}$. When using the mild one-electron oxidant [Ru(bpy)$_3$]$^{3+}$, complex **72** was able to produce a high TON of 4000 and an initial TOF of >7 s^{-1}, which is the highest reported for a metal-based WOC when employing this mild one-electron oxidant. [51]

Insight into the catalytically important intermediates was also provided by the observation of a high-valent Ru^V-oxo species by mass spectrometry. This suggests that H_2O oxidation is triggered from this Ru^V species or from a catalytic intermediate of even higher valency. The study also provided support that the designed ligand motifs offered molecular catalysts that can participate in proton transfer reactions and have a rich redox chemistry, which should stimulate the circumvention of high-energy intermediates. [51]

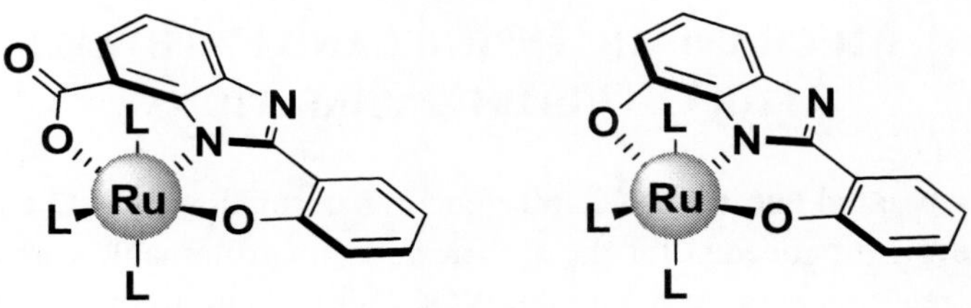

Figure 17. The two Ru complexes 72 and 73 housing bio-inspired ligand motifs.

Further elaboration consisted of incorporating amide functionalities into the engineered ligand scaffolds. Since it is established that the amide motif offers strong σ-donation, this feature should stabilize the metal center(s) in high oxidation states. A symmetric tetradentate ligand carrying two amide entities was therefore incorporating into a Ru complex to construct $[Ru(bpb)(pic)_2]^+$ **74** (Figure 18; H_2bpb = *N,N'*-1,2-phenylene-bis(2-pyridine-carboxamide). The inclusion of the tetradentate amide-based ligand afforded a Ru WOC that was capable of promoting H_2O oxidation driven by the mild oxidant $[Ru(bpy)_3]^{3+}$. However, more captivating was the discovery of a previously unknown deactivation for (Ru-based) WOCs. In postreaction mixtures, the authors were able to detect the CO-containing Ru complex **75**, $[Ru(bpb)(CO)(OH_2)]$, which suggests that this complex is not catalytically active. By independent synthesis of Ru complex **75** and evaluating it as a potential WOC, it could be confirmed that it only produced negligible amounts of O_2. The formation of the $[Ru(bpb)(CO)(OH_2)]$ complex **75** from the $[Ru(bpb)(pic)_2]^+$ complex **74** is a vital observation and constitutes a novel deactivation pathway for Ru-based WOCs. [52]

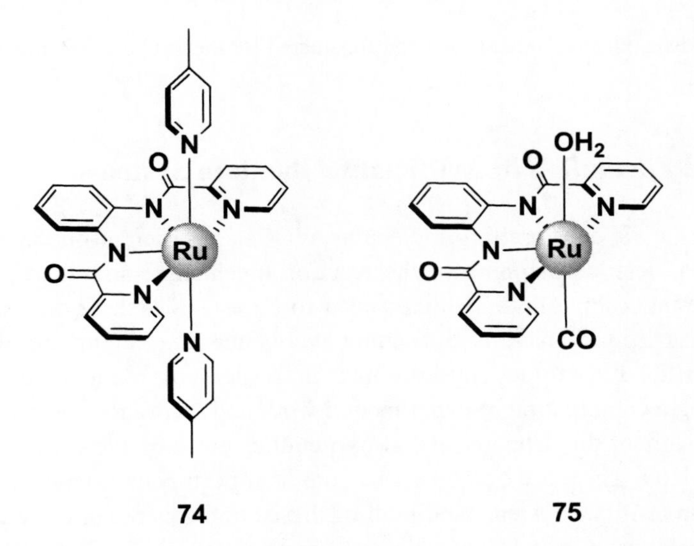

Figure 18. Structures of the two mononuclear Ru complexes 74 and 75 containing the amide-based tetradendate ligand.

4. MECHANISTIC INSIGHT AND PATHWAYS FOR O-O BOND FORMATION

As previously pointed out in this Chapter, the transformation of H_2O to O_2 is not easy to accomplish, however, it is needed for the advancement of sustainable carbon-neutral energy platforms. Severe requirements are put on the WOCs with regard to the catalysts being robust, highly efficient, selective and affordable. In order to understand and to rationally improve WOCs, it is of utmost importance to review how they are able of promoting the four-electron-four-proton oxidation of H_2O to O_2.

The different mechanistic portrayals for O-O bond formation that have been proposed for the Mn_4CaO_5 cluster are depicted in Figure 19. Four different mechanisms have been suggested for the generating the O-O bond and they include: (a) nucleophilic attack on a high-valent Mn^V-oxo or Mn^{IV}-oxo intermediate, [53, 54] (b) coupling of two oxo-bridges, [55, 56] (c) coupling between a terminal oxyl-radical and a bridging oxo-ligand, [57, 58] and (d) reductive elimination of two coordinated hydroxy groups. [59]

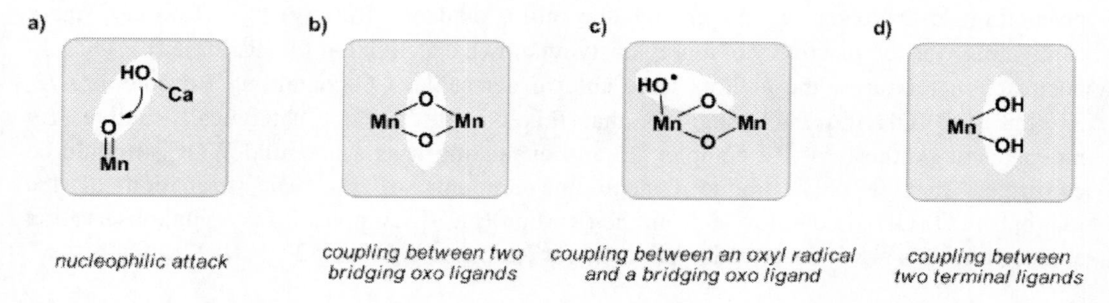

Figure 19. Mechanistic portrayals that have been considered for the O-O bond formation by the natural Mn_4CaO_5 cluster.

4.1. O-O Bond Formation in Artificial Ruthenium Systems

To advance the field of crafting molecular WOCs, in order to obtain more stable and efficient catalysts, detailed mapping of the reaction mechanism and characterization of the plethora of different reactive intermediates need to be established. So far several important pieces of this jigsaw puzzle have been accumulated concerning the nature of H_2O oxidation promoted by artificial catalytic entities, both in respect of mononuclear and dinuclear catalysts, by using a combination of experimental work and theoretical calculations. [60, 61]

As seen throughout this Chapter, metal-oxo entities are key intermediates for managing the activation of H_2O. There are currently two dominant portrayals existing for initiating O-O bond formation in artificial systems and both of these strategies assume the generation of an intermediate involving a metal-oxo species derived from H_2O. These two qualitatively different mechanistic pathways, shown schematically in Scheme 2, can thus be classified into: 1) nucleophilic attack of water/hydroxide on high-valent metal-oxo species (or acid-base mechanism), and 2) radical coupling mechanism. [62]

In the acid-base mechanism, the water/hydroxide acts as the nucleophile and attacks the electrophilic oxygen center in a high-valent metal-oxo unit. Here, the geometry and the redox state(s) of the metal center(s) are critical for governing the electrophilicity of the metal-oxo entity. From an orbital perspective, this event can be explained by the interaction of a σ orbital of water/hydroxide (highest occupied molecular orbital, HOMO) with a π^* orbital (lowest unoccupied molecular orbital, LUMO) of the metal-oxo moiety. This attack leads to a formal two-electron reduction of the metal center with the subsequent formation of the key O-O bond. [62]

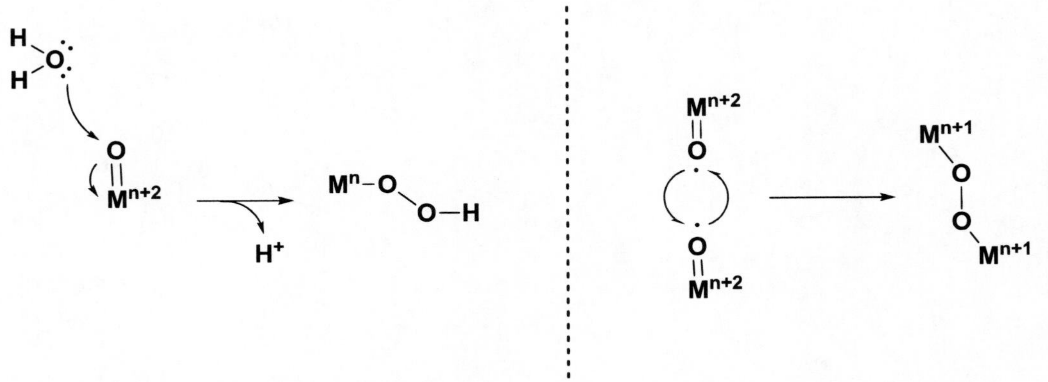

H
O
H
O
M^{n+2}
H^+
M^n–O
O–H
M^{n+2}
O
O
M^{n+2}
M^{n+1}
O
O
M^{n+1}

water nucleophilic attack (or acid-base) mechanism

radical coupling mechanism

Scheme 2. Schematic representations of the water nucleophilic attack (or acid-base) mechanism and the radical coupling mechanism.

The radical coupling mechanism involves the interaction of two metal-oxos. In this alternative scenario, two metal-oxo fragments bearing significant radical character couple to afford a peroxo intermediate. A description of the orbital interactions is characterized by the coupling of two singly occupied molecular orbital (SOMO) with π^* character, which results in the creation of the [M-O-O-M] segment with possible rearrangements and further oxidations leading to O_2 liberation. [62] From the collective mechanistic understanding that has been achieved, it is clear that the production of the essential O-O bond is a chemical step and might be highly dependent on small alterations of the local environment as will be highlighted in the following sections.

4.2. Pathways for O_2 Formation in Ruthenium Systems Comprised of Neutral Polypyridyl Ligand Frameworks

The first developed artificial WOC, “blue dimer” (**1**), is certainly the most well-studied molecular Ru catalyst. Several mechanistic studies have been performed on the “blue dimer” and are consitent with the stepwise oxidation of the initial $Ru_2^{III,III}$ to yield the $Ru_2^{V,V}$ state, which appears to be a potent catalyst for H_2O oxidation. The mechanism for H_2O oxidation by the “blue dimer” is outlined in Scheme 3 and starts from the paramagnetic $Ru_2^{III,III}$ state. The catalytically active form of the “blue dimer”, the $[(bpy)_2(O)Ru^VORu^V(O)(bpy)_2]^{4+}$ (**76**) state, is reached by stepwise PCET oxidation. This intermediate does not accumulate in solution and at pH 0 (in 0.1 M HNO_3) the rate-determining step is the oxidation of the $Ru_2^{IV,V}$

state. The $Ru_2^{V,V}$ reacts rapidly with a H_2O solvent molecule, with subsequent rearrangement, to yield the peroxidic intermediate $[(bpy)_2(HO)Ru^{IV}ORu^{IV}(OOH)(bpy)_2]^{4+}$ (**78**). From this intermediate, O_2 can be liberated which closes the catalytic cycle and regenerates the starting complex $[(bpy)_2(OH_2)Ru^{III}ORu^{III}(OH_2)(bpy)_2]^{4+}$ **1**. [62, 63, 64]

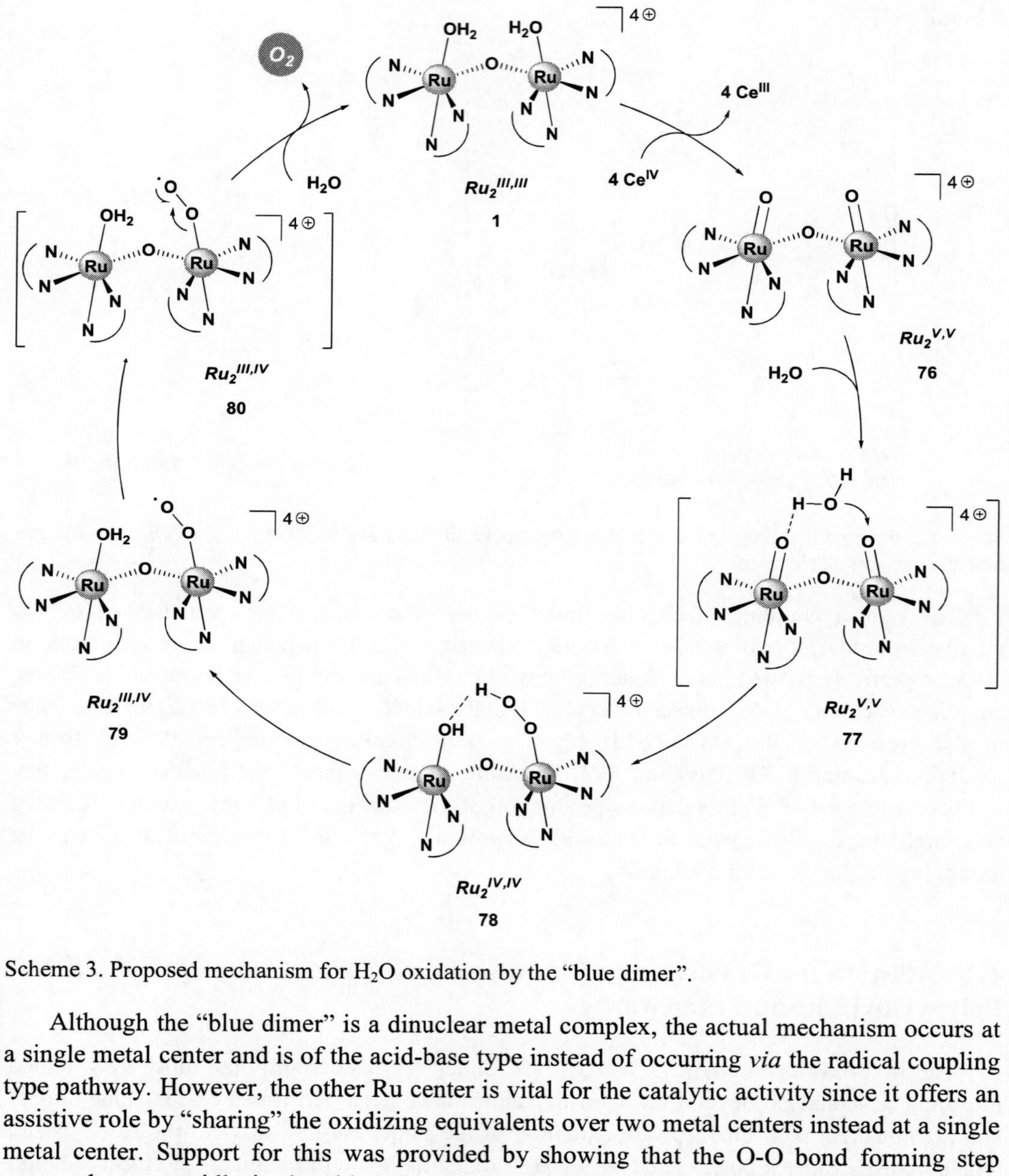

Scheme 3. Proposed mechanism for H_2O oxidation by the "blue dimer".

Although the "blue dimer" is a dinuclear metal complex, the actual mechanism occurs at a single metal center and is of the acid-base type instead of occurring *via* the radical coupling type pathway. However, the other Ru center is vital for the catalytic activity since it offers an assistive role by "sharing" the oxidizing equivalents over two metal centers instead at a single metal center. Support for this was provided by showing that the O-O bond forming step occurred more rapidly in the "blue dimer" compared to the mononuclear analogs. This was explained by the fact that in the "blue dimer" a hydrogen bonding interaction can arise (see structure **77** in Scheme 3), which enables the concerted movement of protons and electrons and circumvents the generation of a high-energy intermediate comprising the hydroperoxo Ru-OOH_2 motif. [64, 65]

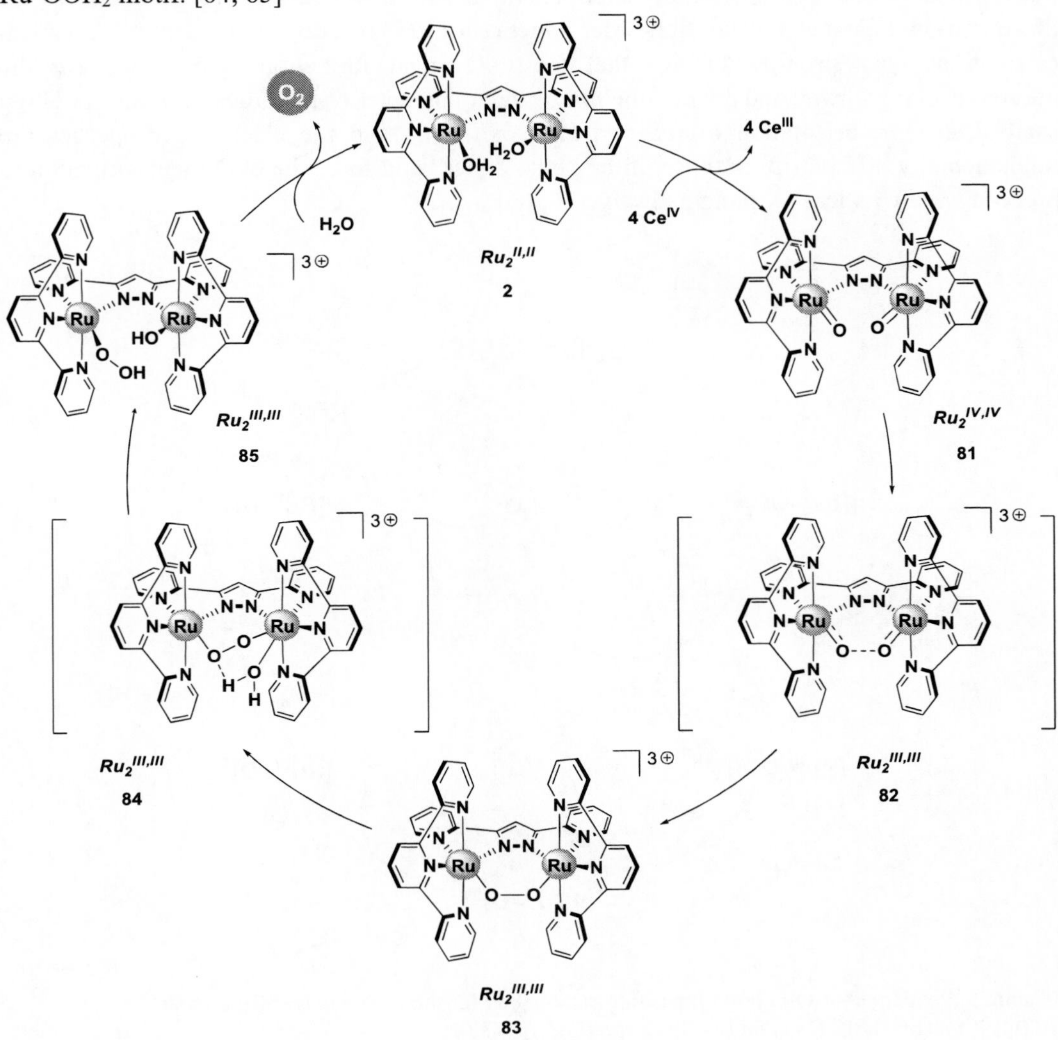

Scheme 4. O-O bond formation catalyzed by the Ru-Hbpp catalyst 2.

The O-O bond formation in the “blue dimer” proceeds through the acid-base mechanism even though the two metal centers are placed in close proximity by the bridging μ-oxo ligand to allow for intramolecular coupling of the two resulting oxo ligands. However, one example of a dinuclear WOC where the placement of the two metal centers in a suitable arrangement promotes the intramolecular O-O coupling is the Ru-Hbpp catalyst **2**. The Ru-Hbpp catalyst **2** has been studied in depth and it has been shown that the ligand structure in this catalyst enforces a geometry in which the aqua ligands are oriented towards each other. Kinetic measurements in combination with ^{18}O-isotopic labeling studies have been conducted and indicate that oxidation with Ce^{IV} proceeds *via* four sequential one-electron oxidations to bring the complex up to the $Ru_2^{IV,IV}$ state (**81**). From this species, *in,in*-$[Ru_2^{IV,IV}(O)_2(bpp)(tpy)_2]^{3+}$, the two oxo moieties can couple in an intramolecular fashion to produce the important O-O bond. The generated 1,2-peroxo species, $[(bpp)(tpy)Ru^{III}\text{-}(OO)\text{-}Ru^{III}(tpy)]^{3+}$ (**83**), is transformed to the hydroperoxidic intermediate **85** from which O_2 evolution occurs, as illustrated in Scheme 4. The first-order kinetics of the reaction and quantum chemical calculations also strongly support that the O-O bond formation takes place *via* the intramolecular pathway and dismiss the bimolecular character of the process. In the Ru-Hbpp catalyst, the pre-orientation of the two Ru^{IV}-oxo units and the electronic properties are fundamentally different from those of the "blue dimer" and force the O-O bond formation to proceed *via* the radical coupling pathway. [16, 66]

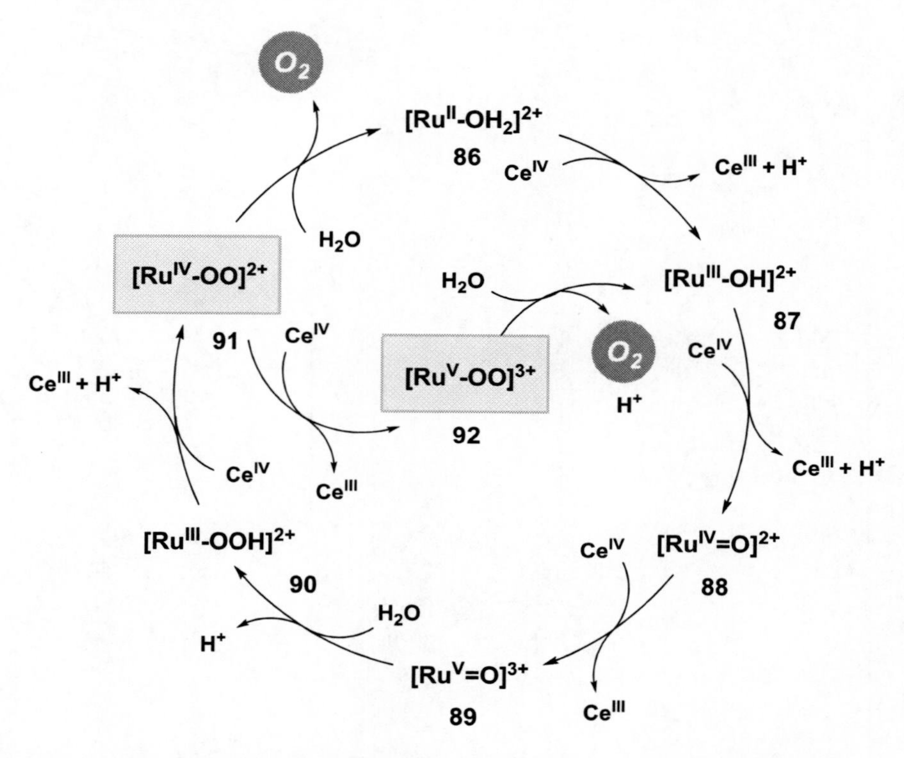

Scheme 5. Pathways for O-O bond formation established for the mononuclear Ru complexes $[Ru(tpy)(bpm)(OH_2)]^{2+}$ **(29)** and $[Ru(tpy)(bpz)(OH_2)]^{2+}$ **(30)**.

The knowledge that H_2O oxidation occurred at a single metal center in the "blue dimer" might have inspired Meyer and co-workers to design the two mononuclear Ru complexes $[Ru(tpy)(bpm)(OH_2)]^{2+}$ (**29**) and $[Ru(tpy)(bpz)(OH_2)]^{2+}$ (**30**) for evaluation as WOCs. The mechanistic details associated with these two mononuclear Ru WOCs were elegantly and systematically exposed by kinetic measurements under catalytic conditions in acidic solutions. The key intermediate for both complexes is the generation of high-valent $Ru^V{=}O$, which triggers O-O bond formation (Scheme 5). The addition of three equivalents of the chemical oxidant Ce^{IV} to the starting aqua complexes, $[Ru^{II}(OH_2)]^{2+}$ (**86**), resulted in a spectroscopically and electrochemically identifiable species, the peroxo species $[Ru^{III}(OOH)]^{2+}$ (**90**). This peroxo species is thus generated from the corresponding $[Ru^V{=}O]^{3+}$ intermediate in a first-order catalytic process by rapid reaction with H_2O, where the solvent H_2O molecule reacts by nucleophilic attack with subsequent loss of a proton to create the essential O-O bond. The $[Ru^{III}\text{-}OOH]^{2+}$ peroxo species is then reacted in a one-electron oxidation step to yield the $[Ru^{IV}(OO)]^{2+}$ peroxo species **91**. The $[Ru^{IV}(OO)]^{2+}$ species represents a branching point in the catalytic cycle and is a striking example that small alterations in the reaction environment can lead to drastic changes in the reaction mechanism. In 0.1 M HNO_3 solutions, the $[Ru^{IV}(OO)]^{2+}$ peroxo intermediate **91** is subsequently decomposed to release O_2 *via* displacement by a solvent H_2O molecule and thus converted to the starting aqua complex $[Ru^{II}(OH_2)]^{2+}$ (**86**). [32, 66]

Another pathway dominates in strongly acidic conditions (1.0 M HNO_3) and involves additional rate-limiting oxidation of the $[Ru^{IV}(OO)]^{2+}$ peroxo species **91** to $[Ru^{V}(OO)]^{3+}$ (**92**). This change in the catalytic cycle is thought to be related to the difference in the redox potential of the Ce^{IV}/Ce^{III} redox couple in the two reaction media, with the access to $[Ru^{V}(OO)]^{3+}$ being limited under less acidic conditions. The liberation of O_2 from the $[Ru^{V}(OO)]^{3+}$ peroxo species closes the catalytic cycle and regenerates the Ru^{III} state. [32,66] It should be pointed out that calculations on the $[Ru(tpy)(bpm)(OH_2)]^{2+}$ (**29**) and $[Ru(tpy)(bpz)(OH_2)]^{2+}$ (**30**) complexes have shown that the corresponding $[Ru^{IV}{=}O]^{2+}$ complexes do not possess the ability to promote O-O bond formation and access to the higher redox state $[Ru^{V}{=}O]^{3+}$ (**89**) is necessary in order to initiate the generation of the vital O-O bond. The calculations also revealed that the radical coupling, which involves the $[Ru^{V/IV}(O)$-$(O)Ru^{V/IV}]$ framework, requires significantly higher activation energy than the pathway involving H_2O nucleophilic attack at a single Ru center. These findings agree with the experimentally observed results and make the radical coupling pathway improbable. [67]

By contrast, Thummel and co-workers proposed that the closely related catalysts **26-28** do react *via* nucleophilic attack of a solvent H_2O molecule on $Ru^{IV}{=}O$ species. [68, 69] This further highlights the difficulties and the different mechanistic portrayals that might exist when examining WOCs.

4.3. Mechanistic Details for O-O bond formation in Ruthenium Systems Based on Negatively Charged Ligand Scaffolds

As previously described in this Chapter, the $[Ru(bda)(pic)_2]$ catalyst **65** has significantly reduced redox potential so that even a high-valent Ru^{IV} intermediate can be isolated. The $[Ru(bda)(pic)_2]$-type catalysts are also interesting from a mechanistic perspective, since O-O bond formation proceeds through a radical coupling type of mechanism (Scheme 6). Support for this pathway originated from the rate law, which followed a second-order dependence in [Ru]. These findings coupled with the fact that the Ru^{IV} dimer **71** was found to be catalytically active suggest that O_2 formation proceeds through a bimolecular process. The origin of the radical coupling pathway is the flexible bda ligand that offers a large O-Ru-O cleft, thus allowing a H_2O molecule to coordinate to the Ru core without the need for ligand exchange processes.[46, 70] It should be noted that the occurrence of seven-coordinated intermediates in H_2O oxidation catalysis was also proposed by the groups of Meyer and Thummel in their catalytic systems but without clear experimental proof. [32, 33] Sequential oxidation converts the starting Ru^{II} complex to the corresponding seven-coordinated Ru^{IV}-$O^{\bullet}$ oxyl radical species **95**, which can be seen as a resonance form to the $Ru^{V}{=}O$ (**95'**). When the Ru^{IV}-$O^{\bullet}$ oxyl radical **95** has been generated, two of these entities couple to produce the peroxo species Ru^{IV}-O-O-Ru^{IV} (**96**). From this species, liberation of O_2 readily occurs, or in the presence of excess Ce^{IV}, the Ru^{IV}-O-O-Ru^{IV} species can be further oxidized to Ru^{IV}-$O^{\bullet}$-O-

Ru^{IV} that decomposes to generate O_2, Ru^{III} and Ru^{IV}. Quantum chemical calculations revealed that the O-O bond forming step has an activation energy of only 12 kcal mol^{-1}. [46,71] The distinguishing feature of this work is the occurrence of seven-coordinated Ru intermediates in the catalytic cycle and the provision of support for O_2 formation *via* the direct interaction of Ru^{IV}-$O^{\bullet}$ radicals.

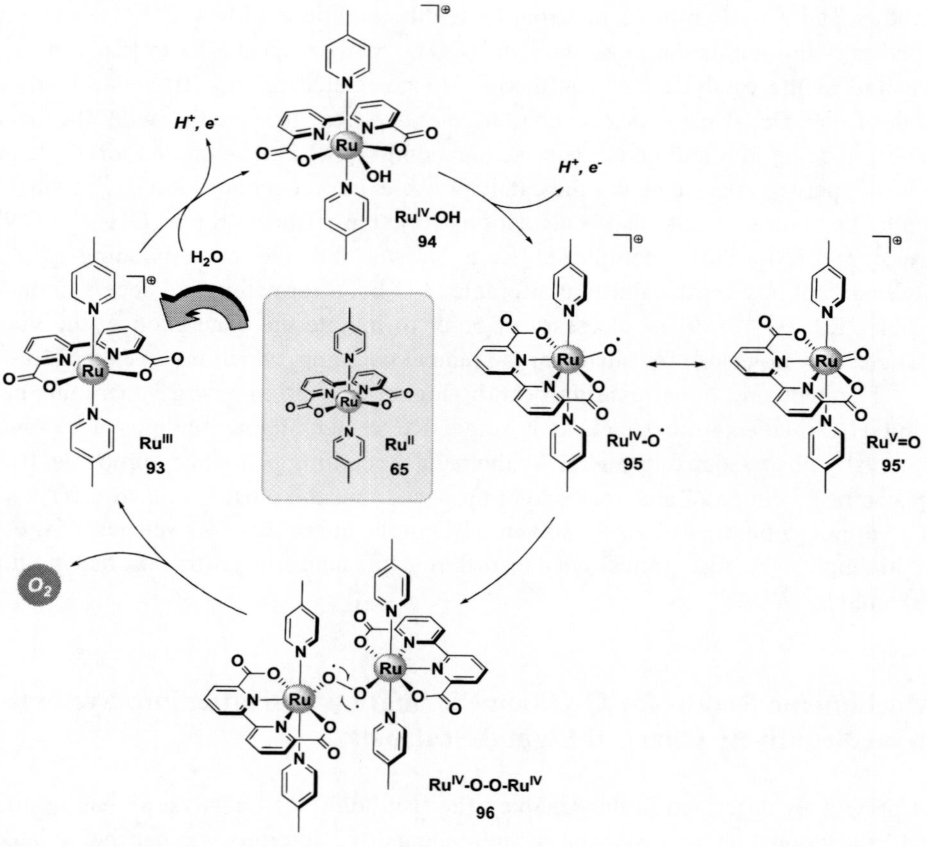

Scheme 6. Portrayal of the radical coupling pathway for conversion of H_2O to O_2 for the $[Ru(bda)(pic)_2]$ catalyst 65.

Replacing the flexible bda ligand backbone by the more rigid pda ligand (H_2pda = phenanthroline dicarboxilic acid) to yield the $[Ru(pda)(pic)_2]$ complex **97** switched the mechanistic pathway for H_2O oxidation. The kinetics changes from second-order in catalyst to first-order, implying that the mechanism now proceeds through a mononuclear process. The coordination features in the developed $[Ru(pda)(pic)_2]$ complex **97** are that the O-Ru-O bite angle is slightly larger than that of the $[Ru(bda)(pic)_2]$ complex **65**, ~131° vs. ~125°, respectively, and in the $[Ru(pda)(pic)_2]$ complex **97**, the pda ligand backbone is essentially planar. The large O-Ru-O cleft in $[Ru(pda)(pic)_2]$ complex **97** allows a hydroxide ligand to directly coordinate to the Ru center to generate a seven-coordinated Ru^{IV} species, analogous to what was found for the $[Ru(bda)(pic)_2]$ complex. However, for the $[Ru(pda)(pic)_2]$ complex, calculations revealed that the H_2O nucleophilic attack pathway is preferred over the radical coupling mechanism, which dominates in the previous developed $[Ru(bda)(pic)_2]$

complex (Scheme 7). The calculations thus support the experimental observations and shows that a small alteration in the ligand backbone can change the mechanistic outcome of the studied catalytic system. [71]

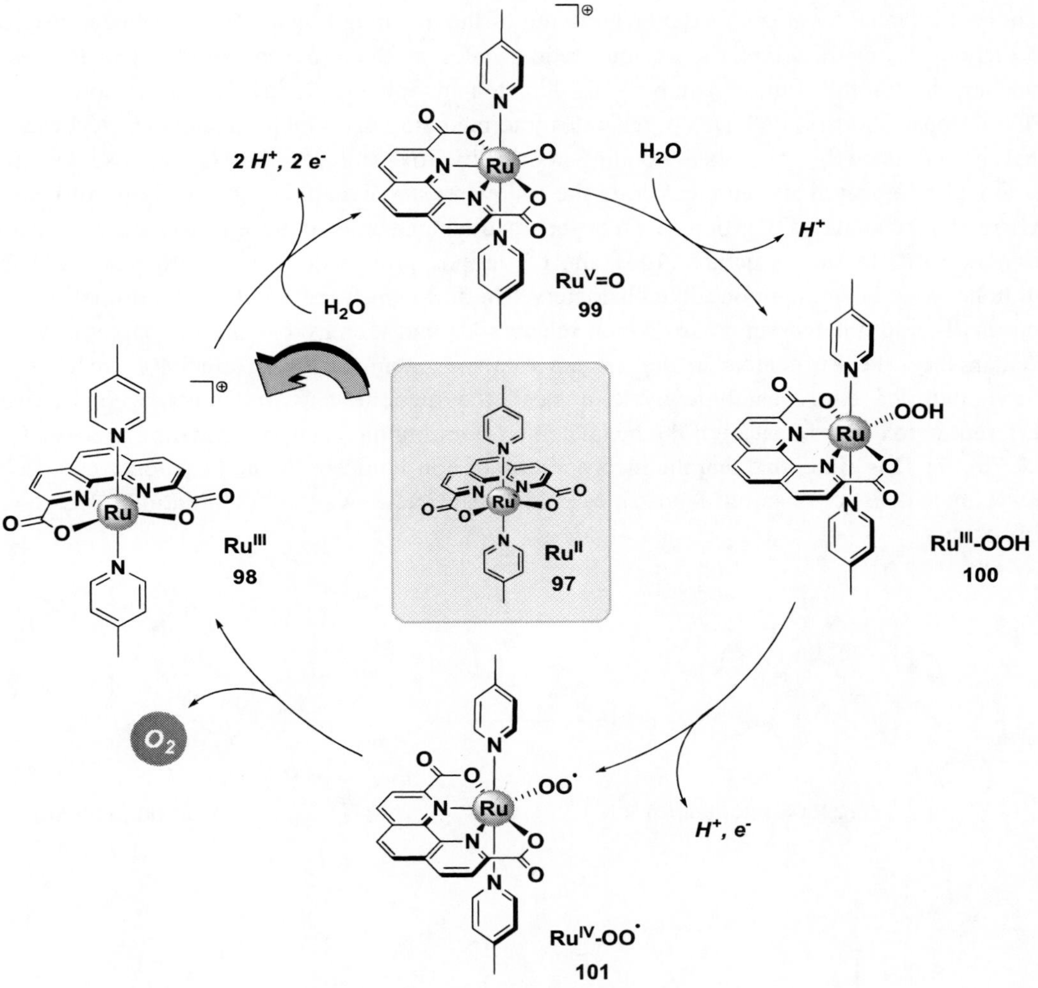

Scheme 7. Mechanistic pathway for O-O bond formation for the [Ru(pda)(pic)$_2$] catalyst 97.

4.5. Other Pathways for O_2 Evolution Based on Non-innocent Ligands

In transition metal complexes, the active place where the catalysis usually occurs is at the metal center. The ligand backbones are usually treated as innocent, as spectators, and do not participate in the catalytic processes. However, this view might be incorrect in a few occasions – the ligand frameworks can be actively participating. These types of ligands are called non-innocent and can be responsible for cooperating, assisting the metal center(s) during the catalytic processes. The design and use of cooperative catalysis could thus offer novel approaches for carrying out selective transformations. [72, 73]

From a mechanistic perspective, the Tanaka catalyst (**16**) represents an interesting example. This catalyst is comprised of two hydroxo units in close proximity to accommodate for intramolecular O-O bond formation to occur. However, the quinone ligands have a more important role during catalysis due to their non-innocence. In complexes containing non-innocent ligands, there is an extensive mixing of the metal and ligand-based orbitals, making it difficult to characterize the various redox states at the different atoms. The proposed mechanism for the Tanaka catalyst **16**, depicted in Scheme 8, involves four consecutive PCET steps. The first PCET step generates intermediate **102**, which contains an oxyl radical that is stabilized by hydrogen bonding to the hydroxo moiety that is in close vicinity. Removal of a proton and an electron in the following step eventuates in O-O bond formation where the generated O_2 group is proposed to transfer some of its electron density to the quinone unit. In this structure (**103**), the O_2 unit is proposed to be of superoxo and the quinone to be of semiquinone-like characters. The following step involves the formation of a terminally coordinated superoxo, which releases O_2 and thereby closing the catalytic cycle. Remarkably, the Ru centers in the Tanaka catalyst remain in their formal Ru^{II} redox state throughout the entire catalytic cycle. Instead the quinone and oxo units cycle between different redox states instead of the metal center(s) during the catalytic oxidation process. [74, 75, 76, 77] This highlights that the incorporation of non-innocent ligand backbones can evoke novel mechanistic reaction landscapes and create new ways for initiating O-O bond formation.

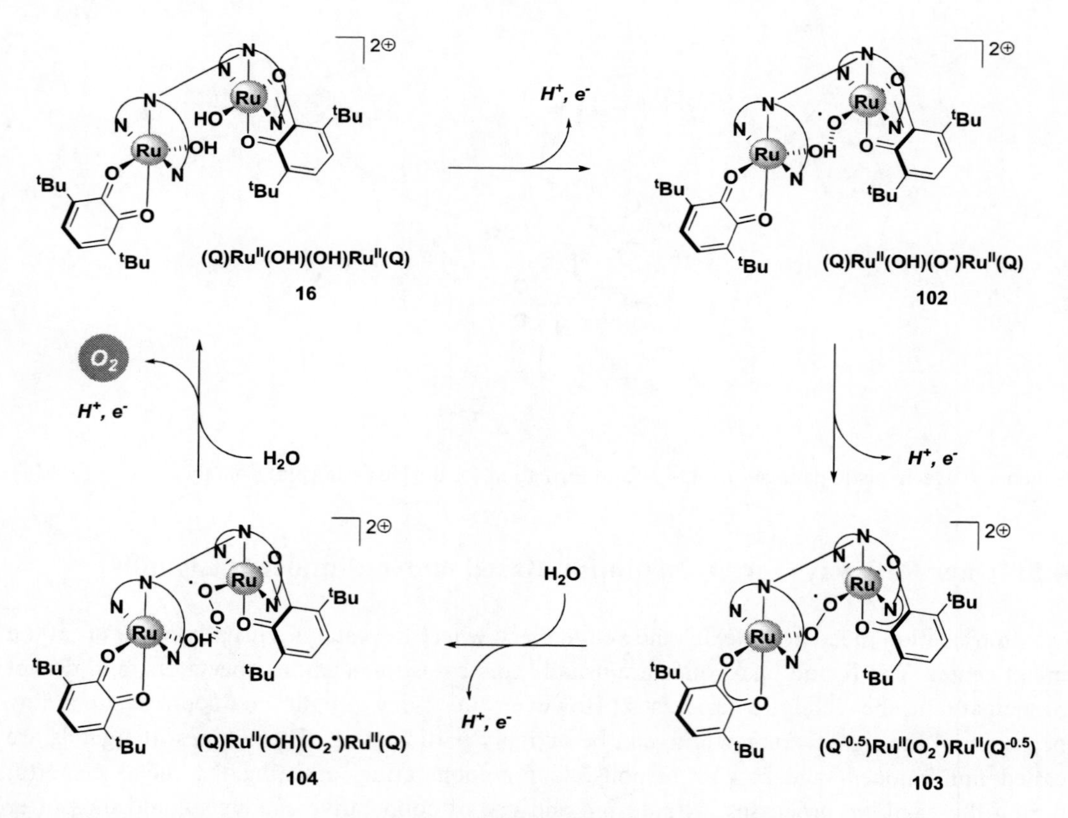

Scheme 8. Proposed mechanism for O_2 evolution by the so-called Tanaka catalyst (16).

Another example where the ligand backbone has a central role and participates in the catalytic process was reported by Milstein and co-workers. They utilized a PNN–Ru pincer-type complex (**105**) and showed that this complex was able to split H_2O into both O_2 and H_2 (Scheme 9). This complex is able to generate both H_2 and O_2 in a consecutive fashion *via* thermally and photolytically induced steps at a single metal center. Here the ligand scaffold cooperatively participates in the catalytic process where the ligand pincer ligand goes through a series of deprotonation-protonation events at one of the methylene centers of the pincer arms. H_2 can then be generated in a thermal step which is accompanied by the formation of the Ru dihydroxo species **107**. From the dihydroxo species **107**, liberation of O_2 occurs through the intramolecular coupling of the two hydroxyl groups to generate H_2O_2, which subsequently decomposes to generate O_2. This completes the catalytic cycle in which H_2O is fully split into H_2 and O_2. [68, 79] Calculations have also revealed that the release of H_2 is the rate-determining step of the reaction and associated with a high activation barrier, which could explain why the H_2 evolving process is slow. [80] Although the overall reaction is quite inefficient and slow, in regard to the generated yields of O_2 and H_2, it highlights the potential of molecular Ru complexes in H_2O splitting schemes.

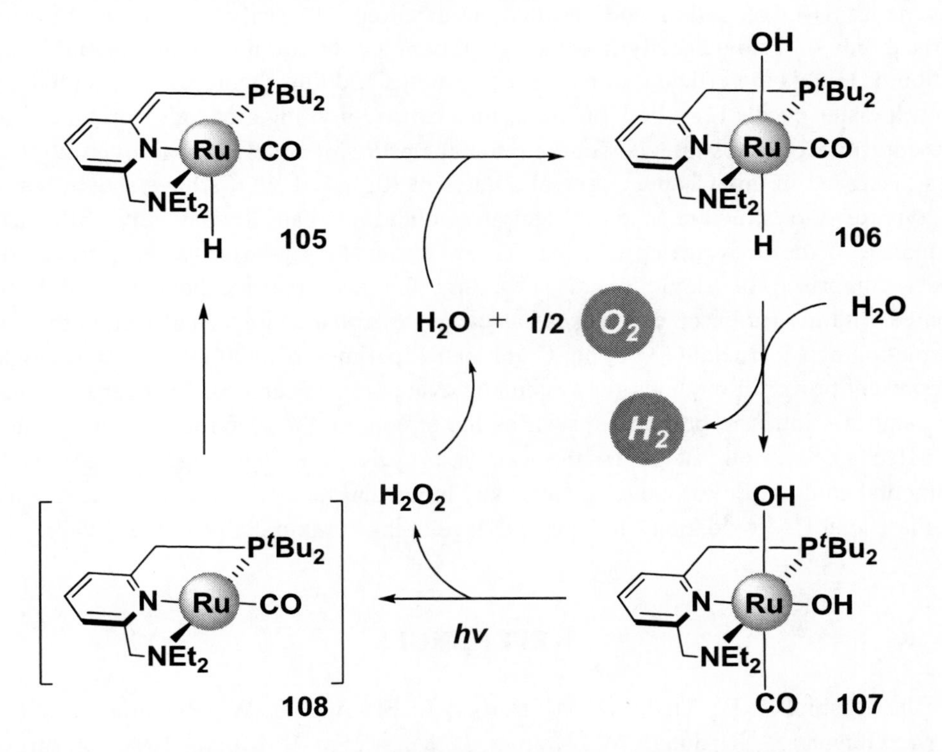

Scheme 9. Reaction scheme for consecutive generation of H_2 and O_2 by the Ru pincer-type complex 105.

Conclusion

The urgent need for development of "green" and carbon-neutral energy sources constitutes an essential, if not the most essential challenge of the 21st century for the human society. A way of accomplishing this would be to convert abundant and energy-poor materials to energy-rich molecules by the help of the energy provided by sunlight. Solving the problem of viable renewable energy systems could be envisioned by splitting H_2O into O_2 and H_2, or other solar fuels. In such systems, WOCs play an important role and are currently being cited as the bottleneck in artificial systems for conversion of solar energy to fuels. Significant efforts have thus been addressed to design stable and efficient catalysts that are able to overcome the kinetic and thermodynamic constraints that are associated with the oxidation of H_2O. Here, the use of mono- or dinuclear Ru complexes has provided a key foundation for understanding and advancing the field of artificial H_2O oxidation. These single or multimetallic catalysts offer several desirable properties, such as robustness, efficiency and redox flexibility, which is in accordance with the requirements needed to bring about the conversion of H_2O to O_2.

Since the initial report by Meyer, more than 30 years ago, of the "blue dimer" which was able to catalyze the four-electron-four-proton oxidation of H_2O to O_2, numerous Ru complexes have been developed to carry out this demanding reaction. The realization that H_2O oxidation could occur at a single metal center has greatly expanded the field of homogeneous H_2O oxidation and resulted in a variety of easily accessible Ru catalysts comprised only of a single catalytic center. Important aspects for managing the multi-electron oxidation of H_2O is the efficient movement of protons and thus the access to coupled proton-electron transfer events (*i.e.,* PCET). Here, mechanistic investigations also provide essential insight and contribute to strategies for the rational crafting of novel and improved WOCs.

As discussed in this Chapter, several studies of Ru-based WOCs have shown that small alterations of the structure and/or catalytic conditions can dramatically influence the performance of the investigated catalyst. The work on the Ru-based WOCs, especially the catalysts comprised of single metal sites, and the acquired mechanistic understanding associated with the Ru-based complexes has clearly established important factors that govern the formation of the crucial O-O bond. Combined experimental and theoretical investigations thus represent powerful methods for systematic evaluation of catalysts in order to get insight in the catalyst's intrinsic properties, such as the structural and electronic features, and how these affect the various steps in the catalytic cycle. The merging of theoretical and experimental studies allows one to uncover key molecular design elements for advancing the field of artificial H_2O oxidation catalysis and developing commercially viable WOCs.

References

[1] Blankenship, R. E.; Tiede, D. M.; Barber, J.; Brudvig, G. W.; Fleming, G.; Ghirardi, M.; Gunner, M. R.; Junge, W.; Kramer, D. M.; Melis, A.; Moore, T. A.; Moser, C. C.; Nocera, D. G.; Nozik, A. J.; Ort, D. R.; Parson, W. W.; Prince, R. C.; Sayre, R. T. Comparing photosynthetic and photovoltaic efficiencies and recognizing the potential for improvement. *Science* 2011, *332*, 805-809.

[2] Kärkäs, M. D.; Johnston, E. V.; Verho, O.; Åkermark, B. Artificial photosynthesis: From nanosecond electron transfer to catalytic water oxidation. *Acc. Chem. Res.* 2014, *47*, 100-111.

[3] Chow, J.; Kopp, R. J.; Portney, P. R. Energy resources and global development. *Science* 2003, *302*, 1528-1531.

[4] Sun, L.; Hammarström, L.; Åkermark, B.; Styring, S. Towards artificial photosynthesis: Ruthenium–manganese chemistry for energy production. *Chem. Soc. Rev.* 2001, *30*, 36-49.

[5] Umena, Y.; Kawakami, K.; Shen, J. -R.; Kamiya, N. Crystal structure of oxygen-evolving photosystem II at a resolution of 1.9Å. *Nature* 2011, *473*, 55-61.

[6] Romain, S.; Vigara, L.; Llobet, A. Oxygen-oxygen bond formation pathways promoted by ruthenium complexes. *Acc. Chem. Res.* 2009, *42*, 1944-1953.

[7] Joya, K. S.; Joya, Y. F.; Ocakoglu, K.; van de Krol, R. Water-splitting catalysis and solar fuel devices: Artificial leaves on the move. *Angew. Chem. Int. Ed.* 2013, *52*, 10426-10437.

[8] Swierk, J. R.; Mallouk, T. E. Design and development of photoanodes for water-splitting dye-sensitized photoelectrochemical cells. *Chem. Soc. Rev.* 2013, *42*, 2357-2387.

[9] Gersten, S. W.; Samuels, G. J.; Meyer, T. J. Catalytic oxidation of water by an oxo-bridged ruthenium dimer. *J. Am. Chem. Soc.* 1982, *104*, 4029-4030.

[10] Gilbert, J. A.; Eggleston, D. S.; Murphy Jr., W. R.; Geselowitz, D. A.; Gersten, S. W.; Hodgson, D. J.; Meyer, T. J. Structure and redox properties of the water-oxidation catalyst $[(bpy)_2(OH_2)RuORu(OH_2)(bpy)_2]^{4+}$. *J. Am. Chem. Soc.* 1985, *107*, 3855-3864.

[11] Nagoshi, K.; Yamashita, S.; Yagi, M.; Kaneko, M. Catalytic activity of $[(bpy)_2(H_2O)Ru–O–Ru(H_2O)(bpy)_2]^{4+}$ for four-electron water oxidation. *J. Mol. Catal. A: Chem.* 1999, *144*, 71-76.

[12] Collin, J. P.; Sauvage, J. P. Synthesis and study of mononuclear ruthenium(II) complexes of sterically hindering diimine chelates. Implications for the catalytic oxidation of water to molecular oxygen. *Inorg. Chem.* 1986, *25*, 135-141.

[13] Lebeau, E. L.; Adeyemi, S. A.; Meyer, T. J. Water Oxidation by $[(tpy)(H_2O)_2Ru^{III}ORu^{III}(H_2O)_2(tpy)]^{4+}$. *Inorg. Chem.* 1998, *37*, 6476-6484.

[14] Sens, C.; Romero, I.; Rodríguez, M.; Llobet, A.; Parella, T.; Benet-Buchholz, J. A new Ru complex capable of catalytically oxidizing water to molecular dioxygen. *J. Am. Chem. Soc.* 2004, *126*, 7798-7799.

[15] Romero, I.; Rodríguez, M.; Sens, C.; Mola, J.; Kollipara, M. R.; Francás, L.; Mas-Marza, E.; Escriche, L.; Llobet, A. Ru complexes that can catalytically oxidize water to molecular dioxygen. *Inorg. Chem.* 2008, *47*, 1824-1834.

[16] Bozoglian, F.; Romain, S.; Ertem, M. Z.; Todorova, T. K.; Sens, C.; Mola, J.; Rodríguez, M.; Romero, I.; Benet-Buchholz, J.; Fontrodona, X.; Cramer, C. J.; Gagliardi, L.; Llobet, A. The Ru-Hbpp water oxidation catalyst. *J. Am. Chem. Soc.* 2009, *131*, 15176-15187.

[17] Zong, R.; Thummel, R. P. A new family of Ru complexes for water oxidation. *J. Am. Chem. Soc.* 2005, *127*, 12802-12803.

[18] Deng, Z.; Tseng, H.-W.; Zong, R.; Wang, D.; Thummel, R. Preparation and study of a family of dinuclear Ru(II) complexes that catalyze the decomposition of water. *Inorg. Chem.* 2008, *47*, 1835-1848.

[19] Wada, T.; Tsuge, K.; Tanaka, K. Electrochemical oxidation of water to dioxygen catalyzed by the oxidized form of the bis(ruthenium-hydroxo) complex in H_2O. *Angew. Chem. It. Ed.* 2000, *39*, 1479-1482.

[20] In this Chapter redox potentials are presented against the normal hydrogen electrode (NHE). Occasionally the referenced potentials have been determined versus different electrodes and have been converted to NHE for the purpose of comparison. For conversion constants, see: (a) Pavlishchuk, V. V.; Addison, A. W. Conversion constants for redox potentials measured versus different reference electrodes in acetonitrile solutions at 25°C. *Inorg. Chim. Acta* 2000, *298*, 97-102. (b) Bard, Allen J.; Faulkner, Larry R. *Electrochemical Methods: Fundamentals and Applications* (2 ed.). John Wiley & Sons Inc. New York 2001.

[21] Wada, T.; Tsuge, K.; Tanaka, K. Syntheses and redox properties of bis(hydroxoruthenium) complexes with quinone and bipyridine ligands. Water-oxidation catalysis. *Inorg. Chem.* 2001, *40*, 329-337.

[22] Campagna, S.; Puntoriero, F.; Nastasi, F.; Bergamini, G.; Balzani, V. Photochemistry and photophysics of coordination compounds: Ruthenium. *Top. Curr. Chem.* 2007, *280*, 117-214.

[23] Kalyanasundaram, K. Photophysics, photochemistry and solar energy conversion with tris(bipyridyl)ruthenium(II) and its analogues. *Coord. Chem. Rev.* 1982, *46*, 159-244.

[24] Thompson, D. W.; Ito, A.; Meyer, T. J. $[Ru(bpy)_3]^{2+*}$ and other remarkable metal-to-ligand charge transfer (MLCT) excited states. *Pure. Appl. Chem.* 2013, *85*, 1257-1305.

[25] Lee, B.-L.; Kärkäs, M. D.; Johnston, E. V.; Inge, A. K.; Tran, L.-H.; Xu, Y.; Hansson, Ö.; Zou, X.; Åkermark, B. Synthesis and characterization of oligonuclear Ru, Co and Cu oxidation catalysts. *Eur. J. Inorg. Chem.* 2010, 5462-5470.

[26] Norrby, T.; Börje, A.; Åkermark, B.; Hammarström, L.; Alsins, J.; Lashgari, K.; Norrestam, R.; Mårtensson, J.; Stenhagen, G. Synthesis, structure, and photophysical properties of novel ruthenium(II) carboxypyridine type complexes. *Inorg. Chem.* 1997, *36*, 5850-5858.

[27] Lomoth, R.; Huang, P.; Zheng, J.; Sun, L.; Hammarström, L.; Åkermark, B.; Styring, S. Synthesis and characterization of a dinuclear manganese(III,III) complex with three phenolate ligands. *Eur. J. Inorg. Chem.* 2002, 2965-2974.

[28] Xu, Y.; Åkermark, T.; Gyollai, V.; Zou, D.; Eriksson, L.; Duan, L.; Zhang, R.; Åkermark, B.; Sun, L. A new dinuclear ruthenium complex as an efficient water oxidation catalyst. *Inorg. Chem.* 2009, *48*, 2717-2719.

[29] Xu, Y.; Fischer, A.; Duan, L.; Tong, L.; Gabrielsson, E.; Åkermark B.; Sun, L. Chemical and light-driven oxidation of water catalyzed by an efficient dinuclear ruthenium complex. *Angew. Chem. Int. Ed.* 2010, *49*, 8934-8937.

[30] Xu, Y.; Duan, L.; Tong, L.; Åkermark, B.; Sun, L. Visible light-driven water oxidation catalyzed by a highly efficient dinuclear ruthenium complex. *Chem. Commun.* 2010, *46*, 6506-6508.

[31] Kärkäs, M. D.; Johnston, E. V.; Karlsson, E. A.; Lee, B.-L.; Åkermark, T.; Shariatgorji, M.; Ilag, L.; Hansson, Ö.; Bäckvall, J.-E.; Åkermark, B. Light-induced water oxidation by a Ru complex containing a bio-inspired ligand. *Chem. Eur. J.* 2011, *17*, 7953-7959.

[32] Concepcion, J. J.; Jurss, J. W.; Templeton, J. L.; Meyer, T. J. One site is enough. Catalytic water oxidation by $[Ru(tpy)(bpm)(OH_2)]^{2+}$ and $[Ru(tpy)(bpz)(OH_2)]^{2+}$. *J. Am. Chem. Soc.* 2008, *130*, 16462-16463.

[33] Tseng, H.-W.; Zong, R.; Muckerman, J. T.; Thummel, R. Mononuclear ruthenium(II) complexes that catalyze water oxidation. *Inorg. Chem.* 2008, *47*, 11763-11773.

[34] Concepcion, J. J.; Jurss, J. W.; Norris, M. R.; Chen, Z.; Templeton, J. L.; Meyer, T. J. Catalytic water oxidation by single-site ruthenium catalysts. *Inorg. Chem.* 2010, *49*, 1277-1279.

[35] Yagi, M.; Tajima, S.; Komi M.; Yamazaki, H. Highly active and tunable catalysts for O_2 evolution from water based on mononuclear ruthenium(II) monoaquo complexes. *Dalton Trans.* 2011, *40*, 3802-3804.

[36] Wasylenko, D. J.; Ganesamoorthy, C.; Koivisto, B. D.; Henderson, M. A.; Berlinguette, C. P. Insight into water oxidation by mononuclear polypyridyl Ru catalysts. *Inorg. Chem.* 2010, *49*, 2202-2209.

[37] Wasylenko, D. J.; Ganesamoorthy, C.; Henderson, M. A.; Koivisto, B. D.; Osthoff, H. D.; Berlinguette, C. P. Electronic modification of the $[Ru^{II}(tpy)(bpy)(OH_2)]^{2+}$ scaffold: Effects on catalytic water oxidation. *J. Am. Chem. Soc.* 2010, *132*, 16094-16106.

[38] Yoshida, M.; Masaoka, S.; Sakai, K. Oxygen evolution from water catalyzed by mononuclear ruthenium complexes with a triazamacrocyclic ligand in a facial fashion. *Chem Lett.* 2009, *38*, 702-703.

[39] Topics in heterocyclic chemistry vol. 21: *N*-Heterocyclic carbenes in transition metal catalysis (Ed. Glorius, F.). Springer-Verlag, Heidelberg, 2007.

[40] Grossmann, A.; Enders D. *N*-Heterocyclic carbene catalyzed domino reactions. *Angew. Chem. Int. Ed.* 2012, *51*, 314-325.

[41] Bugaut, X.; Glorius, F. Organocatalytic umpolung: *N*-heterocyclic carbenes and beyond. *Chem. Soc. Rev.* 2012, *41*, 3511-3522.

[42] Chen, Z.; Concepcion, J. J.; Meyer, T. J. Rapid catalytic water oxidation by a single site, Ru carbene catalyst. *Dalton Trans.* 2011, *40*, 3789-3792.

[43] Bernet, L.; Lalrempuia, R.; Ghattas, W.; Müller-Bunz, H.; Vigara, L.; Llobet, A.; Albrecht, M. Tunable single-site ruthenium catalysts for efficient water oxidation. *Chem. Commun.* 2011, *47*, 8058-8060.

[44] Duan, L.; Xu, Y.; Gorlov, M.; Tong, L.; Andersson, S.; Sun, L. Chemical and photochemical water oxidation catalyzed by mononuclear ruthenium complexes with a negatively charged tridentate ligand. *Chem. Eur. J.* 2010, *16*, 4659-4668.

[45] An, J.; Duan, L.; Sun, L. Ru complexes containing pyridine dicarboxylate ligands: Electronic effects on their catalytic activity toward water oxidation. *Faraday Discuss.* 2012, *155*, 267-275.

[46] Duan, L.; Fischer, A.; Xu, Y.; Sun, L. Isolated seven-coordinate Ru(IV) dimer complex with $[HOHOH]^-$ bridging ligand as an intermediate for catalytic water oxidation. *J. Am. Chem. Soc.* 2009, *131*, 10397-10399.

[47] Duan, L.; Xu, Y.; Zhang, P.; Wang, M.; Sun, L. Visible light-driven water oxidation by a molecular ruthenium catalyst in homogeneous system. *Inorg. Chem.* 2010, *49*, 209-215.

[48] Wang, L.; Duan, L.; Tong, L.; Sun, L. Visible light-driven water oxidation catalyzed by mononuclear ruthenium complexes. *J. Catal.* 2013, *306*, 129-132.

[49] Duan, L.; Bozoglian, F.; Mandal, S.; Stewart, B.; Privalov, T.; Llobet, A.; Sun, L. A molecular ruthenium catalyst with water-oxidation activity comparable to that of photosystem II. *Nature Chem.* 2012, *4*, 418-423.

[50] Duan, L.; Moyses Araujo, C.; Ahlquist, M. S.G.; Sun, L. Highly efficient and robust molecular ruthenium catalysts for water oxidation. *Proc. Natl. Acad. Sci. U. S. A.* 2012, *109*, 15584-15588.

[51] Kärkäs, M. D.; Åkermark, T.; Johnston, E. V.; Karim, S. R.; Laine, T. M.; Lee, B.-L.; Åkermark, T.; Privalov, T.; Åkermark, B. Water oxidation by single-site ruthenium complexes: Using ligands as redox and proton transfer mediators. *Angew. Chem. Int. Ed.* 2012, 11589-11593.

[52] Kärkäs, M. D.; Åkermark, T.; Chen, H.; Sun, J.; Åkermark, B. A tailor-made molecular ruthenium catalyst for the oxidation of water and its deactivation through poisoning by carbon monoxide. *Angew. Chem. Int. Ed.* 2013, *52*, 4189-4193.

[53] Messinger J.; Badger M.; Wydrzynski T. Detection of one slowly exchanging substrate water molecule in the S_3 state of photosystem II. *Proc. Natl Acad. Sci. U. S. A.* 1995, *92*, 3209-3213.

[54] McEvoy, J. P.; Brudvig, G. W. Water-splitting chemistry of photosystem II. *Chem. Rev.* 2006, *106*, 4455-4483.

[55] Barber, J.; Tran, P. D. From natural to artificial photosynthesis. *J. R. Soc. Interface* 2013, *10*, 20120984.

[56] Yachandra, V. K.; Sauer, K.; Klein, M. P. Manganese cluster in photosynthesis: Where plants oxidize water to dioxygen. *Chem. Rev.* 1996, *96*, 2927-2950.

[57] Messinger, J. Evaluation of different mechanistic proposals for water oxidation in photosynthesis on the basis of Mn_4O_xCa structures for the catalytic site and spectroscopic data. *Phys. Chem. Chem. Phys.* 2004, *6*, 4764-4771.

[58] Siegbahn, P. E. M. Structures and energetics for O_2 formation in photosystem II. *Acc. Chem. Res.* 2009, *42*, 1871-1880.

[59] Kusunoki, M. Mono-manganese mechanism of the photosytem II water splitting reaction by a unique Mn_4Ca cluster. *Biochim. Biophys. Acta* 2007, *1767*, 484-492.

[60] Mavros, M. G.; Tsuchimochi, T.; Kowalczyk, T.; McIsaac, A.; Wang, L.-P.; Van Voorhis, T. What can density functional theory tell us about artificial catalytic water splitting? *Inorg. Chem.* 2014, DOI: 10.1021/ic5002557.

[61] Privalov, T.; Åkermark, B.; Sun L. The O-O bonding in water oxidation: The electronic structure portrayal of a concerted oxygen atom-proton transfer pathway. *Chem. Eur. J.* 2011, *17*, 8313-8317.

[62] Betley, T. A.; Wu, Q.; Van Voorhis, T.; Nocera, D. G. Electronic design criteria for O-O bond formation via metal-oxo complexes. *Inorg. Chem.* 2008, *47*, 1849-1861.

[63] Liu, F.; Concepcion, J. J.; Jurss, J. W.; Cardolaccia, T.; Templeton, J. L.; Meyer, T. J. Mechanisms of water oxidation from the blue dimer to photosystem II. *Inorg. Chem.* 2008, *47*, 1727-1752.

[64] Yang X.; Baik, M. H. *cis,cis*-$[(bpy)_2Ru^VO]_2O^{4+}$ catalyzes water oxidation formally via *in situ* generation of radicaloid Ru^{IV}-$O^•$. *J. Am. Chem. Soc.* 2006, *128*, 7476-7485.

[65] Moonshiram, D.; Alperovich, I.; Concepcion, J. J.; Meyer, T. J.; Pushkar, Y. Experimental demonstration of radicaloid character in a Ru^V=O intermediate in catalytic water oxidation. *Proc. Natl. Acad. Sci. U. S. A.* 2013, *110*, 3765-3770.

[66] Concepcion, J. J.; Tsai, M.-K.; Muckerman, J. T.; Meyer, T. J. Mechanism of water oxidation by single-site ruthenium complex catalysts. *J. Am. Chem. Soc.* 2010, *132*, 1545-1557.

[67] Romain, S.; Bozoglian, F.; Sala, X.; Llobet, A. Oxygen-oxygen bond formation by the Ru-Hbpp water oxidation catalyst occurs solely via an intramolecular reaction pathway. *J. Am. Chem. Soc.* 2009, *131*, 2768-2769.

[68] Wang, L.-P.; Wu, Q.; Van Voorhis, T. Acid-base mechanism for ruthenium water oxidation catalysts. *Inorg. Chem.* 2010, *49*, 4543-4553.

[69] Polyansky, D. E.; Muckerman, J. T.; Rochford, J.; Zong, R.; Thummel, R. P.; Fujita, E. Water oxidation by a mononuclear ruthenium catalyst: Characterization of the intermediates. *J. Am. Chem. Soc.* 2011, *133*, 14649-14665.

[70] Lewandowska-Andralojc, A.; Polyansky, D. E.; Zong, R.; Thummel, R. P. ; Fujita, E. Enabling light-driven water oxidation *via* a low-energy Ru^{IV}=O intermediate. *Phys. Chem. Chem. Phys.* 2013, *15*, 14058-14068.

[71] Nyhlén, J.; Duan, L.; Åkermark, B.; Sun L.; Privalov, T. Evolution of O_2 in a seven-coordinate Ru^{IV} dimer complex with a $[HOHOH]^-$ bridge: A computational study. *Angew. Chem. Int. Ed.* 2010, *49*, 1773-1777.

[72] Tong, L.; Duan, L.; Xu, Y.; Privalov, T.; Sun, L. Structural modifications of mononuclear ruthenium complexes: A combined experimental and theoretical study on the kinetics of ruthenium-catalyzed water oxidation. *Angew. Chem. Int. Ed.* 2011, *50*, 445-449.

[73] van der Vlugt, J. I.; Reek, J. N. H. Neutral tridentate PNP ligands and their hybrid analogues: Versatile non-innocent scaffolds for homogeneous catalysis. *Angew. Chem. Int. Ed.* 2009, *48*, 8832-8846.

[74] Lyaskovskyy, V.; de Bruin, B. Redox non-innocent ligands: Versatile new tools to control catalytic reactions. *ACS Catal.* 2012, *2*, 270-279.

[75] Muckerman, J. T.; Polyansky, D. E.; Wada, T.; Tanaka, K.; Fujita, E. Water oxidation by a ruthenium complex with noninnocent quinone ligands: Possible formation of an O-O bond at a low oxidation state of the metal. *Inorg. Chem.* 2008, *47*, 1787-1802.

[76] Boyer, J. L.; Rochford, J.; Tsai, M.-K.; Muckerman, J. T.; Fujita, E. Ruthenium complexes with non-innocent ligands: Electron distribution and implications for catalysis. *Coord. Chem. Rev.* 2010, *254*, 309-330.

[77] Wada, T.; Muckerman, J. T.; Fujita, E.; Tanaka, K. Substituents dependent capability of bis(ruthenium-dioxolene-terpyridine) complexes toward water oxidation. *Dalton Trans.* 2011, *40*, 2225-2233.

[78] Ghosh, S.; Baik, M.-H. The mechanism of O-O bond formation in Tanaka's water oxidation catalyst. *Angew. Chem. Int. Ed.* 2012, *51*, 1221-1224.

[79] Kohl, S. W.; Weiner, L.; Schwartsburd, L.; Konstantinovski, L.; Shimon, L. J. W.; Ben-David, Y.; Iron, M. A.; Milstein, D. Consecutive thermal H_2 and light-induced O_2 evolution from water promoted by a metal complex. *Science* 2009, *324*, 74-77.

[80] Hetterscheid, D. G. H.; van der Vlugt, J. I.; de Bruin, B.; Reek, J. N. H. Water splitting by cooperative catalysis. *Angew. Chem. Int. Ed.* 2009, *48*, 8178-8181.

[81] Yang, X.; Hall, M. B. Mechanism of water splitting and oxygen-oxygen bond formation by a mononuclear ruthenium complex. *J. Am. Chem. Soc.* 2010, *132*, 120-130.

In: Ruthenium
Editor: Gary P. Keeler
ISBN: 978-1-63321-657-0

Chapter 8

RUTHENIUM COMPOUNDS WITH SCHIFF BASES: DESIGN AND PROMISING APPLICATIONS OF SALICYLIDENEIMINE COMPLEXES

Emira Kahrović*
Department of Chemistry, Faculty of Science,
University of Sarajevo, Bosnia and Herzegovina

ABSTRACT

The design and study of new drugs is one of the main challenges in different areas of science for at least two reasons: (i) the cancer has not been defeated and (ii) many bacteria rapidly develop resistance to existing drugs. Development of new drugs is strongly connected with the model of transport, activation of compounds in biological environment, and by the mode of interaction with molecule which is considered the primary target. That is why the recognition of target molecules and processes that determine the activity in biological environment is an imperative for the development of new drugs. A DNA molecule is particularly important for the functioning of biological systems and is considered to be the primary target for anticancer agents. DNA tends to interact by covalent binding with metal complex or non-covalently through two general modes: (i) major and minor groove-bound way stabilized by hydrophobic, electrostatic, and hydrogen-bonding interactions and (ii) through an intercalative interaction in which planar, hetero-aromatic moiety slides between the DNA base pairs. In the case of antimicrobial agents, the drug diffusion through the cell wall is usually major barrier and determining process for the drug activity into the cell. Progressive study of ruthenium complexes with Schiff bases derived from salicylaldehyde and various amines, as candidates for the development of new drugs, is based on several reasons: (i) Ru(III) is isoelectronic with Fe(III) and is found to be readily transported by plasma proteins, (ii) Salicyilideneimines derived from extended planar aromatic amines intercalate DNA, (iii) Many Schiff bases derived from salicyladehyde exhibit antimicrobial activity, especially significant activity against gram-positive bacteria *S. Aureus* and (iv) Since lipid membranes of bacteria favors diffusion of lipid-soluble materials, lipophilicity may be

* Corresonding author: Emira Kahrović. Department of Chemistry, Faculty of Science, University of Sarajevo, Bosnia and Herzegovina. E-mail: emira_kahrovic@yahoo.com.

systematically varied on both, salicylaldehyde and amines aromatic rings. Syntheses of salicylideneimines and their complexes are not demanding. Imines, also known as azomethines or Schiff bases, are compounds represented by the general formula $R_1R_2C{=}NR_3$. A common method for the preparation of the imines is the condensation reaction of salicylaldehyde with the appropriate amine. The reaction can be accelerated by acid catalysis and is generally carried out by refluxing a mixture of a carbonyl compound and an amine.

Syntheses of ruthenium complexes are usually carried out in reaction of $RuCl_3$ with appropriate imine(s) in absolute alcohol solution. From chemical point of view ruthenium complexes with salicylideneimine ligands are thermodynamically stable and resistant to hydrolysis. Kinetically, Ru(II) compounds are more labile than Ru(III). The Ru(III)/Ru(II) electrode potentials depend on the type and number of donor atoms. The electronic effect of nitrogen from azomethine group and phenolate oxygen on reduction potential is different. More electronegative and smaller oxygen atom, hard in character, stabilizes Ru(III), while nitrogen as softer, prefers lower oxidation state.

Systematic alteration of the coordination mode of salicylideneimine ligands in octahedral ruthenium complexes and the consequent fine-tuning of the formal electrode potential are crucial for prospective use of these compounds as electron-transfer mediators and the development of new sensors and catalysts.

INTRODUCTION

Since the time of Werner's theory, development and study of complex compounds has a progressive growth, due to its importance in technique, living systems and theoretical considerations. Hundreds of new complex compounds are being synthesized annually for different purposes. Especially extensive research of metal complexes was found after discovering the anticancer properties of cisplatin in the sixties of the last century. Afterward, more than 2000 new compounds of platinum were synthesized, but only few, like oxaliplatin and carboplatin, have been reached clinical use. Basically, there are three main avenues in research of metal complexes: development of new anticancer, antimicrobial and antiviral drugs, progressive study of new efficient catalysts, and research in the field of electron-transfer mediators for development of new sensors and biosensors.

In addition to platinum compounds, among platinum-group metals ruthenium complexes are the most investigated. Some of them, such as NAMI, NAMI-A and KP1019 have endured several phases of clinical trials as promising anticancer or antimetastatic agents with enhanced selectivity and lower systemic toxicity compared to platinum complexes. Ruthenium complexes are also known as efficient in catalysis, such as Grubb's catalysts of the first and second generation which catalyze olefin metathesis reactions [1]. By searching for new compounds, especially those who might be active in catalysis or who can meet requirements for potentials drugs, many ruthenium complexes with Schiff bases were synthesized and studied.

SYNTHESES AND PROPERTIES

Salicylideneimine Schiff Bases As Ligands

Schiff bases derived from salicyladehyde and various amines are known as salicylideneimines or salicyladimines. They are particularly suitable ligands for at least two reasons: they have great stereochemical flexibility and ability to adjust redox potentials of metal ions in the complex species.

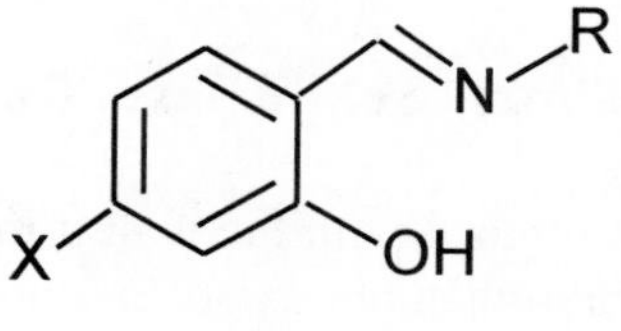

Figure 1. *N*-substituted-5-X-salicylideneimine.

Along with two potential donor atoms, the azomethine nitrogen and phenolic oxygen, amine component can bring additional coordinating atoms. As a result, salicylideneimines may act as monodentate N-donor ligands or chelating ONX_n ligands wherein X is usually oxygen or nitrogen. The mode of coordination and the type of donor atoms allow the tuning of the redox potentials of the metal complex species since the oxygen is hard in character while nitrogen is a softer base.

Syntheses of salicylideneimines are not demanding and take places by condensation of salicylaldehyde and appropriate amines in stoichiometric ratio, mostly from absolute ethanol solutions. The presence of dehydrating agents, e.g., $MgSO_4$ or Na_2SO_4 supports the formation of Schiff bases. In the case of reactive amines, such as low-weight alkyl amines or aniline, the reactions take place at room temperature and Schiff bases are isolated as liquids. In the case of less reactive amines and substituted salicylaldehydes which are solids, heating under reflux is needed, giving the crystalline solids with good yield. Purification of salicylideneimines can cause the decomposition (hydrolysis) of the compounds. A suitable method for the purification is recrystallization, which can be carried out from non-polar solvents such as hexane and cyclohexane, or even from polar ethanol.

The Synthesis of Metal-Salicylideneimine Schiff Bases Complexes

Generally, the preparations of metal complexes with Schiff bases do not require the special conditions. Synthetic methods can be classified into two groups: (i) reaction between appropriate metal compounds and Schiff base, (ii) reaction between the metal-aldehyde complex and the appropriate amine or *vice versa.* In the case of first route, it is possible to use different metal compounds as starting material: metal-alkoxides, although in limited cases due to moisture sensitivity of most metal alkoxides and ability to hydrolyze, metal amides $M(NR_2)$, where R is usually methyl, as very suitable precursors for in the case of early transition metals. Reaction occurs with the deprotonation of the phenolic oxygen on salicylideneimine-Schiff base and with formation of NHR_2. Metal salts, like chlorides or acetates, are often used starting compounds in the synthesis of metal-salicylideneimine Schiff base complexes.

The preparation method of metal complexes with salicylidenimine ligands, introduced by H. Schiff, is based on the reaction of amines with salycilaldehydato-metal complexes near neutral pH.

Salicylaldehyde can act as chelating O,O ligand which coordinates metal *via* phenolic and carbonyl oxygen atoms. After the attack of an amine to the carbonyl group, C=N azomethine group is formed and Schiff base is being coordinated as an anionic ligand.

Ruthenium(III)-Salicylideneimine Schiff Bases Complexes

Ruthenium is a platinum-group metal with the widest range of oxidation from -2 (d^{10}) to +8 (d^0). In most of the compounds ruthenium exists in oxidation states +2 (d^6) and +3 (d^5). Ru(III) complexes are octahedral, low-spin compounds with one unpaired electron. Generally, in low oxidation states, ruthenium demonstrates affinity toward N-, S-, and O-donor ligands. Ru(II) shows higher affinity for N-, and S-donor ligands, while Ru(III) prefers both, N-and O-donor ligands. Therefore, by the modification of the primary coordination sphere is possible to manipulate the electrode potentials and redox properties of the ruthenium complex species. Salicylideneimines give stable and, from kinetically point of view, inert Ru(III) complexes, while Ru(II) complexes are more labile. The complexes are mostly water insoluble, unless contain the polar ligands. In the case of small metal ions like Ru(III) which readily hydrolyze, the chelating ligands significantly reduce the ability of hydrolysis.

The Synthesis of Complexes

In this chapter the principle of synthesis and significant properties of anionic, cationic and neutral Ru(III) complexes with Schiff bases derived from 5-X- substituted salicyladehyde where X = H, Cl, Br, NO_2 and various R-NH_2 amines are presented. The formulation of the compounds was made based on various analytical measurements and here only IR spectra are discussed. As the starting material, $RuCl_3$ was used in the absolute alcohol solution. Depending on stoichiometric ratio of $RuCl_3$ and Schiff base, and the amine component that can bring an extra binding atom, the complex species with $RuO_2N_2Cl_2$, RuO_4N_2, RuO_2N_4 skeletons, were prepared. Reactions were carried out under mild conditions, by refluxing $RuCl_3$ and appropriate Schiff base in absolute alcohol solution and in the presence of triethylamine if needed, as deprotonated agent for phenolic oxygen atoms. Anionic complex species were precipitated with tetraethylammonium cation from $(C_2H_5)_4NBr$ or with Na^+ from aqueous solution. With respect to the stability of the resulting complex species, the removal of $(C_2H_5)_3NH^+Cl^-$ can be done by heating solids at 80 °C and washing with 0.1 M HCl. Otherwise, the complexes might be isolated as triethylamine solvates. In the case of cationic species, the suitable counter ion is Cl^- from starting $RuCl_3$. Solids are insoluble in water and non-polar organic solvents, but soluble in many polar organic solvents like alcohols, acetone, dichloromethane, dimethyl sulfoxide, acetonitrile and dimethylformamide. The complexes can be recrystallized from hot ethanol.

The excess of ligands can be removed with ether. Some ruthenium(III) complexes with Schiff bases derived from 5-substituted salicylaldehyde and primary amines R-NH_2, where R represents –alkyl, phenyl, naphthyl or heterocyclic aromatic pyridyl, were presented in Table 1.

N-Alkyl-5-Substituted-Salicylideneimine Ruthenate(III) Complexes

Dihloro-bis(*N*-butyl-5-chlorosalicylidenimine)ruthenate(III) (3a) was obtained as sodium salt [2]. The homologues (1a-2a, 1b-3b, 3c-1c, 1d-3d) in which alkyl = methyl, propyl and butyl and 5-X-substituent on salicylaldehyde represent H, Cl, Br, NO_2, were prepared from $RuCl_3$ and appropriate Schiff bases in molar ratio 1: 2 respectively, in absolute alcohol solution by refluxing at 75-80 °C. Ligands of general formula (*N*-alkyl-5-X-salimH), wherein X = H, are obtained in the direct reaction from salicylaldehyde and alkyl amines in molar ratio 1:1, while in the case of 5-substituted derivatives, the alcoholic solution of aldehydes and appropriate amines were used. Schiff bases are obtained as liquids with suspended water and were used in the synthesis of the complexes without the removal of water.

Complex anions of the general formula $[RuCl_2(N\text{-alkyl-5-X-Salim})_2]^-$, dichloro-bis(*N*-alkyl-5-substituted-salicylideneimine)ruthenate(III) are dark solids, soluble in polar organic solvents. In the complex species Schiff bases act as O,N-bidentate anionic ligands, giving $RuCl_2O_2N_2$ octahedral skeleton. IR spectra of free ligands and complexes confirmed the coordination of two Schiff bases through azomethine group and phenolic oxygen.

In non-coordinated ligands azomethine asymmetric stretching appears in the range 1636-1607 cm^{-1}, and after coordination is being shifted towards lower values of wave numbers for 9-32 cm^{-1} as a result of the weakening of C=N bond.

Coordination of imines *via* phenolic oxygen after deprotonation is followed by shifts of C-O(H) frequencies in free ligands (1277-1297 cm^{-1}) towards higher values of wave numbers for 11-12 cm^{-1}.

Relatively weak absorptions around 550 and 480 cm^{-1} are attributed to Ru-N and Ru-O absorptions.

N-Phenyl-5-Substituted-Salicylideneimine Ruthenate(III) Complexes

Ruthenate(III) complexes with *N*-phenyl-5-substituted salicylideneimine Schiff bases were obtained as sodium salt (4b) or tetraethylammonium salts (4a, 4c) from $RuCl_3$ and Schiff bases in molar ratio 1:2 respectively [2, 3].

IR spectra are in accordance with coordination *via* atomethine nitrogen and phenolic oxygen.

N-2-Oxyphenyl-5-Substituted-Salicylideneimine Ruthenate(III) Complexes

Due to an extra binding O-atom from 2-aminophenol, *N*-2-oxyphenyl-5-substituted-salicylideneimine can act as O_2N-chelating ligands. The anionic Ru(III) complexes with these ligands are obtained from $RuCl_3$ and Schiff bases in molar ration 1:2 as tetraethylammonium salts (5a) and sodium salts in the case of Cl, Br and NO_2 substituent in position 5- on salicyilaldehyde (5b-5d) [4].

Table 1. Ru(III) complexes containing N-R-substituted-5-X-salicylideneimine Schiff bases

	R from R-NH_2				
Substituent on salicylaldehyde in position 5 (X)	Alkyl (C_2H_5-, C_3H_7-, C_4H_9-)	Phenyl (C_6H_5-)	2-oxyphenyl (C_6H_4O-)	2-pyridyl (C_5H_4N-)	1-naphthyl ($C_{10}H_7$-)
H	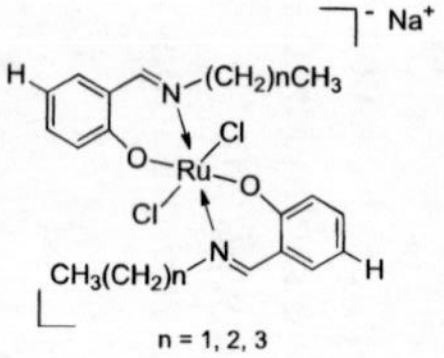 $]^{-}$ Na^{+} H, N, $(CH_2)nCH_3$, Cl, O, Ru, O, Cl, N, $CH_3(CH_2)n$, H n = 1, 2, 3 1a – 3a	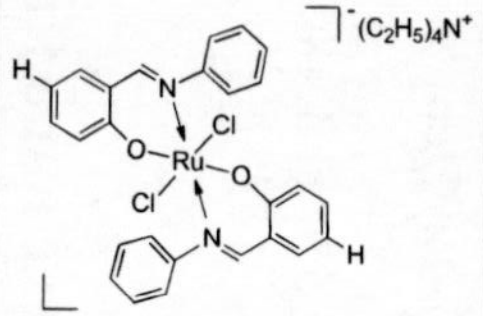 $]^{-}$ $(C_2H_5)_4N^{+}$ H, N, Cl, O, Ru, O, Cl, N, H 4a	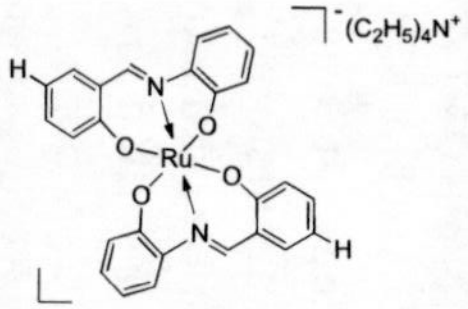 $]^{-}$ $(C_2H_5)_4N^{+}$ H, N, O, O, Ru, O, O, N, H 5a	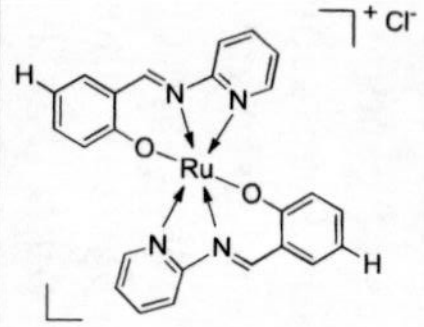 $]^{+}$ Cl^{-} H, N, N, O, Ru, O, N, N, H 6a	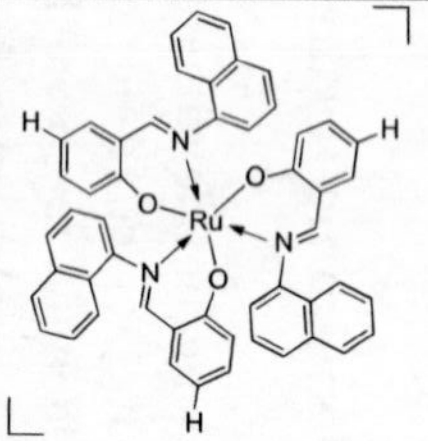 H, N, O, H, O, Ru, N, N, O, H 7a
Cl	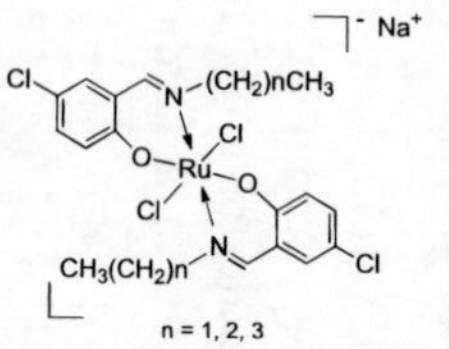 $]^{-}$ Na^{+} Cl, N, $(CH_2)nCH_3$, Cl, O, Ru, O, Cl, N, $CH_3(CH_2)n$, Cl n = 1, 2, 3 1b – 3b	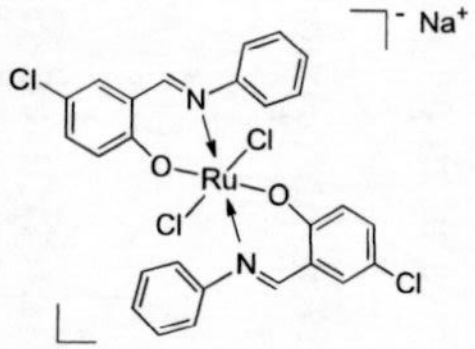 $]^{-}$ Na^{+} Cl, N, Cl, O, Ru, O, Cl, N, Cl 4b	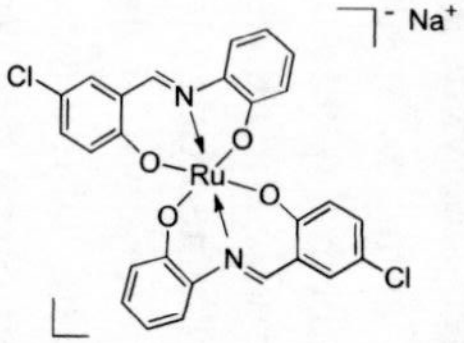 $]^{-}$ Na^{+} Cl, N, O, O, Ru, O, O, N, Cl 5b		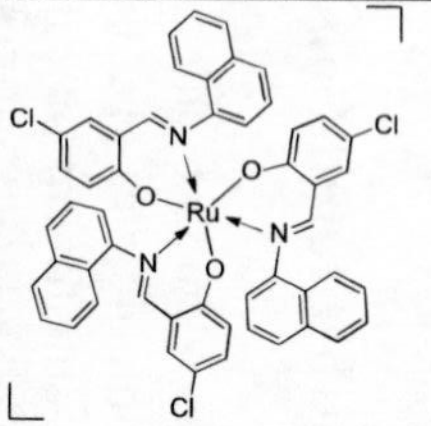 Cl, N, O, Cl, O, Ru, N, N, O, Cl 7b

	R from R-NH_2				
Substituent on salicylaldehyde in position 5 (X)	Alkyl (C_2H_5-, C_3H_7-, C_4H_9-)	Phenyl (C_6H_5-)	2-oxyphenyl (C_6H_4O-)	2-pyridyl (C_5H_4N-)	1-naphthyl ($C_{10}H_7$-)
Br	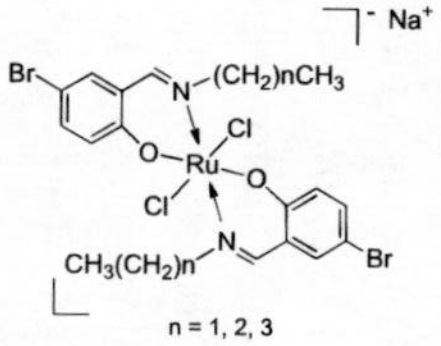 n = 1, 2, 3 1c – 3c	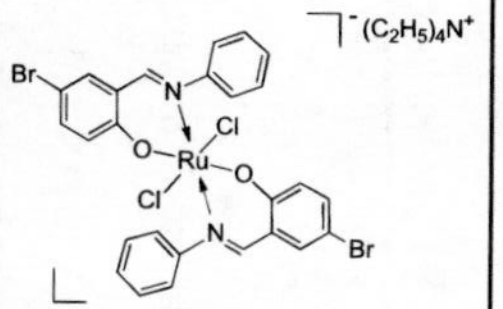 4c	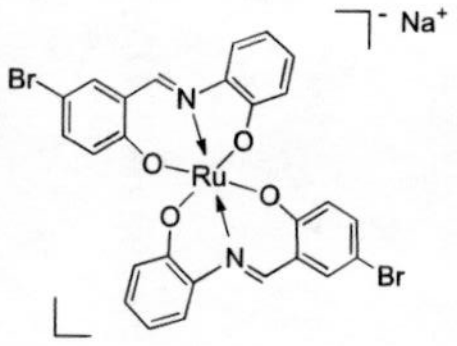 5c		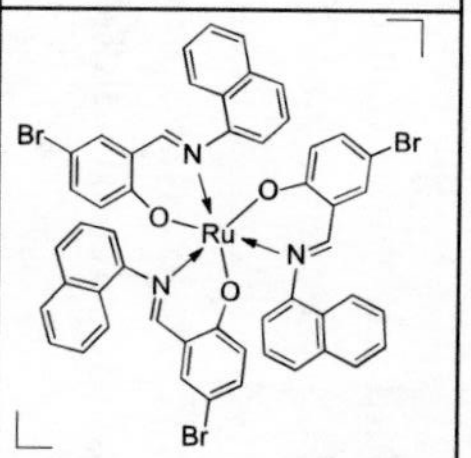 7c
NO_2	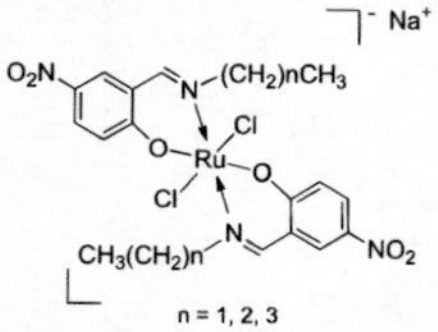 n = 1, 2, 3 1d – 3d		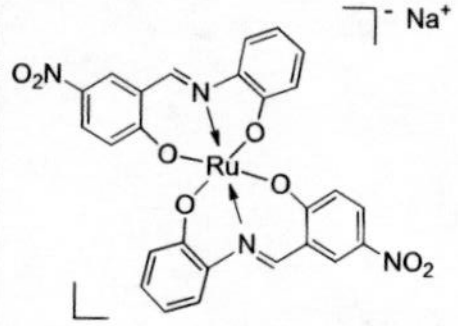 5d		

N-2-Pyridyl-Salicylideneimine Ruthenium(III) Complex

A cationic complex Bis[*N*-(2-pyridyl)salicylideneiminato-*ONN*]ruthenium (III) chloride (6a) is synthesized by refluxing absolute alcohol solution containing $RuCl_3$ and *N*-(2-pyridyl)salicylideneimine in molar ratio 1:2 respectively at 70 °C for 4 hours (Figure 2). Dark solid is washed with cold ethanol, 0.1 M hydrochloric acid and ether.

[*N*-(2-pyridyl)salicylideneimine Schiff base was prepared by condensation of 2-aminopyridyne and salicyladehyde in absolute ethanol solution under the reflux at 70 °C for 2 hours (Figure 3).

$RuCl_3$ + 2 [Schiff base] — EtOH, reflux, 4h, Et_3N, 70 °C → [complex]$^+$ Cl^-

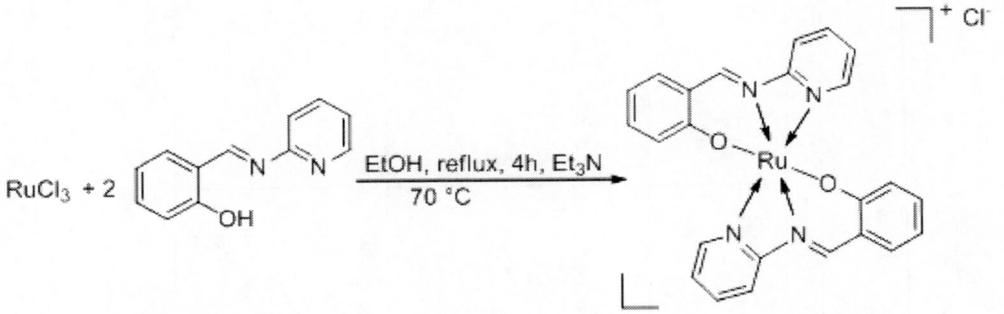

Figure 2. Synthesis of Bis[*N*-(2-pyridyl)salicylideneiminato-*ONN*]ruthenium(III) chloride.

CHO / OH + H_2N — EtOH, reflux → OH

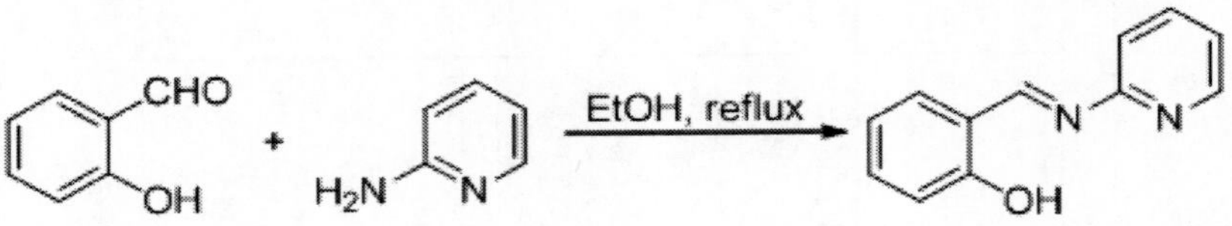

Figure 3. Synthesis of [*N*-(2-pyridyl)salicylideneimine Schiff base.

IR spectrum confirmed coordination of two ON_2 chelating Schiff bases. The azomethine asymmetric stretching frequency, after coordination to Ru(III), is moved from 1609 to1604 cm^{-1}. Coordination of Schiff base to Ru(III) through phenolic oxygen is in accordance with shift of phenolic C-O(H) from 1147 to 1151 cm^{-1} which belong to C-O(Ru) stretching frequency. The coordination through pyridyl nitrogen affected notably the frequencies δ(C=N-C) in-, and out-of-plane of Schiff bases which appear in the range of low wave numbers. As a result, the frequencies are moved from 452 to 466 cm^{-1} and 516 to 525 cm^{-1} respectively. Other peaks in the range 1450-1600 cm^{-1} mainly arise from pyridine ring vibrations. Some of weak absorptions represent overtons or combination of bands and are not affected significantly by chelating. The band at 996 cm^{-1} is attributed to pyridine breathing mode and after chelating is moved to 1010 cm^{-1} which is explained by the formation of coordinative covalent bond between pyridyl nitrogen and ruthenium.

Tris(*N*-1-Naphthyl-5-Substituted Salicylideneimine)Ruthenium (III) Complexes

Neutral Ru(III) complexes with ON-chelating *N*-1-naphthyl-5-substituted-salicylideneimine Schiff bases were prepared (7a-7c).

The complexes of general formula Ru(*N*-R-5-X-salim)$_3$, where R represents 1-naphthyl and X = H, Cl, Br, were obtained from $RuCl_3$ and *N*-1-naphthylsalicyilideneimine Schiff base, used in molar ration 1:3 respectively at 70 °C in rotary evaporator. Ligands were prepared by condensation of 5-X-salicyladehyde and 1-naphthylamine in absolute alcohol solution.

Deprotonation of phenolic oxygen from Schiff bases is achieved by adding a stoichiometric amount of triethylamine in ligand solution which is used in the synthesis of Ru(III) complexes. IR spectra confirmed coordination of three ON- chelating ligands. Characteristic frequencies of azomethine group in free ligands appear at 1611, 1615, 1613 cm^{-1} for H, Cl, Br derivatives in position 5- respectively, and after coordination are being shifted toward lower wave numbers at 1605, 1597 and 1600 cm^{-1}. Generally, the coordination of Schiff bases through phenolic oxygen, when C-O(H) is being transformed to C-O(M), results in a shift of stretching frequency to high energy, depending on the capability of metal to polarize MO bond. In free *N*-1-naphthyl-5-substituted-salicylideneimines phenolic C-O(H) frequencies appear at 1147 cm^{-1} for X=H, at 1163 cm^{-1} for chloro- and bromo-derivatives while in corresponding complexes at 1155, 1175 and 1167 cm^{-1}, respectively.

The Properties of Complexes and Behavior in Solution

Ru(III) complexes with salicylideneimine Schiff bases are dark solids, stable in air, insoluble in water and soluble in polar organic solvents. Behavior in solution is one of the key features for potential use of complexes in different fields. The ruthenium complexes, described in the Chapter, show significant resistance to hydrolysis as a result of ON, ON_2 or O_2N chelating. The hydrolytic profile of complex species is of particular importance, especially for proper interpretation of spectral changes in study of interaction with different biomolecules. Usually, the electronic spectra of Ru(III) complexes with salicylideneimine Schiff bases in non-aqueous solvent, e.g., in CH_2Cl_2, show three bands which belong to ligand intramolecular transitions: (i) bands centered around 230 nm corresponding to $\pi_{aromat} \rightarrow \pi^*$, (ii) bands about 290-300 nm are related to $\pi(O) \rightarrow \pi^*$ and (iii) absorptions around 330-350 nm arising from $\pi(N) \rightarrow \pi^*$ that might be superimposed with LMCT, Cl→Ru(III). In complex species, two new bands appear. The broad absorption at the higher wavelength, usually in the region 370-420 nm, arise from LMCT, L(Schiff base)→Ru(III). The relative position of the absorption bands, that correlates with the electron acceptor properties of 5-X-substituents on salicyladehyde ring, are typically arranged in descending order of wavelength H ~ Cl < Br < NO_2. The electron-acceptor nitro-group reduces the electron density on the ligand making LMCT more difficult. In the spectra of the complexes, a weak and poorly differentiated absorption also appears in the region of spin allowed d-d transition of low spin t_{2g}^5 Ru(III) at 570-600 nm which can be assigned to $^2T_{2g} \rightarrow {}^2A_{2g}$. Schiff base, as condensation products of carbonyl compounds and amines, rapidly hydrolyze. However, after coordination to the metal center, the azomethine group and Ru(III), both of which are stabilized, show significant resistance to hydrolysis. General hydrolytic profile of Ru(III) complexes with salicylideneimines show hypochromism and weak blue shift of the LMCT bands over the time. The blue shift is a result of hidroxo- or aqua-binding into the first coordination sphere of Ru(III). The constants of hydrolysis in buffered 0.1 M Tris-HCl solution at pH = 7.40, calculated for the kinetic of pseudo-first order, are about 10^{-3} min^{-1}. Electrochemical characterization of complex compounds is very important since the electrode potentials have a crucial role in many fields, e.g., catalysis, electron-transfer mediation, in the processes of activation of drugs. Electrode potentials of the metal center in the complex species essentially depend on the type of ligand's environment and the metal affinity for particular donor atoms. Ruthenium occurs in a wide range of oxidation states however its oxidation states II, III and IV are of particular importance. Ru(III) and Ru(II) have significant affinity for N-donor ligands which decreases with the degree of alkylation. Ru(II) are stabilized with the π-acceptor ligands, while Ru(IV) requires acido- and oxo-ligands. Ru(III) and Ru(II) in the complex species with Schiff bases derived from 5-substituted salicylideneimine, exhibit a strong affinity for azomethine nitrogen, while phenolic oxygen rather stabilize Ru(III). Cyclic voltammetry is very useful technique for electrochemical characterization of complex compounds. The general feature of cyclic voltammograms of Ru(III)-salicylideneimine complex species in non-aqueous solutions, measured with glassy carbon electrode as working, Ag/AgCl as reference electrode and Pt wire in the range of negative potentials, is quasi-reversibility of one-electron processes. Quite negative values of half wave electrode potentials, $E_{1/2}$ confirmed stabilization of Ru(III) through phenolic oxygen atoms. In aqueous solutions of complexes, obtained after the initial dissolution in an organic solvent, the anodic and chatodic peaks are not noticeably differentiated. Half wave electrode potentials $E_{1/2}$ for Ru(III)/Ru(II) appear in the range of negative potentials, depending on amine R. For the Ru(III) complexes that contain ON-donor atoms and R-alkyl (1a-3a, 1b-3b, 1c-3c, 1d-3d), phenyl- (4b), and 1-naphthyl (7a-7c), $E_{1/2}$ values in dimethylformamide solution and sodium perchlorate as supporting electrolyte, vary from -0.5 to -0.7 V with significant peak separations of approximately 0.6 V.

For 1-naphthyl derivatives, with extended π-acceptor electron system, the peak separation is 0.8-0.9 V. Half wave potentials $E_{1/2}$ and peak separations ΔE_p, for complexes containing RuO_4N_2 skeleton (5b-5d) are close to values -0.5 V and 0.5-0.7 V respectively. The $E_{1/2}$ and ΔE_p for RuO_2N_4 complexes have close corresponding values, about 0.5V and 0.7V.

The cyclic voltammograms of Ru(III)-salicylideneimine complexes in acetonitrile solutions with tetraethylammonium perchlorate as supporting electrolyte show half wave potentials in the range -0.7 to -0.9 V, but significantly lower values of ΔE_p, 0.2-0.3 V, as a result of poor coordinating abilities of acetonitrile compared to dimethylformamide (Figure 4).

Possibilities and Perspectives in Chemotherapy

Salicylideneimine Scfiff bases provide significant opportunities and different scenarios to modify the modes of coordination, stereochemistry and electronic effects of ligands in octahedral ruthenium complexes:

1 The mode of coordination is possible through azomethine nitrogen (N), azomethine nitrogen and phenolic oxygen (ON); further modifications of the coordination mode can be achieved with amine groups which carry additional donor atoms, e.g., 2-pyridyl (ON_2) or 2-oxyphenyl groups (O_2N).
2 Different charge of Schiff base (1-, 2-) can be obtained by deprotonation of phenolic oxygen or more additional XH groups on R-amine; number and charge of coordinated Schiff bases result in cationic, anionic and neutral complexes of Ru(III).
3 Stereochemistry can be affected by small or voluminous R-amine.
4 Salicyladehyde aromatic ring is suitable for the introduction of substituents, with electron-acceptor or electron withdrawal properties, in different positions.
5 By different donor atoms from Schiff bases, commonly O and N, the fine-tuning of the redox potentials of complex species is possible.

Based on these possibilities, Ru(III) complexes with salicylideneimine Schiff bases are candidates for applications in different fields, particularly in drug development and the electron-transfer meditation.

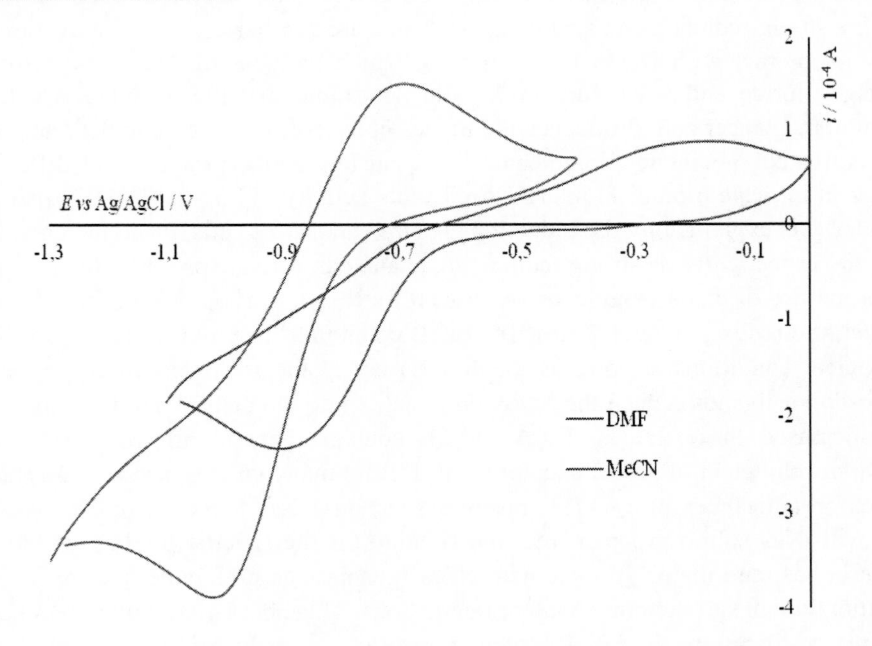

Figure 4. The cyclic voltammograms of $[Ru(N\text{-}2\text{-}py\text{-}salim)_2]Cl$ in dimethylformamide / sodium prechlorate and acetonitrile / tetraethylammonium prechlorate solutions.

Ruthenium complexes have a special place in the medical inorganic chemistry, the scientific discipline whose serious development began with the discovery of anticancer properties of cisplatin in the second half of the last century. Other platinum compounds that have found application as chemotherapeutics are essentially derived from cisplatin, *Cis*-diaminedichloroplatinum(II) by modification of the acido-ligands (carboplatin, *cis*-diammine(1,1-cyclobutanedicarboxylate)platinum or amine ligands, Oxaliplatin, [(1R,2R)-cyclohexane-1,2-diamine](ethanedioato-O,O') platinum(II). General disadvantages of platinum-based drugs are significant side-effects and development of drug resistance. Among the non-platinum drugs, ruthenium(III) complexes have been the subject of huge interest. (ImH)[*trans*-$RuCl_4$(DMSO-S)(Im)] where Im = imidazole, DMSO-S denotes S-bound DMSO, under protected name NAMI-A, has antimetastatic activity [5]. Structurally similar compounds (ImH)[*trans*-$RuCl_4(Im)_2$], under the name ICR or KP418 and (InH)[*trans*-$RuCl_4(In)_2$] (KP1019) are promising anticancer drugs [6]. Other compounds with significant anticancer properties belong to Clarke's class, [*cis*-$RuCl_2(NH_3)_4$)]Cl and [*fac*-$RuCl_3(NH_3)_3$] [7]. In the design of potential drugs it must be considered that the drug activity essentially depends on the model of transport, activation and potential targets. Complexes of Ru(III), which is isoelectronic with Fe^{3+} (d^5 system), are readily transported by plasma proteins, transferrin and albumin.

Due to much higher consumption of oxygen, cancer cells have developed extra transferrin receptor system which can be used for the transport of ruthenium compounds to target cancer cells. In the classical concept of anticancer drug activity, cell nucleus and nucleic acids are thought to be the key targets, although recently the cellular receptors are intensively investigated as possible targets of anticancer agents since their function are being fundamentally changed in the metastatic processes. From the chemical point of view, solid cancers are strong reducing and acidic agents. There are two basic ways of activation of metal complex to interact with DNA: (i) hydrolysis, which includes one or more easily leaving group, e.g chloride and (ii) reduction "*in situ*", meaning that the complex is activated by reduction in the cancer cell. Products and kinetics of hydrolysis depend on the relative affinity of aqua-activated species to biomolecules e.g., nucleic acids, proteins and different small molecules in intricate biological matrix. Anticancer activity of [*cis*-$RuCl_2(NH_3)_4$]Cl and [*fac*-$RuCl_3(NH_3)_3$] is explained by the reduction "*in situ*", in cancer cells. From the chemical point of view, the cancer cells, as strong reducing reactant, can activate pro-drug to an active form. Redox properties of metal complexes are crucial for this activation mechanism. According to this model, the redox potential of Ru(III)/Ru(II) couple has to provide stability of Ru(III) in the biological conditions as long as the Ru(III) enters the hypoxic cancer. Generally, the anionic σ-donor ligands reduce the redox potential, while the neutral and cationic π-acceptor ligands increased these values. DNA, which contains genetic information essential for biological development of all cellular forms of life and many viruses, presents the main target molecule for anticancer drugs. The reactive sites on DNA helix are nucleobases, minor grooves with N2- amino group of guanine suitable for the specific binding of the drug *via* hydrogen bonds, and major grooves with N7 of guanine, as preferable site for many drugs. Intercalation belongs to the non-covalent interactions. This „host-guest" interaction can cause significant modifications in DNA structure resulting in reduced and altered function in physiological processes. The intercalating agents unwind DNA in order to π-stack between two base pairs.

Many pharmacologically interesting compounds, including anticancer drugs and antibiotics, correlate their biological and pharmacological activity with the ability to intercalate the structure of DNA.

Some ruthenium complexes are described as good intercalating agents, $[Ru(phen)_2(dppz)]^{2+}$ and $[Ru(tap)_2(dppz)]^{2+}$ where phen=1,10-phenanthroline; tap=1,4,5,8-tetraazaphenanthrene; dppz=dipyridophenazine [8, 9].

External binding in the grooves can also causes significant changes in the local DNA structure. Ru(III) complexes with Schiff bases derived from salicylaldehyde and amines have some assumptions to be studied and developed as potential drugs: stability, reasonable inertness toward hydrolysis and redox potentials that prevent their reduction in biological environment before they enter the hypoxic targets cells. For Ru(III) complexes, presented in the Chapter, there is the evidence on their ability to bind Calf Thymus DNA with binding constants K_b of order 10^4 M^{-1}. The interaction was investigated by spectroscopic titration and cyclic voltammetry, suggesting that an extended study is needed for Ru(III)-salicylidenimine complexes. The screening of the antiproliferative effects of $[RuCl_2(N\text{-R-5-Cl-salim})_2]^-$, where R= phenyl (4b) on human tumor cell lines, HeLa (cervical carcinoma), SW620 (colorectal adenocarcinoma, metastatic), CFPAC-1 (pancreatic carcinoma), HEp-G2 (hepatocellular carcinoma) and WI38 (normal diploid human lung fibroblast-like cells), as well as on normal (diploid) human fibroblasts (control cell line) showed weak antiproliferative effect and substantially inhibited the cell growth only the high concentration (100 μM). Promising modification of these complexes with extended π-electron-acceptor system of amine components, or with amines obtained by modification from natural products, could provide tighter binding to DNA by intercalation or external binding which can be assisted by additional π-π-interactions.

Progressive study of natural, semi-synthetic and synthetic compounds as potential antimicrobial agents is an imperative in different fields of science, especially due to ability of pathogens to readily and rapidly develop resistance to existing antibiotics. Many organic molecules exhibit antimicrobial activity, but it is known that metal complexes of such molecules exhibit substantially improved activity. The role of metals in the antimicrobial activity of metal complexes have still remained exactly unclear, however complexes of those metals which demonstrate significant activity towards DNA also show significant antimicrobial activity. Many salicylideneimine Schiff bases have shown antimicrobial activity, especially against gram-positive pathogens [10, 11]. Due to the considerable activity of ruthenium complexes toward many biological molecules and targets in living systems, the complexes of Ru(III) are good candidates to develop new potential antibiotics. There is an evidence on significant *in vitro* antimicrobial activity of Sodium dichloro-bis[*N*-phenyl-5-chlorosalicylideneiminato-*N,O*]ruthenate(III) (4b) against gram positive bacteria including *Staphylococcus aureus* (MRSA) and *Bacillus strains,* and *Enterococcus faecalis* while *N*-2-oxyphenyl-5-substituted-salicylideneimine-ruthenate(III) complex (6a) is active only against a narrow spectrum of MRSA pathogens [12, 13]. On the basis of the degree of zone of inhibition and low minimal inhibitory concentration values of 11-50 μg/mL, which reach up to 70-80% of reference antibiotics vancomycin and gentamicin, these complexes are good candidates for further testing and modification, especially taking into account the activity at low concentrations only against gram-positive bacteria.

Electrochemical Application of Ru(III)-Salicylideneimine Schiff Bases Complexes

The development of new amperometric sensors based on chemically modified electrodes is very progressive over the past few decades, particularly due to the growing needs for highly sensitive and selective methods for determination of various analytes. Electrochemical methods are simple, efficient and highly sensitive, especially in flow systems. Many methods for the construction of modified electrodes, modifying agents, and the mechanisms of their actions to substrates are being investigated extensively, especially electrochemical sensors based on carbon electrodes.

Unlike the metal electrodes, the rate of transfer of electrons on the surface of carbon is lower and depends on the structure of the electrode surface. The most used carbon materials are glassy carbon, carbon paste and carbon fiber. The electrodes based on carbon materials are very suitable in electroanalysis, mainly due to the wide "potential window", small background current, low cost and simple options for modifications.

Although ruthenium has ability to accede more oxidation states, the range of potentials related to Ru(III)/Ru(II) is very operational. Some ruthenium modifiers are used for the determination of inorganic and organic analytes e.g., ruthenium red, $[(NH_3)_5Ru^{III}$-O-$Ru^{IV}[(NH_3)_4$-O- $Ru^{III}[(NH_3)_5]^{6+}$ for $S_2O_8^{2-}$ and L-Dopa, $[Ru(bpy)_2(PVP)_{10}Cl]Cl$, for NO_2^- determination, *mer*-Ruthenium(III) bis[1,4-bis(diphenylphosphino)butane]picoline trichloride for ascorbic acid and dopamine, and $Ru(bpy)_3^{2+}$ for determination of N6-isopentrnyl-adenine [14]. Complexes of Ru(III) with salicylideneimine Schiff bases have good properties of the electron-transfer mediators for the carbon-based electrodes: (i) insolubility in water, (ii) small background current of modified electrodes, (iii) low operating potentials and (iv) long-term stability of modified electrodes. Dichloro-bis[*N*-phenyl-5-X-salicylideneiminato-*N,O*]ruthenate(III), wherein X= Cl, Br (4b-c) in bulk modified carbon screen printed electrode was used for determination of ascorbic acid in phosphate buffered solution.

The amperometric measurements in hydrodynamic and flow injection mode at applied potentials of 0.11 and 0.22 V *vs* Ag/AgCl, respectively to 5-X substituent, showed fast current responses with increasing ascorbic acid concentration that is a base of new amperometric sensors for ascorbic acid [15, 16].

Simple sensor constructed by bulk modification of carbon ink with tetraethylammonium dichloro-bis[*N*-phenyl-5-bromo-salicylideneiminato-*N,O*] ruthenate(III) (4c) operate as an amperometric detector for L-cysteine determination in flow injection mode. The sensor works at 0.22 V in phosphate buffer solution, pH=7.4 [17]. The compounds containing SH group like cysteine can be oxidized in the electrochemical processes on different conventional electrodes, though at the high potentials. Modification of electrodes with suitable electron-transfer mediators reduces the overpotential, increase the sensitivity of the method by suppressing the interferences in real samples. The inspection of surface modified carbon pasta electrode with Dihloro-bis[*N*-phenyl-5-bromo-salicylideneiminato-*N,O*]ruthenate(III) (4c) in flow injection mode, at flow rate 0,40 mL/min and operating potential 0.15 V *vs* Ag/AgCl, indicates rapid and reproducible response to the thiol compounds in descending order: dimercaptothiadiazole(2,5-dimercapto-1,3,4-thiadiazole), thiosemicarbazide, thiourea and reduced form of glutathione (GSH).

Carbon paste electrode modified with Sodium bis[*N*-2-oxyphenyl-5-bromosalicylideneiminato-*ONO*]ruthenate(III) (5c) in flow injection mode at 0.15 V *vs.* Ag/AgCl quickly and reproducibly responds to adrenaline and particularly dopamine increase of concentration.

CONCLUSION

Complexes of Ru(III) with salicylideneimines, derived from 5-X-substituted salicylaldehyde and amines R-NH_2 in which R is alkyl, phenyl, naphthyl and pyridyl are stable and inert complexes which can be easily prepared.

The significant biological activity of the complexes is a premise for further examination and modification in order to develop new potential drugs, especially antibiotics. They are promising chemical modifiers, especially for carbon-based electrodes, operating as low potential sensors for different analytes.

Many other properties of these compounds, that might be modified, make them a promising class of compounds, valuable to further investigate.

REFERENCES

[1] Scholl, M., Ding, S., Lee, C. W., Grubbs, R. H. Org. Lett. 1999, 1(6), 953–956.

[2] Ljubijankic, N., Zahirovic, A., Turkusic, E., Kahrovic, *Croat. Chem. Acta.* 2013, 86(2), 215-222.

[3] Kahrovic, E., Dehari, S., Dehari, D., Reci, H., Begic, S., Ljubijankic, N. *Technics Technologies Education Management-TTEM*. Volume, 2010, 5 (4), 799-803.

[4] Kahrovic, E., Zahirovic, A., Turkusic, E. *J. Chem. Chem. Eng*. 2014, 8, 335-343.

[5] Sava, G., Alessio, E., Bergamo, A., Mestroni, G. *Topics in Biological Inorganic Chemistry*. 1999, 1, 143-169.

[6] Keppler, B. K. *Metal Complexes in Cancer Chemotherapy*, Weinheim and New York, 1993.

[7] Clarke, M. J. *Coord. Chem. Rev*. 2003, 236, 209-233.

[8] Greguric, A., Collins, J. G., Clarke, A., Wise, S., Aldrich-Wright, J. 2000, In: *The International Conference of Coordination Chemistry*, Edinburg, UK.

[9] Ambrosek, D., Loos, P. F., Assfeld, X., Daniel, C., *J. Inorg. Biochem*. 2010, 104(9), 893–901.

[10] Shi, L., Ge, H. M., Tan, S. H., Li, H. Q., Song, Y. C., Zhu, H. L., Tan, R. X. *E. J. Med. Chem*. 2007, 42(4), 558-564.

[11] Vinita, Gg., Sanchita, S., Gupta, Y. K. *Res. J. Chem. Sci*. 2013 *3(9), 26-29.*

[12] Kahrovic, E., Bektas, S., Turkusic, E., Zahirovic, A. *SYLWAN*. 2014, 158(5) 482-493.

[13] Zahirovic, A., Bektas, S., Graca, I., Puska, M., Turkusic, E., Kahrovic, E. In: *12th European Biological Inorganic Chemistry Conference*, 2014, Zürich, Swiss.

[14] Svancera, I., Kalcher, Walcarius, A., Vytras, V. *Electroanalysys with Carbon Paste Electrodes*, CRC Press, Taylor and Francis Group, 2102.

[15] Kahrovic, E., Turkusic, E. *HealthMED*. 2012, 6(3), 1046-1049.

[16] Kahrovic, E., Turkusic, E., Ljubijankic, N., Dehari, S., Dehari, D., Bajsman, A. *HealthMED*. 2012, 6(2), 699-702.

[17] Turkusic, E., Kahrovic, E. *Technics Technologies Education Management-TTEM*. 2012, 7(3), 1300-1303.

In: Ruthenium
Editor: Gary P. Keeler

ISBN: 978-1-63321-657-0

Chapter 9

POLYMERIC RUTHENIUM COMPOUNDS: SYNTHESIS AND EMPLOYMENT AS SYNTHONS

Frederick P. Malan, Eric Singleton and Reinout Meijboom
Department of Chemistry, University of Johannesburg,
Auckland Park, Johannesburg, South Africa

ABSTRACT

Polymeric organometallic ruthenium systems have been known for more than 50 years, and their chemistry and synthetic pathways have been extensively studied mainly for their reaction patterns to give an array of neutral and cationic ruthenium complexes which in turn shows to be highly reactive complexes. Worldwide research over the last few decades on the synthesis and reactivity of ruthenium complexes in solution gave rise to a range of different versatile and stable catalysts which are increasingly employed in organic synthesis. These complexes find widespread use in the synthesis of complex organic molecules which have application in the pharmaceutical, plastic and other commercial industries. The ongoing search for inexpensive and trivial synthetic routes to these chemo- and regio-selective ruthenium complexes have in many accounts made use of polymeric ruthenium precursors, and is still of interest to date. Some of these polymeric complexes also exhibit other interesting physical properties which renders them useful for other applications. This chapter covers the initial discovery of selected organometallic polymeric- and oligomeric Ru(0), Ru(I), and Ru(II) species for the specific application as highly reactive synthons to fine organo- and inorganic ruthenium complexes, their associated solid state structures that has been investigated, and their reactions involving both stoichiometric and catalytic amounts of these complexes with a wide range of ligands under various reaction conditions. Modern approaches to other polymeric ruthenium species that has been synthesized in the last 15 years are also discussed. Selected reactions, reactions with ligands, and selected characterization of the polymeric complexes have been tabulated and are included herein.

INTRODUCTION TO POLYMERIC RUTHENIUM(II) SPECIES

One of the great interests of organic chemists has always been focused on the developments in the design and use of homogeneous catalysts employed in chemical transformation reactions. The motive was, and still is, to convert readily available commercial compounds into sought after and expensive organic compounds. Therefore, an overwhelming amount of research has been dedicated to this area of synthetic chemistry (both organic and inorganic). From these studies high catalytic activities with impressive turn over numbers, as well as instances with a high degree of selectivity and enantiomeric excess for products obtained were achieved. The concept and term of catalyst tailoring [1] originated from the process of optimizing the catalytic capability and efficiencies in the organic reactions that transition metal complexes are found to catalyse. The optimization of the catalytic efficiencies and therefore applicability of these catalysts involves the ease of variation of the nature of the ligands, geometric arrangement of the complex, and the valence state of the metal. A common problem encountered in the synthesis of these and other materials is the difficulty associated with obtaining a compound of specific geometrical arrangement of atoms or molecules in three-dimensional space. Therefore, a great deal of research is focused on the synthesis of crystalline compounds having sought after chemical and physical properties. With this in mind, finding synthetic methodologies to control or guide the arrangement of the crystalline material's ligands or substituents in a predictable manner is of high importance [2]

For a specific class of catalysts such as hydrogenation catalysts, and certainly for other classes of catalysts, complexes have been synthesised to contain mainly group 8, 9, and 10 transition metals: Fe, Ru, Os, Rh, Ir, Ni, Pd, and Pt. [1] Acquiring highly active catalysts is dependent on effective combinations of d^8 spin-paired (low-spin) configurations due to strong ligand fields and electron delocalizing (strong π-acceptor) ligands. The identification and elaboration of the mechanisms that are involved in the hydrogenation reactions are frequently reported on. These mechanisms generally include the mode of activation of molecular hydrogen by a homogeneous catalyst, the activation of the substrate, and the subsequent transfer of the activated hydrogen to the substrate, often with a significant degree of stereospecificity.

Spanning more than 45 years, chemists have devoted much attention and research to the vast area of supramolecular species obtained by assembling transition metal complexes as molecular components – specifically the synthesis and more importantly, the application thereof. Provided that the monomeric units exhibit suitable properties and the assembly as a whole behaves accordingly, many useful features, functions and applications for this class of molecules exist. These include fascinating features such as information recording, conversion of light into chemical energy, electrical properties, electrochemical properties, magnetic properties, luminosity, and the direct use of these species as highly stable and reactive synthons. Reactive synthetic precursors allow for the synthesis of wide arrays of different groups of neutral and cationic transition metal complexes, of which these themselves often turn out to be reactive synthetic precursors. [3]

However, in the case of transition metal complex polynuclear compounds, few routes exist to the well-defined and structured synthesis of supramolecular species with specialized functions. Some of the limitations encountered in these syntheses are the number of metal atoms that remain small (mostly cluster compounds such as di-, tri-, tetra-, and penta-nuclear metal and mixed-metal complexes), or in the other extreme large and/or not well-defined polymeric species are obtained. [3] Well-defined polymeric transition metal compounds tend to be remarkably stable and can provide routes to highly reactive starting materials in synthetic schemes designed for specific and product-directed reaction outcomes.

A number of different polymeric species exist, but few are useful as precursors to a wide variety of neutral and cationic ruthenium(II) complexes. The most prominent example in the literature is $[RuCl_2(1,5\text{-cod})]_x$ (x > 2). In this thesis we investigate further reactions of $[RuCl_2(1,5\text{-cod})]_x$ (x > 2). This complex has been used to synthesise a wide range of neutral and cationic Ru(II) complexes which will be discussed in this chapter.

Many complexes containing triphenylphosphine ligands were synthesised from the reactions of $RuCl_3.xH_2O$ in alcohol solvents. These include the neutral monomeric ruthenium(II) complexes $[RuHCl(PPh_3)_3]$, [4] $[RuCl_2(PPh_3)_3]$, [5] $[RuH_2(PPh_3)_4]$, [5] and $[RuHCl(CO)(PPh_3)_3]$. [5] Reactions [6] of $RuCl_3.xH_2O$ in alcohol solvents with diaryl-, alkyl- or aryldialkyl-phosphines by comparison form triply-chloro bridged cationic ruthenium(II) dimers. However, these syntheses often involve complex reduction reactions employing hazardous reagents such as sodium amalgams, often in relatively low yield after extensive purification procedures. This is in strong contrast to the more simplistic synthetic routes developed to employ the more convenient polymeric species and react it under milder conditions. Furthermore, few routes exist which fully utilize the effective and straightforward methodology of ruthenium(II) polymeric species of which the syntheses and applications are described in the following sections.

1) Chloride-Bridged Cyclooctadiene Ruthenium(II) Polymer: $[RuCl_2(1,5\text{-cod})]x$ (x > 2)

$[RuCl_2(1,5\text{-cod})]_x$ (x > 2) was first synthesised in 1958 by Abel and co-workers. [7] An optimized, general procedure was published later by Albers et al. [8] which entailed the reaction of commercially available $RuCl_3.xH_2O$ with 1,5-cyclooctadiene in EtOH under reflux conditions which gave the polymeric compound in high yield (> 96%). Diene ruthenium(II) dichloride polymers are air- and light stable, insoluble complexes. However, extensive investigations on these polymers with nitrogen-donor ligands in alcohol solvents have led to an extensive range of neutral and cationic ruthenium(II) complexes in moderate to high yields. [9,10]. Specifically the cationic complexes $[RuX(1,5\text{-cod})(NH_2NR_2)_3]^+$ (X = H, R = H, Me; X = Cl, R = Me) and dicationic complexes $[Ru(1,5\text{-cod})(NH_2NH_2)_4]^{2+}$ were synthesised from the reactions of the polymer with NH_2NR_2 (R = H, Me) in alcohol solvents which gave clear pale red solutions from which the complexes were isolated as the PF_6-, BF_4- or BPh_4-salts. Reactions of these salts led to a plethora of different neutral- and cationic ruthenium(0), (I), (II), (III) and (IV) complexes [9,11-13].

2) Carboxylato and Carboxylato-Bridged Ruthenium(I) and (II) Polymeric Species

When $RuCl_3.xH_2O$ is heated under reflux with ethanoic acid and ethanoic anhydride, a green solution with a brown precipitate from the solution is observed, which subsequently analysed for $[Ru_2(O_2CCH_3)_4Cl]$. [14] Higher yields of the brown compound were obtained with the addition of an excess of LiCl to the reaction mixture being heated [15] Various analogues have been synthesized [16] as a series with general formula $[Ru_2(O_2CR)_4X]_x$ ($x > 2$; R = H, X = Cl, Br; R = Me, X = Cl, Br, I, SCN, NO_3, CH_3COO; R = Ph, X = Cl, Br; R = CH_2Cl, X = Cl). Considering the insoluble nature of the latter compounds, complete and meaningful characterization of these compounds proved to be challenging. The butanoate counterpart, however, has been found to be soluble in, amongst others, butanoic acid from which it has been recrystallized to give brown tetragonal crystals. An X-ray crystal structure determination revealed for the first time the polymeric nature of these compounds having a basic dimeric $[Ru_2(O_2CC_3H_7)_4]^+$ unit, linked indefinitely by chloride anions [17]

The high yield synthesis of a carboxylato-bridged ruthenium(I) polymer, $[Ru(\mu\text{-}O_2CR)(CO)_2]_x$ ($x > 2$; R = H, Me, Et, Pr, C_9H_{19}), has also been reported from the ruthenium carbonyl cluster compound of $[Ru_3(CO)_{12}]$ together with carboxylic acids under reflux conditions. [18,19] An X-ray crystal structure of the analogous Os-derivative, $[Os(\mu\text{-}O_2CMe)(CO)_3]_2$, has been determined and revealed a C_{2v} point group symmetry with the carboxylato groups bridging the metal centers and with terminal carbonyl ligands as shown in Figure 1.1.[19] The polymeric complex $[Ru(\mu\text{-}O_2CMe)(CO)_2]_x$ was shown to be a useful precursor to a range of neutral and cationic dimeric complexes containing alkyl cyanides, [19] isocyanides, [20] mono- and bidentate tertiary phosphorous ligands, [21,22] and the dimeric species of $[\{Ru(\eta^5\text{-}L)(CO)_2\}_2]$ (L = Cp, Cp*) and $[\{Ru(HB(pz)_3)(CO)_2\}_2]$. [23]

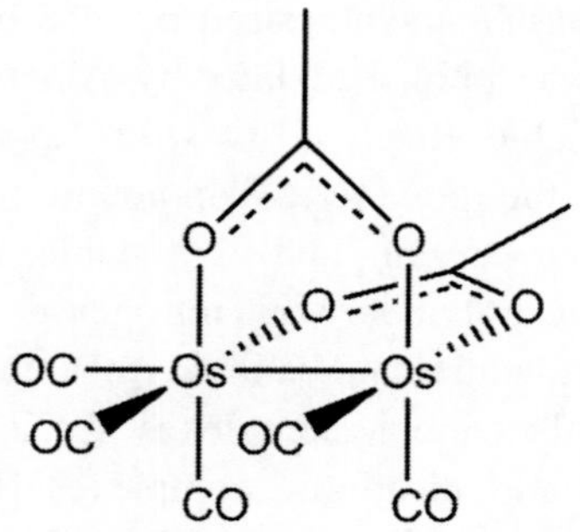

Figure 1.1. Graphical representation of the complex $[Os(\mu\text{-}O_2CMe)(CO)_3]_2$ with bridging carboxylato groups.

De Villiers Steyn et al. [19,21,22] showed in their work that the dinuclear complexes of $[Ru(\mu\text{-}O_2CMe)(CO)_2(NCMe)]_2$ and the polymeric dimers of $[Ru_2(\mu\text{-}O_2CR)_2(CO)_4]_x$ ($x > 2$; R = Me, Et) reacts with one molar equivalent of diphosphine ligands to give the air-stable, sparingly soluble polymers of ruthenium(I) of formula $[Ru_2(\mu\text{-}O_2CR)_2(CO)_4(L_2)]_x$ ($x > 2$; L_2 = dmpm, dppm, dpam, dppe, arphos, dpppr, dppb, dppp). The structure of the analogous complex, $[Ru_2(\mu\text{-}O_2CMe)_2(CO)_4(MeSCH_2SMe)]_x$ ($x > 2$), has been determined and confirmed the structure proposed for the above polymers. [19,21,22] When two molar equivalents of dppm are reacted with $[Ru_2(\mu\text{-}O_2CR)_2(CO)_4]_x$ (x > 2) in THF the neutral disubstituted dimer $[Ru_2(\mu\text{-}O_2CMe)_2(CO)_4(\eta^1\text{-dppm})_2]$ is formed in quantitative yields. In alcoholic solvents $[Ru_2(\mu\text{-}O_2CR)_2(CO)_4]_x$ (x > 2) reacts with the diphosphines dppm and dppe to form cationic species of the type $[Ru_2(\mu\text{-}O_2CMe)(CO)_4(L_2)_2]$ (L_2 = dppm, dppe) [22] and the unusual salt $[Ru_2(\mu\text{-}O_2CMe)(CO)_3(dppm)(\eta^1\text{-dppm})(\mu\text{-dppm})](PF_6).C_2H_5OH$. [24]

From interpretations of FTIR, ^1H- and $^{31}P\{^1H\}$-NMR spectra Singleton et al. [24] inferred a synthetic pathway involving three distinct bonding modes of the bidentate phosphine ligand in this latter cationic salt. This synthetic scheme is illustrated in Scheme 1.1.

The polymeric $[Ru_2(\mu\text{-}O_2CMe)_2(CO)_4]_x$ reacts [25] with L = CH_3CN, PPh_3 to form the carboxylate-bridged dimeric species of $[Ru_2(\mu\text{-}O_2CMe)_2(CO)_2(L)_2]$. From the reactions of the salts K[HB(pz)₃] and K[B(pz)₄] with $[Ru_2(\mu\text{-}O_2CMe)_2(CO)_4]_x$ in boiling alcoholic solutions forms dimeric complexes $[Ru_2\{RB(pz)_3\}_2(CO)_4]$ (R = H, pz) in which the dimer is held together by a metal-metal bond. [26] Interestingly, the complex of $[Ru_2(\mu\text{-}pz)_2(CO)_4(PPh_3)_2]$ can be synthesised from the reaction of the polymeric $[Ru_2(\mu\text{-}O_2CMe)_2(CO)_4]_x$ with $NaEt_2B(pz)_2$ and PPh_3 in boiling MeOH. It is not clear[25] how fragmentation of the pyrazolylborate ligand occurred. These reactions of the neutral polymer of $[Ru_2(\mu\text{-}O_2CMe)_2(CO)_4]_x$ and $[Ru_2(\mu\text{-}O_2CMe)_2(CO)_2(L)_2]$ demonstrate the versatility of these compounds for the synthesis of a range of neutral and cationic dimeric compounds having coordinated isocyanide, [20] mono- and bidentate tertiary phosphine,[22] and bidentate amine ligands. [23]

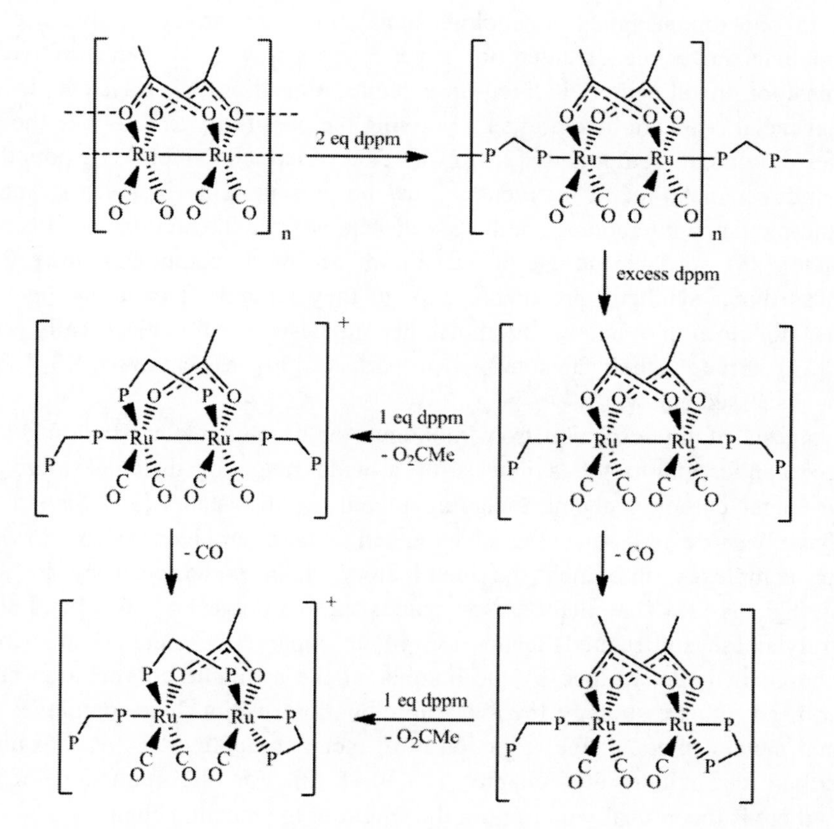

Scheme 1.1. Synthetic pathway to the formation of, amongst other, the salt of $[Ru_2(\mu\text{-}O_2CMe)(CO)_3(dppm)(\eta^1\text{-dppm})(\mu\text{-dppm})](PF_6)$. [24].

Interestingly, Wilkinson et al. [27] have synthesised the mixed valent Ru(II)/Ru(III) air stable orange polymeric compound $\{Na_3[Ru_2(\mu\text{-}O_2CMe)_2].6H_2O\}_x$ (x > 2). The product was isolated in moderate yields (~ 40%) from the disproportionative reaction of $[Ru_2(\mu\text{-}O_2CMe)_4]$ with an aqueous solution of excess Na_2CO_3. This complex is water soluble, but insoluble in organic solvents. It has been characterised by FTIR (KBr), UV/Vis spectroscopy and cyclic voltammetry methods. SXRD characterization has revealed an unusual bonding mode for the carboxylate anion(s). [27]

The crystal structure determination showed that the carbonato groups behave as unusual bidentate ligands which are linked together into a layer through axial Ru-O interactions to a free carbonato oxygen of a neighboring dimeric unit. [27] Hence, in each dimeric unit two free oxygen atoms are involved, with the water molecules interacting only with the Na ions. This compound has also been found to possess catalytic abilities; high activity was identified in a two-phase aqueous-alkene system in the hydrogenation of terminal and internal alkenes [27].

3) Extended Metal Atom Chain Compounds

i. Examples Prevalent in the Literature

The field of coordination chemistry with respect to an extension of mono- or dinuclear complexes to one dimensional, three dimensional multinuclear, and polymeric transition metal compounds have been studied for several years now [28]. Constructive interplay between transition metal centers is likely in extended transition metal systems in which the mononuclear metal units are linked together, giving the possibility to fine-tune the properties of these transition metal compounds [28] In the case of extended metal compounds, various direct and indirect metal-metal interactions may be present. This includes strong covalent bonds, ligand-mediated interactions, and weak dispersion type interactions observable only in the solid state. [28] To date, the use of this line of polymeric compounds have found little application as direct synthetic precursors, though they remain an exciting topic for other applications; for example acting as molecular metal-wires for electrically conducting purposes, [29] through their anisotropic properties, [30] as catalysts, [31] and other applications discussed below.

The synthesis of linear chains from mononuclear or oligonuclear building blocks has found direct application to the synthesis of a wide range of different oligonuclear or polynuclear metal carbonyl chains including mixed-metal systems [32] Several synthetic strategies have been devised to synthesise extended metal atom chains, also known as metal atom string complexes, in which the metal atom chain is wrapped by its supporting multidentate ligands [28] One method uses ligands such as polyenes [33-35] and polydentate oligo-α-pyridylamino and related ligands [36-40] to support the metal chain, whereby the length of the chain is determined by the number of the available coordination sites of the ligand. Another synthetic strategy involves the oxidation of dinuclear complexes having d^8 square-planar metal centers, or the reduction of d^7 metal compounds. Several examples have been described throughout this chapter [28,30,41,42] For the reduction of d^7 metal compounds there is theoretically no limit in the length of the metallic chain.

Another synthetic strategy for the synthesis of oligomeric, linear transition metal carbonyl chains uses transition metal cluster compounds as precursors. These reactions usually involve metal-metal bond fission, especially in the clusters $[Ru_3(CO)_{12}]$, $[Os_3(CO)_{12}]$, $[Os_3(CO)_{11}L]$, and $[Os_3(CO)_{10}L_2]$ (L = RCN, RNC, PPh_3, $SbPh_3$) which do not contain bridging carbonyl ligands. These cluster opening reactions occur with the use of halogens, polyenes, 2,7-disubstituted naphtyridines, monoazadienes, 2,2'-dimethyl-3,5-heptane-dionate, silanes, oxadienes, and RN=NNHR moieties.[32] Generally, with $[M_3(CO)_{12}]$ (M = Ru, Os) either a trinuclear or a linear transition metal chain is formed in these reactions in which one of the metal-metal bonds of the trinuclear clusters is broken [32]. To date most of the linear metal-metal bonded complexes are formed from the trinuclear carbonyl clusters from reactions of complexes of Cr(II), Cr(III), Co(II), Ni(II), Pt(II), Cu(II), Ru(II), and Rh(II). [30,43]

Rare linear zero-valent metal atom chains with no supporting ligands of general formula $[M(bpy)(CO_2)]_x$ ($x > 2$; M = Ru, Os) were prepared by electrochemical reduction of the mononuclear d^6-species $[MCl_2(bpy)(CO)_2]$. [28,44-47] Jia et al. [48] have found a route to dimeric and polymeric ruthenium complexes containing Ru-vinyl linkages. These syntheses entail reaction of the carbonyl hydrido complex $[RuHCl(CO)(PPh_3)_3]$ with diene-ynes HC=CRC≡CH (R = *para*-C_6H_4) to yield five-coordinate vinyl ruthenium dimeric compounds with general formula $[\{RuCl(CO)(PPh_3)_2\}_2(\mu\text{-}CH{=}CHRCH{=}CH)]$ in quantitative yields. Subsequent reactions with the latter dimer and isocyanides or bipyridines gave rise to the formation, isolation and partial characterization of polymeric ruthenium compounds with general formula $[RuCl(CO)(PPh_3)_2(\mu\text{-}CH{=}CHRCH{=}CH)RuCl(CO)(PPh_3)_2(\mu\text{-}L)]_x$ ($x > 2$; L = 2,3,5,6-tetramethylphenyl diisocyanide; 4,4'-bipyridine). [48]

ii) Synthesis of $[Ru(CO)_4]_x$ ($x > 2$) and the catalytic application thereof

The linear polymeric species $[Ru(CO_4)]_x$ ($x > 2$) are other examples of zero-valent linear polymeric compounds. These were synthesised by Baird et al. from the photochemical cluster opening of $[Ru_3(CO)_{12}]$. [49] The polymeric structure was confirmed by powder X-ray diffraction (PXRD). [50] The compound $[Ru(CO_4)]_x$ ($x > 2$) may also be synthesised from the direct reductive carbonylation of $RuCl_3$. [32] This compound has been shown to react with high pressures of CO (~5.1 kPa) to form mixtures of $[Ru(CO)_5]$ and the thermodynamically stable $[Ru_3(CO)_{12}]$; with H_2 to yield $[Ru_4H_4(CO)_{12}]$; with halogens to yield the neutral ruthenium(II) *cis*-$[RuX_2(CO)_4]$ (X = I, Br); with CCl_4 to form $[Ru_2(CO)_6Cl_4]$ exclusively; and with tertiary phosphines to yield ruthenium(0) products with a major product of $[Ru(CO)_4(L)]$ (L = PMe_2Ph, PMe_3), and another minor product of $[Ru(CO)_3(L)_2]$. [49]

This complex, $[Ru(CO_4)]_x$, is amongst a selected few polymeric compounds that have been shown to be active catalysts in, the activation of carbon dioxide in the water-gas shift reaction, [51-53] the reduction of CO_2 gas, [44-46] and in C-H activation of arene systems [54]. Haukka et al. [28,31] have reported the successful application of $[Ru(CO)_4]_x$ ($x > 2$) to the hydroformylation of 1-hexene, which apparently showed higher activity with the employment of ionic liquids as promoters. This is similar to reactions reported for well-known trinuclear cluster of $[Ru_3(CO)_{12}]$. [31]

The industrially significant process of hydroformylation which involves the homogeneous carbonylation of olefins is the most researched transformation process to date. The industrial process involves the conversion of olefins with synthesis gas ($CO + H_2$) using a Rh or Co transition metal catalyst [55] Some reports have used the reverse water-gas shift reaction (RWGS) as a prelude to the hydroformylation process. The WGSR is an industrial significant reaction in that it produces hydrogen gas as a product which can be employed directly in amongst other Fischer-Tropsch type syntheses, ammonia syntheses, and organic chemicals [53]. It has been reported in a few reports that CO_2 is used as an alternative source to CO through the reverse water shift reaction (RWGS). These reactions lead to a catalytic system for hydroformylation employing CO_2 and H_2. [56] This is an attractive process, in that the same active catalysts employed in the RWGS reaction, can be used [57-60] in the subsequent hydroformylation reaction (Scheme 1.2). Therefore, the RWGS conversion route to hydroformylation is a green and hence sustainable industrially reaction [61]

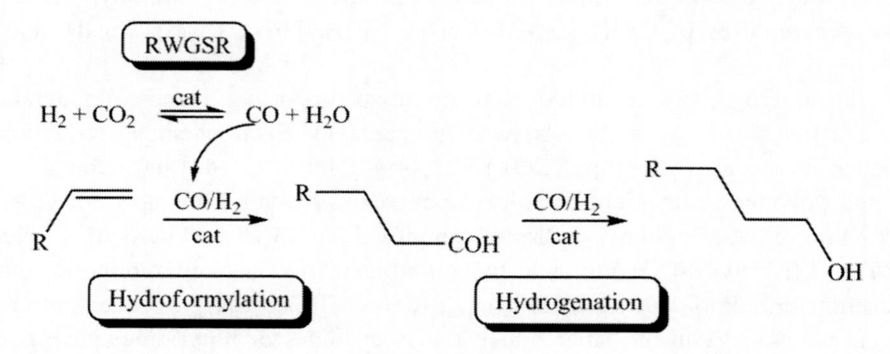

Scheme 1.2. The one-pot activation of CO_2 through the RWGSR, followed by hydroformylation of alkenes, and subsequent hydrogenation to the end alcoholic products [28].

The abundant and readily available carbon resource of carbon dioxide gas (CO_2) has the advantages of being non-toxic, abundant and economical [62] CO_2 is also known to be attractive as an environmentally friendly chemical reagent and is especially useful as a phosgene substitute. A major challenge remains the high energy input required to convert CO_2 gas in industrial processes. Therefore, for CO_2 to be reactive in chemical transformations, the large energy input is not environmentally friendly or efficient [63]. If the thermodynamics of the RWGS equation is taken into account, the catalysts active at relatively lower temperatures would necessarily lead to increased reaction efficiency and a lower thermal input requirement [56,63]

Haukka et al. [58] have previously undertaken a study where they investigated the effect of ruthenium carbonyl-based catalysts and the role of promoters for hydroformylation of 1-hexene with CO_2 as a reactant at 60 bar pressure and a temperature of 150°C. They have also revealed that numerous ruthenium precursors could be used for the reaction, and that cluster compounds as catalyst precursors were not necessary. The hydroformylation process by Tominaga et al. [64] were made more efficient by using different ionic liquids as solvents for the simple and easy synthesis of desired products.

4) Tetraamidato- and Tetracarboxylatodiruthenium Compounds

Renewed interest in a specific subset of the field of supramolecules, commonly referred to as paddlewheel complexes, employing transition metals occurred in the last few years. This is because of their fascinating magnetic and electronic properties, as well as their potential applications as molecular materials for use in the booming nanochemistry industry [65]

Therefore, over the past three decades the synthesis, structure, bonding, and reactivity patterns of these complexes have been duly reported on [65]

For instance, the substitution of acetate moieties in $[Ru_2Cl(\mu\text{-}O_2CMe)_4]$ by other carboxylate or formamidinate ligand systems has allowed for the development of a range of supramolecular compounds with either the $[Ru_2(\mu\text{-}O_2CR)_4]^+$ or $[Ru_2(\mu\text{-}NRCHNR)_4]^+$ dimeric cations as repeating units. Depending on the R group in these ligands, as well as the choice of solvent employed, synthesis routes may be optimized to yield either molecular or polymeric compounds [65]. The first chloridotetraamidatodiruthenium complexes were obtained by the reaction of $[Ru_2Cl(\mu\text{-}O_2CMe)_4]$ with molten amide ligands, with structural elucidation of two of these resulting polymeric compounds, $[Ru_2Cl(\mu\text{-}NHOCR)_4]_x$ ($x > 2$; R = Ph, 4-Cl-C_6H_4) by SXRD reported afterwards (see Figure 1.2).

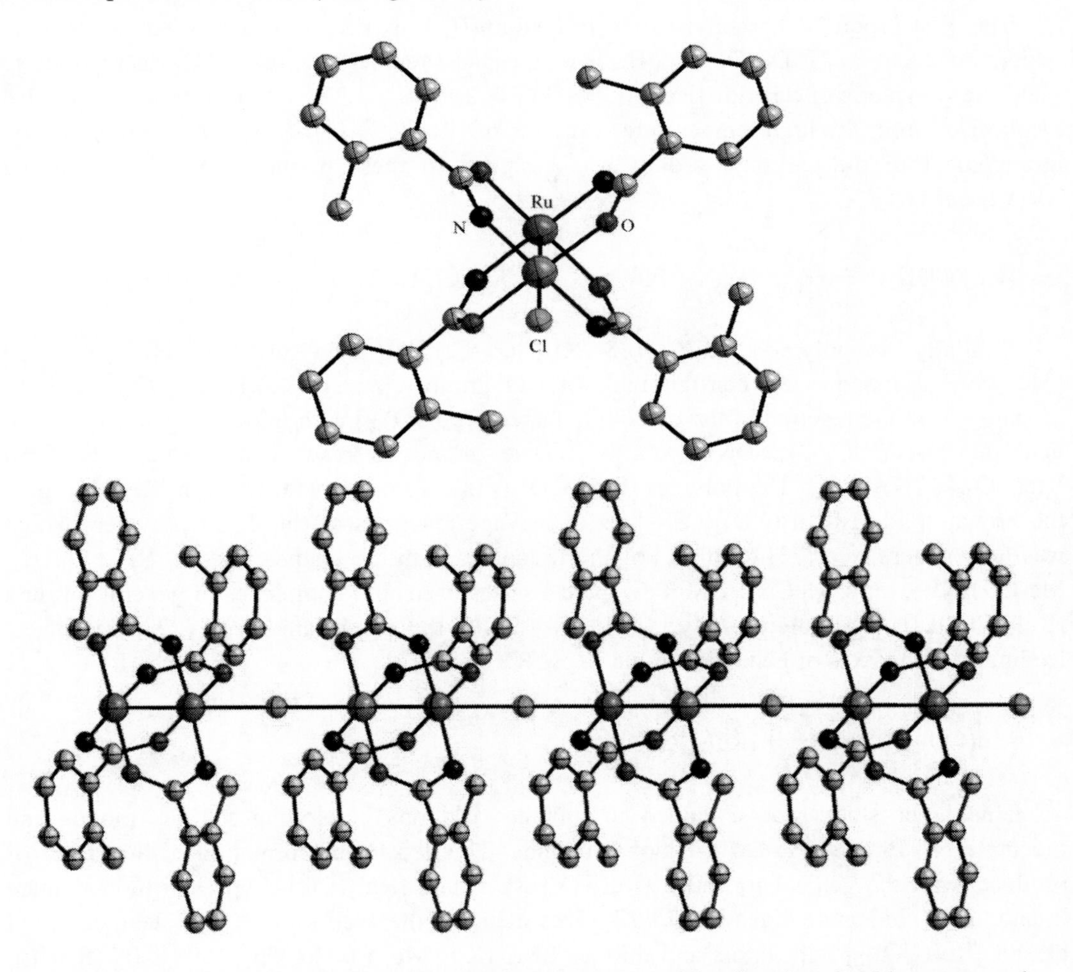

Figure 1.2. (a) Molecular diagram of the X-ray crystal structure of the dimeric unit of the compound $[Ru_2Cl(\mu\text{-}2\text{-}Me\text{-}C_6H_4CONH)_4]$, drawn as 50% ellipsoids. (b) Molecular diagram of the resulting linear chain of $[Ru_2Cl(\mu\text{-}2\text{-}Me\text{-}C_6H_4CONH)_4]_x$ ($x > 2$), with the hydrogen atoms being omitted for clarity. Diffraction data extracted from the CSD database [65].

Priego et al. [65] has however, shown that their solvothermal and microwave assisted synthesis of polymeric amidato and carboxylato species has led to the isolation, as well as the spectroscopic and structural characterization of compounds with general formulae $[Ru_2Cl(\mu\text{-}NHOCR)_4]_x$ (x > 2; R = 2-Me-C_6H_4, 3-Me-C_6H_4, 4-Me-C_6H_4) and $[Ru_2Cl(\mu\text{-}O_2CMe)_4]_x$ (x > 2; R = 2-Me-C_6H_4, 3-Me-C_6H_4, 4-Me-C_6H_4). These compounds have been synthesised in optimized yields under more environmentally friendly reaction conditions from the substitution reactions of the acetate groups in $[Ru_2Cl(\mu\text{-}O_2CMe)_4]$ by the *N,N*-donor ligands triazenide, formamidinate, or guanidinate ligands.

5) Carbonyl Ruthenium(II) Polymeric Species

i. Synthesis And Reaction Patterns

The first report of carbonyl-halide ruthenium(II) polymers was published in 1924, in which the reaction of RuX_3 (X = Cl, Br, I) with CO at a temperature of 270°C was reported to yield the polymeric species of $[RuX_2(CO)_2]_x$ (x > 2). [66,67] The latter polymers were also synthesised from the high temperature reactions of $[Ru_3(CO)_{12}]$ [68,69] with halides. A *cis*-arrangement of the carbonyl groups was assigned to these polymers based on infrared spectroscopy.

$$[Ru_3(CO)_{12}] \xrightarrow{X_2;\ >140°C} [RuX_2(CO)_2]_x \ (x > 2;\ X = Cl, Br, I)$$

Similarly, the polymers $[Ru(CO)_2(SCN)_2]_x$ (x > 2) [70] and $[RuCl_2(CO)(H_2O)]_x$ (x > 2) [71] were assigned a *cis* configuration of CO groups. $[RuCl_2(CO)(H_2O)]_x$ (x > 2) was prepared from the reaction of the carbonyl cluster $[Ru_3(CO)_{12}]$ with thiocyanogen, $(SCN)_2$, in benzene [70] $[Ru(CO)_2(SCN)_2]_x$ (x > 2) was found to react with pyridine to form $[Ru(CO)_2(SCN)_2(py)_2]$. The polymer $[RuI_2(CO)_2]_x$ (x > 2) reacts with KCN in MeOH to give the brown solid $K_2[RuI_2(CO)_2(CN)_2]$. [72]Cleavage reactions of this latter polymer (which was later generalized [73] to other polymeric halides with the ligands L = py, NH_3, $PhNH_2$, Me-$C_6H_4NH_2$, bipy, MeCN, $AsMePh_2$) gave a series of neutral complexes of general formula $[RuI_2(CO_2)L_2]$. [74] Interestingly, when L = RNC, the displacement of CO takes place, leading to complexes of general formula $[RuI_2(RNC)_4]$: [72]

$$[Ru(CO)_2I_2]_x \xrightarrow{RNC;\ C_6H_6} [RuI_2(RNC)_4]$$

This latter study was extended to include reactions employing various mono- and bidentate N-, P-, As-, Sb-, and S-donor ligands. This led to the formation of the series of products with the general formulae $[RuI_2(CO)_2(L)_2]$ and $[RuI_2(CO)_2(L_2)]$ (L = monodentate ligand; L_2 = bidentate ligand). [75-77] Treatment of the well-known trinuclear carbonyl cluster $[Ru_3(CO)_{12}]$ with thiols and thiones RSH (R = Me, Et, Bu, Ph); [69] S_2R_2 (R = Et, Ph);[78] and E_2Ph_2 (E = Se, Te) [79] lead to the formation of the polymeric products of general formula $[Ru(CO)_2(ER)_2]_x$ (x > 2). Interestingly, other polymeric clusters and chains differing in the chain length (x) were also obtained from the reaction mixture upon separating the species by column chromatography [78,79]

It has been found [80] that when ethene (50 – 60 atm) is bubbled through a benzene solution of $[RuCl(\eta^3\text{-}C_3H_5)(CO)_3]$ a pale yellow oligomeric complex of $[RuCl(CO)_2(COEt)]_x$ (x > 2) is obtained. This oligomer was found to react with L (L = PPh_3, py) in a range of different solvents (THF, C_6H_6, CH_2Cl_2) to form the neutral complexes [RuCl{C(O)Et}(CO)(L)$_2$(solvent)]. An X-ray crystallographic determination of the monoclinic crystals of the oligomer characterised this product [8] as [$Ru_6Cl_2(\mu_2\text{-}Cl)_4(\mu_3\text{-}OH)_2(\mu\text{-}COEt)_4$].$C_6H_6$, with a complex bridging structure involving six Ru atoms in its molecular structure with two {$Ru_3(\mu\text{-}OH)$} units linked together by two asymmetric chloride bridges (Figure 1.3). [77,81]. Researchers have shown that polymers and oligomers, such as [$Ru_6Cl_2(\mu_2\text{-}Cl)_4(\mu_3\text{-}OH)_2(\mu\text{-}COEt)_4$], are highly selective and active electrocatalysts for the reduction of CO_2 in aqueous media, or as previously described, for the WGSR [82].

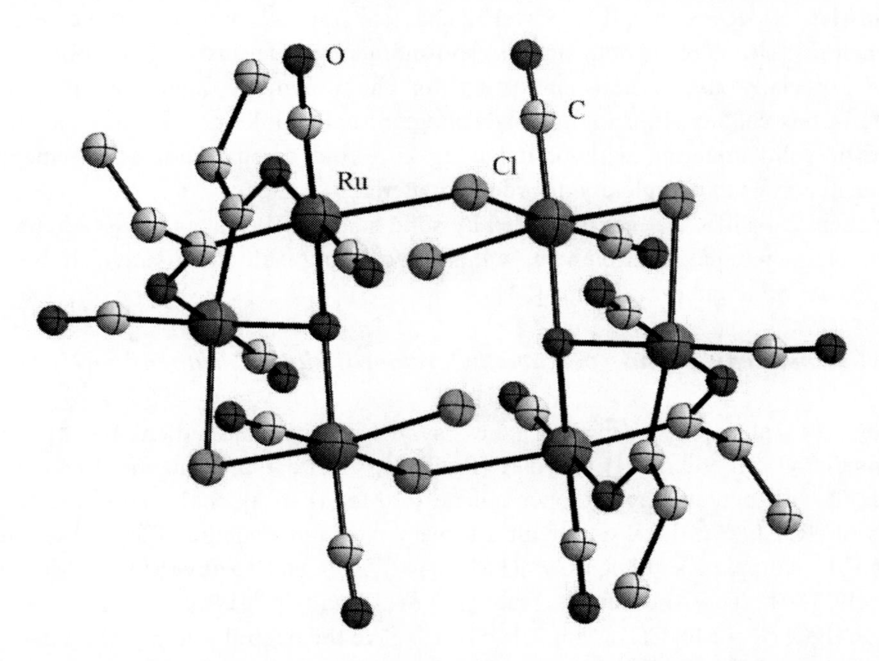

Figure 1.3. Molecular diagram of the X-ray crystal structure of the oligomer with molecular formula [$Ru_6Cl_2(\mu_2\text{-}Cl)_4(\mu_3\text{-}OH)_2(\mu\text{-}COEt)_4$].$C_6H_6$. H-atoms and the C_6H_6 solvent molecule omitted for clarity. Diffraction data extracted from the CSD Database [81].

ii. Structural Characterization Employing Advanced Methods

As with carbonyl ruthenium(II) polymers and most other ruthenium polymeric species, the highly insoluble nature and in some instances air sensitivity has precluded it from thorough and unequivocal identification by means of characterization. The proposed molecular structures of most of these polymeric compounds have been inferred from detailed physicochemical analyses in the solid state including techniques such as electrochemistry, elemental analysis, FAB-MS, UV/Vis, and FTIR spectroscopy, most of which the assumption was made that these polymers were based on metal-metal bond chains [82]. However, through pioneering work the structure determination of various transition metal polymeric compounds can be significantly enhanced with the employment of calculations in combination with powder X-ray diffraction (PXRD) structure determinations. Examples are the work of Masciocchi and co-workers and other researchers with the structural determination of the organometallic polymeric species of Ru, Re and Pd: $[Ru(CO)_4]_x$, $[Re(\mu\text{-}H)(CO)_4]_x$, and $[PdCl(CH_2COCH_3)]_x$ (in all cases $x > 2$). [82] They made use of PXRD methods to resolve the nature of the neutral ruthenium polymeric complexes $[Ru(L)(CO)_2]_x$ (x

> 2, L = 2,2'-bipyridine, 4,4'-dimethyl-2,2'-bipyridine, 1,10-phenanthroline). With these methods they have shown how these molecules are packed in-plane, showing that flat monomeric species, staggered by either 45° or 135° rotations (as in $[Ru(CO)_4]_x$ {x > 2}), pack in a random fashion along the chain [82] Using these methods they have also obtained an estimate average chain length of 60 Å for the compound $[Ru(bpy)(CO)_2]_x$ (x > 2).

Furthermore, by employing the combination of high-resolution solid-state NMR experiments with DFT chemical-shift calculations Gerbaud et al. [83] inferred the structure and properties of the organometallic ruthenium(0) polymer of $[Ru(bpy)(CO)_2]_x$ (x > 2)

Solid-state NMR is generally a powerful characterization tool to use for the determination of the chemical structure of both organic and inorganic materials in their solid phase. This becomes especially useful and interesting for the polymeric materials that have been described in this chapter. It has a huge advantage of being able to determine the structure of any type of solid material, without it having any kind of structural arrangement – from crystalline materials to completely disordered material.

The chemical shifts that are measured by solid-state NMR makes it possible to probe the structural and chemical environment, whilst also being able to distinguish between the electronic state of neighboring atoms [83]

iii. Cyclopentadienyl- and pentamethylcyclopentadienyl ruthenium(II) polymeric species

Tilley et al. [84] reported the synthesis of the dichloro (pentamethyl-cyclopentadienyl)ruthenium(III) polymer $[RuCl_2(Cp^*)]_x$ (x > 2) from the direct reaction of $RuCl_3.xH_2O$ with pentamethylcyclopentadiene (C_5Me_5H) in alcoholic solvents. Subsequent reactions of $[RuCl_2(Cp^*)]_x$ (x > 2) with a tertiary phosphine such as PMe_3 gave the neutral ruthenium(II) complexes $[RuCl(Cp^*)(PMe_3)_2]$ (50%) and *trans*-$[RuCl_2(PMe_3)_4]$ (20%) respectively [84]. The subsequent reactions of $[RuCl(Cp^*)(PMe_3)_2]$ with the Grignard reagents RMgCl (R = Me, CH_2CMe_3, CH_2SiMe_3) gave the neutral primary alkyl derivatives.[84] Nagashima et al. [85] have found that the reaction of $[RuCl_2(Cp^*)]_x$ (x > 2) with allyl chloride in a solution of CH_2Cl_2 with traces of $EtOH/H_2O$ gave, after heating the reaction mixture for 2 hours at 40°C, the Ru(IV) compound of $[RuCl_2(Cp^*)(\eta^3\text{-allyl})]$ in almost quantitative yield.

The synthesis of a dichloro(pentamethylcyclopentadienyl)ruthenium(III) oligomer was also reported by Oshima et al. [86] from similar reactions of $RuCl_3.H_2O$ with C_5Me_5H in boiling EtOH. They also reported[86] that when either MeOH or isopropanol was used instead of EtOH, that a higher oligomer of the same compound had formed. This oligomer was soluble enough to obtain a ^{1}H-NMR spectrum ($CDCl_3$) which contained one broad signal at δ_H 4.90 ppm for the methyl protons of Cp*. When the oligomer, $[RuCl_2(Cp^*)]_x$, is reacted with bidentate phosphines or cyclic dienes, neutral ruthenium(II) complexes of the formula $[RuCl(Cp^*)(L_2)]$ (L_2 = dppe, dpppr, dppb) or $[RuCl(Cp^*)(diene)]$ (diene = 1,5-cod, nbd) respectively, were isolated in low yields [86].

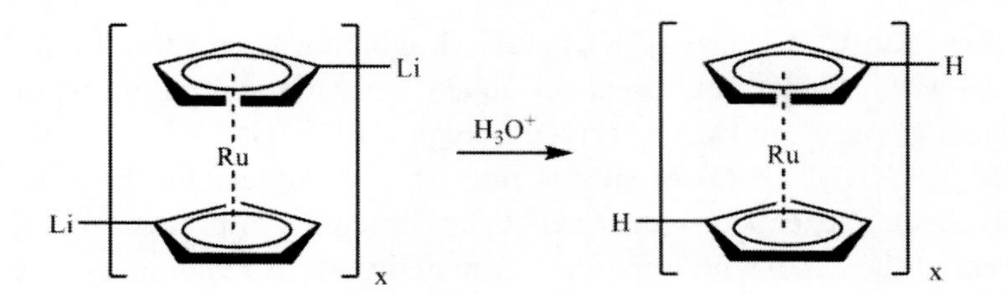

Scheme 1.3. Simplistic scheme representing the synthesis of $[RuCp_2]_x$ (x = 2, 3, 4) from the corresponding dilithiated polymeric precursor [87].

Shaver et al. [88] have, however, reported a convenient high yield synthesis of ruthenocene and osmocene together with their decamethyl derivatives from the reaction of the insoluble metal polymer, $[MCl_2(1,5\text{-cod})]_x$ (x > 2), with $SnBu_3(C_5R_5)$ (R = H, Me) to give $[M(\eta^5\text{-}C_5R_5)_2]$ (M = Ru, R = H, Me; M = Os, R = H). A series of oligomeric derivatives of general formula $[Ru(Cp)_2]_x$ (x = 2, 3, 4; Scheme 1.3) has been synthesised in low-yield from the reaction of the dilithiated species $Li_2[Ru(C_5H_4)_2]_x$ (x = 2, 3, 4; chelated with tmen) with $[Ru(C_5H_4I_2)_2]_x$. [87]

6) Oligomeric Arene Ruthenium(II) Complexes

The insoluble complexes $[RuX_2(C_6H_6)]_x$ (X = Cl, I) were first synthesised in 1967 and their structures were inferred from microanalytical data [89]. Later far-IR, and ^{1}H-NMR studies [90] indicated these complexes to be dimeric species with the general formula $[Ru_2Cl_2(\mu\text{-}Cl)_2(C_6H_6)_2]$. These compounds are insoluble in common organic solvents, but moderately soluble in coordinating solvents such as $(CH_3)_2SO$, CH_3CN, or H_2O, in which the dimeric structure is broken down [90]. An interesting observation is made that three apparent species of $[Ru_2Cl_4(C_6H_6)_2]$ are observed in the ^{1}H-NMR spectra recorded using D_2O, and include $[RuCl_2(C_6H_6)(D_2O)]$, $[RuCl(C_6H_6)(D_2O)_2]^+$, $[Ru(C_6H_6)(D_2O)_3]^{2+}$, and $[Ru_2Cl_3(C_6H_6)_2]^+$. [90] The series of dimeric complexes $[Ru_2X_2(\mu\text{-}X)_2(C_6H_6)_2]$ (X = Cl, Br, I) proves to be an extremely reactive precursor to a comprehensive range of different neutral and cationic arene-adduct complexes [91-94].

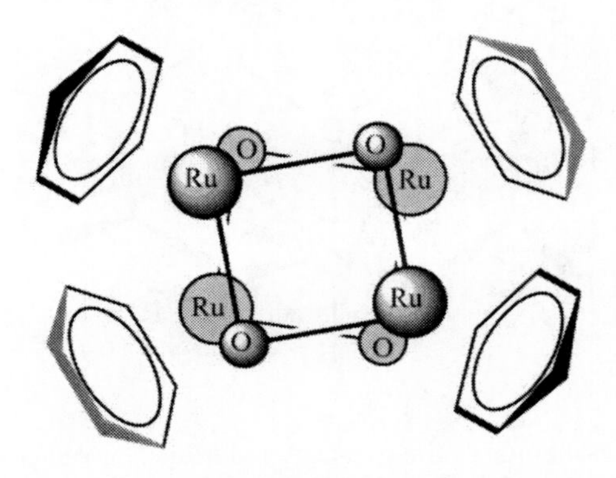

Figure 1.4. Schematic illustration of a distorted cubic structure, $[\{Ru(\eta^6\text{-}C_6H_6)(OH)\}_4]^{4+}$, an intermediate for $[Ru_4(C_6H_6)_4(OH)_4](SO_4)_2.12H_2O$. [92].

The complex $[Ru_4(C_6H_6)_4(OH)_4](SO_4)_2.12H_2O$, which was prepared from the reaction of $[Ru_2(C_6H_6)_2Cl_4]$ with 2 molar equivalents of aqueous $NaCO_3$ and an excess of Na_2SO_4, was structurally characterised by X-ray crystallography [92] The orange cubic crystals of $[Ru_4(C_6H_6)_4(OH)_4](SO_4)_2.12H_2O$ revealed a rare (rare in ruthenium chemistry, common in iron and molybdenum chemistry) distorted cube structure with four ruthenium atoms at alternate corners of the cube, with bridging OH-moieties at the remaining corners of the cube (Figure 1.4). [92]

The complex $[Ru(chd)Cl_2]_x$ ($x > 2$, chd = 1,3-cycloheptadiene) was synthesised from $RuCl_3.xH_2O$ and 1,3,5-cycloheptatriene in refluxing EtOH. [89,95] This complex was initially proposed to be polymeric with the chd ligand η^4-bound to each ruthenium atom. Later, work done by Lewis et al. [96] has shown that the correct formulation is the dimer $[Ru_2(C_7H_8)_2Cl_4]$ with η^6-bound triene ligands. A number of syntheses have made use of this compound together with the Grignard reagent ^iPrMgBr and a carbocycle, which includes the synthesis of $[Ru(\eta^5\text{-}C_7H_9)_2]$ and $[Ru(\eta^6\text{-arene})(\eta^4\text{-carbocycle})]$. [95,97-99]

7) Ligand-Bridged Cyclic Polymeric Cluster Compounds

i. Synthesis and Structural Aspects

An interesting series of polymeric ruthenium species involves the trinuclear μ-oxo-centered ruthenium-carboxylate cluster compounds with general formula $[Ru_3O(\mu\text{-}O_2CR)_6L_3]^n$ (R = H, [100] CH_3, [101-103] C_2H_5, [102,104] C_3H_7, [102] C_3F_7, [105] C_6H_5, [102,106,107] C_7H_{15}, [102] C_8H_{16}; [102] L = H_2O, PPh_3, MeOH, CO, N-heterocycles, $OS(CH_3)_2$). This series of complexes has been the topic of interest for various research groups over the last 20 years, particularly for their promising catalytic abilities and their rich mixed-valence chemistry [108]

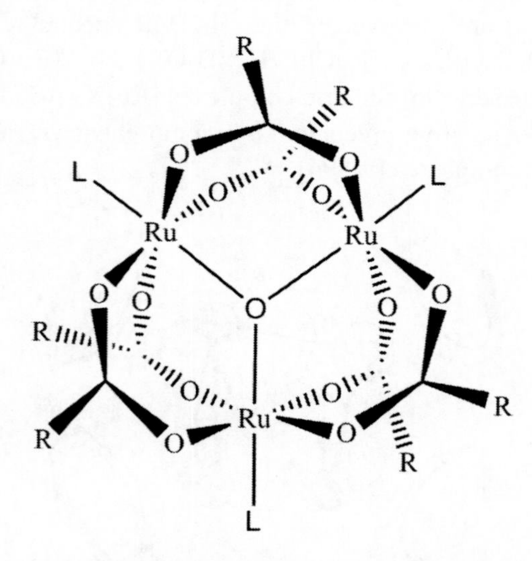

Figure 1.5. A schematic representation of the oxo-centered trinuclear ruthenium cluster structure as described. In this figure R = carboxylate ligands and L = H_2O, MeOH or *N*-heterocyclic ligands [108].

It has been shown that this series of complexes exhibits a triangular structure with each mononuclear ruthenium carboxylate species being bridged in a rather strongly held configuration of both a μ_3-O moiety as well as bridging carboxylato ligands (Figure 1.5). As a result of the ruthenium metal ions being in close proximity of each other, strong electronic and magnetic interactions are caused. This in turn rationalizes the stabilization of a series of different oxidation states for the ruthenium ions, including Ru(II), Ru(III), and Ru(IV). [108]

The synthetic route to these complexes is derived from that of Wilkinson et al., [102] in which the precursor complex with formula $[Ru_3O(\mu\text{-}O_2CR)_6(Sol)_3]^+$ (Sol = H_2O, MeOH, EtOH) is formed from the reaction of boiling EtOH solutions of $RuCl_3.xH_2O$ with RCO_2H and RCO_2Na. The latter complex forms part of a series of green solids of general formula $[Ru_3O(\mu\text{-}O_2CR)_6(Sol)_3]X$ (Sol = H_2O, MeOH, EtOH; X = $\{RCO_2^-\}$, [102] $\{ClO_4^-\}$, [109] $\{BF_4^-\}$, [100] $\{PF_6^-\}$ [110]) and exhibits remarkable stability as solids or in solution over prolonged periods of time without any noticeable signs of decomposition or degradation [101,108].

Toma et al. [111] reported that the reaction of the compound $[Ru_3O(\mu\text{-}O_2CR)_6(CO)(MeOH)_2]$ (R = CH_3) with pyrazine in MeOH gave rise to the formation and subsequent isolation of the polymeric compound of $[Ru_3O(\mu\text{-}O_2CR)_6(pz)(CO)]_x$ ($x > 2$, R = CH_3). Contrary to the usual insoluble nature of ruthenium polymeric species in general, this latter polymer was quite soluble in $CDCl_3$ and a subsequent ^{1}H-NMR analysis showed relatively simple ^{1}H-NMR spectra containing a single pyrazine signal resonating at δ_H 8.81 ppm, and two signals from the acetate moieties at δ_H 2.13 and 2.29 ppm in the ratio of 1:2 respectively [111]

Complimentary FTIR and Raman spectra included a single ν(CO) peak at 1951 cm^{-1}, pointing to the symmetric cyclic nature of this compound. It is known that the Ru_2O core moiety exhibits an equilateral triangular geometrical arrangement, which changes to a slightly distorted equilateral triangle upon coordination of one molecule of CO to the core moiety [112].

From spatial constraints, energy arguments, and molecular mechanics simulations, hexagonal structures are preferred with the triangular clusters in which each vertex of the resulting hexamer is occupied by one $[Ru_3O(\mu\text{-}O_2CR)_6(CO)(MeOH)_2]$ unit, as can be seen in Figure 1.6.

ii. Catalytic Applications

The catalytic applications of complexes containing oxo-centered trinuclear ruthenium species have been investigated [108] by various groups over the years. Wilkinson et al. [15,113] as well as Fouda et al. [114] have reported the catalytic activity of these oxo-bridged clusters in the hydrogenation of unsaturated hydrocarbons.

Both intramolecular and intermolecular hydrogen transfer efficiencies were investigated and evaluated for a selected range of ruthenium catalysts, and amongst these is the example of μ_3-oxo-triruthenium(III) acetate which exists in dimethylformamide as the weakly dissociated 1:1 electrolyte, $[Ru_3O(OCOCH_3)_6(DMF)](OCOCH_3)$. [108,114]

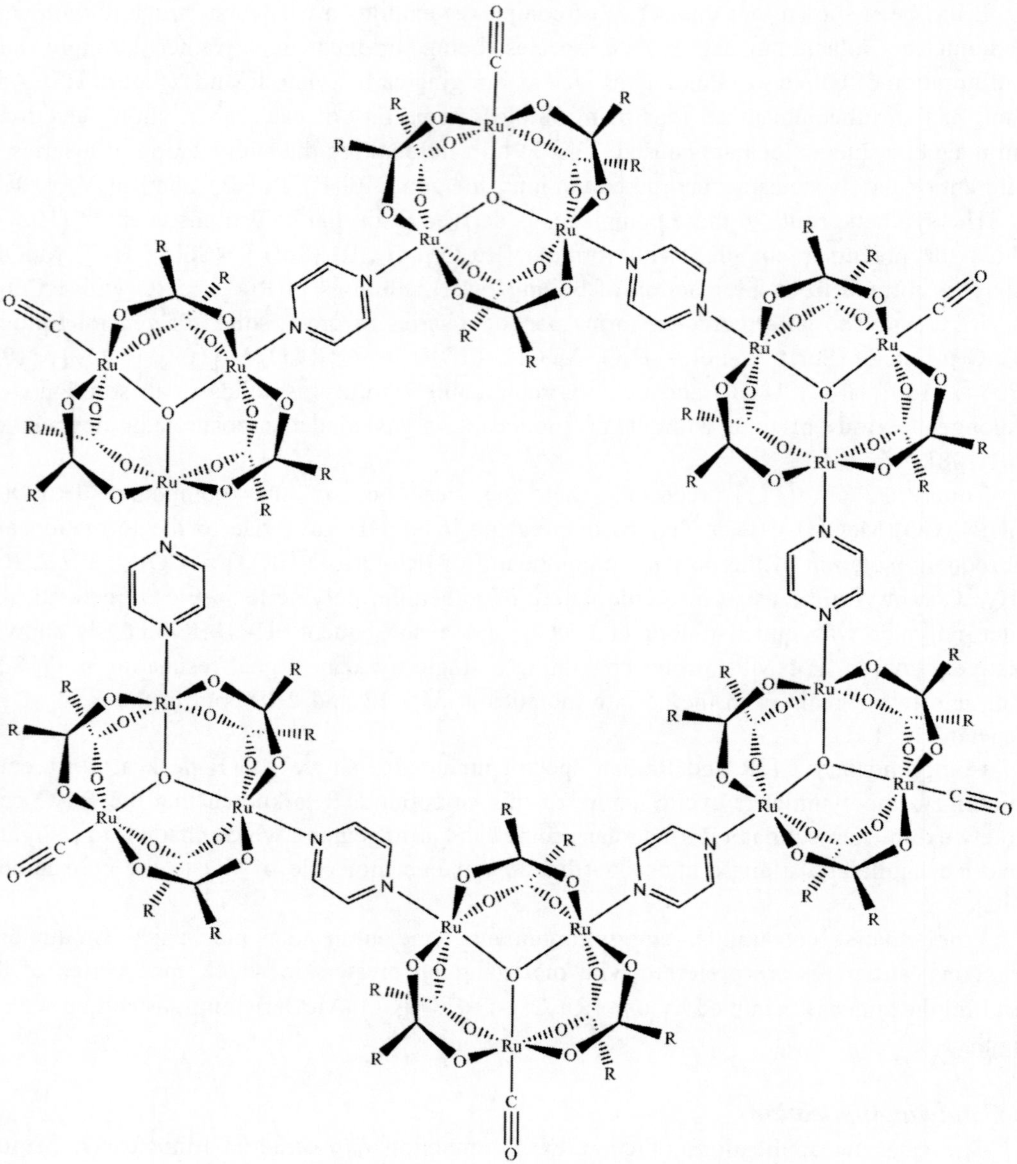

Figure 1.6. A schematic representation of the favorable hexagonal structure of the triangular clusters of $[Ru_3O(Ac)_6(CO)]$ in which each vertex of the hexamer is occupied by one such a $[Ru_3O(Ac)_6(CO)]$ unit [108].

This complex then undergoes a series of spontaneous reduction reactions and intramolecular transfer reactions in which intermediate ruthenium hydride and dimeric ruthenium(I) complexes are formed. This in turn leads to the heterolytic splitting of hydrogen and the eventual isolation of a mixture of products containing the dimer $[Ru_2(OCOCH_3)_2(CO)_4L_2]$ and the polymeric hydridoruthenium carbonyl complex $[RuH(CO)_3]_x$ ($x > 2$). [114] The latter compound was found to be active in the carbonylation of amines, but not in the hydrogenation of unsaturated hydrocarbons.

Another example of the catalytic application of the oxo-centered ruthenium clusters is the conversion of hex-1-ene-3-ol to hexan-3-one at 98% yield within 30 minutes by the $[Ru_3O(Ac)_6(H_2O)_3]^+$ cluster compound. This is compared to the identical reaction using the reference catalyst of $[RuHCl(PPh_3)_3]$ which was reported to reach a maximum of only 92% yield after 1 hour. Other catalytic reactions reported were the efficient conversion of acrylonitrile to propionitrile and 1,4-dicyano-1,3-butadiene using the acetate cluster $[Ru_3O(Ac)_6(H_2O)_3]^+$; [108] the conversion of butadiene with formaldehyde and acetic acid to give $CH_2CHCH(Ac)CH_2CH_2OH$ in a moderate yield of 59%; [108] and the efficient oxidation of alkenes and phenols with hydroperoxides to give 2,3,6-trimethylbenzoquinone, a vital precursor in the synthesis of Vitamin E. [108]

The oxidation of primary and secondary alcohols to aldehydes with O_2 in the presence of $[Ru_3O(RCO_2)_6(L)_3]^n$ (R = Me, Et; L = H_2O, PPh_3; n = 0,1) has a selectivity comparable to that of $RuCl_3.xH_2O$ and $[RuCl_2(PPh_3)_3]$, albeit with a ten-fold increase in activity [108]

8) Ruthenium Nitrosyl Halide Polymeric Species

This series of polymers were synthesised by Irving et al. [115] in 1966 from the reaction of $[RuX_2(CO)_2]_x$ (x > 2; X = I) with NO at 230°C and formulated as the diamagnetic, air stable polymeric species of $[RuI_2(NO)]_x$ (x > 2). Other polymeric species are derived from $[RuI_2(NO)]_x$ (x > 2) upon treatment with bipy, $AsMePh_2$, or heated pyridine to give the complexes $[RuI_2(NO)(bipy)]_x$ (x > 2), $[RuI_2(NO)(AsMePh_2)_2]_x$ (x > 2), and $[RuI_2(NO)(py)_2]_x$ (x > 2) respectively.[115] The reaction of the five-coordinate complex of $[RuCl_2(PPh_3)_3]$ with $[ArN_2][BF_4]$ (Ar = 4-R-C_6H_4-; R = Me, OMe) in dichloromethane was proposed to form the cationic polymeric complex of $\{[RuCl_2(N_2Ar)(PPh_3)_2](BF_4)\}_x$ (x > 2). This complex was shown to be dimeric in nature, [5,116] from the reaction with LiCl which gave the complex $[RuCl_3(N_2Ar)(PPh_3)_2]$. [117,118]

9) Other Ruthenium(II) Polymeric Species of the Type $[RuX_2(diene)]_x$ (x > 2; X = Cl, Br; diene = nbd, cht)

It is well known that the reaction of the commercially available $RuX_3.xH_2O$ (X = Cl, Br, I) with cyclic dienes, trienes or tetraenes produces neutral ruthenium(II) polymeric complexes. The unsaturated carbocyclic ligands employed include 1,5-cod, [119,120] 1,4-cod, [121] nbd, [120,122] 2,3-dicyanobicyclo[2.2.2]octa-2,5,7-triene (dcno), [123] 1,4,5,6,7,8-hexamethyl-2,3-dicyanobicyclo-[2.2.2]octa-2,5,7-triene (hmdcno), [123] chd, [95] cht, [89,95,96] and cot. [119] The reactions are performed in either EtOH or Me_3COH [121] under N_2 and yields between 30 – 40% of the corresponding polymeric complexes with general formula $[RuX_2(diene)]_x$ (x > 2); where cht and cot are bound as dienes) were obtained [77]

The first account of the synthesis and isolation of the norbornadiene (nbd) ruthenium(II) complex of $[RuCl_2(nbd)]_x$ was reported by Abel et al. [122] in 1959. The preparation of $[RuCl_2(nbd)]_x$ was also reported to form from the reaction of the ruthenium(II) blue solution (solution of reduced $RuCl_3$) and nbd. [124] A route to the bromide $[RuBr_2(nbd)]_x$ (x > 2) was reported whereby a propanone solution of $RuCl_3.xH_2O$ was treated with LiBr and nbd. [122]

The formation of $[RuBr_2(cht)]_x$ (x > 2; cht = 1,3,5-cycloheptatriene) was also isolated from treatment of $[Ru(cht)_2]$ with *N*-bromosuccinimide. [125] Accounts of the synthesis and use of the analogous $[RuX_2(nbd)]_x$ (x > 2; X = Cl, Br) polymer[4] with excess of phosphorous ligand and $NaBPh_4$ as well as the $[RuCl_2(cht)]_x$ (x > 2) polymer [9] are also known to give, amongst other, the hydrides $[RuHL'_5]^+$, the dinuclear species $[L_3RuX_3RuL_3]^+$, and the mononuclear cations $[RuL_6]^{2+}$ (L' = $P(OMe)_2Ph$; L = $P(OR)_2Ph$, $P(OR)Ph_2$; R = Me, Et; X = Cl, Br).

Interestingly, the formation of two yellow-brown complexes of general formulation $[\{RuCl_2(diene)\}_x\{Ru(diene)(C_2O_4)\}_y]_n$ (x, y, n > 2; diene = 1,5-cod, nbd), were prepared from the reactions of heated aqueous ethanol mixtures of $RuCl_3.xH_2O$ and oxalic acid with the relevant diene [126] These polymeric complexes form the series of binuclear cationic complexes $[L'_3RuX_3RuL'_3]^+$ (X = Cl, Br) in alcohols with phosphonite and phosphinite ligands [4] The symmetrical nature of the bound phosphonite/phosphinite ligands were confirmed by ^{1}H-NMR through the symmetrical virtual coupling constant for the methyl resonances of these ligands. A noticeable difference in reactivity of *catena*-dibromo(nbd)ruthenium is the reaction involving the polymer with L' = $P(OMe)_2Ph$ in boiling MeOH gave the dicationic complex of the formula $[Ru(L')_6]^{2+}$, which was isolated as the tetraphenylborate salt in high yield [4] When blue solutions (methanolic solutions of reduced species of $RuCl_3.xH_2O$) of Ru(II) are treated with pyridine-2-thiol (py-2-SH), 2-vinylpyridine (py-2-CH=CH_2), or $NC(CH_2)_nCN$ (n = 2, 3) the polymeric species of formula $[RuCl_2(py\text{-}2\text{-}SH)_2]_x$ (x > 2), $[RuCl_2(py\text{-}2\text{-}CH{=}CH_2)_2]_x$ (x > 2), and $[RuCl_2(NC(CH_2)_nCN)_2]_x$ (x > 2) respectively were reported.[124] $[RuCl_2(py\text{-}2\text{-}SH)_2]_x$ subsequently reacts with PPh_3 to give the monomeric complex $[Ru(py\text{-}2\text{-}S)_2(PPh_3)_2]$, of which the X-ray crystal structure has been reported [127] Furthermore, the sulphoxide exchange reactions with $[Ru\{(CH_3)_2SO\}_4Cl_2]$ and bulky racemic ligands such as methyl phenyl sulphoxide gave rise to complexes of novel stoichiometries, and in particular the polymeric $[Ru(mpso)_2Cl_2]_x$ (x > 2) with the aforementioned ligand [128] Treatment of benzene solutions of the trinuclear cluster of $[Ru_3(CO)_{12}]$ with S_2Et_2 or E_2Ph_2 (E = S, Se, Te) gives a wide range of different neutral ruthenium(I) species, together with the polymeric species $[Ru(SPh)(CO)_3]_x$ (x > 2). [78,79] The reaction of the trinuclear carbonyl cluster with bis(perfluoromethyl)dithietene, $(CF_3)_2C_2S_2$, in heptanes leads to the polymeric species $[Ru_2\{(CF_3)_2C_2S_2\}(CO)_6]_x$ (x > 2), albeit without sufficient or convincing characterization [129]. King et al. [130] found that the carbonylation reaction of $[RuCl_2(diene)]_x$ with CO gas at 1 atm in the absence of a reducing agent gave the ruthenium carbonyl chloride $[RuCl_2(CO)_3]_2$, which was able to undergo a reversible reaction with EtOH to give the polymeric compound of $[RuCl_2(CO)_2(EtOH)]_x$ (x > 2). The same carbonylation reaction in the presence of hydrazine as a reducing agent gave a mixture of ruthenium(II) amine products with general formula $[Ru(NH_3)_5L]Cl_2$ (L = CO, N_2). If the latter reaction is repeated together with added PPh_3, a mixture of products, including $[Ru(NH_3)_5L]Cl_2$ (L = CO, N_2) as well as *trans*-$[Ru(CO)_3(PPh_3)_2]$ were formed. When the above reactions were performed in the presence of zinc as a reducing agent, the carbonyl cluster $[Ru_3(CO)_{12}]$ was the main product of the reaction with $[Ru(OH)_2(nbd)(CO)_2]$ and the tetrametallic carbonyl hydride complex $[Ru_4H_4(CO)_{12}]$ as by-products. [130] Atmospheric pressure carbonylation of an ethanolic solution of the bidentate benzene complex $[RuCl_2(C_6H_5)]_x$ (x > 2) and lithium acetate in the presence of zinc gave a moderate yield of the carbonyl hydride complex of formula $[Ru_4H_2(CO)_{13}]$. Table 1.1 summarizes the reactions discussed, employing the polymeric $[RuCl_2(nbd)]_x$ (x > 2) as a synthon. Other examples of ruthenium(II) polymeric species emanated from the work of Wilkinson et al. [124] includes the use of the so-called blue solutions of Ru(II) presumed to be $[Ru_5Cl_{12}]^{2-}$. They found that the reaction of $[Ru_5Cl_{12}]^{2-}$ with pyridine-2-thiol and 2-vinylpyridine form highly insoluble species of the formula $[RuCl_2L_2]_x$ (L = C_5H_5NS, $CH_2CHC_5H_4N$) respectively. It was thought that these complexes contain bridging ligand groups and terminal chloride ligands. Also, it has been found that the same blue Ru(II) solutions react with L = *ortho*-aminobenzenethiol and *para*-toluenethiol to give the highly insoluble polymeric species of $[Ru(L)_2]_x$ (x > 2; L = *ortho*-$NH_2C_6H_4S$, *para*-MeC_6H_4S) which were thought to contain sulphur bridges [124] When the same reaction is repeated with L = toluene-3,4-dithiol, polymeric species of the formula $[Ru_2(L)_3]_x$ (x > 2; L = *ortho*-$MeC_6H_3S_2$) were obtained. Table 1.2 and Table 1.3 contains information regarding the neutral and cationic ruthenium(I) and (II) species derived from the different polymeric ruthenium compounds discussed in this chapter, as well as some characterization reported on these compounds, respectively.

10) Reactions Involving the Polymeric Species of the Formula $[RuCl_2(1,5\text{-}cod)]_x$ (x > 2)

In the sections above, involving the synthesis and related applications of each of the different classes of polymeric ruthenium compounds, specific subsections for those employed as synthetic precursors in the relevant reactions involved were discussed.

However, the use of $[RuCl_2(1,5\text{-}cod)]_x$ (x > 2) as a synthetic precursor has been extensively investigated in reactions that lead to, amongst others, the formation, isolation and characterization of neutral and cationic ruthenium(0), and (II) hydrazine, substituted hydrazine and acetonitrile adduct species.

All of the latter species were further employed as synthetic precursors in the formation of an extensive range of various products of ruthenium which were catalytically active, or synthetically reactive. These neutral and cationic Ru(II) complexes are highly reactive because of high ligand labilities in a variety of organic solvents, [9,138,139] and as a result, it was decided to focus on specific reactions as a separate section. As a compact summary, Table 1.4 shows the products isolated from these and other reactions all making use of $[RuCl_2(1,5\text{-}cod)]_x$ (x > 2) as a synthon.

i. Hydrazine Complexes

Initial investigations by Hough et al. [149] have shown that the polymeric species, $[RuCl_2(1,5\text{-}cod)]_x$ (x > 2), which is insoluble in most solvents, when suspended in either methanol or ethanol reacts rapidly with anhydrous NH_2NH_2 to give clear red-yellow solutions. From these clear solutions hydrazine-diene ruthenium(II) complexes could be isolated as the cationic salt upon addition of $NaBPh_4$. It was later found by Ashworth et al. [9,139] that a suspension of $[RuCl_2(diene)]_x$ (diene = 1,5-cod, nbd) in MeOH with excess anhydrous hydrazine rapidly gave pale red solutions from which the complexes of the type $[Ru(diene)(NH_2NH_2)_4](BPh_4)_2$ (diene = 1,5-cod, nbd) were isolated in high yield using BPh_4^- as an anion. Attempts to isolate the products of the BF_4^- and PF_6^- anions were however, reported to be unsuccessful [139]

Table 1.1. Selected neutral and cationic ruthenium(II) species derived from the polymeric $[RuCl_2(nbd)]_x$ (x > 2) precursor [77]

Entry	Ligand, reaction conditions	Product(s)	Reference
1	Aqueous glycine (glyH); Reflux	$[Ru(nbd)(gly)_2].H_2O$	[131]
2	$Na[S_2CNMe]$; DMF	$[Ru(nbd)(SCNMe_2)_2]$	[132]
3	acacH; Reflux	$[Ru(nbd)(acac)_2]$	[132]
4	$K_2[C_8H_8]$; THF	$[Ru(nbd)(C_8H_8)] + [Ru(nbd)(C_8H_{10})]$	[133]
5	Py; 120°C	$[Ru(py)_4Cl_2]$	[122]
6	$4\text{-}NH_2\text{-}C_6H_4Me$; 100°C	$[RuCl_2(nbd)(4\text{-}NH_2\text{-}C_6H_4Me)_2]$	[122]
7	NH_2NH_2; $NaBPh_4$; MeOH; H_2O	$[Ru(nbd)(NH_2NH_2)_4](BPh_4)_2$	[9]
8	L (L = Me_2NH; $C_6H_{11}NH_2$, piperidine)	$[RuH(Cl)(nbd)(L)_2]$	[134]
9	CO; without reducing agent	$[Ru_2Cl_4(CO)_6]$; $[RuCl_2(CO)_3]_2$	[130]
	CO; with added NH_2NH_2	$[Ru(N_2)(NH_3)_5]Cl_2 + [Ru(CO)(NH_3)_5]Cl_2$	[130]
	CO; with added NH_2NH_2 and PPh_3	$[Ru(N_2)(NH_3)_5]Cl_2 + [Ru(CO)(NH_3)_5]Cl_2 + [Ru(CO)_3(PPh_3)_2]$	[130]
	CO; with added NH_2NH_2 and dppe	$[Ru(N_2)(NH_3)_5]Cl_2 + [Ru(CO)(NH_3)_5]Cl_2$	[130]
	CO; with added zinc as reducing agent	$[Ru_3(CO)_{12}] + [Ru(OH)_2(nbd)(CO)_2]$	[130]

Table 1.2. Selected polymeric species of ruthenium(II) as precursors to selected neutral and cationic ruthenium(II) species that have resulted from the relevant polymeric species

Entry	Precursor[a]	Ligand L	Cationic/Neutral products	Reference
1	$[RuCl_2L_2]_x$	L = C_5H_5NS, $CH_2CHC_5H_4N$	$[RuCl_2(PPh_3)_4]$; $[Ru(C_5H_5NS)_2(PPh_3)_2]$	[123]
2	$[RuCl_2(L)]_x$	L = bicyclo[2.2.1]hepta-2,5-diene	$[L'_3RuCl_3RuL'_3]$ (L' = $P(OMe)_2Ph$, $P(OEt)_2Ph$, $P(OMe)Ph_2$, $P(OEt)Ph_2$); *trans*-$[Ru(py)_4Cl_2]$	[4, 122]
3	$[RuBr_2(L)]_x$	L = bicyclo[2.2.1]hepta-2,5-diene	$[RuL'_6]^{2+}$ (L' = $P(OMe)_2Ph$); $[L'_3RuBr_3RuL'_3]$ (L' = $P(OEt)_2Ph$, $P(OEt)Ph_2$)	[4]
4	$[RuCl_2(Cp^*)]_x$	-	$[RuCl(Cp^*)(PMe_3)_2$; *trans*-$[RuCl_2(PMe_3)_4]$; $[RuCl(Cp^*)(diene)$ (diene = 1,5-cod, nbd); $[RuCl(Cp^*)(L'_2)]$ (L'_2 = dppe, dpppr); $[RuCl(Cp^*)(L'_2)(CHCl_3)$	[84, 86]
5	$[Ru_2(\mu\text{-}O_2CR)_2(CO)_4]_x$	R = Me, Et	$[Ru_2(\mu\text{-}O_2CR)_2(CO)_4(L'_2)]_x$ (L'_2 = dmpm, dppm, dpam, dppe, arphos, dpppr, dppb, dppp); $[Ru_2(\mu\text{-}O_2CMe)_2(CO)_2(L)_2]$ (L = CH_3CN, PPh_3); $[Ru_2(\mu\text{-}Pz)_2(CO)_4(PPh_3)_2]$; $[Ru_2(\mu\text{-}O_2CMe)(CO)_3(dppm)(\eta^1\text{-}dppm)(\mu\text{-}dppm)](PF_6).C_2H_5OH$	[19, 21, 25]
6	$[Ru(\mu\text{-}O_2CR)(CO)_2]_x$	R = Me	$[Ru_2(CO)_2(^tBuNC)_8](PF_6)_2$; $[Ru_2(CO)_2(RNC)_9](PF_6)_2$ (R = $C_6H_5CH_2$, 2,6-$Me_2C_6H_3$); $[Ru_2(RNC)_{10}](PF_6)_2$ (R = $C_6H_5CH_2$, 2,6-$Me_2C_6H_3$); $[Ru_2(2,6\text{-}Me_2C_6H_3NC)_{10}](BPh_4)_2$; $[\{Ru(\eta^5\text{-}L)(CO)_2\}_2]$ (L = Cp, Cp*); $[Ru_2(\mu\text{-}pz)_2(CO)_4(PPh_3)_2]$; $[\{Ru(RB(pz)_3)(CO)_2\}_2]$ (R = H, pz)	[20,22, 26]
7	$[RuCl_2(py\text{-}2\text{-}SH)_2]_x$	-	$[Ru(py\text{-}2\text{-}S)_2(PPh_3)_2]$	[124]
8	$[RuCl_2(PPh_3)_2]_x$	-	*trans*-$[Ru(py)_4Cl_2]$; $[RuCl_2L_4]$ (L = py-2-NH_2, py-2-Me, quin)	[124, 135]

Table 1.2. (Continued)

Entry	Precursor[a]	Ligand L	Cationic/Neutral products	Reference
9	$[Ru_2Cl(O_2CR)_4]_x$	R = Me, Et	*trans*-$[Ru(O_2CR)_2(py)_4]$ (R = Me, Et); *trans*-$[Ru(O_2CR)_2(py)_2]$ (R = Me, Et)	[136]
10	$[Ru(CO)_2(SCN)_2]_x$	-	$[Ru(CO)_2(SCN)_2(py)_2]$	[70]
11	$[RuI_2(CO)_2]_x$	-	$[Ru_2(Cp)_2(CO)_4]$; $K_2[RuI_2(CO)_2(CN)_2]$; $[RuI_2(CO_2)L_2]$ (L = py, NH_3, $PhNH_2$, Me-$C_6H_4NH_2$, bipy, MeCN, $AsMePh_2$); $[RuI_2(RNC)_4]$ (L = RNC); $[RuI_2(CO)_2(L)_2]$ (L = monodentate N-, P-, As-, Sb-, or S-donor ligand); $[RuI_2(CO)_2L_2]$ (L_2 = bidentate N-, P-, As-, Sb-, or S-donor ligand).	[75-77]
12	$[RuCl_2(CO)_2]_x$	-	$[RuCl_2(CO)(NH_3)_5]$	[130]
13	$[RuCl(CO)_2(COEt)]_x$	-	$[RuCl\{C(O)Et\}(CO)(L)_2(solvent)]$ (L = PPh_3, py)	[80]
14	$[RuCl_2(chd)]_x$	-	$[Ru(\eta^5\text{-}C_7H_9)_2]$	[95]
15	$[RuCl_2(C_6H_6)]_x$	-	$[Ru(CO)_3Cl_2]_2$; $Ru(N_2)(NH_3)_5]Cl_2$; $Ru(CO)(NH_3)_5]Cl_2$; $[Ru_3(CO)_{12}]$; $[Ru_4H_4(CO)_{12}]$; $[Ru_4H_2(CO)_{13}]$; $[RuCl_2(CO)_3]_2$;	[130]
16	$[RuI_2(NO)]_x$	-	$[RuI_2(NO)(bipy)]_x$ ($x > 2$); $[RuI_2(NO)(AsMePh_2)_2]_x$ ($x > 2$); $[RuI_2(NO)(py)_2]_x$ ($x > 2$)	[115]

[a] For all the polymeric species, $x > 2$ in general.

Table 1.3. Selected characterization and properties of the polymeric species of ruthenium(II) as discussed in above sections [77]

Entry	Complex[a]	Colour	m.p (°C)	FTIR bands (ν, δ; cm^{-1})	FTIR method	Reference
1	$[RuCl_2(1,5\text{-}cod)]_x$	Brown	> 200[f]	-	-	[119]
		Brown	265[e]	-	-	[121]
2	$[RuCl_2(mpso)_2]_x$	Yellow	-	1130 (ν(SO)); 330 (ν(RuCl))	-	[128]
3	$[RuCl_2(nbd)]_x$	Red	-	-	-	[122]
4	$[RuBr_2(nbd)]_x$	Brown	-	-	-	[122]
5	$[Ru(CO)_2(SMe)_2]_x$	-	-	2102; 2022; 1962; 1930	Nujol	[69]
6	$[Ru(CO)_2(SEt)_2]_x$	-	-	2096; 2023; 1963; 1932	Nujol	[69]
		Yellow-orange	59-60	2110; 2041; 1986	CCl_4	[78]
7	$[Ru(CO)_2(SBu)_2]_x$	-	-	2100; 2022; 1962; 1930	Nujol	[69]
8	$[Ru(CO)_2(SPh)_2]_x$	-	-	2105; 2080; 2060; 2018	Nujol	[69]
		Orange	100[e]	2112; 2052; 1996	CCl_4	[78]
9	$[Ru(CO)_2(SPh)_2]_x$[b]	Orange	150-155[e]	2106; 2046; 1991; 1945	CCl_4	[78]
10	$[Ru(CO)_2(SPh)_2]_x$[c]	Yellow	200[e]	2073; 2051; 2020; 2008; 1995; 1973; 1966	CCl_4	[78]
11	$[Ru(CO)_2(SePh)_2]_x$[b]	Orange	~200[e]	2096; 2037; 1974	$CHCl_3$	[79]
12	$[Ru(CO)_2(SePh)_2]_x$[b]	Yellow	~200[e]	2105; 2037; 1974	$CHCl_3$	[79]
13	$[Ru(CO)_2(TePh)_2]_x$[b]	Orange	> 200[f]	2085; 2030; 1974	$CHCl_3$	[79]
14	$[Ru(CO)_2(TePh)_2]_x$[b]	Orange-brown	200-220[e]	2095; 2027; 1974	$CHCl_3$	[79]
15	$[RuCl_2(NC(CH_2)_2CN)]_x$	Brown	-	2275 (ν(CN)); 310 (ν(RuCl))	-	[124]
16	$[RuCl_2(NC(CH_2)_3CN)]_x$	Brown	-	2270 (ν(CN)); 320 (ν(RuCl))	-	[124]
17	$[RuCl_2(dcno)]_x$	Red-brown	310[e]	-	-	[123]
18	$[RuCl_2(hmdcno)]_x$	Red	330-332[e]	-	-	[123]

Table 1.3. (Continued)

Entry	Complex[a]	Colour	m.p (°C)	FTIR bands (v, δ; cm^{-1})	FTIR method	Reference
19	$[Ru(\mu\text{-}O_2CH)(CO)_2]_x$	Yellow	-	2068; 2061; 2054; 2040; 2012; 2006; 1998; 1947; 1957; 1950; 1947; 1942-1913[g]	Nujol	[18]
20	$[Ru(\mu\text{-}O_2CMe)(CO)_2]_x$	Yellow	-	2049; 1994; 1967; 1952; 1916; 1908[g]	Nujol	[18]
		Yellow	-	2049; 1994; 1966; 1952; 1916; 1908[g]	Nujol	[18]
		-	-	2049; 1994; 1966; 1952[g]	KBr	[137]
21	$[Ru(\mu\text{-}O_2CEt)(CO)_2]_x$	Orange-yellow	-	2041; 1996; 1984; 1974; 1946; 1920; 1905[g]	Nujol	[18]
22	$[Ru(\mu\text{-}O_2CC_9H_{19})(CO)_2]_x$	Orange	-	2038; 2033; 1992; 1979; 1974; 1942; 1916[g]	Nujol	[18]
23	$[Ru_2\{(CF_3)_2C_2S_2\}(CO)_6]_x$	Orange	-	2139; 2084; 2035[g]	KBr	[129]
24	$[RuI_2(NO)]_x$	Black	-	1847 (v(NO)); 1666	-	[115]
25	$[RuI_2(NO)(bipy)]_x$	Brown	-	1848 (v(NO)); 1795 (v(NO))	-	[115]
26	$[RuI_2(NO)(AsMePh_2)_2]_x$	Brown	168	1835 (v(NO))	-	[115]
27	$[RuI_2(NO)(py)_2]_x$	Red	-	1823 (v(NO)); 1784 (v(NO))	-	[115]
28	$\{[RuCl_2(N_2C_6H_4\text{-}4\text{-}Me)(PPh_3)_2](BF_4)\}_x$	Red	-	1861 (v(NN))	CH_2Cl_2	[5]
29	$\{[RuCl_2(N_2C_6H_4\text{-}3\text{-}OMe)(PPh_3)_2](PF_6)\}_x$	Orange	-	1870 (v(NN)); 1836 (v(NN))	$CHCl_3$	[5]
30	$\{[RuCl_2(N_2C_6H_4\text{-}2\text{-}OMe)(PPh_3)_2](PF_6)\}_x$	Orange	-	-	-	[5]

[a] For all the polymeric species, $x > 2$ in general. [b] $6 \leq x \geq 7$. [c] $x \sim 4$. [d] $12 \leq x \geq 14$. [e] Melt with decomposition. [f] Decomposition without melt. [g] All FTIR frequencies from the carbonyl-carboxylato species are assigned to v(CO).

Table 1.4. Selected neutral and cationic ruthenium(II) species derived from the polymeric $[RuCl_2(1,5\text{-cod})]_x$ (x > 2) precursor

Entry	Ligand, reaction conditions	Product(s)	Reference
1	CH_3CN; NH_4PF_6	$[RuCl(1,5\text{-cod})(CH_3CN)_3](PF_6)$	[140]
2	CH_3CN; NH_4PF_6; $AgPF_6$	$[Ru(1,5\text{-cod})(CH_3CN)_4](PF_6)_2$	[140]
3	RCN (R = CH_3, HC=CH_2, CH_2CH_3)	$[RuCl_2(1,5\text{-cod})(CH_3CN)_2].H_2O$; $[RuCl_2(1,5\text{-cod})(CH_3CN)_2].NCCH_3$; $[Ru[RuCl_2(1,5\text{-cod})(H_2CCHCN)_2]$; $[Ru[RuCl_2(1,5\text{-cod})(H_3CCH_2CN)_2]$	[141-144]
4	LiBr; CH_3CN	$[RuBr_2(1,5\text{-cod})(CH_3CN)_2]$	[141]
2	4-NH_2-C_6H_4Me	$[RuCl_2(1,5\text{-cod})(4\text{-}NH_2\text{-}C_6H_4Me)_2]$	[119]
3	C_7H_8; $Me_2CHMgBr$; Et_2O; $h\nu$	$[Ru^0(1,5\text{-cod})(C_7H_8)]$[a]	[125]
4	C_8H_{10}; $Me_2CHMgBr$; Et_2O; $h\nu$	$[Ru^0(1,5\text{-cod})(C_8H_{10})]$[a]	[125]
5	C_6H_8; $Me_2CHMgBr$; Et_2O; $h\nu$	$[Ru^0(1,5\text{-cod})(C_6H_6)] + [Ru(C_6H_6)(C_6H_8)]$[a]	[125]
6	$K_2[C_8H_8]$	$[Ru^0(1,5\text{-cod})(C_8H_{10})]$	[133]
7	Aqueous glycine (glyH); Reflux	$[Ru(1,5\text{-cod})(gly)_2].H_2O$	[131]
8	$Na[S_2CNMe]$; DMF	$[Ru(1,5\text{-cod})(SCNMe_2)_2]$	[132]
9	$[chelate]^-$ (chelate = acac, bzac, sal, C_5H_4N-2-S, ox, mbt); Reflux	$[Ru(1,5\text{-cod})(chelate)_2]$	[132]
10	NH_2NH_2; $NaBPh_4$; MeOH; H_2O	$[Ru(1,5\text{-cod})(NH_2NH_2)_4](BPh_4)_2$	[9]

Table 1.4. (Continued)

Entry	Ligand, reaction conditions	Product(s)	Reference
11	NH_2NMe_2; NH_4PF_6/$NaBPh_4$; MeOH; H_2O	$[RuH(1,5\text{-cod})(NH_2NMe_2)_3](PF_6)$; $[RuH(1,5\text{-cod})(NH_2NMe_2)_3](BPh_4)$	[9]
12	NH_2NHMe; NH_4PF_6; MeOH; H_2O	$[Ru(1,5\text{-cod})(NH_2NHMe)_4](PF_6)_2$	[9]
13	(all)MgBr (all = allyl, 2-methylallyl); Et_2O	$[Ru(all)_2(1,5\text{-cod})]$	[18]
14	$SnBu_3(C_5R_5)$ (R = H, Me); EtOH	$[Ru(\eta^5\text{-}C_5R_5)_2]$	[145]
15	CH_2CRCH_2MgCl; H_2O; Et_2O	$[Ru(1,5\text{-cod})(CH_2CRCH_2)_2]$	[146]
16	L (L = Me_2NH; $C_6H_{11}NH_2$, piperidine)	$[RuH(Cl)(1,5\text{-cod})(L)_2]$	[134]
17	(L = PEt_3, PPh_3)	*trans*-$[RuH_2L_4]$	[147]
18	(L_2 = dppe, dpppr, dppb, dppf, dcpe, dcpm, depe, dpph)	*cis*- and *trans*-$[RuH_2(L_2)_2]$	[148]

[a]Analogous reactions have been reported from $[Ru(chd)Cl_2]_x$ ($x > 2$) and/or $[Ru_2(cht)_2Cl_4]$. [95].

The ^1H-NMR spectrum of $[Ru(1,5\text{-}cod)(NH_2NH_2)_4](BPh_4)_2$ showed a broad resonance at δ_H 2.1 ppm for the aliphatic protons of the 1,5-cod ligand, resonances between δ_H 3.3 – 4.2 ppm for the diene protons of the 1,5-cod ligand, a singlet at δ_H 3.7 ppm for the uncoordinated NH_2 protons of NH_2NH_2, and peaks at δ_H 4.72 and 6.04 ppm (broad singlets) for the NH_2 protons of the hydrazine ligand [139] The integration of NH_2 protons to a total of only 4H has been ascribed to ligand exchange reactions, including possibly with the deuterated solvent [139]

Recently Owalude et al. [150] has found that the polymer, $[RuCl_2(1,5\text{-}cod)]_x$ ($x > 2$), reacts with hydrazine hydrate in boiling EtOH to give the complex $[RuH(1,5\text{-}cod)(NH_2NH_2)_3](BPh_4)$ upon addition of $NaBPh_4$, of which the X-ray crystal structure determination was reported. The analogous polymer $[OsCl_2(1,5\text{-}cod)]_x$ ($x > 2$), has been shown to react differently in similar reactions performed previously by Singleton and co-workers [151] when compared to the ruthenium counterpart. For example, it has been shown that methanolic suspensions of $[OsCl_2(1,5\text{-}cod)]_x$ reacts with anhydrous NH_2NH_2 at room temperature to form $[OsCl(1,5\text{-}cod)(NH_2NH_2)_3](BPh_4)$, but in boiling methanol to give $[Os(1,5\text{-}cod)(NH_2NH_2)_4](BPh_4)$, both of which were isolated by addition of $NaBPh_4$. [151]

ii. N,N-dimethylhydrazine Complexes

Ashworth [139] showed that when a suspension of the polymer, $[RuCl_2(1,5\text{-}cod)]_x$, in a 1:1 mixture of methanol and aqueous NH_2NMe_2 (90%) was heated for 15 minutes, a dark brown solution was obtained from which the complex $[RuH(1,5\text{-}cod)(NH_2NMe_2)_3](Y)$ (Y = BPh_4, PF_6) was isolated upon addition of $NaBPh_4$ or NH_4PF_6 respectively. Interestingly, the complex $[RuH(1,5\text{-}cod)(NH_2NMe_2)_3](BPh_4)$ precipitated either as plates (ν(RuH) = 2050 cm^{-1}) or colorless needles (ν(RuH) = 2000 cm^{-1}) upon addition of $NaBPh_4$ depending on the water-methanol ratio [9,139] Initially Hough et al. [149] observed two different geometrical isomers from these two different stretching frequencies observed in the FTIR-spectra. It was later reported by Ashworth et al. [139,152] that these two crystal forms are indeed identical *facial* geometrical isomers, as seen from identical ^1H-NMR spectra, and that the differences in the RuH stretching frequencies seen in the FTIR-spectra is due to crystal packing differences in the two forms. The FTIR spectra of these complexes all contain stretching frequencies in the regions 3360 – 3100 cm^{-1} (ν(NH)), 1640 – 1590 cm^{-1} (asym δ(NH)), 915 – 930 cm^{-1} (ν(NN)). [139] Ashworth et al. [9,139] concluded from the ν(NN) frequencies (~ 930 cm^{-1}) of the hydrazine complexes to be coordinated in a monodentate fashion.

The ^1H-NMR spectra of both $[RuH(1,5\text{-}cod)(NH_2NMe_2)_3](BPh_4)$ and $[RuH(1,5\text{-}cod)(NH_2NMe_2)_3](PF_6)$ reported by Ashworth [139] showed similar resonances, i.e., broad resonances for the NH_2 protons between δ_H 4.52 – 4.90 (centre of an AB quartet [153-155]) ppm and between δ_H 5.97 – 6.17 ppm. Singlets for the methyl resonances of the NMe_2 moieties were reported between δ_H 2.52 – 2.75 (*trans* to the hydride ligand) ppm and between δ_H 2.20 – 2.43 (*trans* to the 1,5-cod ligand) ppm. The slight upfield signals of the PF_6^- counterpart, as opposed to the BPh_4^-, is reasoned to be partly due to anisotropic shielding effects of the phenyl groups on the coordinating tetraphenylborate anion [139]. The X-ray crystal structure of $[RuH(1,5\text{-}cod)(NH_2NMe_2)_3](PF_6)$ had been determined in 1977 by Ashworth et al. [152] as a further substantiation in the nature and geometry assigned to the bound NH_2NMe_2 ligands.

iii. Other Substituted Hydrazine Complexes

Other hydrazine ruthenium(II) species $[RuH(1,5\text{-cod})(NH_2NHR)_3](BPh_4)$ (R = H, Me) were synthesised from reactions of the hydride species $[RuH(1,5\text{-cod})(NH_2NMe_2)_3]^+$ by ligand exchange reactions [139]. Due to steric constraints brought about by alkyl or aryl substituents on substituted hydrazines (NH_2NHR or NH_2NR_2), the ability of coordination *via* the substituted nitrogen atom is limited. As a result, coordination of the hydrazine occurs usually in a monodentate fashion *via* the NH_2 atom in octahedral transition metal complexes, though exceptions have been reported with dimeric hydrazine complexes, $[RuH(1,5\text{-cod})(\mu\text{-}H)(\mu\text{-}X)(\mu\text{-}NH_2NMe_2)RuX(1,5\text{-cod})]$ (X = Cl, Br) [12,156]

11) Phosphine-Adduct Ruthenium(II) Complexes

Grubbs et al. [147] devised an elegant and simple route to the synthesis of ruthenium(II) dihydrido complexes making direct use of the ruthenium polymer of $[RuCl_2(1,5\text{-cod})]_x$ (x >2). In a typical reaction, to a vessel containing a slurry of $[RuCl_2(1,5\text{-cod})]_x$ (x >2) and excess NaOH in butan-2-ol was added the appropriate amount of mono- or bidentate phosphine and the complete reaction mixture left to heat under reflux under inert conditions. Afterwards, H_2O would be added to the reaction mixture to dissolve excess NaOH, after which the mixture would be filtered and washed with dry MeOH. Following this synthetic route high yields of dihydrido mono- and bidentate phosphine adduct products were obtained in high purity [147] The series of products included *trans*-$[RuH_2L_4]$ (L = PEt_3, PPh_3) and *trans*-$[RuH_2(L_2)_2]$ (L_2 = dppe, dpppr, dppb, dppf, dcpe, dcpm, depe). The neutral dihydride complexes may then readily be converted to the corresponding cationic complexes by the protonation with acids HX (X = PF_6, BF_4), which have been reported by Grubbs et al. [147] to give complexes with the formulae $[RuH(L_2)_2](BF_4)$ (L = dcpe, dpppr, dppb).

Another synthetic route to ruthenium(II) dihydrido complexes was reported later on by Nolan et al., [148] which involved stirring a butan-2-ol slurry of the polymer, $[RuCl_2(1,5\text{-cod})]_x$ (x > 2), with excess NaOMe in the presence of two molar equivalents of the bidentate dpph phosphine ligand. The reaction mixture is then heated under reflux for 20 hours. With L_2 = $Ph_2PNMeNMePPh_2$ a mixture of *cis*- and *trans*-dihydrido products was formed. From ^1H- and ^{31}P-NMR spectroscopy experiments on $[RuH_2(Ph_2PNMeNMePPh_2)_2]$ they have found c.a. 70% of the *cis* isomer and 30% of the *trans* isomer. From ^{31}P-NMR spectra two triplets were present at δ_P 140.8 and 134.0 ($^2J_{PP}$ = 25 Hz) ppm respectively and a singlet at δ_P 140.4 ppm representing the *cis*- and *trans*-isomers respectively [148]. The ^1H-NMR spectrum furthermore revealed two triplets at δ_H 2.36 and 2.73 ppm for the diastereotopic NMe groups in the *cis*-isomer, whereas a singlet at δ_H 2.74 ppm was assigned to the equivalent NMe moiety in the *trans*-isomer [148].

The cation, $[RuH(1,5\text{-cod})(NH_2NMe_2)_3]^+$, formed from the inter-reaction of *N,N*-dimethylhydrazine with the ruthenium polymer $[RuCl_2(1,5\text{-cod})]_x$ (x > 2), was also found to be useful in the synthesis of a series of neutral and cationic mono- and dihydrido complexes with mono- and bidentate phosphine, phosphonite, phosphinite, and phosphite ligands [11,12,157,158]

12) Acetonitrile Ruthenium(II) Complexes

The polymer $[RuCl_2(1,5\text{-cod})]_x$ reacts in boiling acetonitrile after several hours to give the neutral complex $[RuX_2(1,5\text{-cod})(RCN)_2].Y$ (X = Cl, Br; R = Me, Ph, HC=CH_2, CH_2CH_3; Y = H_2O, CH_3CN). [142-144] When NH_4PF_6 is added to the mother liquors of these reactions the cationic salts of $[RuX(1,5\text{-cod})(CH_3CN)_3](PF_6)$ (X = Cl, Br) and dicationic salts of $[Ru(1,5\text{-cod})(CH_3CN)_4](PF_6)_2$ were isolated.[141] The crystal structure of the water monosolvate complex $[RuCl_2(1,5\text{-cod})(CH_3CN)_2].H_2O$ and recently of the acetonitrile monosolvate complex $[RuCl_2(1,5\text{-cod})(CH_3CN)_2].CH_3CN$ were reported [141,142]

Further reaction of the complex, $[RuCl(1,5\text{-cod})(CH_3CN)_3](PF_6)$, was isolated, with $AgPF_6$ gave the dicationic complex $[Ru(1,5\text{-cod})(CH_3CN)_4](PF_6)_2$. This latter product formed a series of complexes of formula $[RuL_2(CH_3CN)_4](PF_6)$ with the ligands L = PPh_3, $PMePh_2$, PMe_2Ph, $P(OMe)_2Ph$ and $P(OMe)_3$. [140] Refluxing acetone solutions of the neutral and cationic species $[RuX(1,5\text{-cod})(CH_3CN)_3](PF_6)$ (X = Cl, Br) gave the triply-halo-bridged species $[RuX(1,5\text{-cod})(\mu\text{-}X)_3Ru(1,5\text{-cod})(RCN)]$ (X = Cl, Br; R = Me, Ph). [141]

13) Cyclopentadienyl Ruthenium(II) Complexes

Many of the cyclopentadienyl- or pentamethylcyclopentadienyl ruthenium(II) complexes used as catalysts in a plethora of different organic reactions find their origin either directly from the ruthenium(II) polymer, $[Ru(1,5\text{-cod})Cl_2]_x$ ($x > 2$), or similar neutral and cationic derivatives thereof. [159] One of these routes involved the reaction of $[Ru(1,5\text{-cod})Cl_2]_x$ ($x > 2$) directly with TlCp in dimethoxyethane to have given ruthenocene, $[RuCp_2]$, in relative high yield [159] Simple routes [159] to the pentamethylcyclopentadienyl counterpart, $[RuCp^*{}_2]$, have also been reported.

14) Other Carbocyclic Organoruthenium(II) Complexes

In the reaction of $[RuCl_2(1,5\text{-cod})]_x$ ($x > 2$) with the potassium salt KC_9H_7 in THF gives the complex $[RuCl(1,5\text{-cod})(\eta^5\text{-}C_9H_7)]$, whereas if NaC_9H_7 was used in the same reaction, the complex $[Ru(\eta^5\text{-}C_9H_7)(\eta^2\text{-}\eta^5\text{-}C_8H_{11})]$ is formed [10] The complex $[RuCl(1,5\text{-cod})(\eta^5\text{-}C_9H_7)]$ reacts with a range of mono- and bidentate phosphines to give the five- and six coordinated complexes $[RuCl(\eta^5\text{-}C_9H_7)(L)]$ (L = PCy_3, P^iPr_3). [10]

Shaw et al. [160] reported that the polymer $[RuCl_2(1,5\text{-cod})]_x$ ($x > 2$) reacts with an allylic Grignard reagent to form the allyl-ruthenium(II) complexes $[Ru(all)_2(diene)]$ (all = allyl, 2-methylallyl; diene = C_8H_{12}, C_7H_8) which were isolated as white powders. The ^1H-NMR signals from the 1,5-cod ligand in the allyl complex $[Ru(all)_2(1,5\text{-cod})]$ were reported as multiple broad resonances at δ_H 1.42, 1.98 and 3.93 ppm respectively. This is due to the fluctionality of the allyl-ligand in the molecule in solution.

Conclusion

Significant progress has been made over the last 50 years in the synthesis of various neutral and cationic ruthenium(II) species employing ruthenium oligomeric and polymeric compounds as precursors. Many of these Ru(II) species are actively employed as reactive synthetic precursors in the production of modern catalysts incorporating exotic ligand systems, with the polymeric complex of $[RuCl_2(1,5\text{-cod})]_x$ ($x > 2$) remaining to be the preferred compound to a vast range of Ru(0), Ru(I), Ru(II) and Ru(IV) neutral and cationic complexes synthesised. With new contributions continually being made, the indication is that these ruthenium systems are still of interest in synthesis as well as for their applications, and further investigations thereof would be beneficial.

Acknowledgments

This work is based on the research supported in part by the National Research Foundation of South Africa (Grant specific unique reference number (UID) 85386. The New Generation Scholarship (NGS) of the University of Johannesburg (UJ) is gratefully acknowledged for a stipend for FPM.

References

[1] Harmon, R.E., Gupta, S.K., Brown, D.J., *Chem. Rev.*, 1973, *73*, 21.
[2] Fagan, P.J., Ward, M.D., Calabrese, J.C., *J. Am. Chem. Soc.*, 1989, *111*, 1698.
[3] Denti, G., Campagna, S., Serroni, S., Mauro, C., Balzani, V., *J. Am. Chem. Soc.*, 1992, *114*, 2944.
[4] Couch, D.A., Robinson, S.D., *Inorg. Chem.*, 1974, *13*, 456.
[5] McCleverty, J.A., Seddon, D., Whiteley, R.N., *J.C.S. Dalton Trans.*, 1975, 839.
[6] Crabtree, R.H., Pearman, A.J., *J. Organomet. Chem.*, 1978, *157*, 335.
[7] Abel, E.W., Bennett, M.A., Wilkinson, G., *Chem. Ind.*, 1959, 1516.
[8] Albers, M.O., Ashworth, T.V., Oosthuizen, H.E., Singleton, E., *Inorg. Synth.*, 1989, *26*, 68.
[9] Ashworth, T.V., Singleton, E., Hough, J.J., *J.C.S. Dalton Trans.*, 1977, 1809.
[10] Alvarez, P., Gimeno, J., Lastra, E., García-Granda, S., Van der Maelen, J.F., Bassetti, M., *Organometallics*, 2001, *20*, 3762.
[11] Ashworth, T.V., Singleton, E., Laing, M., Pope, L., *J.C.S. Dalton Trans.*, 1978, 1032.
[12] Ashworth, T.V., Reimann, R.H., Singleton, E., *J.C.S. Dalton Trans.*, 1978, 1036.
[13] Naota, T., Takaya, H., Murahashi, S-I., *Chem. Rev.*, 1998, *98*, 2599.
[14] Stephenson, T.A., Switkes, E., *Inorg. Nucl. Chem. Lett.*, 1971, *7*, 805.
[15] Mitchell, R.W., Spencer, A., Wilkinson, G., *J.C.S. Dalton Trans.*, 1973, 846.
[16] Mukaida, M., Nomura, T., Ishimori, T., *Bull. Chem. Soc. Jpn*, 1972, *45*, 2143 and references therein.
[17] Bennett, M.J., Caulton, K.G., Cotton, F.A., *Inorg. Chem.*, 1969, *8*, 1.

[18] Crooks, C.R., Johnson, B.F.G., Lewis, J., Williams, I.G., Gamlen, G., *J. Chem. Soc. (A)*, 1969, 2761.

[19] De Villiers Steyn, M.M., *PhD Thesis*, University of South Africa, 1989.

[20] Albers, M.O., Liles, D.C., Singleton, E., Stead, J.E., De Villiers Steyn, M.M., *Organometallics*, 1986, *5*, 1262.

[21] Hilts, R.W., Sherlock, S.J., Cowie, M., Singleton, E., De Villiers Steyn, M.M., *Inorg. Chem.*, 1990, *29*, 3161.

[22] Sherlock, S.J., Cowie, M., Singleton, E., De Villiers Steyn, M.M., *Organometallics*, 1988, *7*, 1663.

[23] De Villiers Steyn, M.M., Singleton, E., *Acta Cryst.*, 1988, *C44*, 1722.

[24] Singleton, E., Van Rooyen, P.H., De Villiers Steyn, M.M., *S. Afr. J. Chem.*, 1989, *42*, 57.

[25] Sherlock, S.J., Cowie, M., Singleton, E., De Villiers Steyn, M.M., *J. Organomet. Chem.*, 1989, *361*, 353.

[26] De Villiers Steyn, M.M., Singleton, E., Hietkamp, S., Liles, D.C., *J.C.S. Dalton Trans.*, 1990, 2991.

[27] Lindsay, A.J., Motevalli, M., Hursthouse, M.B., Wilkinson, G., *J.C.S. Chem. Comm.*, 1986, 433.

[28] Kontkanen, M.-L., Oresmaa, L., Moreno, A., Jänis, J., Laurila, E., Haukka, M., *Applied Catalysis A: General*, 2009, *365*, 130 and references therein.

[29] Chen, Y.-H., Lee, C.-C., Wang, C.-C., Lee, G.-H., Lai, S.-Y., Li, F.-Y., Mou, C.-Y., Peng, S.-M., *J.C.S. Chem. Comm.*, 1999, 1667.

[30] Sakai, K., Takeshita, M., Tanaka, Y., Ue, T., Yanagisawa, M., Kosaba, M., Tsubomura, T., Ato, M., Nakano, T., *J. Am. Chem. Soc.*, 1998, *120*, 11353 and references therein.

[31] Oresmaa, L., Moreno, M.A., Jakonen, M., Suvanto, S., Haukka, M., *Appl. Catal. A*, 2009, *353*, 113 and references therein.

[32] Hirva, P., Haukka, M., Jakonen, M., Pakkanen, T.A., *Inorg. Chim. Acta*, 2006, *359*, 853 and references therein.

[33] Kurosawa, H., *J. Organomet. Chem.*, 2004, *689*, 4511.

[34] Murahashi, T., Nagai, T., Okuno, T., Matsutani, T., Kurosawa, H., *J.C.S. Chem. Comm.*, 2000, 1689.

[35] Murahashi, T., Mino, Y., Chiyoda, K., Ogoshi, S., Kurosawa, H., *J.C.S. Chem. Comm.*, 2008, 4061.

[36] Benard, B., Berry, J.F., Cotton, F.A., Gaudin, C., Lopez, X., Murillo, C.A., Rohmer, M.-M., *Inorg. Chem.*, 2006, *45*, 3932.

[37] Berry, J.F., Cotton, F.A., Lu, T., Murillo, C.A., Roberts, B.K., Wang, X., *J. Am. Chem. Soc.*, 2004, *126*, 7082.

[38] Ismayilov, R.H., Wang, W.-Z., Wang, R.-R., Hang, Y.-L., Yeh, C.-Y., Lee, G.-H., Peng, S.-M., *Eur. J. Inorg. Chem.*, 2008, 4290.

[39] Kuo, C.-K., Chang, J.-C., Yeh, C.-Y., Lee, G.-H., Wang, C.-C., Peng, S.-M., *J.C.S. Dalton Trans.*, 2005, 3696.

[40] Wang, W.-Z., Ismayilov, R.H., Lee, G.-H., Liu, I.P.-C., Yeh, C.-Y., Peng, S.-M., *J.C.S. Dalton Trans.*, 2007, 830.

[41] Arai, S., Ochiai, M., Ishihara, K., Matsumoto, K., *Eur. J. Inorg. Chem.*, 2007, 2031.

[42] Pruchnik, F.P., Jakimowicz, P., Ciunik, Z., Stanislawek, K., Oro, I.A., Tejel, C., Ciriano, M.A., *Inorg. Chem. Comm.*, 2001, *4*, 19.

[43] Cotton, F.A., Daniels, D.M., Lu, T.B., Murillo, C.A., Wang, X.P., *J.C.S. Dalton Trans.*, 1999, 517 and references therein.

[44] Chardon-Noblat, S., Deronzier, A., Hartl, F., Van Slageren, J., Mahabiersing, T., *Eur. J. Inorg. Chem.*, 2001, 613.

[45] Collomb-Dunand-Sauthier, M.-N., Deronzier, A., Ziessel, R., *J.C.S. Chem. Comm.*, 1994, 189.

[46] Collomb-Dunand-Sauthier, M.N., Deronzier, A., Ziessel, R., *Inorg. Chem.*, 1994, *33*, 2961.

[47] Hartl, F., Mahabiersing, T., Chardon-Noblat, S., Da Costa, P., Deronzier, A., *Inorg. Chem.*, 2004, *43*, 7250.

[48] Jia, G., Wu, W.F., Yeung, R.C.Y., Xia, H.P., *J. Organomet. Chem.*, 1997, *539*, 53.

[49] Hastings, W.R., Baird, M.C., *Inorg. Chem.*, 1986, *25*, 2913.

[50] Maschiocchi, N., Moret, M., Ciarati, P., Ragaini, F., Sironi, A., *J.C.S. Dalton Trans.*, 1993, 471.

[51] Luukkanen, S., Kallinen, M., Haukka, M., Pakkanen, T.A., *Catal. Lett.*, 2000, *70*, 123.

[52] Luukkanen, S., Haukka, M., Laine, O., Venäläinen, T., Vainiotalo, P., Pakkanen, T.A., *Inorg. Chim. Acta*, 2002, *332*, 25.

[53] Moreno, M.A., Haukka, M., Venäläinen, T., Pakkanen, T.A., *Catal. Lett.*, 2004, *96*, 153.

[54] Grushin, V.V., Marshall, W.J., Thorn, D.L., *Adv. Synth. Catal.*, 2001, *343*, 161.

[55] Frohning, C.D., Kohlpaintner, C., Bohnen, H.-W., *Applied Homogeneous Catalysis with Organometallic Compounds*, 2nd ed., Wiley-VCH: Weinheim, 2002.

[56] Dérien, S., Dixneuf, P. H., *J. Organomet. Chem.*, 2004, *689*, 1382 and references therein.

[57] Fujita, S., Okamura, S., Akiyama, Y., Arai, M., *Int. J. Mol. Sci.*, 2007, *8*, 749.

[58] Jääskeläinen, S., Haukka, M., *Appl. Catal. A*, 2003, *247*, 95.

[59] Tominaga, K., Sasaki, Y., *J. Mol. Catal. A*, 2004, *220*, 159.

[60] Tominaga, K., *Catal. Today*, 2006, *115*, 70.

[61] Tominaga, K.-I., Sasaki, Y., *J. Mol. Catal. A*, 2004, *220*, 159.

[62] Yin, X., Moss, J.R., *Coord. Chem. Rev.*, 1999, *181*, 27.

[63] Chen, X.-Y., Zhao, Y.-X., Wang, S.-G., *J. Phys. Chem. A*, 2006, *110*, 3552.

[64] Tominaga, K.-I., Sasaki, Y., *Chem. Lett.*, 2004, *33*, 14.

[65] Delgado, P., González-Prieto, R., Jiménez-Aparicio, R., Perles, J., Priego, J.L., Torres, R.M., *J.C.S. Dalton Trans.*, 2012, *41*, 11866 and references therein.

[66] Manchot, W., Enk, E., *Chem. Ber.*, 1930, *63*, 1635.

[67] Manchot, W., König, E., *Chem. Ber.*, 1924, *57*, 2130.

[68] Johnson, B.F.G., Johnston, R.D., Lewis, J., *J. Chem. Soc (A)*, 1969, 792.

[69] Johnson, B.F.G., Johnston, R.D., Josty, P.L., Lewis, J., Williams, I.G., *Nature (London)*, 1967, *213*, 901.

[70] Faraone, F., Sergi, S., *J. Organomet. Chem.*, 1976, *112*, 201.

[71] Colton, R., Farthing, R.H., *Aust. J. Chem.*, 1969, *22*, 2011.

[72] Hieber, W., Heusinger, H., *J. Inorg. Nucl. Chem.*, 1957, *4*, 179.

[73] Colton, R., Farthing, R.H., *Aust. J. Chem.*, 1967, *20*, 1283.

[74] Irving, R.J., *J. Chem. Soc.*, 1956, 2879.

[75] Hieber, W., John, P., *Chem. Ber.*, 1970, *103*, 2161.

[76] John, P., *Chem. Ber.*, 1970, *103*, 2178.

[77] Seddon, E.A., Seddon, K.R., *The Chemistry of Ruthenium*, Elsevier Science Publishing Co. Inc.: New York, 1984, Vol. 19.
[78] Cetini, G., Gambino, O., Sappa, E., Valle, M., *J. Organomet. Chem.*, 1968, *15*, P4.
[79] Schermer, E.D., Baddley, W.H., *J. Organomet. Chem.*, 1971, *30*, 67.
[80] Braca, G., Sbrana, G., *Chim. Ind. (Milan)*. 1974, *56*, 110.
[81] Merlino, S., Montagnoli, G., Braca, G., Sbrana, G., *Inorg. Chim. Acta*, 1978, *27*, 233.
[82] Maschiocchi, N., Sironi, A., Chardon-Noblat, S., Deronzier, A., *Organometallics*, 2002, *21*, 4009 and references therein.
[83] Gerbaud, G., Mouesca, J.-M., Hediger, S., Chardon-Noblat, S., Lafolet, F., Deronzier, A., Bardet, M., *Phys. Chem. Chem. Phys.*, 2010, *12*, 15428.
[84] Tilley, T.D., Grubbs, R.H., Bercaw, J.E., *Organometallics*, 1984, *3*, 274.
[85] Nagashima, H., Mukai, K., Shiota, Y., Yamaguchi, K., Ara, K., Fukahori, T., Suzuki, H., Akita, M., Moro-oka, Y., Itoh, K., *Organometallics*, 1990, *9*, 799.
[86] Oshima, N., Suzuki, H., Moro-Oka, Y., *Chem. Lett.*, 1984, 1161.
[87] Bednarik, L., Neuse, E., *J. Org. Chem.*, 1980, *45*, 2032.
[88] Liles, D.C., Shaver, A., Singleton, E., Wiege, M.B., *J. Organomet. Chem.*, 1985, C33.
[89] Winkhaus, G., Singer, H., *J. Organomet. Chem.*, 1967, *7*, 487.
[90] Bennett, M.A., Smith, A.K., *J.C.S. Dalton Trans.*, 1974, 233.
[91] Arthur, T., Stephenson, T.A., *J. Organomet. Chem.*, 1979, *168*, C39.
[92] Gould, R.O., Jones, C.L., Robertson, D.R., Stephenson, T.A., *J.C.S. Chem. Comm.*, 1977, 222.
[93] Restivo, R.J., Ferguson, G., O'Sullivan, D.J., Lalor, F.J., *Inorg. Chem.*, 1975, *14*, 3046.
[94] Robertson, D.R., Stephenson, T.A., Arthur, T., *J. Organomet. Chem.*, 1978, *162*, 121.
[95] Müller, J., Kreiter, C.G., Mertschenk, B., Schmitt, S., *Chem. Ber.*, 1975, *108*, 273.
[96] Johnson, B.F.G., Lewis, J., Ryder, I.E., *J.C.S Dalton Trans.*, 1977, 719.
[97] Bennet, M.A., Matheson, T.W., Robertson, G.B., Smith, A.K., Tucker, P.A., *J. Organomet. Chem.*, 1976, *121*, C18.
[98] Pertici, P., Simonelli, G., Vitulli, G., Deganello, G., Sandrini, P., Mantovani, A., *J.C.S. Chem. Comm.*, 1977, 132.
[99] Pertici, P., Vitulli, G., Porri, L., *J.C.S. Chem. Comm.*, 1975, 846.
[100] Almog, O., Bino, A., Garfinkel-Shweky, D., *Inorg. Chim. Acta*, 1993, *213*, 99.
[101] Baumann, J.A., Salmon, D.J., Wilson, S.T., Meyer, T.J., Hatfield, W.E., *Inorg. Chem.*, 1978, *17*, 3342.
[102] Spencer, A., Wilkinson, G., *J.C.S. Dalton Trans.*, 1972, 1570.
[103] Toma, H.E., Cunha, C.J., Cipriano, C., *Inorg. Chim. Acta*, 1988, *154*, 63.
[104] Zhilyaev, A.N., Fomina, T.A., Katser, S.B., Baranovskii, I.B., *Russ. J. Inorg. Chem.*, 1994, *39*, 856.
[105] Davis, S., Drago, R.S., *Inorg. Chem.*, 1988, *27*, 4759.
[106] Abe, M., Sasaki, Y., Yamaguchi, T., Ito, T., *Bull. Chem. Soc. Jpn*, 1992, *65*, 1585.
[107] Ohto, A., Tokiwa-Yamamoto, A., Abe, M., Ito, T., Sasaki, Y., Umakoshi, K., Cannon, R.D., *Chem. Lett.*, 1995, 97.
[108] Toma, H.E., Araki, K., Alexiou, A.D.P., Nikolaou, S., Dovidauskas, S., *Coord. Chem. Rev.*, 2001, *219-221*, 187 and references therein.
[109] Sasaki, Y., Tokiwa, A., Ito, T., *J. Am. Chem. Soc.*, 1987, *109*, 6341.
[110] Abe, M., Sasaki, Y., Yamada, Y., Tsukahara, K., Yano, S., Ito, T., *Inorg. Chem.*, 1995, *34*, 4490.

[111] Toma, H.E., Nikolaou, S., *J. Chem. Res. (S)*, 2000, 326.
[112] Abe, M., Sasaki, Y., Yamada, Y., Tsukahara, K., Yano, S., Yamaguchi, M., Tominaga, M., Taniguchi, I., Ito, T., *Inorg. Chem.*, 1996, *35*, 6724.
[113] Legzdins, P., Mitchell, R.W., Rempel, G.L., Ruddick, J.D., Wilkinson, G., *J. Chem. Soc (A)*, 1970, 3322.
[114] Fouda, S.A., Hui, B.C.Y., Rempel, G.L., *Inorg. Chem.*, 1978, *17*, 3213.
[115] Irving, R.J., Laye, P.G., *J. Chem. Soc (A)*, 1966, 161.
[116] McCleverty, J.A., Whitely, R.N., *J. Chem. Soc (D)*, 1971, 1159.
[117] Laing, K.R., Robinson, S.D., Uttley, M.F., *J.C.S. Chem. Comm.*, 1973, 176.
[118] Laing, K.R., Robinson, S.D., Uttley, M.F., *J.C.S Dalton Trans.*, 1973, 2713.
[119] Bennett, M.A., Wilkinson, G., *Chem. Ind. (London)*, 1959, 1516.
[120] Müller, J., Fischer, E.O., *J. Organomet. Chem.*, 1966, *5*, 275.
[121] Tayim, H.A., Mahmoud, F.T., *J. Organomet. Chem.*, 1975, *92*, 107.
[122] Abel, E.W., Bennett, M.A., Wilkinson, G., *J. Chem. Soc.*, 1959, 3178.
[123] Iqbal, M.Z., *Pak. J. Sci. Res.*, 1972, *24*, 299.
[124] Gilbert, J.D., Rose, D., Wilkinson, G., *J. Chem. Soc. (A)*, 1970, 2765.
[125] Müller, J., Schmitt, S., *J. Organomet. Chem.*, 1975, *97*, 275.
[126] Potvin, C., Manoli, J.M., Dereigne, A., Pannetier, G., *J. Less-Common Met.*, 1971, *25*, 373.
[127] Fletcher, S.R., Skapski, A.C., *J.C.S. Dalton Trans.*, 1972, 635.
[128] James, B.R., McMillan, R.S., Morris, R.H., Wang, D.K.W., *Adv. Chem. Ser.*, 1978, *167*, 122.
[129] Miller, J.B., A.L., *Inorg. Chem.*, 1971, *10*, 1410.
[130] King, R.B., Kapoor, P.N., *Inorg. Chem.*, 1972, *11*, 336.
[131] Potvin, C., Davignon, L., Pannetier, G., *Bull. Soc. Chim. Fr.*, 1975, 507.
[132] Powell, P., *J. Organomet. Chem.*, 1974, *65*, 89.
[133] Schrock, R.R., Lewis, J., *J. Am. Chem. Soc.*, 1973, *95*, 4102.
[134] Potvin, C., Pannetier, G., *Bull. Soc. Chim. Fr.*, 1974, 783.
[135] Poddar, R.K., Agarwala, U., *J. Inorg. Nucl. Chem.*, 1973, *35*, 3769.
[136] Stephenson, T.A., Wilkinson, G., *J. Inorg. Nucl. Chem.*, 1966, *28*, 2285.
[137] Braca, G., Carlini, Ciardelli, F., Sbrana, G., *Proc. Int. Cong. Catal.*, 1976, *1*, 528.
[138] Swanepoel, H.E., *Ph.D. Thesis*, Randse Afrikaanse Universiteit, 1980.
[139] Ashworth, T.V., *Ph.D. Thesis*, University of South Africa, 1977.
[140] Ashworth, T.V., Singleton, E., *J. Organomet. Chem.*, 1974, *77*, C31.
[141] Ashworth, T.V., Liles, D.C., Robinson, D.J., Singleton, E., Coville, N.J., Darling, E., Markwell, A.J., *S. Afr. J. Chem.*, 1987, *40*, 183.
[142] Chiririwa, H., Meijboom, R., Owalude, S.O., Eke, U.B., Arderne, C., *Acta Cryst.*, 2011, *E67*, m1096.
[143] Chiririwa, H., Meijboom, R., *Acta Cryst.*, 2011, *E67*, m1335.
[144] Chiririwa, H., Meijboom, R., *Acta Cryst.*, 2011, *E67*, m1336.
[145] Albers, M.O., Liles, D.C., Robinson, D.J., Shaver, A., Singleton, E., Wiege, M., *Organometallics*, 1986, *5*, 2321.
[146] Schrock, R.R., Johnson, B.F.G., Lewis, J., *J.C.S. Dalton Trans.*, 1974, 951.
[147] Nolan, S.P., Belderrain, T.R., Grubbs, R.H., *Organometallics*, 1997, *16*, 5569.
[148] Shen, J., Stevens, E.D., Nolan, S.P., *Organometallics*, 1998, *17*, 3875.
[149] Hough, J.J., Singleton, E., *J.C.S. Chem. Comm.*, 1972, 371.

[150] Owalude, S.O., Eke, U.B., Odebunmi, E.O., Nesterov, V.N., Meijboom, R., Coville, N.J., *X-ray Structure Analysis Online*, 2012, *28*, 29.
[151] Oosthuizen, H., Singleton, E., Field, J.S., Van Niekerk, G.C., *J. Organomet. Chem.*, 1985, *279*, 433.
[152] Ashworth, T.V., Nolte, M.J., Singleton, E., *J. Organomet. Chem.*, 1977, *139*, C73.
[153] Clark, H.C., Kurosawa, H., *Inorg. Chem.*, 1972, *11*, 1275.
[154] Clark, H.C., Jablonski, C.R., Wong, C.S., *Inorg. Chem.*, 1975, *14*, 1332.
[155] Pople, J.A., Schneider, W.G., Bernstein, H.J., *High Resolution Nuclear Magnetic Resonance*, McGraw-Hill Book Co., 1959.
[156] Ashworth, T.V., Nolte, M.J., Reimann, R.H., Singleton, E., *J.C.S. Dalton Trans.*, 1978, 1043.
[157] Ashworth, T.V., Liles, D.C., Singleton, E., *Organometallics*, 1984, *3*, 1851.
[158] Ashworth, T.V., Nolte, M.J., Singleton, E., *J.C.S. Dalton Trans.*, 1977, 1816.
[159] Albers, M.O., Robinson, D.J., Singleton, E., *J. Organomet. Chem.*, 1986, *311*, 207 and references therein.
[160] Powell, J., Shaw, B.L., *J. Chem. Soc. (A)*, 1968, 159.

INDEX

A

B

C

D

E

F

G

H

I

K

L

M

N

O

Q

R

S

T

U

V

W

X

Y

Z